Eugene Giles

THE ESSENTIALS
OF ORGANIC CHEMISTRY

REVISED EDITION

By

C. W. PORTER *and* T. D. STEWART

Department of Chemistry

University of California

Berkeley

GINN AND COMPANY

BOSTON · NEW YORK · CHICAGO · ATLANTA · DALLAS · COLUMBUS

SAN FRANCISCO · TORONTO · LONDON

PRINTED IN THE UNITED STATES OF AMERICA

PREFACE

THIS BOOK provides material for a short course in organic chemistry. It covers most of the established facts and theories of organic chemistry which have basic significance. The general reactions commonly used in synthetic work and in industrial processes are explained and illustrated. The aim has been to develop in a concise manner, without sacrifice of precision, the essential facts and viewpoints which are necessary for an understanding of the applications of organic chemistry to related fields. The book is designed primarily for students of medicine, pharmacy, dentistry, home economics, and agriculture, and for students in the general curricula of arts and sciences.

There are exercises and problems at the end of each chapter. The exercises are intended to test the student's assimilation of the factual material; they represent the minimum that every student should master. Direct answers to the exercises may be found in the text. The problems, as a rule, are a little more difficult than the exercises. Answers to the problems are not given in the book, but methods of solving the problems are fully explained.

In this revision of the text some new material has been added and some discussions have been more fully detailed, for instance, a quantitative use of the mass law as related to the strengths of acids and compositions of buffer solutions, the idea of chain reactions as illustrated by chlorination, the qualitative use of resonance in accounting for the relative acidities of alcohols and acids, and the interpretation of double and triple bonds. The opportunity has been taken to rephrase, without expansion, many facts and ideas in keeping with current usage and increased understanding. The introductory chapters have been essentially rewritten; here, as throughout the text, the aim has been to increase the correlation between organic and general chemistry and to make evident the paths through which organic chemistry has developed.

C. W. P.
T. D. S.

CONTENTS

THE ESSENTIALS
OF ORGANIC CHEMISTRY

1 · ORGANIC COMPOUNDS

The terms *organic* and *inorganic*, as applied to chemistry, were used, originally, to designate the origins of compounds. All compounds formed in the tissues of living organisms—plants and animals—were called organic compounds. Those found in the mineral kingdom were called inorganic compounds. At a later period it became evident that nearly all compounds which are formed in living cells contain carbon, and gradually the emphasis was shifted from origin to composition. We now define organic chemistry as the chemistry of the carbon compounds.

There is no sharp distinction between organic and inorganic chemistry. The same principles are encountered in both fields, and we do not make a strict segregation of compounds on the basis of composi-

---

SUBSTANCES CONTAINING CARBON

Crystalline forms of carbon

Diamond   Graphite

Materials of indefinite and varying composition but mostly carbon

Coal   Lampblack   Charcoal   Coke

Carbonaceous mixtures

Petroleum   Peat   Asphalt

Carbonates

Limestone   Calcite   Magnesite
Dolomite   Witherite   Many other minerals

Animal and vegetable products

Celluloses   Sugars   Fats   Proteins
Rubber   Waxes   Gums   Resins
Essential oils   Vitamins   Hormones   Dyes

Technological products

Plastics   Solvents   Dyes
Drugs   Perfumes   Flavors
                    Insecticides

---

tion. Carbon dioxide and the carbonates are commonly classed as inorganic compounds, although carbon dioxide is a product of both animal and vegetable metabolism, and calcium carbonate is found in the bones and shells of animals. The inclusion of carbonates in the study of general chemistry and the segregation of other carbon compounds into a separate course is reasonable, even if it is arbitrary, because most other compounds of carbon bear little resemblance to the carbonates. The table on page 3 presents a partial list of substances which are familiar to all, at least in name, and which contain carbon.

Chemists who are mainly interested in the occurrence, composition, reactions, and synthesis of carbon compounds are termed organic chemists. This specialization reflects the magnitude of the tasks of identifying the compounds associated with animal and vegetable metabolism, and of describing and synthesizing all of the possible compounds of carbon. Neither of these tasks is completed; yet over a million compounds containing the element carbon have been isolated, either from natural sources or through laboratory operations.

The organic chemist has left to others—physical chemists—the detailed study of the basic principles applicable to all problems in chemistry, such as the factors which control equilibria, rates of reaction, and the physical properties of compounds and mixtures. This does not mean that he is not concerned with the results of such studies or does not participate at all. It does mean that he has not waited for the development of theory before finding out what compounds of carbon can exist.

The isolation and identification of organic compounds. The composition of a pure substance is expressed in terms of a molecular formula; an elementary analysis of a mixture of compounds has little meaning. The examination of a substance, therefore, entails ascertaining whether it is a compound or a mixture, and if the latter, the separation or isolation of the components. If the isolated components have been described by other investigators, the chemist is able to identify them from the recorded descriptions. Otherwise he is faced with the problem of determining the molecular formulas and such other facts as may serve to identify them. The problems of separation and identification are enormously complicated by the facts that compounds of carbon which are different may still have the same molecular composition, and that sometimes compounds of different molecular formulas differ from each other in barely perceptible degree.

Progress in the study of the compounds of carbon and much of our material welfare have been dependent upon the ability of organic chemists to isolate, purify, analyze, and identify the compounds which occur in nature or which appear during laboratory syntheses. A few instances in which separation processes and analyses have been advantageous may serve to make clear this dependence. For centuries the art of healing utilized minerals and herbs as medicines, and in most of those cases in which therapeutic value can be demonstrated, chemists have succeeded in isolating the responsible ingredient as a definite chemical compound. Examples are quinine, from the bark of the cinchona tree, isolated in 1820; morphine, a constituent of opium, from the seed of the white poppy (1806); one of the heart stimulants, digitoxigenin, from various species of digitalis; ascorbic acid (vitamin C), responsible for the control of scurvy through inclusion of citrus fruits in the diet. One may compare the procedure for the isolation of a biologically active component with that for the isolation of radium from pitchblende, a uranium ore. In all cases one must have a quantitative measure of potency. In the detection of radium there was radioactivity to detect the degree of separation and concentration as fractional crystallizations were made. In biological properties small animals, or often bacteria and molds, are used to determine the minimum doses needed to produce a given effect. The effects looked for may be rate of growth, or incidence of some abnormality. A separation process which is fruitful will result in a fraction of high potency, eventually of maximum potency; if other criteria of purity agree, then the isolation problem is solved and the purely chemical work can begin.

Not all useful substances owe their utility to a single component. At times a mixture of compounds is to be preferred, as in the cases of perfumes and flavors. Natural products as complex as rubber, shellac, resins, and amber may not be divisible into precise components, but their examination has led to an understandnig of why, in terms of composition, they have certain characteristic properties, with the result that "synthetics" of similar properties, often better, are designed. Reasonably simple (low-molecular-weight) compounds found in nature are eventually synthesized in exact reproduction; an example is thiamine (vitamin B_1). Quinine has but recently (1944) been prepared, and not by a process of commercial advantage; cane sugar has not been made without the help of enzymes; insulin, while a definite substance, will probably never be synthesized *in vitro*. There is increasing use, in synthetic procedures, of microörganisms and enzymes to produce specific chemical products not obtainable expediently in any other way. For example, the antibiotic penicillins are isolated from the medium in which the common green mold, *Penicillium notatum*, is grown.

The isolation of organic compounds present in natural products was haphazard until late in the 18th century. In the years (1769–1785) overlapping those of the American Revolution, a Swedish chemist, Carl W. Scheele, isolated not only oxygen and a number of other inorganic substances, but also a series of organic acids—tartaric, malic, citric, lactic, oxalic, and uric acids. Simultaneously Antoine Lavoisier, in France, was developing the analytical procedures necessary for the examination of pure substances. Prior to this time relatively few substances were known as compounds. Of these, cane sugar was known as early as the fourth century because of its ease of isolation. Products of fermentation processes such as tartar (potassium acid tartrate), grain alcohol, and acetic acid had long been familiar as substances, but the alcohol and acid were not obtained free from water until 1796 and 1789 respectively.

Isolation procedures. The methods and tools for the isolation and identification of compounds are constantly being improved and increased in number. Of these, the basic ones are distillation, crystallization, and extraction. They depend upon the facts that substances differ in volatility and solubility and hence the more volatile can be removed from the less volatile and the more soluble from the less soluble components of a mixture. Extractions always involve two or more phases. Two immiscible liquids divide a solute between them, but in different concentrations. Or a component of a gas or solution may be adsorbed on a solid surface, such as an activated charcoal, and thereby be removed from its previous environment. For instance, sugar is separated from brown impurities by adsorption of the latter on charcoal; the colored pigments in carrots may be separated from each other by filtering a solution of them slowly through a column of a powdered solid substance such as calcium carbonate or a clay. Those pigments that are strongly adsorbed remain near the top of the column, those less strongly adsorbed are found further down. Where similarities in chemical and physical properties exist, but differences in molecular weights occur, the different rates of diffusion of gaseous components serve to effect separations. Isotopes of some of the elements have been separated in this way. The fluoride of uranium 235 can be separated from the fluoride of uranium 238 by diffusion.

Criteria of purity. Interest in the isolation of naturally occurring compounds coincided with the growth of other aspects of chemistry. This is not surprising because, in order to achieve isolation, some understanding of what constitutes purity in a compound had to be reached. Today we recognize a pure compound as a substance of definite composition with respect to the elements present, of a given molecular weight, and of specific physical and chemical properties. Actually, purity is defined in terms of separation processes, composition, and properties. If one is unable, by any physical process, to separate a substance into fractions which differ in some respect, the substance is said to be pure. However, not until composition could be expressed, qualitatively and quantitatively, in terms of the elements present and procedures for the quantitative measurement of physical and chemical properties were available, could the purity of a compound be certain. The isolation and description of compounds, which were the main aims of chemistry in its early days, then depended for progress upon the following factors:

(1) Development of separation processes, namely, crystallization, distillation, extraction.

(2) Recognition of the existence of elements, and discovery of the elements.

(3) Development of the concept of molecules and of methods of obtaining molecular weights.

(4) Discovery and refinement of analytical methods.

(5) Development of valence concepts.

(6) Discovery of the physical laws governing the behavior of gases, liquids, solids, solutions, and chemical changes.

There are cases today in which certification of purity is debatable and recourse is had to some aspect of each of the above factors. Usually, however, the problem reduces to a simple routine. A liquid compound, if pure, distills at a single temperature when the barometric pressure is constant; a pure solid compound melts (or freezes) entirely at one temperature. Other physical properties, such as density, index of refraction, and absorption spectrum remain unchanged upon subjection of the substance to any separation process. Strictly speaking, the elementary composition and molecular weight need not be known, but these factors are confirmatory of purity if they indicate a molecular formula which is predictable from valence concepts.

It is evident that organized progress in chemical knowledge had to await discovery of methods and recognition of basic ideas. Neither composition, reactions, or physical properties had definite meaning until they could be expressed in terms of atomic and molecular theory, and criteria of purity had been established. After centuries of fumbling, during which a chaos of facts and ideas existed, a few key discoveries were made. The one which may be taken as opening the epoch of modern physical science entailed the conversion from qualitative to quantitative methods of investigation. In 1661 Robert Boyle announced the relation between the pressure and volume of a given amount of gas at constant temperature. Yet over a century more was to elapse before there was any extended and systematic isolation of pure organic compounds (about 1780), and it was still later that the age-long search for the elementary substances which pervade all matter found a true expression in Dalton's Atomic Theory (1803). In the meantime oxygen had been discovered (1774) and the nature of combustion had been explained (1775). The basis for molecular theory was soon laid by Gay-Lussac (Law of Combining Volumes of Gases (1808)) and Avogadro (Avogadro's Hypothesis (1811)), but the inherited confusion regarding atoms and molecules persisted until as late as 1858, when Cannizzaro reviewed the existing facts. By that time experimental procedures for the isolation, synthesis, and analysis of compounds were highly developed. The nature of valence and chemical affinity were current problems, and physical chemistry (study of the physical laws governing all kinds of systems) had a beginning. Upon this slowly built foundation a rapidly growing body of facts regarding compounds of carbon has risen.

Identification of compounds. The identification of an organic compound, once its purity is established, is a problem of great technical complexity. It has a counterpart in the identification of a person whose fingerprints are on record. Normally a simple description of his major characteristics—the analogs of melting-point, boiling-point, index of refraction, absorption spectrum or color—suffices for a stranger to place him, particularly if he is habitually located in a limited area. To use fingerprints alone, a system of classification had to be developed and a filing system devised; and the possibility of two sets of identical prints had to be excluded. There is no analog of fingerprints among the properties of compounds, but there are systematic classifications, starting with elementary content, which lead one to a sure identification of any known and previously described compound.

SOME PROPERTIES BY WHICH COMPOUNDS MAY BE IDENTIFIED

    1. Volatility and boiling point (applied to liquids and to some solids)
    2. Melting point
    3. Solubility in various solvents
    4. Index of refraction
    5. Color or absorption spectrum
    6. Chemical reactions

The characteristics of carbon as an element. The crystalline allotropic forms of carbon are diamond and graphite. Diamond is the stable form at very high temperatures and pressures, while graphite is the stable form under ordinary conditions. At about 2000° C a diatomic gas, C_2, exists.

The position of carbon in the fourth group of the periodic table suggests that in chemical behavior it should lie between the metallic, or electropositive, elements and the nonmetallic, or electronegative, elements. This it seems to do. For instance, while a lithium atom loses its valence electron to become the cation (Li^+), and fluorine tends to acquire an electron to become the anion (F^-), carbon does neither. Its simplest hydride, methane (CH_4), is not ionized at all, nor are any of its halogen compounds ionized. In fact hydrogen and chlorine can combine with carbon in the same molecule, as in the series CH_4, CH_3Cl, CH_2Cl_2, $CHCl_3$, CCl_4. Carbon has been made to form bonds with almost every element, but its most outstanding

---

ELEMENTS OF THE FIRST TWO ROWS OF THE PERIODIC TABLE

[The dots represent valence electrons]
[Numerals are atomic numbers and atomic weights]

1 H· 1.008							2 :He 4.003
3 Li· 6.94	4 ·Be· 9.02	5 ·B 10.82	6 ·C· 12.01	7 :N· 14.01	8 :O: 16.00	9 :F· 19.00	10 :Ne: 20.18
11 Na· 23.00	12 ·Mg· 24.32	13 ·Al 26.97	14 ·Si· 28.06	15 :P· 30.98	16 :S· 32.06	17 :Cl· 35.46	18 :A: 39.94

reaction is to form bonds with itself. Compounds of nitrogen exist with eight nitrogen atoms combined with each other, but in the case of carbon there seems to be no limit to the number of carbon atoms which can be joined together in a single molecule. This property accounts for the enormous number and variety of carbon compounds. The other elements usually present are, in the order of their frequency, hydrogen, oxygen, nitrogen, sulfur, and the halogens.

The compositions of molecules and their properties must be considered in connection with the nature of the chemical bond and atomic structure. The concept of an atom composed of a positive nucleus, the charge of which is called the atomic number, surrounded by an equal number of electrons, is a familiar one. The existence of the inert gases helium, neon, and argon indicates that certain electronic arrangements are so stable as to preclude either loss or gain of electrons to or from other atoms. These arrangements are called shells; the first is the K (or helium) shell, of two electrons only; the next is the L (or neon) shell of eight electrons. For the smaller atoms the tendency is either to lose electrons by ionization to simulate a lower shell, or acquire electrons to fill the outer shell. The electrons outside a stable shell are called valence electrons. Thus carbon, with four valence electrons, associates with four more electrons from other atoms to complete its L shell of eight electrons. These eight electrons are shared by the carbon atom and the other atoms concerned, in the sense that the orbital motions of the bonding electrons include two atomic nucleii. Moreover, each bond requires two electrons in that orbital. This was deduced by Gilbert N. Lewis in 1916 from the statistical observation that the sum of the valence electrons in practically all compounds is an even number. This pairing of electrons requires also that the magnetic fields of the two electrons neutralize each other; and to achieve this their directions of spin must be opposed. Atoms or molecules with unpaired electrons have magnetic moments, and since most substances are diamagnetic rather than paramagnetic, there is clear evidence of pairing. So we picture a chemical bond as a mutual interaction between two nucleii and an electron pair; the bonding electrons have opposing spins and occupy an orbital which includes both nucleii. They also serve to fill the valence shells of both atoms involved.

Electron formulas. There are occasions when it is desirable to represent in a formula all of the valence electrons present, whether they be involved in bonds or not. The conventional formulation is best presented by some examples; such representations are called "electron formulas."

$$: \overset{..}{\underset{H}{O}} : H \qquad H : \overset{H}{\underset{..}{N}} : H \qquad H : \overset{H}{\underset{H}{C}} : H \qquad H : \overset{H}{\underset{H}{C}} : \overset{..}{\underset{..}{Cl}} :$$

Water   Ammonia   Methane   Chloromethane

The usual valences are represented by a pair of electrons; the total number of electrons to be shown is the sum of the valence electrons contributed by each atom, and they are arranged in pairs in such a way as to complete the octet of electrons in the L shells of the oxygen, nitrogen, and carbon atoms.

The valence of carbon is uniformly four as required for completion of its octet of electrons. It has no unshared pairs of electrons, as have oxygen and nitrogen in water and ammonia. Carbon monoxide (CO) seems to be an exception, but all diatomic molecules have unique electron-valence arrangements.

Isotopes of carbon. There are five isotopes of carbon; two of them, represented by the symbols $_6C^{12}$ and $_6C^{13}$, occur in nature and are not radioactive. In this symbolism the upper figure is the atomic weight and the lower the atomic number. Ordinary carbon is composed of 98.9% of $_6C^{12}$ and about 1.1% of $_6C^{13}$; a minute amount of a radioactive isotope, $_6C^{14}$, which is continually being synthesized through cosmic ray absorption, is also present. It has a half-life of 5700 years, that is, half of any given amount disintegrates (into $_7N^{14}$ and a β^- particle) in that time. Two other isotopes are prepared in nuclear reactors; the one, $_6C^{10}$, has a half-life of 19 seconds; the other, $_6C^{11}$, has a half-life of 20.5 minutes. The nuclear reactions are as follows, where $_0n^1$ is the neutron, and $_1H^1$ and $_1H^2$ are hydrogen and deuterium respectively.

$$_5B^{10} + {}_1H^1 \longrightarrow {}_6C^{10} + {}_0n^1$$
$$_5B^{10} + {}_1H^2 \longrightarrow {}_6C^{11} + {}_0n^1$$
$$_7N^{14} + {}_0n^1 \longrightarrow {}_6C^{14} + {}_1H^1$$

The radioactive isotopes, particularly $_6C^{14}$, are useful tracer atoms. Through the radioactivity the fate of a given molecule or even that part of a molecule which is active can be traced during metabolism or reaction. The radioactive carbon is prepared in the form of carbonates and cyanides.

Oxidation states. The oxidation states of carbon range formally from -4 in CH_4 to $+4$ in CCl_4 and CO_2. These assignments arbitrarily assume that the oxidation state of hydrogen is $+1$, that of chlorine is -1, and that of oxygen is -2. Since the proton and chloride do not ionize there could be some question as to the electron distribution in the bonds. The problem is not peculiar to organic chemistry. For instance, the assignment of an oxidation state of $+6$ to the sulfur atom in sulfate ion ($SO_4^=$) tacitly assumes an oxidation state of -2 for the oxygen atoms. In un-ionized bonds the bonding electrons are *shared* and are not in possession of either atom alone, hence the oxidation state is indeterminate in terms of electron transfer. The term *covalent* bond is used to denote an essentially nonpolar or un-ionized bonding.

EXERCISES

1. Name and describe briefly three procedures which may be used for the separation of the components of a mixture.

2. Is it possible to be sure that a substance is a pure compound and not a mixture? What criteria of purity are normally applied?

3. Define a pure compound in terms of (*a*) molecular composition, (*b*) experimental observation.

4. Why did the wide-spread isolation of pure organic compounds coincide approximately in time with the development of analytical and physical chemistry?

5. Suggest five physical measurements which could be used to describe a compound.

6. What isotopes of carbon exist in nature? How many are known as synthetic isotopes?

7. Define and illustrate (*a*) isotope, (*b*) atomic number, (*c*) valence electrons, (*d*) orbital, (*e*) unshared electron pairs, (*f*) electron formulas, (*g*) valence.

8. What behavior of carbon as an element is the most distinctive?

9. Specify the oxidation states of (*a*) Mn in $KMnO_4$, (*b*) Cr in $Na_2Cr_2O_7$, (*c*) C in H_2CO_3, (*d*) C in CH_2O, (*e*) C in $H_2C_2O_4$ (average value).

10. Specify for each of the following changes whether an oxidizing agent, reducing agent, or neither would be required.

(*a*) $CH_4 \longrightarrow CH_3OH$

(*b*) $CH_3OH \longrightarrow CH_3Cl$

(*c*) $CH_3OH \longrightarrow HCO_2H$

(*d*) $CO \longrightarrow HCO_2Na$

(*e*) $H_2C_2O_4 \longrightarrow 2\ CO_2 + H_2O$

(*f*) $H_2O_2 \longrightarrow \frac{1}{2} O_2 + H_2O$

2 · FORMULAS AND STRUCTURES
OF COMPOUNDS WHICH CONTAIN
A SINGLE CARBON ATOM

The formula for a compound represents, in addition to elementary composition and molecular weight, the structure of its molecules. In some compounds, such as HCN and CO_2, the atoms are arranged in a straight line; in others, such as H_2CO, the atoms are in a plane. In methane, CH_4, and methyl alcohol, CH_3OH, three-dimensional figures are needed to describe the arrangements of the atoms. To arrive at such conclusions organic chemists established the order of attachment of the atoms to each other and the angles between bonds on any one carbon atom. The major deductions of the organic chemist have been confirmed by physicists. Through the use of X-ray and electron diffraction, and micro wave absorption, the distances apart of atoms in simple molecules may be determined.

Molecular composition. The kinds of atoms present in a compound and their relative numbers are determined through qualitative and quantitative analysis. The procedures for carbon and hydrogen detection and measurement involve combustion to carbon dioxide and water respectively. For the qualitative detection of nitrogen, sulfur, and the halogens the sample is heated strongly in the presence of metallic sodium. Any nitrogen present is then found in the form of cyanide (NaCN); sulfur becomes sulfide (Na_2S), and a halogen attached to carbon is converted to inorganic halide (NaCl). The ions, CN^-, Cl^-, Br^-, I^-, S^{--}, are then detected in the usual ways. For quantitative analysis, weighed samples are subjected to various procedures which convert each element present into a form of known composition and which can be weighed or measured. These procedures, based upon combustion of the sample, are summarized on page 15. The per cent of oxygen present is usually obtained by subtracting from 100% the sum of the percentages of the other elements. From the percentage composition the ratios of the different atoms present are calculated.

Molecular weights. It is essential to know the molecular weights of compounds because many substances may have the same percent-

13

COMPOUNDS CONTAINING A SINGLE CARBON ATOM

Systematic Name	Common Name	Formula	Structure
Carbon dioxide	Carbonic acid gas	CO_2	$O=C=O$
Carbonic acid	Soda water	H_2CO_3	$HO-C(\!=\!O)-OH$
Methanoic acid	Formic acid	H_2CO_2	$H-C(\!=\!O)-OH$
Carbon monoxide	Carbon monoxide	CO	$C=O$
Methanal	Formaldehyde, formalin (in water)	CH_2O	$H-C(H)\!=\!O$
Methanol	Methyl alcohol, wood alcohol	CH_4O	$H-C-OH$
Methane	Natural gas, marsh gas, fire damp	CH_4	$H-C-H$
Chloromethane	Methyl chloride	CH_3Cl	$H-C-Cl$
Dichloromethane	Methylene chloride	CH_2Cl_2	$H-C-Cl$
Trichloromethane	Chloroform	$CHCl_3$	$Cl-C-Cl$
Tetrachloromethane	Carbon tetrachloride	CCl_4	$Cl-C-Cl$
Triiodomethane	Iodoform	CHI_3	$I-C-I$

Systematic Name	Common Name	Formula	Structure
Carbon disulfide	Carbon disulfide	CS_2	$S=C=S$
Aminomethane	Methyl amine	CH_5N	$H-C-NH_2$
Formonitrile	Hydrocyanic acid, prussic acid	HCN	$H-C\equiv N$ or $H-N=C$
Iodomethane	Methyl iodide	CH_3I	$H-C-I$
Dichlorodifluoromethane	Freon	CCl_2F_2	$Cl-C-F$ (with F, Cl)
Carbamide	Urea	CON_2H_4	$O=C(NH_2)(NH_2)$
Carbonyl chloride	Phosgene	$COCl_2$	$O=C(Cl)(Cl)$
Nitromethane		CH_3O_2N	$H-C-NO_2$
Methyl nitrite		CH_3O_2N	$H-C-O-NO$
Methyl mercaptan		CH_4S	$H-C-SH$
Methyl sulfate		CH_4SO_4	$H-C-O-SO_3H$

age of each element present but differ in molecular formula. Such a situation exists between formaldehyde and grape sugar; the one is CH_2O, the other $C_6H_{12}O_6$ or $(CH_2O)_6$. The molecular weight of formaldehyde (or any gas) may be obtained by measuring the volume, temperature, pressure, and weight of a sample of the gas, and then applying the gas laws to these measurements to find how much of the gas would be present in 22.4 liters at 0° C and 760 mm of Hg pressure (the molal volume under standard conditions). For the sugar one would observe the freezing point of a solution in water of known composition. The freezing point of a water solution is − 1.86° C if one gram-mole of solute is present in 1000 g of water. Other solvents have, similarly, molal freezing point depressions characteristic of each solvent. The lowering of the freezing point from that of the pure solvent is proportional to the concentration of the solute expressed in gram-moles per 1000 grams of solvent.

QUANTITATIVE COMBUSTION METHODS			
Element	Combustion Medium and Name of Process	Product Measured	Absorbent
C	O_2 and CuO (Liebig)	CO_2	KOH
H	O_2 and CuO (Liebig)	H_2O	H_2SO_4 or $CaCl_2$
N	CuO and CO_2 (Dumas)	N_2 (gas)	_ _ _ _
N	Conc. H_2SO_4 (Kjeldahl)	NH_3	Standard acid
S	HNO_3 (Conc.)(300°)(Carius)	$BaSO_4$	_ _ _ _
Halogen	HNO_3 (Conc.)(300°)(Carius)	AgX	_ _ _ _

Valences and electron distribution. The valence of an atom is the number of points of attachment of that atom to other atoms or radicals. We may assume, as a first approximation, that carbon has a valence of four, oxygen two, hydrogen one, nitrogen three or four, and sulfur two, four, or six. Each bond involves a pair of electrons. These occupy an orbital which includes the two atomic centers. With a valence of four, carbon is associated with four pairs of electrons (eight electrons) and its neon shell is complete. In the case of trivalent nitrogen in ammonia a fourth (unshared) electron pair is present and it completes the octet. In carbon dioxide one must write double bonds (O=C=O) to satisfy the assumed valences of carbon and oxygen, but this does not mean that four electrons occupy a given orbital. In such multiple bonds the electron distribution is not quite that of two single bonds; one pair of electrons occupies what one may term a normal single-bond orbital, while the other pair occupies a different kind of orbital, differing in shape and in energy of bond formation. Two atoms joined by double bonds are not as far apart as they are when held by single bonds; moreover, one of the bonds, since its energy of rupture is less, is much more reactive than is a normal single bond.

An alternative to writing double bonds is to represent one of the bonds as being ionized. For instance, the molecule H_2CO could be written

$$\begin{array}{c} H \\ \diagdown \\ \diagup \\ H \end{array} C{=}O \quad \text{or} \quad \begin{array}{c} H \\ \diagdown \\ \diagup \\ H \end{array} C^{+}{-}O^{-},$$

corresponding to the electron formulas $\overset{H}{\underset{H}{\cdot}} C :: \overset{\cdot\cdot}{\underset{\cdot}{O}}$ and $\overset{H}{\underset{H}{\cdot}} C^{+} : \overset{\cdot\cdot}{\underset{\cdot\cdot}{O}} :^{-}.$

Such ionization, or charge separation, could be detected by physical tools. The substance would not conduct electricity, but it would have a high dielectric constant if it were to any large degree in the polarized form; the heat of vaporization would be high due to molecular attractions through the high electrical field. However, this substance, formaldehyde, is a gas at room temperature and the double bond more nearly represents its electron distribution. Neither structure precisely describes the electron distribution; the electrons settle into orbitals of such shape as to have some of the features of both structures.

Another case of valence uncertainty is to be found in the molecule $H_3C{-}NO_2$. To write its structure as

$$H_3C{-}N \begin{array}{c} \diagup O \\ \diagdown O \end{array}$$

implies that nitrogen shares ten electrons. Since this is impossible the issue is compromised by writing

$$H_3C{-}N \underset{+}{\overset{\diagup O}{\diagdown O^{-}}} \quad \text{or} \quad H_3C{-}\overset{+}{N} \begin{array}{c} \diagup O^{-} \\ \diagdown O \end{array},$$

where the ionization, or dipole, results from the stability of the neon shell, but where the position of the negative charge is indeterminate.

Once again, we assume that the actual molecule, in its electron distribution, is neither one nor the other, but a composite of both. This substance, in its physical properties, does show a marked charge separation. To be explicit, the electrical moment of a $> C = O$ group is about 1.5 Debye units, while that of a $- NO_2$ group is about 3 Debye units; if the charge separation were the maximum possible the moments would be of the order of 7 Debye units. The net result is a molecular structure which closely satisfies the assignments of valences given above, and satisfies the octet rule. Any structure so written as to give a carbon atom less than four valences as covalent bonds must be justified by physical and chemical properties of an unusual sort; such structures do exist, but are very rare.

Nomenclature. A table of some of the compounds which contain but one carbon atom per molecule is given on page 14. The list illustrates the variety and types of simple substances and raises the question of names and structures. Common, or trivial, names are inherited from associations of various sorts. For instance, we have wood alcohol, a by-product of charcoal manufacture; dry ice, a refrigerant; phosgene, a substance prepared with the aid of light. The systematic names are based upon the hydride, or hydrocarbon, methane. Its formula is CH_4, and if hydrogen atoms in this molecule are replaced by other atoms or radicals we have such names as chloromethane for CH_3Cl, aminomethane for CH_3NH_2, and nitromethane for CH_3NO_2. The oxygen-containing compounds are alcohols, aldehydes, and acids; they are named by dropping the final letter in the hydrocarbon and adding the suffixes *ol*, *al*, and *oic*, to give methanol, methanal, and methanoic acid. A further variation in nomenclature uses an analogy from inorganic chemistry. Thus a chlorine derivative, CH_3Cl, becomes methyl chloride; this is misleading because the substance is not a salt, but it does picture the radical, methyl ($\cdot CH_3$), in combination with a chlorine atom. Other methyl derivatives are evident. The inherent confusion in current nomenclature is being dissipated by a growing use of systematic names; for the present, whenever a name appears, one must inquire as to its basis, whether it be systematic, trivial, or a trade name for advertising purposes.

The basis of structural determination. The structures of the compounds listed on page 14 are based upon the tetravalence of carbon, with two exceptions. In the cases of carbon monoxide and one of the structures for hydrocyanic acid, an apparent divalent carbon is written; but the actual structures involve the disposition of ten valence electrons in each case, and only two (CO) or four (HCN) are needed respectively to give the primary bonds. The remaining electrons participate in bonding, but not in orbitals equivalent to simple co-valent bonds. The simplest electron structure for cyanide ion, $(: C ::: N :)^-$, is seen to have two positions for acquisition of hydrogen ion, one on carbon, one on nitrogen. Probably the former prevails.

FACTS REPRESENTED BY A STRUCTURAL FORMULA

1. Composition of the compound
2. Molecular weight of the compound
3. Order of attachment of atoms in the molecule
4. Presence of characteristic groups, such as methyl ($-CH_3$), hydroxyl ($-OH$), amino ($-NH_2$), carboxyl

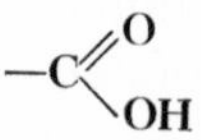

$$-C{\overset{O}{\underset{OH}{\diagup\diagdown}}}$$

and aldehyde

$$-C{\overset{O}{\underset{H}{\diagup\diagdown}}}$$

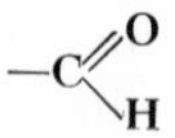

groups
5. Chemical and physical properties as judged by the reactions given by the characterizing groups present and by properties associated with these groups
6. Valence (number of points of attachment) of each atom
7. Methods of synthesis, as judged by the general methods used to prepare compounds containing the characterizing groups
8. Systematic name of the compound

The tetravalence of carbon is virtually inviolable and the main problem is order of attachment. For instance, since a definitely monovalent chlorine atom may replace one oxygen and one hydrogen atom in methyl alcohol, it is concluded that an hydroxyl radical is present in the alcohol.

$$H_3C-OH + HCl^{(Conc.)} \overset{Heat}{\rightleftarrows} H_3C-Cl + H_2O$$

The reaction is slow and reversible.

Similarly, the formula of carbonic acid (H_2CO_3) could be written in two ways, either of which would satisfy conventional valence numbers.

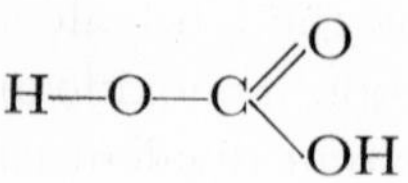

$$H-O-C{\overset{O}{\underset{OH}{\diagup\diagdown}}} \quad \text{or} \quad H-C{\overset{O}{\underset{O-O-H}{\diagup\diagdown}}}$$

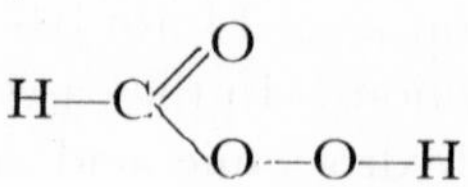

A substance of the second structure would be expected to oxidize hydriodic acid to iodine, as does hydrogen peroxide, H—O—O—H, and as carbonic acid does not. Moreover, carbonic acid is dibasic and rarely does a proton attached to carbon have a detectable degree of ionization, so the first formula is favored.

Two compounds have the formula CH_3O_2N. One of them, known as nitromethane, boils at $101.9°$ C: the other, methyl nitrite, boils at $-12°$ C. Upon reduction with iron in hydrochloric acid the one gives a salt of methyl amine, the other gives methanol and ammonium ion.

$$CH_3NO_2 + 2\ Fe + 7\ H^+ \longrightarrow CH_3\overset{+}{N}H_3 + 2\ \overset{+++}{Fe} + 2\ H_2O$$

$$CH_3ONO + 2\ Fe + 7\ H^+ \longrightarrow \overset{+}{N}H_4 + 2\ \overset{+++}{Fe} + CH_3OH + H_2O$$

The one which gives a product containing a carbon-nitrogen bond is presumed to possess that bond; while the one which yields the alcohol is assigned a carbon-oxygen bond.

A similar set of facts and arguments may be used to show that in a sodium salt of the composition CH_3SO_3Na the carbon atom is attached directly to the sulfur atom. Upon reduction it retains the sulfur atom; H_3C—SH, methyl mercaptan, is formed.

Bond angles and bond distances. These critical factors, which govern the sizes and shapes of molecules, are discussed in succeeding chapters.

EXERCISES

1. Assign two names to each of the following: (a) CH_3Cl, (b) CH_3NH_2, (c) $CHCl_3$, (d) CH_3OH, (e) HCO_2H, (f) CCl_2F_2.

2. Write possible structures for each of the following compounds to show the order of attachment and valences of the atoms: (a) H_2CO_2, (b) H_2CO_3, (c) CH_5N, (d) CON_2H_4, (e) CH_4S, (f) CH_3NO_2, (g) CH_4SO_4.

3. Write the electron formula corresponding to each structure written in Exercise 2.

4. What facts indicate (a) that carbonic acid is $O{=}C(OH)_2$ and not H—C—O—O—H? (b) that methyl nitrite has no carbon-nitrogen bond, while nitromethane has such a bond?

5. Write the electron structures of nitromethane and methyl nitrite and in terms of the charge distribution account for the large difference in the boiling points of the two compounds.

6. What is meant by the terms (a) *molecular formula*? (b) *structural formula*?

3 · METHANE
AND ITS OXIDATION PRODUCTS

Methane. This compound is composed of carbon and hydrogen only, and it is the simplest member of the class of compounds called *hydrocarbons*. It is a colorless, odorless, inflammable gas, and with air it forms a highly explosive mixture. Natural gas, which is used in some districts as a fuel, is largely methane; the odor associated with such gas is due to sulfur compounds which are added deliberately in very small amounts to permit detection of the gas if it should escape. Methane is not poisonous, but in high concentration it causes asphyxiation through displacement of air. Water gas, on the other hand, is highly toxic. Water gas is made by passing steam over hot coal, and it consists mainly of carbon monoxide and hydrogen.

The formula of methane is CH_4; hence its molecular weight is comparable to the molecular weights of water and ammonia. However, it is much more difficult to liquefy than is ammonia; the boiling points of the two liquids are $-161.5°$ and $-33.3°$ respectively.

Methane is usually found associated with petroleum, which is a mixture of hydrocarbons. The decay of vegetable matter due to the action of microorganisms under oxygen-free conditions leads to the production of methane. The gas bubbles from the water of marshes and issues from deposits of coal and peat; it is a source of danger in coal mines. The old names *marsh gas* and *fire damp* are still sometimes applied to methane; the former indicates one of the natural sources of the gas, and the latter reflects the danger of gas explosions in coal mines.

The commercial value of methane, in addition to its value as a fuel, is due largely to the availability of the hydrogen present in it. At very high temperatures (1000°) methane dissociates into carbon and hydrogen.

$$CH_4 \xrightarrow{\text{Heat}} C + 2\,H_2$$

This is a major source of hydrogen for nitrogen fixation, that is, for the conversion of atmospheric nitrogen into ammonia. The carbon black which is formed can be prepared in such a way that it is suitable for use in the manufacture of rubber tires. Carbon which is not good enough for use in tires can be made into briquettes and burned as fuel.

20

Methane, ammonia, and water differ markedly not only in melting points and boiling points but in chemical properties. Methane is very slightly soluble in water, while ammonia dissolves in and reacts with water. Water reacts vigorously with metallic sodium; liquid ammonia reacts slowly with the metal; liquid methane does not react with sodium. The electrical conductivity of methane is *nil*, whereas both water and liquid ammonia are slightly ionized and are poor conductors. Ammonia and water react rapidly with chlorine and bromine under ordinary conditions, but methane requires heat or light to initiate a reaction:

$$H_2O + Cl_2 \underset{\xrightarrow{\text{Fast; 20°}}}{\rightleftarrows} HOCl + HCl$$

$$NH_3 + Cl_2 \underset{\xrightarrow{\text{Fast; 20°}}}{\rightleftarrows} NH_2Cl + HCl$$

$$CH_4 + Cl_2 \xrightarrow{\text{Heat}} CH_3Cl + HCl$$

Molecular structures. Water and ammonia combine with the HCl formed in the reactions with chlorine, but methane does not. These differences in properties and reactivities between the compounds methane, ammonia, and water are associated with differences in molecular structures.

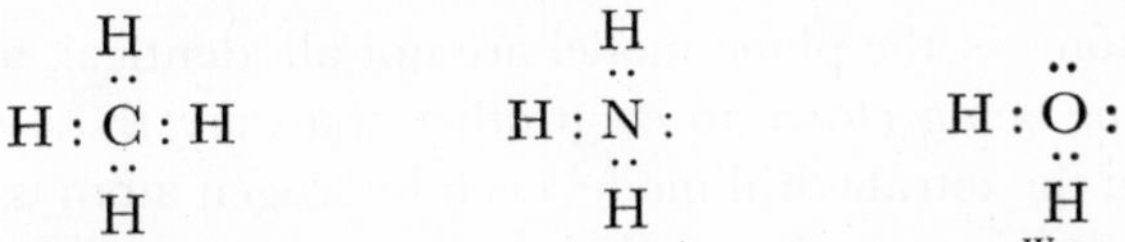

Methane   Ammonia   Water

When formulas which show the valence electrons are compared, it is seen that the carbon compound has no unshared electron pairs, and its four valences are satisfied. Both water and ammonia, through their capacities to contribute electron pairs to a possible reagent, react more readily. The chemical inertness of methane and similar hydrocarbons toward most reagents at room temperature is a major characteristic of this class of compounds. The inertness of paraffin wax illustrates the resistance to chemical change of a hydrocarbon of the methane type.

The structure of methane—that is, the way in which the hydrogen atoms are arranged about the carbon atom—might be pictured in one of two ways:

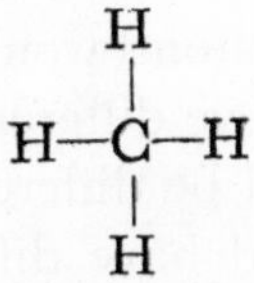

Plane Model 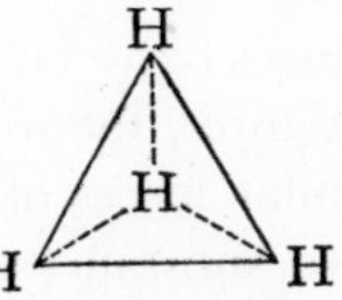   Tetrahedral Model

In the planar structure the carbon atom corresponds to the hub of a wheel with a hydrogen atom on each of four spokes, and the five atoms lie in a single plane. In the tetrahedral, three-dimensional model the carbon atom is located at the center of a tetrahedron with a hydrogen atom at each apex. In the first case the bond angle subtended by two adjacent hydrogen atoms at the center of the molecule is 90°; in the tetrahedral model it is 109° 28′. The distances between

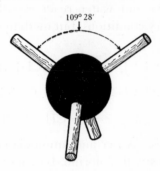

109° 28′

FIG. 1. A Model of the Carbon Atom · *Atoms or groups attached to the ends of the pegs would be at the points of a tetrahedron*

hydrogen atoms in the plane model are not all identical, adjacent hydrogen atoms being closer to each other than are those on opposite sides; but in the tetrahedral model each hydrogen atom is equidistant from each of the other three. This suggests a means of determining which is the actual form of the molecule. If methane has the planar structure, we should be able to prepare from it two different dichloromethanes, CH_2Cl_2. On the plane model the structures of the two compounds would be as follows:

```
        H                           H
        |                           |
   H—C—Cl                      Cl—C—Cl
        |                           |
       Cl                           H
```

Two Hypothetical Planar Models for Dichloromethane

Since the distances between the two chlorine atoms would be different in the two structures, the molecules would have different shapes, and the intermolecular forces of attraction would be different in the two cases. The two substances, therefore, would have different boiling points and different solubilities, and they could be separated. On the other hand, only one substance of the formula CH_2Cl_2 could exist in the tetrahedral form. The fact is that after a century of search, only one dichloromethane has been obtained, and the planar structure is eliminated.

Many other facts indicate a tetrahedral arrangement of atoms or groups attached to a carbon atom. Long after the organic chemists considered the issue closed in favor of the tetrahedral model, physicists discovered methods by which the relative positions and the distances between atoms attached to carbon could actually be measured. The methods of measuring the distances and the angles between atoms depend upon X-ray diffraction and electron diffraction. By these methods it has been proved that carbon tetrachloride, CCl_4, has the form of a regular tetrahedron, and the bond angle subtended by two chlorine atoms in carbon tetrachloride and in dichloromethane is found to be about 109°. We shall often use the formula

for methane, but we shall use it only as a simplified representation of a tetrahedron. It must be remembered that formulas of this type, as used in this book and in the chemical journals, do not imply planar structures.

Methanol, or methyl alcohol, CH_3OH, was at first called wood alcohol, because it belongs to the class of compounds known as alcohols and is obtained commercially as a by-product in the destructive distillation of wood. Actually the wood is not distilled; it is heated in a kiln for the purpose of manufacturing charcoal and is partially decomposed by the heat treatment. In the general process of disintegration, water and many volatile organic substances are formed, and these volatile products are removed from the charcoal by distillation. The distillate separates into a layer of tar and a layer of water. In the water layer methanol, acetic acid, acetone, and other products are held in solution. A ton of dried wood yields about 500 pounds of charcoal, 30 to 40 pounds of methanol, 75 pounds of acetic acid, 100 pounds of tar, and 3500 cubic feet of gas (mainly carbon monoxide and carbon dioxide). Methanol may be regarded as an oxidation product of methane, but it is not actually made from methane.

The direct oxidation of methane cannot be stopped at the methanol stage, but indirect methods of making the alcohol from methane are available.

An alcohol contains an —OH group attached to carbon. This fact is indicated in the systematic naming of alcohols through the use of the suffix *ol*, substituted for the final *e* in the name of the most closely related hydrocarbon. Methanol, CH_3OH, is a derivative of methane, and ethanol, CH_3—CH_2OH, the ordinary alcohol which is produced in the fermentation of sugars and fruit juices, is a derivative of ethane. Since alcohols and water have one group of atoms (the hydroxyl group) in common, they have some similar properties. Some of the properties of water, methane, methanol, ammonia, and methyl chloride are listed in the table below.

PROPERTIES OF SOME SIMPLE COMPOUNDS

Substance	Boiling Point °C	Melting Point °C	Density g/cc	Solubility g/100 g H_2O
HOH	100	0	1 (4°)	
CH_3OH	64.6	− 97.8	0.796 (15°)	*
CH_3Cl	− 23.7	− 97.6	0.991 (− 25°)	0.8
NH_3	− 33.3	− 77.7	0.817 (− 79°)	50.
CH_4	− 161.5	− 184	0.46 (− 164°)	0.006

Only two of these substances, water and methanol, are liquids at ordinary temperatures and pressures; the others are gases. Methane and methyl chloride are sparingly soluble in water, while methanol is miscible with water in all proportions. Ammonia is very soluble in water. Within this group of compounds methane has the lowest boiling point, lowest melting point, and lowest density. Comparisons of many compounds of these types have led to the following conclusions:

1. The introduction of the OH group in the place of a hydrogen atom in a hydrocarbon raises the boiling point, increases the solubility in water, and increases the density.

2. The exchange of a chlorine atom for a hydrogen atom in a hydrocarbon increases the density, but makes only minor changes in boiling point and solubility.

*Soluble in all proportions.

3. Substances of low boiling points, such as hydrocarbons, boil at low temperatures because the molecules do not attract each other strongly.

4. High-boiling substances, such as water and methanol, have strong intermolecular attractions, and they evaporate relatively slowly.

The methanol molecule is composed of two parts, one like methane, the other like water. Because of the presence of the hydroxyl group, methanol mixes well with water; and because it has a CH_3 group, methanol dissolves methane and methyl chloride to a greater extent than water does. The chemical properties of methanol bear some resemblance to those of water. Metallic sodium reacts with both to form hydrogen gas and an ionized sodium compound:

$$Na + HOH \longrightarrow Na^+ + OH^- + \tfrac{1}{2} H_2$$
$$Na + CH_3OH \longrightarrow Na^+ + CH_3O^- + \tfrac{1}{2} H_2$$

The organic product, CH_3ONa, is an oxide, in this case sodium methoxide. In the presence of water the methoxide is almost completely hydrolyzed:

$$CH_3ONa + H_2O \; \rightleftarrows \; CH_3OH + Na^+ + OH^-$$

The fact that hydrolysis is nearly complete shows that methanol is a weaker acid than water and that methoxide ion is a stronger base than is hydroxide ion. In round numbers the degree of dissociation of an alcohol is about 1 per cent of the degree of dissociation of water.

Like most alcohols, methanol is a poison; as little as ten grams will produce illness, and a larger dose may cause blindness or death. The reasons for such physiological reactions, and for the large variation in physiological properties among different alcohols, are not known. Methanol is used to prepare formaldehyde, methyl chloride, and many esters and ethers. It is commonly used as a solvent for shellac.

Formaldehyde, HCHO, is an oxidation product of methanol. The oxidation is accomplished with oxygen of the air in the presence of metallic silver or copper:

$$2 \underset{\text{Methanol}}{CH_3OH} + O_2 \xrightarrow[\text{Heat}]{Ag} 2 \underset{\text{Formaldehyde}}{CH_2O} + 2 H_2O$$

The product is a gas, which condenses to a liquid under atmospheric pressure at $-21°$. Formaldehyde is very soluble in water; it associates or polymerizes slowly and forms a solid waxy substance called *paraform wax.* When the latter is heated, formaldehyde gas is regenerated. The vapor is very irritating and toxic. The gas has been used as a fumigant.

The more important uses of formaldehyde depend upon its ability to combine with a variety of substances, including phenols and urea, to form plastics and resins. Such substances are complex, of very high molecular weight, tough rather than brittle, and they can be cast or molded into desired shapes. The urea-formaldehyde resins may be made as clear and colorless as glass.

Formaldehyde belongs to a class of compounds known as aldehydes, each member of which contains the group —CHO, or

$$-C\overset{\displaystyle H}{\underset{\displaystyle O}{\diagup\diagdown}}$$

Many perfumes and flavors contain aldehydes; examples are oil of bitter almonds, vanilla, cinnamon, and oil of violet. Since formaldehyde itself is toxic and irritating in odor, it is clear that the pleasing properties of the other aldehydes mentioned above are due not to the aldehyde group as such but to a combination of the aldehyde group with other organic groups. All these substances have chemical reactions in common which permit their classification as aldehydes.

Formic acid. The name *formic acid* is derived from the Latin name for "ant" (*formica*). The irritation caused by the sting of ants and bees is due to this substance. Formic acid is a colorless liquid (bp 100.8°); it is miscible with water in all proportions. Formic acid is somewhat stronger than acetic acid. A 0.1 N solution of acetic acid is ionized to the extent of 1.3 per cent, while formic acid of the same normality is 4.5 per cent ionized. The equilibrium for the dissociation of formic acid is written as follows:

$$HCOOH \rightleftarrows HCOO^- + H^+$$

In more dilute solutions the ionization increases, as could be predicted from the mass law. The equilibrium shifts with dilution in the direction which increases the number of solute molecules present; that is, it tends to counteract the dilution by producing more solute molecules. Since by dissociation the number of solute molecules is doubled, dissociation is promoted by dilution. In a 0.01 N solution of formic acid the amount ionized is 13 per cent.

The structure of formic acid is

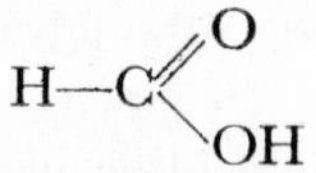

$$H-C\overset{O}{\underset{OH}{\diagup}}$$

This is in accordance with the assignment of a valence of four to carbon, of two to oxygen, and of one to each hydrogen atom in the molecule. The formula is often abbreviated to HCOOH or HCO_2H for the sake of simplicity in writing or printing. The group of atoms responsible for the acidity,

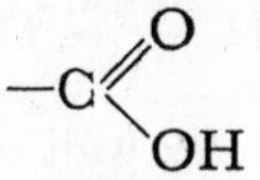

$$-C\overset{O}{\underset{OH}{\diagup}}$$

is called the *carboxyl group*. Any carbon compound of similar acidity contains this group; any structure containing this group is an acid. Acetic acid, $C_2H_4O_2$, has the structure

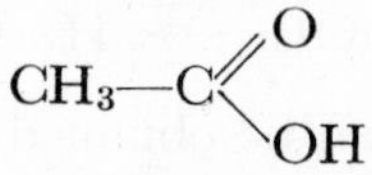

$$CH_3-C\overset{O}{\underset{OH}{\diagup}}$$

Formic acid is readily oxidized to carbonic acid. The oxidation is accomplished by permanganate ion or by mercuric ion. The reaction with mercuric chloride proceeds as follows:

$$HCOOH + 2\ HgCl_2 + H_2O \xrightarrow{Heat} H_2CO_3 + 2\ HgCl + 2\ HCl$$

   Formic acid   Mercuric chloride   Carbonic acid   Mercurous chloride

This reaction is used as a test for the acid, since mercurous chloride is insoluble and its precipitation is easily observed. Acetic acid does not reduce mercuric salts. This difference between the two acids shows that hydrogen attached to a carbon atom which is already holding an oxygen atom is rapidly attacked by an oxidizing agent. Thus formaldehyde,

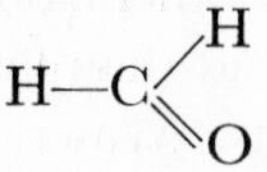

$$H-C\overset{H}{\underset{O}{\diagup}}$$

and formic acid,

$$H-C\overset{OH}{\underset{O}{\diagup}}$$

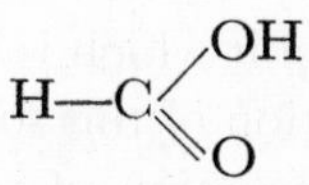

are very readily oxidized. Compounds like acetic acid,

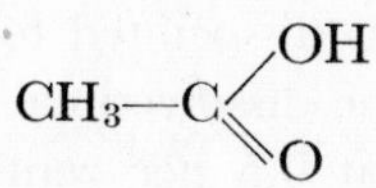

$$CH_3-C\overset{OH}{\underset{O}{\diagup}}$$

which do not have hydrogen and oxygen attached to the same carbon atom, are not readily oxidized, although the possibility of further oxidation exists.

Dehydrogenation of formic acid occurs at 160° or at a higher temperature:

$$H—COOH \xrightarrow{160°} H_2 + CO_2$$

When formic acid is heated in the presence of a little concentrated sulfuric acid, a dehydration to carbon monoxide takes place:

$$H—COOH \xrightarrow[\text{Heat}]{H_2SO_4} CO + H_2O$$

The sulfuric acid is a catalyst, as well as a dehydrating agent. This reaction furnishes a very good method of preparing pure carbon monoxide. Carbon monoxide does not add water again to yield formic acid, but it reacts with fused sodium hydroxide to give sodium formate:

$$CO + NaOH \xrightarrow{\text{Heat}} H—COONa$$

A solution of formic acid can be obtained from the salt, sodium formate, by mixing a saturated aqueous solution of the salt with sulfuric acid and distilling the mixture.

Another useful reaction of carbon monoxide is its addition to chlorine to yield phosgene:

$$CO + Cl_2 \xrightarrow{\text{Light}} \begin{array}{c} Cl \\ \diagdown \\ Cl \diagup \end{array} C{=}O$$

Phosgene

The name *phosgene* implies a generation with the help of light. Such a reaction is called a photochemical reaction. High temperatures suffice as well to promote the addition. Phosgene is a very poisonous gas, but it is widely used in the syntheses of organic compounds.

Carbonic acid, H_2CO_3, is another oxidation product of methane. It seems to be a much weaker acid than formic acid. This conclusion is based upon the following facts: Water saturated at 20° with carbon dioxide at 760 mm pressure contains .0374 mole of carbon dioxide per liter, including any part of it which is in the form of carbonic acid. The hydrogen ion concentration of this solution is only $1.2 \times 10^{-4} N$; this means an apparent dissociation of only 0.33 per cent if all the carbon dioxide dissolved is in the form of carbonic acid. Formic acid at the same concentration is dissociated to the extent of about 8 per cent. Actually, however, the dissolved carbon dioxide is hydrated to only a slight extent. About 0.5 per cent of the carbon dioxide in solution is in the form of carbonic acid, H_2CO_3, and 99.5 per cent of it is in the form of CO_2. The following equilibria are established when carbon dioxide is dissolved in water:

$$CO_2 + H_2O \rightleftarrows H_2CO_3 \rightleftarrows H^+ + HCO_3^-$$

The small amount of H_2CO_3 present in the solution (one half of 1 per cent of the total CO_2) must be dissociated to the extent of about 60 per cent to produce the acidity found in a saturated solution of carbon dioxide. Formic acid of the same low normality is also ionized about 60 per cent because of the dilution. The compound H_2CO_3, therefore, is about as strong as formic acid, but it is impossible to produce a concentration of carbonic acid high enough to give a sour taste. Carbonic acid is represented by the structural formula

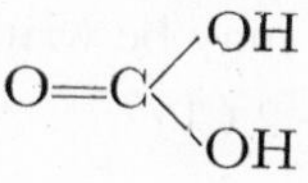

$$O=C{\Large\langle}^{OH}_{OH}$$

It differs from formic acid in having no hydrogen atom attached directly to carbon. In carbonic acid the oxidation state of carbon is at a maximum, and the compound cannot be oxidized further.

THE OXIDATION STATES OF A SINGLE CARBON ATOM					
	Oxidation State				
	+4	+2	0	−2	−4
Oxides	CO_2	CO			
Acids	HOCOOH (Carbonic acid)	HCOOH (Formic acid)			
Salts	$NaHCO_3$ (Sodium bicarbonate) Na_2CO_3 (Sodium carbonate)	HCOONa (Sodium formate)			
Aldehyde			HCHO (Formaldehyde)		
Alcohol				CH_3OH (Methanol)	
Hydrocarbon					CH_4
Halides	CCl_4	$CHCl_3$	CH_2Cl_2	CH_3Cl	

The oxidation of methane by chlorine. If chlorine is used to oxidize methane, a mixture of products is obtained:

$$CH_4 \xrightarrow{Cl_2} CH_3Cl \xrightarrow{Cl_2} CH_2Cl_2 \xrightarrow{Cl_2} CHCl_3 \xrightarrow{Cl_2} CCl_4$$

Methyl chloride   Methylene chloride   Chloroform   Carbon tetrachloride

In each of these successive reactions HCl is formed. The relative amounts of the chloromethanes which are formed depend upon the molal ratio of methane to chlorine at the start and the relative rates of the individual steps. For example, by passing a gaseous mixture of 70% CH_4, 10% Cl_2, and 20% N_2 through a reactor at about 400° C, there is obtained for each mole of CH_3Cl, 0.8 mole $CHCl_2$, 0.36 mole $CHCl_3$, and 0.08 mole CCl_4.

The chlorination of methane is not a spontaneous process; to initiate it there is required light of a wave length shorter than about 4800 Angstrom units $(1 A = 1 \times 10^{-8} cm.)$, or a temperature of 300°–400° C. The initiating step is the absorption of energy which results in the dissociation of chlorine molecules into chlorine atoms. If the symbol $h\nu$ be used to represent the energy of a photon of frequency ν, the initiating step may be written as follows:

$$Cl : Cl + h\nu \longrightarrow 2\ Cl \cdot \qquad \text{Initiating reaction}$$

The chlorine atoms are then consumed and regenerated in a pair of steps which together constitute the chlorination reaction.

$$H_3C : H\ +\ \cdot Cl \longrightarrow H_3C \cdot\ +\ H : Cl$$
$$H_3C \cdot\ +\ Cl : Cl \longrightarrow H_3C : Cl\ +\ Cl \cdot \qquad \text{Propagating reactions}$$

One initiating step may cause thousands of molecules of product to be formed; such a mechanism is called a chain mechanism. The chains may be broken (the reaction stopped) by processes which consume one or the other of the radicals.

$$Cl \cdot + Wall \longrightarrow 1/2\ Cl_2 \qquad \text{Terminating reaction}$$

Methyl chloride is converted to CH_2Cl_2 at the same time by a similar chain reaction.

Radical chain reactions are relatively rare. Usually reactions involve the rupture and making of bonds by ionic-type processes during which the valence electrons remain paired. Some oxidations by oxygen proceed through intermediary radicals.

It would appear feasible to subject methane to a succession of oxidations analogous to successive chlorinations.

$$CH_4 \longrightarrow CH_3OH \longrightarrow H\!-\!CHO \longrightarrow H\!-\!CO_2H \longrightarrow CO_2$$

However, methyl alcohol is never observed as a product of the direct oxidation of methane, for one of two possible reasons, (1) the reaction mechanism does not lead to its formation, or (2) the alcohol is itself too rapidly oxidized to accumulate.

EXERCISES

1. What is the main component of natural gas?

2. Write the structural and electronic formulas of each of the following compounds: water, methane, ammonia, formaldehyde, methanol, formic acid, carbonic acid, chloroform.

3. Ammonia and water react with HCl. Write equations for the reactions.

4. Does methane react with HCl, Na, Cl_2, or O_2? If so, write equations for the reactions and state the conditions under which the reactions occur.

5. What group of atoms is common to formic and carbonic acids? What is it called?

6. What reactions with Na, Cl_2, and HCl are given by H_2O and CH_3OH as a result of the presence of the hydroxyl group?

7. Insert in a rubber ball four pins to represent four equidistant bonds. What is the bond angle in degrees? How many compounds of the formula CH_2Cl_2 would you expect to exist if methane were (a) planar, (b) tetrahedral, in configuration? State the reasons for your answer. How many do exist?

PROBLEMS

1. If evolution of H_2 by Na is an indication of ionization, what conclusion do you reach as to ionization in H_2O, CH_3OH, and CH_4? Could the hydrogen be evolved without prior ionization? Suggest an alternate qualitative test for ionization.

2. Present the facts and argument which show that CO_2 in water does not form an acid weaker than acetic acid, but one much stronger.

3. Define: weak acid; strength of an acid; normality of an acid; change in oxidation state; equivalent of an oxidizing (reducing) agent.

4. What changes, if any, in oxidation state per mole occur during the following conversion:

(a) $CH_3OH \longrightarrow H{-}COOH$,   (b) $CHCl_3 \longrightarrow COCl_2$,

(c) $CH_2Cl_2 \longrightarrow CH_2O + 2\,HCl$,   (d) $H{-}CHO \longrightarrow CH_3OH$.

5. Detail the radical-chain mechanism for the conversion of CH_4 to CH_3Cl; of CH_3Cl to CH_2Cl_2. State how a comparison of the amount of light absorbed to the amount of Cl_2 reacted proves the chain mechanism.

6. Outline in equations methods of commercial production of CH_3OH, H_2, HCHO, HCO_2H, and CO_2.

4 · COMPOUNDS OF TWO CARBON ATOMS; THE CARBON-CARBON BOND

The classes of substances mentioned in our consideration of compounds containing a single carbon atom find their counterparts among the organic compounds containing two carbon atoms. Those composed of carbon and hydrogen and of carbon, hydrogen, and oxygen are listed in the table below.

COMPOUNDS OF CARBON AND HYDROGEN AND OF CARBON, HYDROGEN, AND OXYGEN	
Classes of Compounds	Composition of Compounds
Hydrocarbons	Composed of carbon and hydrogen only
Alcohols	Contain at least one hydroxyl group, but not more than one hydroxyl group attached to a single carbon atom
Aldehydes	Contain the aldehyde group $-C\begin{smallmatrix}\nearrow O\\\searrow H\end{smallmatrix}$
Acids	Contain the carboxyl group $-C\begin{smallmatrix}\nearrow O\\\searrow OH\end{smallmatrix}$
Ethers	Contain oxygen with the two valence bonds of the oxygen atom satisfied by attachment to two carbon atoms, as in CH_3-O-CH_3
Esters	Contain two oxygen atoms, as in an acid, but the acidic hydrogen atom is replaced by an organic group, as in $CH_3-C\begin{smallmatrix}\nearrow O\\\searrow O-CH_3\end{smallmatrix}$

Specific examples of these types of compounds are given in the table below. The table is limited to compounds which are composed of carbon and hydrogen or carbon, hydrogen, and oxygen only. Compounds which contain nitrogen, sulfur, halogens, and other elements will be considered later.

Hydrocarbons

There are three hydrocarbons which have two carbon atoms in the molecule. They are ethane, C_2H_6; ethylene or ethene, C_2H_4; and acetylene or ethyne, C_2H_2. The first of the alternate names is the

	COMPOUNDS OF TWO CARBON ATOMS	
Classes of Compounds	Name of a Specific Example	Formula of the Specific Example

Hydrocarbons
  Alkane
  Alkene
  Alkyne
	Ethane
	Eth*ene*, or ethylene
	Eth*yne*, or acetylene
		H_3C—CH_3
		H_2C=CH_2
		HC≡CH

Alcohols	Ethan*ol*, or ethyl alcohol	CH_3—CH_2—OH
Aldehydes	Ethan*al*, or acetaldehyde	CH_3—$C\begin{smallmatrix}H\\\\O\end{smallmatrix}$
Acids	Acetic acid Oxalic acid	CH_3—$COOH$ $HOOC$—$COOH$
Ethers	Ethylene oxide Dimethyl ether	$\begin{smallmatrix}CH_2-CH_2\\\\O\end{smallmatrix}$ CH_3—O—CH_3
Esters	Methyl formate	H—$C\begin{smallmatrix}O\\\\OCH_3\end{smallmatrix}$

common name; the second has been adopted as the systematic name. These formulas represent the experimentally determined compositions and molecular weights of the compounds, and with the help of valence theory a molecular structure may be assigned to each compound.

Ethane, CH_3—CH_3, is a colorless gas which constitutes from 5 to 10 per cent of the volume of natural gas and is one of the products formed in the process of "cracking" petroleum. The term *cracking* is applied to the process of decomposing petroleum oils by heat. This is a commercial method of breaking heavy hydrocarbon molecules into lighter molecules and thereby increasing the yield of gasoline. In the laboratory, ethane can be prepared from methyl bromide and metallic sodium:

$$2\,CH_3\text{—}Br + 2\,Na \longrightarrow CH_3\text{—}CH_3 + 2\,NaBr$$

Ethylene, or ethene, CH_2=CH_2, is readily obtained through dehydration of ethyl alcohol:

$$H_2C\text{—}CH_2 \xrightarrow[\text{Catalyst}]{\text{Heat}} H_2C\text{=}CH_2 + H_2O$$
$$|\quad|$$
$$H\;\;OH$$

Water is lost from the alcohol; the hydroxyl group held by one carbon atom and a hydrogen atom attached to an adjacent carbon atom are eliminated with the help of an acidic catalyst. Sulfuric acid at about 160° or aluminum oxide at 300° serves as the catalyst.

Acetylene, or ethyne, $CH{\equiv}CH$, is prepared from calcium carbide, which in turn is made from coke and lime:

$$3\ C + CaO \xrightarrow{1,000°} CaC_2 + CO$$

$$CaC_2 + 2\ H_2O \xrightarrow{20°} Ca(OH)_2 + HC{\equiv}CH$$

Acetylene gas is used in welding and as a source of light. It is employed also as a reagent in many synthetic processes.

Unsaturation. The only way in which the tetravalence of carbon can be represented in formulas for ethene and ethyne is to write multiple bonds between the carbon atoms:

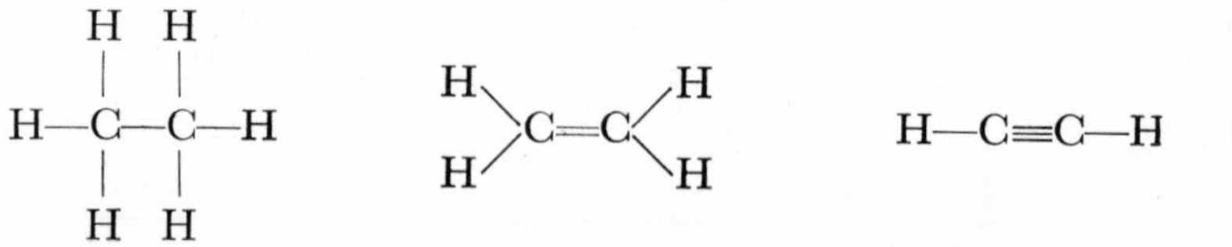

Ethane, saturated, single bond   Ethene, unsaturated, double bond   Ethyne, unsaturated, triple bond

In the presence of hydrogen gas and finely divided nickel both ethene and ethyne add hydrogen and are converted into the saturated compound, ethane:

$$H_2C{=}CH_2 + H_2 \xrightarrow{Ni} H_3C{-}CH_3$$

$$HC{\equiv}CH + 2\ H_2 \xrightarrow{Ni} H_3C{-}CH_3$$

The reaction is carried out at temperatures between 20° and 300°, and at pressures ranging from 1 to 300 atmospheres, the conditions depending upon the activity of the catalyst. No measurable addition of hydrogen occurs in the absence of the catalyst. Ethane does not combine with hydrogen, for to do so would require the breaking of the single bond between the carbon atoms. A single carbon-to-carbon bond is not easily ruptured; multiple bonds break readily.

Another reaction through which the presence of a double or triple bond is made evident is the rapid addition of bromine:

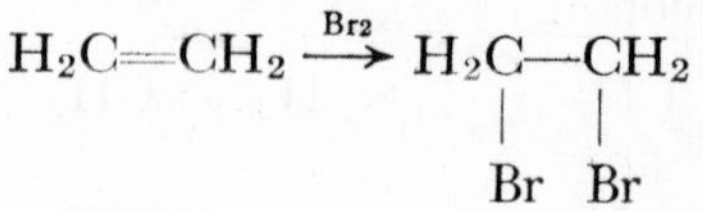

$$H_2C{=}CH_2 \xrightarrow{Br_2} H_2C{-}CH_2$$

$$\qquad\qquad\qquad\qquad\; \underset{Br\ \ \ Br}{|\quad|}$$

Ethylene   Dibromoethane

$$HC\!\equiv\!CH \xrightarrow[\text{Fast}]{\text{Br}_2} \underset{\underset{\text{Br \ Br}}{|\quad|}}{HC\!=\!CH} \xrightarrow[\text{Slow}]{\text{Br}_2} \overset{\overset{\text{Br \ Br}}{|\quad|}}{\underset{\underset{\text{Br \ Br}}{|\quad|}}{HC\!-\!CH}}$$

Acetylene   Dibromoethylene   Tetrabromoethane

A second bromine molecule may add to acetylene, as indicated above, to complete the saturation. This absorption of bromine can be followed readily, as the bromine is a red liquid (brown in solution) and the products of the reactions indicated above are colorless.

A hydrocarbon which adds hydrogen or bromine is said to be *unsaturated*. The rate of addition depends upon the nature of the unsaturated compound. In the case of acetylene the first bromine molecule adds rapidly, the second one slowly. The reactivity of the double bond is lessened when bromine atoms are attached to the carbon atoms.

The saturated hydrocarbons, ethane and methane, are relatively inert. The only ways in which they can react involve the rupture of a carbon-carbon bond or a carbon-hydrogen bond; and the fact that these gases do not react readily shows that carbon-carbon bonds and carbon-hydrogen bonds must be classed as nonpolar. Methane and ethane react with oxygen, but only at high temperatures; chlorine and bromine react with ethane in a manner analogous to that described for methane, the hydrogen atoms being successively replaced by halogen atoms. A replacement of one type of atom by another is called a *substitution reaction*. Chlorine may be substituted for hydrogen in ethane as follows:

$$C_2H_6 \xrightarrow[-HCl]{+Cl_2} C_2H_5Cl \xrightarrow[-HCl]{+Cl_2} C_2H_4Cl_2 \text{--------} C_2Cl_6$$

Here, as in the case of methane, light or a high temperature is required to start the reaction.

Hydrogen gas shows the same kind of inertness, that is, the hydrogen-hydrogen linkage is nonpolar in character. Hydrogen does not react rapidly at room temperature with oxygen or with bromine, or with ordinary oxidizing agents such as permanganate and dichromate ions. At high temperatures hydrogen, as well as the saturated hydrocarbons, react with these reagents, sometimes explosively. In the table on page 36 some reagents are listed which are potentially capable of reacting with both saturated and unsaturated hydrocarbons, but which at room temperature and in the dark do not react at measurable rates with methane or with ethane. It is seen that the oxidizing agents differ markedly in their reactivities toward unsaturated hydrocarbons; apparently their capacities to react are not directly related to their oxidizing potentials. The difference between sulfuric acid (95–100 per cent acid) and concentrated solutions of other strong acids is equally striking. In the table the word *rapid* implies a reaction which is completed in a few minutes at the most, while *very slow* means that no appreciable reaction occurs in hours or even days.

THE RATES OF REACTION OF SOME COMMON REAGENTS WITH UNSATURATED HYDROCARBONS

Reagent	Reaction Rate at 20°C
Bromine	Rapid
Chlorine	Rapid
Iodine	Rapid but incomplete
Oxygen	Very slow
Permanganate in alkali	Rapid
Chromic acid and chromates	Very slow
Sulfuric acid, concentrated	Moderately rapid
Nitric acid, concentrated	Slow at first; may explode

---

The presence of ethylene or acetylene in a gas which is mostly ethane can be detected by passing the gaseous mixture through bromine (dissolved in carbon tetrachloride) or through potassium permanganate (dissolved in sodium carbonate solution) or through concentrated sulfuric acid. In the first case the disappearance of bromine, as shown by loss of color, indicates the presence of an unsaturated gas. A permanganate solution also loses color if an easily oxidized gas is present; the permanganate is reduced to either manganate ion (green solution) or manganese dioxide (brown precipitate). Sulfuric acid dissolves any unsaturated gas without color change, but the decrease in volume of the gas passed through the acid is a measure of the reaction.

The reaction between an alkene and sulfuric acid may be written as follows:

$$H_2C{=}CH_2 + HOSO_3H \longrightarrow \underset{\substack{| \quad \ | \\ H \ \ OSO_3H}}{H_2C{-}CH_2}$$

or
$$\underset{\text{Ethylene}}{C_2H_4} + H_2SO_4 \longrightarrow \underset{\text{Ethyl hydrogen sulfate}}{C_2H_5HSO_4}$$

The reaction is one of *addition*, hydrogen ion going to one carbon atom and bisulfate ion (attached through an oxygen atom) to the other carbon atom. Bromine also reacts with unsaturated hydrocarbons by *addition*. The reaction with permanganate ion is one of *oxidation*; manganese is not found in the organic product.

Acetylene (ethyne) may be detected by a reaction which seems to contradict the usual rule that a hydrogen atom attached to carbon is inert. If the gas is passed through a solution containing silver-ammonia ions, a precipitate is formed. (Cuprous-ammonia ion reacts in the same way.)

$$H-C\equiv C-H + 2\ \overset{+}{Ag}(NH_3)_2 \longrightarrow Ag-C\equiv C-Ag + 2\ \overset{+}{NH_4} + 2\ NH_3$$

Acetylene   Silver acetylide

The silver acetylide thus formed (unless carefully purified) explodes upon gentle heating when it is dry. The formation of the acetylide is rapid and has all the characteristics of a simple ionic displacement of hydrogen ion by silver ion. Acetylene, however, is not appreciably ionized, as shown by the fact that a dilute solution of the gas in water is not a better conductor of electricity than is water alone. Another test is made by dissolving acetylene gas in heavy water (deuterium oxide D_2O or $_1H^2{}_2O$).* If acetylene ionizes in pure water, we should be able to prepare a heavy hydrogen derivative of the gas by shaking acetylene with heavy water. The following exchange should occur:

$$H-C\equiv C-H + DOD \rightleftarrows H-C\equiv C-D + DOH$$

Actually the isotopes H and D do not exchange when acetylene and pure heavy water are shaken together, but do exchange when alkali is present. This means that ionization is not spontaneous, but that alkali can react to a very slight degree with the *un-ionized* acetylene and that the resulting anion may then combine with either H^+ or D^+:

$$H-C\equiv C-H + OH^- \rightleftarrows H-C\equiv C^- + H_2O$$
$$H-C\equiv C^- + DOH \rightleftarrows H-C\equiv C-D + OH^-$$

Aqueous sodium hydroxide does not dissolve acetylene more than does water alone. It must be assumed, therefore, that only a vanish-

---

*When we write equations for reactions involving the nuclei of atoms, we indicate the atomic numbers and atomic weights by small subscripts and superscripts before and after the symbols of the atoms. Thus, to represent the capture of a neutron by ordinary hydrogen to form isotopic hydrogen of mass 2 (deuterium) we write the equation as follows:

$$_1H^1 + _0n^1 \longrightarrow _1H^2$$

The symbol D is commonly used for hydrogen of mass 2.

ingly small amount of acetylene reacts as an acid; yet that small amount is sufficient to allow the exchange reaction to be rapid. Here we have an apparent catalysis of the exchange by alkali. In the presence of alkali the exchange is rapid, while in its absence the exchange is so slow that the rate cannot be measured. The alkali is not consumed or neutralized in the process.

TESTS FOR UNSATURATION IN HYDROCARBONS

A. Double and triple bonds
1. Rapid decolorization of bromine
2. Rapid decolorization of an alkaline permanganate solution
3. Solution in concentrated sulfuric acid
4. Catalytic hydrogenation

B. Triple bond with hydrogen attached to triply linked carbon
1. Formation of copper and silver derivatives

Since ethane and ethene do not form silver salts or cuprous derivatives, or exchange hydrogen isotopes even in strong alkali, we conclude that these reactions are not typical of hydrocarbons as a class but only of hydrocarbons in which at least one hydrogen atom is attached to a triply linked carbon atom. Acetylene differs from ethylene in another respect: it is potentially unstable. When compressed, acetylene sometimes explodes. The products of the explosion are carbon and hydrogen. Heat is evolved when acetylene decomposes; and in the commercial use of compressed acetylene for welding, the energy of decomposition as well as the energy of combustion of the hydrogen and carbon is available. To make the compressed gas safe to handle, substances which inhibit explosion are used. Acetone is one substance which can be used for this purpose.

Alcohols

Ethyl alcohol. The best-known and most commonly used alcohol is ethanol, or ethyl alcohol, CH_3—CH_2OH, a colorless liquid which boils at 78.3°. The major source of the compound is the alcoholic fermentation of glucose. The reaction of fermentation may be written as follows:

$$C_6H_{12}O_6 \xrightarrow{\text{Enzymes}} 2\ C_2H_5OH + 2\ CO_2$$
$$\text{Glucose} \qquad\qquad\qquad \text{Alcohol}$$

Ethanol is commonly called grain alcohol, because grains have been used as the sources of starch from which glucose and, in turn, ethanol are derived. Ethyl alcohol is soluble in water in all proportions.

Alcoholic beverages, such as beer, wine, brandy, whisky, gin, and rum, contain ethanol in varying amounts. The maximum concentration of alcohol which can be produced by fermentation alone is about 15 per cent. A higher concentration of alcohol in a beverage is produced by a distillation process or by the addition of alcohol to the fermentation product.

Commercial ethanol (95 per cent alcohol) is a constant-boiling mixture of ethanol and water. It is made from glucose, derived from starch, or from molasses. The latter is a by-product of the sugar-refining industry. Molasses yields fructose as well as glucose, but both sugars are fermentable. Denatured alcohol is commercial alcohol to which has been added some substance to make it unpalatable but which does not interfere with its projected use. The amount of ethanol used commercially is many times greater than that consumed in beverages. Alcohol is nearly indispensable as a solvent in the drug and chemical industries, and it is one of the major raw materials used in making synthetic rubber. The ethyl group, C_2H_5—, and the ethoxy group, C_2H_5O—, of ethyl alcohol are incorporated by chemical methods in a great variety of drugs, dyes, textiles, and plastics. The use of ethanol as a motor fuel is prevented at present by its cost.

Glycol. A second alcohol related to ethane is glycol, or dihydroxy ethane, CH_2OH—CH_2OH. It is made from ethylene by an oxidation process:

$$CH_2{=}CH_2 + \tfrac{1}{2} O_2 \xrightarrow{300°} \overset{\displaystyle O}{\overset{\displaystyle \diagup \diagdown}{CH_2{-}CH_2}} \xrightarrow{H_2O} CH_2OH{-}CH_2OH$$
Ethylene   Ethylene oxide   Ethylene glycol

Ethylene glycol is termed a dihydric alcohol because of its two hydroxyl groups, and the name *glycol* generally refers to this particular derivative of ethane. Many other glycols (alcohols containing two hydroxyl groups), however, are known. Ethylene glycol is a sirupy liquid which boils at 200° C and which dissolves in water in all proportions. In its general appearance and properties it resembles glycerol. One of its uses is that of an antifreeze agent in automobile radiators; the freezing point of an aqueous solution of glycol is much lower than the freezing point of water alone. It finds extensive use also in the manufacture of plastics.

Aldehydes

There are two aldehydes which may be regarded as derivatives of ethane. Since the aldehydic functional group is by definition

$$-CHO \qquad or \qquad -C\diagup^{H}_{\diagdown O}$$

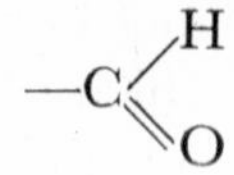

'we may write the formulas for the two possible compounds as follows:

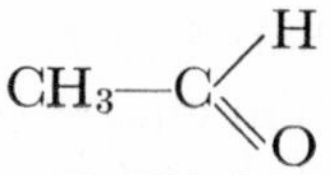

$$CH_3-C\diagup^{H}_{\diagdown O} \qquad\qquad \diagup^{H}_{O\diagdown}C-C\diagup^{H}_{\diagdown O}$$

Acetaldehyde 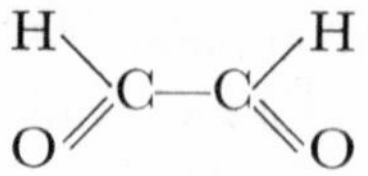   Glyoxal

Both are known; they may be prepared in the laboratory, but they are not made directly from ethane.

The common name of an aldehyde is derived from the name of the acid which the aldehyde yields upon oxidation. Acetaldehyde yields acetic acid. The systematic name of acetaldehyde is *ethanal*, the suffix *al* denoting the presence of an aldehyde group and the first part of the name indicating the relationship of the compound to the hydrocarbon, ethane. Correspondingly, *glyoxal* presents a dual reference to glyoxylic acid, $CHO-COOH$, and oxalic acid, $COOH-COOH$. The latter is found in many plants, particularly in oxalis.

Aldehydes are made from the corresponding alcohols by oxidation, and the aldehydes in turn are readily oxidized to acids. Typical reactions are as follows:

$$3\ CH_3-\underset{\text{Ethanol}}{CH_2OH} + Cr_2O_7^{--} + 8\ H^+$$
$$\longrightarrow 3\ \underset{\text{Acetaldehyde}}{CH_3-CHO} + 2\ Cr^{+++} + 7\ H_2O$$

$$3\ \underset{\text{Acetaldehyde}}{CH_3-CHO} + Cr_2O_7^{--} + 8\ H^+$$
$$\longrightarrow 3\ \underset{\text{Acetic acid}}{CH_3-COOH} + 2\ Cr^{+++} + 4\ H_2O$$

It is noteworthy that the oxidation of ethanol involves the carbon atom which is already partially oxidized, not the carbon of the methyl group. The oxidation of a saturated hydrocarbon seldom results in anything but carbon dioxide and water. For instance, the following oxidation series is possible, but the products indicated cannot be prepared directly from ethane:

$$CH_3-CH_3 \longrightarrow CH_3-CH_2OH \longrightarrow CH_3-CHO \longrightarrow CH_3-COOH$$

The low reactivity of the hydrocarbon demands such strenuous conditions to start the reaction that the ethanol and subsequent products cannot survive; the oxidation continues to the production of carbon dioxide and water. If, however, we begin with CH_3—CH_2OH or CH_3—CHO, stepwise oxidation can be accomplished. As soon as oxygen is introduced into a molecule, the carbon atom to which the oxygen is attached becomes reactive; and from that point on, smooth oxidation can be achieved without danger of attacking the adjacent hydrocarbon groups or breaking the carbon chain.

Acetaldehyde, CH_3—CHO, is a colorless, inflammable liquid which boils at 20.2° (room temperature) and freezes at − 123.5°. Glyoxal, CHO—CHO, is a yellow liquid which boils at 50.4° and freezes at 15°.

Acids

There are two acids which are structurally related to ethane and which have only two carbon atoms in each molecule, namely, acetic acid and oxalic acid. They may be regarded as derivatives of ethane, but they are not made from the hydrocarbon by direct oxidation.

Acetic acid. The acidic component of vinegar is acetic acid, CH_3—COOH. The pure acid is a colorless liquid which boils at 118° and solidifies at 16.6°. The crystalline solid resembles ice, and for that reason the anhydrous acid is called *glacial* acetic acid. The acid is made from ethyl alcohol by oxidation. This is a case where oxygen of the air serves as the oxidizing agent, but the process is not a simple one. It occurs only in the presence of enzymes which are produced by microorganisms. About twenty species of bacteria of the family *Acetobacter* are capable of converting dilute solutions of alcohol into dilute solutions of acetic acid. The organisms are killed by solutions which contain more than 15 per cent alcohol.

Oxalic acid. In oxalic acid both carbon atoms are as fully oxidized as they can be without rupture of the carbon-carbon bond. Oxalic acid therefore represents the end-product of the oxidation of glycol. Successive oxidation stages may be indicated as follows:

$$CH_2OH \rightarrow CH_2OH \rightarrow CH_2OH \rightarrow CHO \rightarrow COOH$$
$$| \qquad\qquad | \qquad\qquad | \qquad\qquad | \qquad\qquad |$$
$$CH_2OH \quad\; CHO \qquad COOH \qquad COOH \qquad COOH$$

Glycol	Glycolic aldehyde	Glycolic acid	Clyoxalic acid	Oxalic acid

The intermediate compounds may or may not appear in appreciable amounts, but they are possible oxidation products. The actual products obtained depend upon the oxidizing agent used, the temperature, the time, and other factors. One other product is possible, namely, glyoxal, which was mentioned in connection with aldehydes. Whenever organic matter is oxidized by concentrated nitric acid, oxalic acid may appear as one of the products. Oxalic acid is easily prepared from sugar or starch by treatment with hot nitric acid. It is not oxidized rapidly by concentrated nitric acid, but it is oxidized by permanganate ions in dilute acid solution and by ferric ions. The first of these reactions is used to standardize permanganate solutions, and the second is used to remove iron-rust stains and some ink stains. Oxalic acid is a crystalline solid which melts at 189°.

Ethers and Esters

The ethers and esters which contain only two carbon atoms are not derived from ethane, since in these compounds the two carbon atoms are separated by an oxygen atom.

$$CH_3—O—CH_3 \qquad\qquad H—C \overset{\displaystyle O}{\underset{\displaystyle O—CH_3}{\big\langle}}$$

Dimethyl ether   Methyl formate

Dimethyl ether may be looked upon as water in which both hydrogen atoms have been replaced by methyl groups, or as methanol which has been dehydrated.

$$2 CH_3OH \xrightarrow[\text{Acid catalyst}]{\text{Heat}} CH_3—O—CH_3 + H_2O$$

Methanol   Dimethyl ether

The compound can be made by heating methanol with sulfuric acid. Methanol boils at 64.6°, while dimethyl ether is a gas at normal temperatures and pressures (bp 23.7°). Moreover, methanol is soluble in water in all proportions, while the ether is very sparingly soluble. We may conclude that the presence of an oxygen atom, as such, does not markedly increase the solubility in water of an organic substance, but that a hydroxyl group is particularly effective in promoting solubility.

Methyl formate is an ester. It is a colorless liquid, has a pleasant odor, boils at a low temperature, and dissolves in about three times its own volume of water. It is made from formic acid and methyl alcohol:

$$HCOOH + CH_3OH \underset{}{\overset{H_2SO_4}{\rightleftarrows}} HCOOCH_3 + H_2O$$

Formic acid   Methanol   Methyl formate
(bp 100.8°)   (bp 64.6°)   (bp 32°)

Ether formation and ester formation are similar in type. Both reactions involve the loss of water from two molecules which possess hydroxyl groups. Esterification is a faster reaction and more readily reversible than ether formation. Esterification is catalyzed by the presence of a mineral acid, but the reaction will take place slowly in the absence of a catalyst.

Esterification is different from the reaction of an acid with a base. In a mixture of an acid and an alcohol there is a low concentration of hydrogen ions, but no hydroxyl ions. The formation of water from such a mixture, therefore, is a slow process if not catalyzed. Furthermore, an ester is in no sense a salt. The chief characteristics of salts are ionization and high melting points. Esters are liquids, or low-melting solids, and they are not ionized at all. It is evident that any two alcohol molecules may form an ether, as, for instance, two ethanol molecules, or one methanol and one ethanol molecule. Likewise any acid, such as acetic acid or oxalic acid, can form an ester with any alcohol.

The Carbon-Carbon Bond

The structures of ethane, ethylene, and acetylene have been represented as containing respectively single, double, and triple bonds between the two carbon atoms, in keeping with the conception of carbon as a tetravalent element. However, the widely differing reactivities of single and multiple bonds raise a question as to whether multiple bonds are definable in terms of single bonds. In the table below some additional facts, associated with bonds of specific types, are summarized. It is seen that (a) carbon-carbon single bonds are very stable, that is, dissociation requires a high energy input, (b) the

COMPARISON OF BOND TYPES					
PROPERTY	C—C	C=C	C≡C	C—H	H—H
(a) Heat of dissociation into radicals	~84 K cal	——	——	~102 K cal	~104 K cal
(b) Heat of rupture by hydrogenation	16 K cal	48 K cal	90 K cal	——	——
(c) Wave length of light absorption	~1600 A	~2000 A	~2600 A	~1600 A	~1100 A
(d) Bond distances	1.54 A	1.32 A	1.22 A	1.06 A	0.58 A

reaction of ethyne with three moles of hydrogen to form two moles of methane liberates about six times as much energy, not three times, as does the corresponding reaction of ethane with one mole of hydrogen, (c) the frequencies of the light absorbed, which measure the energy required to displace the valence electrons, indicate that the electrons of double and triple bonds are less tightly held than are those of single bonds, and (d) multiple bonds are shorter than single bonds. Our problem is the interpretation of these facts in terms of structure.

A chemical bond involves, as we have seen, a pair of electrons which occupy an orbital which includes the bonded atoms. The paired electrons have opposite spins and this results in the neutralization of the magnetic fields of the electrons. Analogously, double and triple bonds involve four and six electrons respectively, but there remains the question of the disposition of the electrons. If the pattern for the geometry of methane is followed, one is led to structures which may be represented as follows:

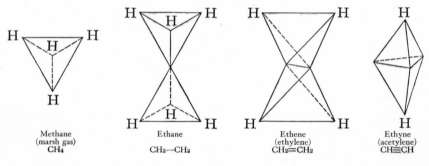

| Methane (marsh gas) CH_4 | Ethane $CH_3—CH_3$ | Ethene (ethylene) $CH_2{=}CH_2$ | Ethyne (acetylene) $CH{\equiv}CH$ |

In ethane two tetrahedra are joined at one apex of each; in ethene they are joined along one edge; in ethyne they are face to face. On the basis of these structures one would predict that the six atoms of ethene lie in a single plane, while in ethyne the four atoms are on a straight line. The facts confirm this prediction.

Ethane is a three-dimensional figure in which one methyl group rotates with respect to the other. During the rotation the hydrogen atoms of the one methyl group alternately move toward and recede from those of the other. Since the hydrogen atoms repel each other the position of greatest stability is the one in which they are furthest apart (in the staggered form as shown above); continued internal rotation requires energy to overcome the repulsive forces between the hydrogen atoms as rotation brings the latter closer together. This is a sort of friction to rotation, and amounts to 3 Kg-cal per mole. On the other hand, in ethene the one methylene (CH_2) group does not rotate with respect to the other unless about 40 Kg-cal per mole are acquired. This is too large an amount for rotation to occur spontaneously at moderate temperatures. In this case some structural feature of the double bond inhibits the rotation.

Some of the above facts are consistent with the classical concept, based on the tetrahedral form of the carbon atom, of the nature of multiple bonds. Yet it is evident that a double bond is not merely two single bonds. In 1885 Baeyer introduced the idea that a bond under strain, like any rod under strain, would be more susceptible to rupture than one not under strain. Through this mechanical analogy he explained the high energy content and high reactivity of multiple bonds, since distortion of the bond angle from the normal angle of 109° 28′ to form the multiple bond would impose strain. The language and idea of the strain theory are still used, but since a molecule is made up of integral parts which adjust themselves to each other and to the energy content of the system, we must interpret the multiple bond in a more realistic manner.

An alternative view of multiple-bond construction assumes that the orbitals of the two (or three) pairs of electrons are not of the same type, but differ in shape, position, and energy content. It pictures two C—C orbitals in ethene, for example, the one termed a σ (sigma) orbital, the other a π (pi) orbital. The former is essentially identical to a single-bond orbital as found in ethane; it is the latter which characterizes the "double bond." In ethyne there are one σ and two π orbitals, the latter perpendicular to each other. Baeyer's strain concept includes the ideas of high energy content and high reactivity. By designating one pair of electrons in a double bond as π electrons and assigning to the bond it represents an energy content and reactivity not observed in single (σ) bonds, we have said the same thing but avoided a mechanically false analogy. We shall continue to write multiple bonds in the conventional manner, without distinguishing their components from each other.

It is evident from the list of reagents given on page 36, that unsaturated compounds react with electron-seeking reagents, that is, acids and oxidizing agents. This fact implies that the π electrons, not the carbon centers, are attacked by reagents.

We may now examine other possible representations of the structure of ethene, bearing in mind that its molecular formula is C_2H_4.

In addition to the simple double-bond formula $H_2C::CH_2$, we might write the following electronic structures:

$$H_2C : CH_2 \qquad H_2\overset{+}{C} : \overset{-}{C}H_2 \qquad H_3C : CH$$

$$\text{I} \qquad\qquad\qquad \text{II} \qquad\qquad\qquad \text{III}$$

In formulas I and II the possible dispositions of the four electrons of the double bond only are presented. In I we have the equivalent of a dissociation of one of the multiple bonds into two free radicals, or into two unpaired electrons. The evidence against this is that ethene is not paramagnetic. Every compound in which there is an unpaired electron is magnetic. Formula II represents the ionization of one of the multiple bonds; one pair of electrons has been transferred completely to one of the carbon atoms. Against this structure we may cite the general nonexistence of ions bearing a charge upon carbon. A more cogent argument rests upon a physical property. The ethene molecule has no electrical dipole moment, as measured by its dielectric constant, and therefore there is no permanent separation of charges in the molecule. Formula III represents a major rearrangement of the atoms; but since bivalent carbon (in CO) is known, this structure must be considered. In this formula the unsaturation concerns only one carbon atom, and the addition of bromine would lead to a dibromide of the structure CH_3—$CHBr_2$, not CH_2Br—CH_2Br. Now two substances of the general formula $C_2H_4Br_2$ are known. One boils at 110°, the other at 131.6°; both react with alkali, giving rise to compounds in which the bromine atoms are replaced by hydroxyl groups:

$$CH_3\text{—}CHBr_2 \xrightarrow{2\ OH^-} CH_3\text{—}CH(OH)_2 \longrightarrow CH_3\text{—}CHO + H_2O$$
$$\text{Acetaldehyde}$$

$$CH_2Br\text{—}CH_2Br \xrightarrow{2\ OH^-} CH_2OH\text{—}CH_2OH$$
$$\text{Glycol}$$

The compound which has both bromine atoms on the same carbon atom yields acetaldehyde,

$$CH_3\text{—}C\overset{\displaystyle H}{\underset{\displaystyle O}{\big\langle}}$$

The compound in which the two bromine atoms are on different carbon atoms yields an alcohol, glycol, corresponding to the formula CH_2OH—CH_2OH. The dibromide which is prepared from ethene boils at 131.6° and yields glycol upon hydrolysis. The other dibromide is prepared by another path. Hence the unsaturation in ethene is divided between the two carbon atoms, not localized on one of them, and formula III cannot be correct. The evidence supports the double-bond structure for ethene, namely, $H_2C::CH_2$.

SUMMARY OF MAJOR VALENCE CONCEPTS

1. Each kind of atom has a normal and a maximum valence; in the case of carbon the normal and the maximum valence is four.
2. Valence has a directional, or vector, quality. The normal angle between two valences of carbon is $109° 28'$, but the bond angle of carbon may vary slightly from this norm.
3. Valence is actuated by bonding electron pairs, the electrons being mutually attracted by the nuclei of the two bonded atoms.
4. Bonded atoms are at a finite distance from each other; the effective radius of the carbon atom in a saturated hydrocarbon is 0.77 A.
5. The energy required to rupture a bond, with the formation of free radicals or of ions, determines the degree of such dissociation; the smaller the energy required, the greater the possibility of dissociation.
6. The energy required to dissociate a single carbon-carbon bond into radicals is about 84,000 calories per mole; to dissociate a carbon-hydrogen bond requires about 102,000 calories per gram-atom of hydrogen released. Such bonds are correspondingly unreactive.
7. Double bonds and triple bonds between carbon atoms are shorter than single bonds, and they are easily converted to single bonds by the addition of certain reagents. This reactivity is ascribed to an instability within the bond which is mechanically analogous to a strain.
8. The double bond distance between carbon atoms is about 1.32 A; that of a triple bond, about 1.20 A.
9. Chemical bonds are called polar bonds if they show some degree of ionization in solution or a high reactivity. Nonpolar bonds are present in molecules of low reactivity, with low dielectric constant, or with no measurable ionization. These terms are relative, with no sharp distinction between polar and nonpolar compounds.
10. Fully ionized substances, such as sodium chloride and potassium iodide, do not contain electron-pair bonds; their ions are held in juxtaposition by electrical (coulombic) attraction of opposite charges. Electron-pair bonds, whether polar or nonpolar, are called co-ordinate bonds.

EXERCISES

1. Name two reagents which react with both ethylene and acetylene, but not with ethane. Write equations for the reactions of these two reagents with ethylene.

2. Name a reagent which acts upon acetylene, but not upon ethane or ethene. Represent the reaction with acetylene by a balanced equation.

3. Describe in words a commercial source of each of the following compounds: ethyl alcohol, ethylene, acetylene, acetic acid, glycol, oxalic acid.

4. Supply the formulas of the reagents required for the following reactions:

$$CH_3\text{—}CH_3 \longrightarrow CH_3\text{—}CH_2Cl \longrightarrow CH_3\text{—}CH_2OH \longrightarrow CH_3CHO$$
$$\longrightarrow CH_3\text{—}COOH \longrightarrow CH_3\text{—}COOCH_3$$

PROBLEMS

1. Why do we we write the structural formula of C_2H_4 as $CH_2\text{==}CH_2$ and not $CH_2\text{—}CH_2$ or $\overset{+}{C}H_2\text{—}\overset{-}{C}H_2$ or $CH_3\text{—}CH$?

2. Are the four atoms in C_2H_2 in a straight line?

3. How could you determine whether kerosene is composed of saturated hydrocarbons only or contains unsaturated hydrocarbons?

4. Give examples of the following types of reactions: addition, substitution, oxidation, reduction.

5. What is a free radical?

5 · THE HIGHER ALKANE HYDROCARBONS

Methane and ethane are the first two members of a series of compounds which are variously termed alkanes, alkane hydrocarbons, saturated hydrocarbons, and paraffins. The next higher members are propane, C_3H_8, butane, C_4H_{10}, and pentane, C_5H_{12}. Each member of this group of compounds has the general formula C_nH_{2n+2}. The successive members of this series of hydrocarbons differ in composition by CH_2, that is, by one carbon atom and two hydrogen atoms, and they are readily formulated by substituting a methyl group, $—CH_3$, for a hydrogen atom in the next lower members of the series. The formulas of the first four members are written as follows:

CH_4 $CH_3—CH_3$ $CH_3—CH_2—CH_3$ $CH_3—CH_2—CH_2—CH_3$
Methane   Ethane   Propane   Butane .

Any group of compounds the successive members of which differ in composition by CH_2 constitutes a *homologous series* of compounds. It will be observed that the formula for ethane is derived from the formula of methane by substituting a CH_3 group for one hydrogen atom. Similarly, the formula for propane is the ethane formula with one hydrogen atom replaced by CH_3.

The actual procedure for replacing a hydrogen atom by a methyl group involves a series of reactions. A hydrogen atom can be displaced directly by chlorine:

$$CH_3—CH_3 + Cl_2 \longrightarrow CH_3—CH_2Cl + HCl$$

The chlorine may then be replaced by CH_3 through the Wurtz reaction (p. 67) or through the Grignard reaction (p. 68).

Propane. Like methane and ethane, propane is found among the hydrocarbon gases obtained from oil wells. Its formula, C_3H_8, permits but one structural interpretation. In formula (1) on page 50 the central carbon atom is not shown. In formula (2) the carbon atoms only are shown; it is understood that the eight hydrogen atoms are held by the free apexes of the tetrahedra. If propane is pictured as a methane molecule in which two hydrogen atoms have been replaced by two CH_3 groups, it is evident that the three carbon atoms of propane do not lie in a straight line. The car-

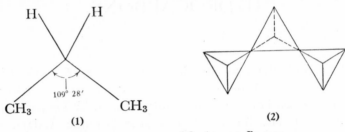

Spatial Arrangements of the Atoms in Propane

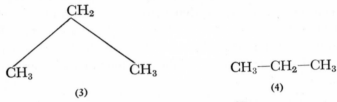

Typographical Representations of Propane

bon atoms are tetrahedral in form, and the angle subtended at the central carbon atom in propane is 109° 28'. For purposes of simplicity in printing, this fact is usually ignored, and chains of carbon atoms are written as if they were straight chains. They are often called straight chains, but it would be more accurate to call them continuous chains.

Instead of beginning with methane and replacing two hydrogen atoms by two methyl groups, we may make propane from ethane by substituting one methyl group for one hydrogen atom. The six hydrogen atoms in ethane are similarly placed in the molecule—they are equivalent. Therefore substitution of any one of them by CH_3 leads to the same structural formula for propane. Only one propane has ever been found. This is not true of the higher members of the series, each of which exists in more than one form.

The butanes. Two substances of the formula C_4H_{10} are known. One boils at $-0.3°$; the other boils at $-13°$. Their existence is readily explained if it can be assumed that a difference in structure would lead to a difference in properties, because two structures are possible. Let us consider that butane is derived from propane by replacing one of the eight hydrogen atoms in propane by a methyl

group. As indicated by the following structural formulas, two butanes should exist:

$$\overset{1}{C}H_3—\overset{2}{C}H_2—\overset{3}{C}H_3$$
Propane

$$CH_3—CH_2—CH_2—CH_3$$

$$\underset{|}{\overset{CH_3}{}}$$
$$CH_3—CH—CH_3$$

Butane derived by substitution at either position 1 or 3.   Butane derived by substitution at position 2.
Normal butane (bp — 0.3⁰)   Isobutane (bp — 13⁰)

Since the hydrogen atoms located on any single carbon atom are
equivalent to each other, and since the two terminal methyl groups
in propane are in the same relative positions, it makes no difference
which one of the six terminal hydrogen atoms is replaced. Only one
structure for butane is obtained by that path. It is called normal butane and abbreviated n-butane. The remaining two hydrogen atoms
of the propane molecule are equivalent to each other, but not equivalent to any of the first six. Substitution of one of these by CH_3 results
in a different butane, which is named *iso*butane. This accounts for all
the possibilities and is in accord with observation. There remains the
question as to which of the two butanes, the one boiling at − 13° or
the one boiling at − 0.3°, should be assigned the *straight chain*, or
normal, form. This is answered by a simple experiment. A butane
can be prepared from ethyl chloride and sodium:

$$CH_3—CH_2—\underset{\underset{+ 2\,Na}{}}{Cl} + Cl—CH_2—CH_3$$

$$\longrightarrow CH_3—CH_2—CH_2—CH_3 + 2\,NaCl$$

The simplest representation of the reaction leaves the carbon atoms
of the ethyl groups ($CH_3—CH_2—$ groups) attached to each other and
joins the two groups through a new carbon-carbon bond. This leads
to the continuous-chain structure,—normal butane,—and the compound formed by this reaction boils at − 0.3°. To obtain the *iso*butane from these reagents, it would be necessary to rupture the original
carbon bonds during the reaction and then induce a recombination of
the fragments. It seems probable from this reasoning that the butane
boiling at − 0.3° is the normal butane—the straight-chain compound.

The pentanes. It is possible to predict the number of compounds
of the formula C_5H_{12} by counting the number of ways the substitution
of a methyl group for a hydrogen atom can be made in the butanes.

There are two different positions in which a methyl group could be placed in normal butane, and two positions for it in isobutane. The possibilities are indicated in the formulas below by assigning similar numbers to positions which would lead to identical structures.

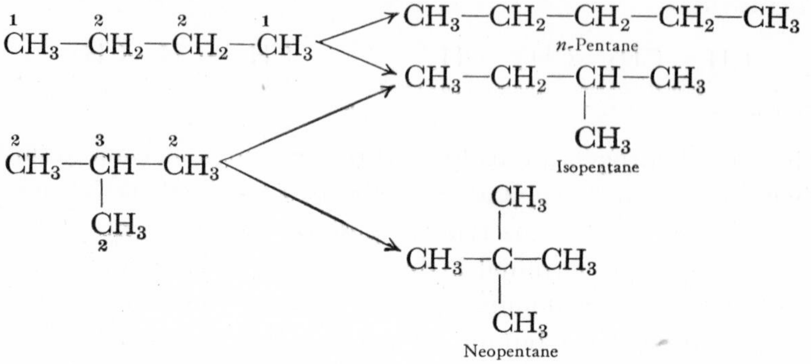

$$\overset{1}{C}H_3-\overset{2}{C}H_2-\overset{2}{C}H_2-\overset{1}{C}H_3$$

$$\overset{2}{C}H_3-\overset{3}{C}H-\overset{2}{C}H_3$$
$$\underset{\overset{|}{2}}{CH_3}$$

$$CH_3-CH_2-CH_2-CH_2-CH_3$$
n-Pentane

$$CH_3-CH_2-CH-CH_3$$
$$\overset{|}{CH_3}$$
Isopentane

$$CH_3-\overset{\overset{CH_3}{|}}{\underset{\underset{CH_3}{|}}{C}}-CH_3$$
Neopentane

Three and only three pentanes are known.

Isomerism. The existence of two or more compounds which have the same composition and the same molecular weight is called isomerism, and the different substances (which have the same molecular formula) are called isomers. Isomers always differ in physical properties, and in many cases they differ also in chemical properties. Isomerism is possible because the properties of compounds are determined not only by composition but also by the structural arrangements of the atoms in the molecules. Examples of different structural arrangements are given in the table below.

ISOMERIC SUBSTANCES	
Molecular Formula	Structural Formulas of Isomers
C_2H_6	CH_3-CH_3. No isomers (only one possible arrangement)
C_3H_8	$CH_3-CH_2-CH_3$. No isomers
C_4H_{10}	$CH_3-CH_2-CH_2-CH_3$; $(CH_3)_3CH$
C_5H_{12}	$CH_3-(CH_2)_3-CH_3$; $(CH_3)_2CH-CH_2-CH_3$; $(CH_3)_4C$
C_2H_6O	CH_3-O-CH_3; CH_3-CH_2OH
$C_2H_4Cl_2$	CH_2Cl-CH_2Cl; CH_3-CHCl_2
C_3H_7Cl	$CH_3-CH_2-CH_2Cl$; $(CH_3)_2CHCl$
C_4H_9Cl	$CH_3-CH_2-CH_2-CH_2Cl$; $CH_3-CHCl-CH_2-CH_3$; $(CH_3)_2CH-CH_2Cl$; $(CH_3)_3CCl$

The number of possible structures, and therefore the number of isomers corresponding to a given molecular formula, increases rapidly as the molecular weight increases. There are five hexanes, C_6H_{14}; nine heptanes, C_7H_{16}; eighteen octanes, C_8H_{18}; and 366,319 possible isomers of the formula $C_{20}H_{42}$. The last number was calculated by mathematical analysis, only a few of the compounds being known.

Petroleum. It would be difficult to overestimate the importance of the role petroleum has played in the industrial development of the world. The dependence of the automobile and airplane upon gasoline and lubricating oils is one example of the usefulness of petroleum products. Petroleum is the great natural source of the alkane hydrocarbons. The crude oil is a dark-colored, viscous liquid which contains the entire list of hydrocarbons included in the table below and many more.

The amount of gasoline now obtained from petroleum is far in excess of the yield which could be secured by fractional distillation alone. The cracking process, which converts high-boiling fractions of the oil into low-boiling mixtures suitable for motor fuels, has vastly increased the yield of gasoline obtainable from petroleum. A more

NORMAL ALKANES				
Name	Formula	Melting Point	Boiling Point	Specific Gravity
Methane	CH_4	$-184°$	$-161.4°$	0.415 (at $-164°$)
Ethane	C_2H_6	$-172°$	$-88.3°$	0.546 (at $-88°$)
Propane	C_3H_8	$-189°$	$-44.5°$	0.585 (at $-44.5°$)
Butane	C_4H_{10}	$-135°$	$-0.3°$	0.600 (at $0°$)
Pentane	C_5H_{12}	$-131.5°$	$36.3°$	0.627 (at $14°$)
Hexane	C_6H_{14}	$-94.3°$	$69.0°$	0.660 (at $20°$)
Heptane	C_7H_{16}	$-90°$	$98.4°$	0.683 (at $20°$)
Octane	C_8H_{18}	$-56.5°$	$124.6°$	0.702 (at $20°$)
Nonane	C_9H_{20}	$-51°$	$150.6°$	0.718 (at $20°$)
Decane	$C_{10}H_{22}$	$-32°$	$174°$	0.747 (at $0°$)
Undecane	$C_{11}H_{24}$	$-26.5°$	$197°$	0.773 (at mp)†
Dodecane	$C_{12}H_{26}$	$-12°$	$216°$	0.774 (at mp)
Tetradecane	$C_{14}H_{30}$	$+5.5°$	$252.5°$	0.775 (at mp)
Hexadecane	$C_{16}H_{34}$	$20°$	$287.5°$	0.775 (at mp)
Eicosane	$C_{20}H_{42}$	$38°$	$205°*$	0.777 (at mp)
Heneicosane	$C_{21}H_{44}$	$40.4°$	$215°*$	0.778 (at mp)
Tricosane	$C_{23}H_{48}$	$47.4°$	$234°*$	0.779 (at mp)
Hentriacontane	$C_{31}H_{64}$	$68.1°$	$302°*$	0.781 (at mp)
Hexacontane	$C_{60}H_{122}$	$101°$		
Heptacontane	$C_{70}H_{142}$	$105°$		

*At 15 mm pressure.   †mp = melting point.

recent development—a method for converting gaseous hydrocarbons into gasoline—has further increased the yield of motor fuels.

The principal products derived from petroleum of the paraffin-base type are the following: ligroin, a very volatile liquid which boils below 70° and which consists mainly of pentanes and hexanes; gasoline, C_6 to C_{12}, with a boiling range of 70° to 200°; kerosene, C_{12} to C_{15}, which boils between 200° and 300°; lubricating oils, C_{16} to C_{20}; greases, C_{18} to C_{24}; and paraffin waxes, C_{20} to C_{26}. Certain kinds of petroleum called asphalt base oils, when distilled, yield a black residue of asphalt or pitch instead of paraffin wax. The asphalt residue is valuable as a material for roofing and for paving.

Alkyl radicals. The groups CH_3—, C_2H_5—, C_3H_7—, and, in general, C_nH_{2n+1} are called alkyl radicals. These groups correspond to the hydrocarbons CH_4, C_2H_6, C_3H_8, and C_nH_{2n+2} with one hydrogen atom removed in each case. An alkyl radical is monovalent and is never obtained in a free state; it is too reactive to have an independent existence except perhaps momentarily in the course of a reaction. The name of a radical is derived from the name of the corresponding hydrocarbon by changing the final *ane* to *yl*, as shown in the following table:

Hydrocarbon		Alkyl Radical	
Name	*Formula*	*Name*	*Formula*
Methane	CH_4	Methyl	CH_3—
Ethane	CH_3—CH_3	Ethyl	CH_3—CH_2—
Propane	CH_3—CH_2—CH_3	Propyl	CH_3—CH_2—CH_2—
n-Butane	CH_3—CH_2—CH_2—CH_3	*n*-Butyl	CH_3—CH_2—CH_2—CH_2—
*Iso*butane	CH_3\\CH_3/CH—CH_3	*Iso*butyl	CH_3\\CH_3/CH—CH_2—

The symbol R is used to represent a radical in a general formula. The actual formula of a radical must be used in connection with a specific compound. Thus, C_2H_5OH is a specific formula for a particular alcohol, and ROH is a general formula which stands for any alcohol. Similarly, the symbol X is used for a halogen atom when any halogen atom would serve the purpose. The formula C_3H_7Br specifies the alkyl radical as the propyl group, and the halogen as bromine; C_3H_7X stands for the propyl group combined with fluorine, chlorine, bromine, or iodine; RCl stands for any alkyl radical in combination with chlorine; and RX is a general formula for a compound comprising any alkyl radical in combination with any halogen atom. In a similar way the formulas of other classes of compounds are generalized. Thus, ROH, RCl, RCN, and RCOOH are general formulas for alcohols, alkyl chlorides, nitriles, and acids respectively.

Radicals which contain three or more carbon atoms exist in isomeric forms. There are, for example, four butyl radicals, C_4H_9—. They correspond to the following structures:

$$CH_3—CH_2—CH_2—CH_2— \quad (1)$$

$$CH_3—CH_2—\underset{|}{C}H—CH_3 \quad (2)$$

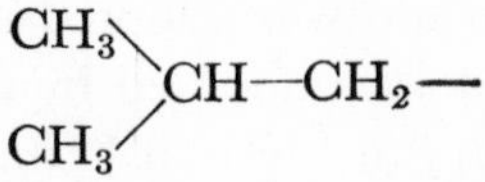

$$\begin{array}{c} CH_3 \diagdown \\ \qquad CH—CH_2— \\ CH_3 \diagup \end{array} \quad (3)$$

$$\begin{array}{c} CH_3 \diagdown \\ CH_3—C— \\ CH_3 \diagup \end{array} \quad (4)$$

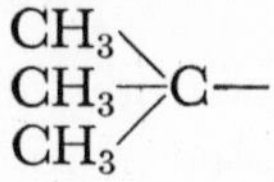

The first is primary normal butyl (straight chain); the second is secondary normal butyl; the third is isobutyl (branching at the end of the chain); and the fourth is tertiary butyl. The carbon which has the free valence in formula (4) is a tertiary carbon atom; that is, it is linked to three other carbon atoms. A carbon atom linked to two other carbon atoms is called secondary, and one which is attached to only one other carbon is said to be a primary carbon atom.

Correspondingly, the halides and alcohols are designated as primary, secondary, or tertiary compounds, according to whether the carbon atom which holds the halogen atom or the hydroxyl group is at the same time attached to one, two, or three other carbon atoms.

Type	Alkyl Radical	Alkyl Halide	Alcohol
Primary	RCH_2—	RCH_2X	RCH_2OH
Secondary	R_2CH—	R_2CHX	R_2CHOH
Tertiary	R_3C—	R_3CX	R_3COH

Nomenclature. In naming isomers various systems have been used. The simpler hydrocarbons were once referred to as substitution products of methane; examples are methylethylmethane, (CH_3)—CH_2—(C_2H_5), and tetramethylmethane, $(CH_3)_4C$. The terms *iso* and *neo* carry specific implications as to structure. The prefix *iso* is used to indicate the presence of the grouping

$$CH_3 \diagdown \atop CH_3 \diagup {\hspace{-0.5em}} CH—$$

at one end of a chain, and the prefix *neo* implies that at least one of the carbon atoms present has four other carbon atoms attached to it and therefore no hydrogen atoms attached. As a molecule becomes more and more complex and the number of isomers grows, a precise system of nomenclature is needed.

The system now in common use was adopted at an international congress at Geneva in 1892 and was modified by a committee of the International Union of Chemistry at Liége in 1930. Its main features as applied to the naming of open-chain hydrocarbons are as follows:

1. The names of the saturated hydrocarbons end in *ane*. Above four carbon atoms Greek numerals are used as root words.

2. The name is based upon the longest continuous chain of carbon atoms in the molecular structure. A normal, or unbranched, hydrocarbon of six carbon atoms is simply hexane, while a branched-chain hydrocarbon of six carbon atoms is named as a derivative of pentane or butane. Prefixes such as *iso*, *neo*, and *normal* are not used in this plan. Three of the hexanes, for example, are named as follows:

$$\overset{1}{C}H_3—\overset{2}{C}H—\overset{3}{C}H_2—\overset{4}{C}H_2—\overset{5}{C}H_3$$
$$|$$
$$CH_3$$

2-Methylpentane

$$\overset{1}{C}H_3—\overset{2}{C}H—\overset{3}{C}H—\overset{4}{C}H_3$$
$$| \quad |$$
$$CH_3 \ CH_3$$

2, 3-Dimethylbutane

$$CH_3$$
$$|$$
$$CH_3—C—CH_2—CH_3$$
$$|$$
$$CH_3$$

2, 2-Dimethylbutane

3. The carbon atoms in the reference chain are numbered, beginning at either end, and the position of each substituent is indicated by using as a prefix the number of the carbon atom to which the substituent is attached. In general, where there is a choice, the numbering is started at that end which gives the lowest possible numbers for the prefixes. The names and formulas of the isomeric heptanes, all of which have been prepared, illustrate the principle:

Formula	Name	Melting Point	Boiling Point
$CH_3—CH_2—CH_2—CH_2—CH_2—CH_2—CH_3$	Heptane	$-90.5°$	$98.4°$
$CH_3—CH_2—CH_2—CH—CH_2—CH_3$ $\quad CH_3$	3-Methylhexane	$-119°$	$92.0°$
$CH_3—CH_2—CH_2—CH_2—CH—CH_3$ $\quad CH_3$	2-Methylhexane	$-118.2°$	$90.0°$
CH_3 $CH_3—CH_2—CH_2—C—CH_3$ $\quad CH_3$	2, 2-Dimethylpentane	$-125.0°$	$78.9°$
CH_3 $CH_3—CH_2—C—CH_2—CH_3$ $\quad CH_3$	3, 3-Dimethylpentane	$-134.9°$	$86.0°$
CH_3 $CH_3—CH_2—CH—CH—CH_3$ $\quad CH_3$	2, 3-Dimethylpentane		$89.4°$
$CH_3—CH—CH_2—CH—CH_3$ $CH_3 \quad CH_3$	2, 4-Dimethylpentane	$-119.3°$	$80.8°$
$CH_3—CH_2—CH—CH_2—CH_3$ $\quad CH_2—CH_3$	3-Ethylpentane	$-119°$	$93.3°$
$CH_3—CH—C(CH_3)_2—CH_3$ CH_3	2, 2, 3-Trimethylbutane	$-25.0°$	$80.8°$

THE NOMENCLATURE AND SOME PROPERTIES OF THE ISOMERIC HEPTANES

The position of any atom or group which has replaced an atom of hydrogen in a hydrocarbon is indicated in the name of the compound in the same way that the position of an alkyl radical is shown. Examples will make this clear:

$$CH_3—CHBr—CH_2—CHCl—CH_3$$
2-Bromo-4-chloropentane

$$CH_3—\overset{\displaystyle Cl}{\underset{\displaystyle CH_3}{C}}—CHCl—CH_2I$$
2-Methyl-2, 3-dichloro-4-iodobutane

Definitions of Terms

Alkane. A hydrocarbon of the saturated or paraffin series.

Derivative. A compound formed from another, formally if not in reality, by substituting an atom or group of atoms for a hydrogen atom in the parent compound.

Homologous series. A group of compounds represented by formulas which differ by a CH_2 or a multiple of CH_2.

Isomer. A compound which has the same composition and the same molecular weight as some other compound.

Isomerism. The existence of two or more compounds to which the same molecular formula must be assigned.

Normal chain. A chain whose atoms are placed successively one after the other, with no branching.

Structure. The order of attachment of the atoms in a molecule or the arrangement of the atoms in space with respect to each other.

Substituent. An atom or group of atoms which has replaced a hydrogen atom.

Radical. A group of atoms which acts as a unit in chemical reactions. Radicals are electrically neutral groups, not ions. Examples are CH_3—, —OH, and —CN in CH_3Cl, CH_3OH, and CH_3CN; R— in the hydrocarbon RH; C_2H_5— and —COOH in C_2H_5—COOH. Only a few types of radicals have independent existence; they are constituents of compounds.

EXERCISES

1. Write structural formulas for *n*-pentane, isopentane, and neopentane. Name each of them according to the Geneva system.

2. As applied to normal hydrocarbons, is the descriptive term *continuous chain* more accurate than *straight chain*? Explain.

3. Write a structural formula for each of the five hexanes.

Note. Begin with the three pentanes, and substitute CH_3 for a hydrogen atom wherever such substitution leads to a new structure.

4. Assign two names to each of the hexanes. Name each compound as a derivative of methane and also as a derivative of the normal hydrocarbon corresponding to the longest continuous chain of carbon atoms in the molecule.

5. Write a structural formula for each of the following compounds:

    a. 2, 4-Dimethyl-4-ethylheptane
    b. 2-Methyl-4-ethyloctane
    c. 2, 2, 4-Trimethylpentane
    d. 3, 4, 4, 5-Tetramethylheptane

6. Name the following compounds:

a. 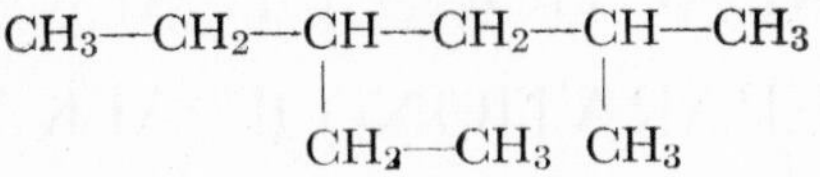 CH_3—CH_2—CH—CH_2—CH—CH_3
$\qquad\qquad\qquad\quad|\qquad\qquad\;|$
$\qquad\qquad\quad CH_2$—$CH_3\;\;CH_3$

b. 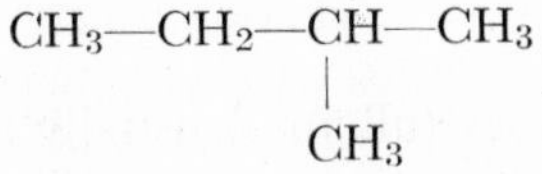 CH_3—CH_2—CH—CH_3
$\qquad\qquad\qquad\;|$
$\qquad\qquad\quad CH_3$

c. 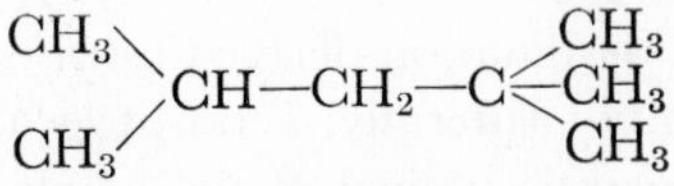
$$CH_3 \diagdown \qquad\qquad\qquad\qquad \diagup CH_3$$
$$\qquad\quad CH-CH_2-C \diagup\!\!\!\diagdown CH_3$$
$$CH_3 \diagup \qquad\qquad\qquad\qquad \diagdown CH_3$$

d. 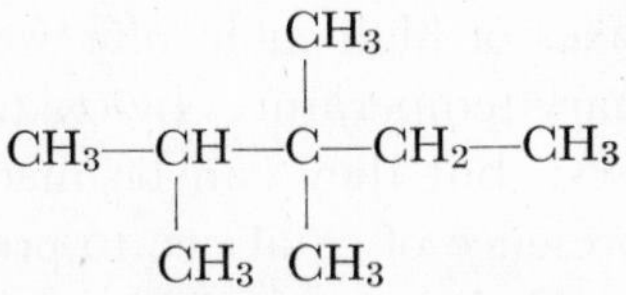
$$\qquad\qquad\qquad CH_3$$
$$\qquad\qquad\qquad\;|$$
$$CH_3—CH—C—CH_2—CH_3$$
$$\qquad\quad|\quad\;|$$
$$\qquad CH_3\;\;CH_3$$

7. What is the range of the molecular weights of the hydrocarbons in gasoline? in kerosene? in paraffin wax?

8. Define (a) alkane, (b) normal chain, (c) homologous series, (d) isomerism.

6 · REACTIONS OF ALKANES;
PREPARATION OF ALKANES

The saturated hydrocarbons (alkanes) usually are described as inert and unreactive compounds. The early chemists called them paraffin hydrocarbons, a designation derived from the Latin *parum affinis*, meaning "slight affinity" (literally, "too little akin"). The familiar inertness of paraffin wax is typical of the whole series, from gaseous methane to the solid waxes of high molecular weight. The alkanes are not attacked at ordinary temperatures by oxidizing agents, reducing agents, acids, or bases; but they can be made to react at high temperatures or in the presence of catalysts, to produce substances of great value and variety. Ordinary gasoline, as we now know it, is not so much a product of natural petroleum as it is a product of complex chemical reactions in which petroleum hydrocarbons are used as starting points. Some of our synthetic rubbers and some of the raw materials for the manufacture of resins, plastics, solvents, and explosives arise from reactions of the alkanes.

Reactions of Alkanes

The primary steps in the utilization of alkanes as reactants may be listed under the headings (*a*) halogenation, (*b*) isomerization, (*c*) cracking, (*d*) oxidation.

Halogenation. In sunlight, or at a high temperature, chlorine and bromine act upon alkanes to produce a variety of substitution products. A reaction between pentane and chlorine is represented by the following equation:

$$C_5H_{12} + Cl_2 \xrightarrow[\text{Dark}]{300°} C_5H_{11}Cl + HCl$$

Pentane · · · · · · · · Chloropentane

It is apparent that even if one starts with a single isomer of pentane, such as *n*-pentane, a number of isomeric chloropentanes would be formed, unless a hydrogen atom in some one position were much more reactive than any of the others. The possibilities in the case of normal pentane are as follows:

$CH_3—CH_2—CH_2—CH_2—CH_2Cl$ 1-chloropentane
$CH_3—CH_2—CH_2—CHCl—CH_3$ 2-chloropentane
$CH_3—CH_2—CHCl—CH_2—CH_3$ 3-chloropentane

In addition to these some dichloro pentanes and still higher chlorination products would be formed. The relative amounts of the three monochloropentanes formed in the chlorination process show that the hydrogen atoms in the different positions have about the same reactivity toward chlorine. Toward some other reagents there are pronounced differences in reactivity in the various positions.

It sometimes happens that there are industrial uses for mixtures of substances of a similar nature. This is true of the chlorination products of pentane. The monochloropentanes obtained from a mixture of isomeric pentanes can be hydrolyzed to alcohols. Dilute alkali promotes the hydrolysis.

$$C_5H_{11}Cl + OH^- \longrightarrow C_5H_{11}OH + Cl^-$$

If the chloropentane used is a mixture of isomers, then a mixture of alcohols is produced; but as a solvent in the manufacture of lacquers the mixed alcohols can be used.

It is possible to generalize the reactions of halogenation and hydrolysis in the following way: Let RH be any hydrocarbon—that is, let H be any one of the hydrogen atoms in a hydrocarbon—and let R be the rest of the molecule. Then chlorination would be written

$$RH + Cl_2 \xrightarrow{\text{Heat}} RCl + HCl,$$

and the hydrolysis of the halogen compound is represented by either of the following equations:

$$RCl + OH^- \xrightarrow{\text{Heat}} ROH + Cl^-$$
$$RCl + H_2O \xrightarrow{\text{Heat}} ROH + HCl$$

The group of atoms designated as R in RH and RCl acts as a unit in a reaction. Such a group is called a *radical*. Groups of this kind which are derived from the saturated hydrocarbons are known as *alkyl radicals* (see page 54).

Iodine is not a sufficiently strong oxidizing agent to react with a hydrocarbon directly. Fluorine, on the other hand, reacts explosively with hydrocarbons to yield free carbon, hydrogen fluoride, and some fluorinated products. In cases where the reactivity of the hydrogen atoms is reduced by other substituents, as in $C_2H_4Cl_2$, direct fluorination may be controlled.

The substitution of a halogen for hydrogen in an alkane is not a common practice, because mixtures of isomers result; but the reaction has a restricted use.

Isomerization. By *isomerization* we mean the changing of one structural isomer into another. For example, when *n*-butane is treated with a mixture of aluminum chloride and dry hydrogen chloride, some of the normal butane changes to isobutane:

$$CH_3-CH_2-CH_2-CH_3 \xrightleftharpoons[]{AlCl_3 + HCl} (CH_3)_2CH-CH_3$$
$$\text{\textit{n}-Butane} \qquad\qquad\qquad\qquad \text{Isobutane}$$

Antimony trichloride may be used as a solvent for the butane and for the catalyst. At 27° equilibrium is reached with about 80 per cent isobutane and 20 per cent *n*-butane. This type of isomerization is applicable to all normal alkanes. It is used largely in connection with butane and pentane, since the branched-chain isomers of these substances are employed in the production of aviation gasoline and in the manufacture of some of the synthetic rubbers. The equilibrium at 600° favors the normal form, so that isomerization at high temperatures is not feasible. Here we have a case of a desired reaction which is normally too slow at low temperatures and cannot be hastened by heating because it goes only part way at high temperatures. The discovery of a catalyst which hastens the reaction at ordinary temperatures solved the problem of preparing the branched-chain isomers of the lower alkanes.

Thermal decomposition and catalytic cracking. At 575° *n*-butane breaks into a mixture of several compounds of lower molecular weights. The principal results of this *cracking* process are represented by the following equations:

$$CH_3-CH_2-CH_2-CH_3 \longrightarrow CH_3-CH=CH_2 + CH_4$$
$$CH_3-CH_2-CH_2-CH_3 \longrightarrow CH_3-CH_3 + CH_2=CH_2$$
$$CH_3-CH_2-CH_2-CH_3 \longrightarrow CH_3-CH=CH-CH_3 + H_2$$

Some of the molecules yield methane, and others lose hydrogen (dehydrogenation); in each case an unsaturated hydrocarbon remains. The cracking may take place between almost any two carbon atoms in the molecule and produce two fragments, one saturated, the other unsaturated.

When hydrocarbons of high molecular weight are subjected to high temperatures in the presence of catalysts composed of the oxides of silicon, aluminum, and manganese, similar reactions occur. Liquid hydrocarbons of low molecular weights and gases are produced. The reactions shown above represent only a few of the possible changes. Isomerization also takes place; some of the hydrogen formed by crack-

Standard Oil Company of California

FIG. 2. Isomerization Unit, 100-Octane Plant at Richmond, California

ing adds again to unsaturated products. The net result is a high yield of branched-chain hydrocarbons with molecular weights lower than the molecular weights of the original materials. This results in an increased yield of gasoline from petroleum.

Oxidation. The alkanes resist oxidation at moderate temperatures, but at elevated temperatures they are attacked by a variety of oxidizing agents. The combustion of hydrocarbons by oxygen is a major source of heat and power. Under ideal conditions carbon dioxide and water are the only products formed, but in the actual operation of an internal-combustion engine carbon monoxide and carbon also are produced. The complete combustion of hexane is represented by the following equation:

$$2 \ CH_3\!\!-\!\!(CH_2)_4\!\!-\!\!CH_3 + 19 \ O_2 \longrightarrow 12 \ CO_2 + 14 \ H_2O$$

When hydrocarbons are oxidized at comparatively low temperatures, some of the terminal methyl groups are converted into carboxyl groups. This is particularly true if the oxidation is carried out in the presence of manganese oxide or osmium oxide at 150° C:

$$2 \ R\!\!-\!\!CH_3 + 3 \ O_2 \xrightarrow{\text{Catalyst}} 2 \ R\!\!-\!\!COOH + 2 \ H_2O$$

The oxidation is accompanied by cracking, that is, by a rupture of carbon-carbon linkages at various points of the chain. When paraffin is oxidized under these conditions, almost all the possible acids are produced. Since the organic acids, particularly the higher ones, find use in the manufacture of soaps and other detergents, the oxidation of paraffin by air is a process of practical value.

Other oxidizing agents, such as potassium permanganate (solution), antimony pentasulfide, chlorosulfonic acid, concentrated sulfuric acid, chromic acid, and nitric acid, react with alkanes under one condition or another. Nitric acid, although an oxidizing agent, reacts with hydrocarbons at elevated temperatures, to form nitro compounds:

$$2 \ CH_3\!\!-\!\!CH_2\!\!-\!\!CH_3 + 2 \ HONO_2 \begin{cases} CH_3\!\!-\!\!CH_2\!\!-\!\!CH_2\!\!-\!\!NO_2 + H_2O \\[2mm] \begin{array}{l} CH_3 \\ \!\!\diagdown \\ CH\!\!-\!\!NO_2 + H_2O \\ \!\!\diagup \\ CH_3 \end{array} \end{cases}$$

Nitromethane, CH_3NO_2, and nitroethane, $C_2H_5NO_2$, are formed as by-products through concurrent oxidation of part of the propane. These nitro compounds are valuable as solvents and as starting points in the manufacture of some other nitrogen compounds.

The combustion of a hydrocarbon in a limited supply of oxygen results in the formation of carbon black. When this condition exists in a kerosene lamp, soot or lampblack is formed. A gas burner which is burning with a yellow flame deposits soot on a cool surface. This formation of carbon is essentially a stripping of the hydrogen from the carbon skeleton—a dehydrogenation—by a combination of the processes of combustion and thermal decomposition. At about 1000° C, in the absence of oxygen, methane dissociates into carbon and hydrogen gas.

$$CH_4 \xrightarrow{1000° C} C + 2 H_2$$

This reaction is used to produce hydrogen, and the carbon black is a by-product. Carbon black is used in inks and in many rubber products, particularly in tire casings. For inks the best carbon is a lampblack, formed in low yield by incomplete combustion of a hydrocarbon. For tires a carbon black is formed by allowing a yellow flame to be suddenly cooled on an iron surface. The role of carbon black in tire rubber is to reduce internal friction (heating) and to help resist abrasion.

Preparation of Alkanes

Petroleum contains nearly all the alkane hydrocarbons, but it is difficult to obtain from petroleum pure individual members of the series. Natural gas is the best source of methane. The butanes—both the normal compound and the branched-chain compound—are present in natural gas and also in the gaseous products which result from the cracking of the higher petroleum products; and since they are needed as starting points in the synthesis of gasoline and rubber, they are removed by fractional distillation from the other hydrocarbons present. Heptane is found in the sap of the Jeffrey pine. Practically all other alkanes, when needed in the pure state, are synthesized from substances which are hydrocarbon derivatives. The synthetic methods fall into three classes:

1. The carbon content of the initial material is retained, and the original structure of the carbon skeleton is not altered.

2. The carbon skeleton used as a starting point is broken.

3. The original carbon skeleton is augmented by the addition of one or more alkyl radicals.

1. In the first of this series of processes some naturally occurring substance, which has the desired structure, is used as the starting point,

and elements other than carbon and hydrogen in the selected compound are replaced by hydrogen. Typical examples are shown below:

1 *a*. **The Berthelot reduction of an alcohol.** Alcohols are difficult to reduce, but at 300°, under pressure and in the presence of phosphorus, they are reduced by concentrated hydriodic acid. The phosphorus reacts with the iodine formed to produce PI_3, which in turn hydrolyzes to phosphorous acid and hydriodic acid:

$$(CH_3)_2CH-CH_2-CH_2OH + 2\ HI\ (conc)$$
$$\xrightarrow[300°]{P} (CH_3)_2CH-CH_2-CH_3 + I_2 + H_2O$$
$$3\ I_2 + 2\ P + 6\ H_2O \longrightarrow 2\ P(OH)_3 + 6\ HI$$

1 *b*. **Reduction of an alcohol by a zinc-copper couple.** The alcohol to be reduced is first converted to the corresponding bromide, and the latter is then warmed in ethyl alcohol solution with a zinc-copper alloy. The zinc is the reducing agent; ethanol is present as a solvent which, like water, can furnish the required proton. The reaction with a zinc-copper alloy is much faster than with zinc alone:

$$ROH + HBr \xrightarrow{Warm} RBr + H_2O$$
$$RBr + Zn + C_2H_5OH \xrightarrow{Cu} RH + Zn(OC_2H_5)Br$$

1 *c*. **Reduction of a halide by magnesium.** Alkyl halides react with pure magnesium metal in the presence of ether to give what is called a Grignard reagent. The reaction was discovered in 1900 by the French chemist V. Grignard.

$$RBr + Mg \xrightarrow{Ether} \underset{\text{Grignard reagent}}{RMgBr}$$

Magnesium derivatives of this type react with acids or with any substance which is even slightly ionized to H^+, such as water or alcohol:

$$RMgBr + H_2O \longrightarrow RH + Mg(OH)Br$$

1 *d*. **The reduction of an alkene.** Unsaturated hydrocarbons may be reduced to alkanes by adding hydrogen gas. The reduction is carried out under pressure in contact with Raney nickel* or palladium oxide:

$$R_2C=CH-CH_3 + H_2 \xrightarrow{Ni} R_2CH-CH_2-CH_3$$

*Raney nickel is a finely divided form of the metal made by treating an alloy of nickel and aluminum with sodium hydroxide solution. The aluminum is dissolved by the base, and the nickel is left in the form of a porous mass.

Since the alkenes are obtainable from alcohols of the same carbon structure, this process is an alternative method of converting an alcohol of known structure into a saturated hydrocarbon of known structure.

2. In the second series of processes carbon dioxide is eliminated from an acid.

2 *a*. **The decarboxylation of an acid.** The lower acids (up to five carbon atoms) give good yields of the hydrocarbon by loss of CO_2 at a temperature of about 400°:

$$R\text{---}CH_2\text{---}COOH \xrightarrow{\text{Heat}} R\text{---}CH_3 + CO_2$$

At higher temperatures, and particularly in the presence of charcoal, pumice, or clay, more deep-seated changes result in the formation of carbon monoxide, hydrogen, resins, and other substances.

2 *b*. **The decarboxylation of salts of organic acids.** Sodium acetate, CH_3COONa, when heated with solid sodium hydroxide, yields methane and sodium carbonate. Salts of other acids react in the same way. Side reactions are inevitable in this process, but sometimes a good yield of the desired hydrocarbon may be obtained.

$$R\text{---}CH_2\text{---}COONa + NaOH \xrightarrow{\text{Heat}} R\text{---}CH_3 + Na_2CO_3$$

3. The third series of processes involves the building of the desired carbon framework, that is, the formation of new carbon-carbon bonds. Only those methods will be considered here which result directly in the formation of hydrocarbons; it is evident that if methods are known which yield alcohols or alkyl halides of desired structures, they, in turn, can be converted into the corresponding hydrocarbons by the methods described above.

3 *a*. **The Wurtz synthesis.** Metallic sodium removes the halogen from an alkyl halide, and the alkyl radicals combine in pairs to form a hydrocarbon:

$$2\ C_4H_9Br + 2\ Na \longrightarrow C_4H_9\text{---}C_4H_9 + 2\ NaBr$$

To secure a hydrocarbon with an odd number of carbon atoms by this method it is necessary to use a mixture of alkyl halides. Thus, a mixture of ethyl iodide and methyl iodide may be used to produce propane:

$$CH_3CH_2I + CH_3I + 2\ Na \longrightarrow CH_3CH_2CH_3 + 2\ NaI$$

The product, however, is not pure propane; it is a mixture of ethane, propane, and butane. The Wurtz synthesis is seldom used to synthesize hydrocarbons that can be derived only from mixed alkyl halides.

Since it is improbable that four molecules will come into contact simultaneously, the Wurtz reaction should be written in two steps:

$$RBr + 2\ Na \longrightarrow RNa + NaBr$$
$$RNa + RBr \xrightarrow{\text{Fast}} R{-}R + NaBr$$

There is experimental justification for this view, since the intermediate, a sodium alkyl, NaR, can be made by another path, and when the isolated sodium alkyl is added to an alkyl halide there is a rapid formation of a hydrocarbon. Wurtz discovered this reaction when he sought to prepare a free radical, —CH$_3$, by displacement of a halogen atom in methyl chloride. He supposed that the reaction would go as follows:

$$CH_3Cl + Na \longrightarrow {-}CH_3 + NaCl$$

The gas which he obtained by this reaction had the right composition for the expected free radical. Several years later a molecular-weight determination of the gas showed it to be C_2H_6 and not CH$_3$.

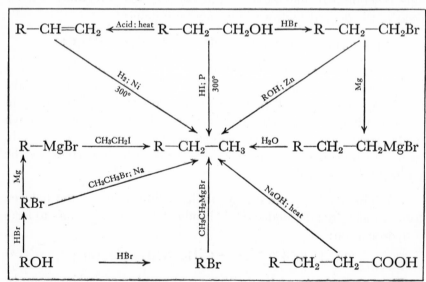

Preparation of an Alkane

3 b. Use of the Grignard reagent. A Grignard reagent acts upon an alkyl chloride, bromide, or iodide, to yield a hydrocarbon. Mercury salts are often used as catalysts. In some cases the reaction is too slow to be of practical value, and side reactions always reduce the yield of the desired product. The general reaction may be written as follows:

$$RMgX + R'X \xrightarrow{\text{HgX}_2} R\text{---}R' + MgX_2$$

A specific example is indicated by the following equation:

$$CH_3\text{---}CH_2I + CH_3MgI \rightarrow CH_3\text{---}CH_2\text{---}CH_3 + MgI_2$$

The three series of processes outlined above may be summarized as follows: replacement of a hydroxyl group, a halogen atom, or a carboxyl group by a hydrogen atom, and replacement of a halogen atom by an alkyl group. These reactions are summarized in the diagram on page 68.

EXERCISES

1. Define (*a*) halogenation, (*b*) alkyl radical, (*c*) alkane, (*d*) isomerization, (*e*) cracking process, (*f*) decarboxylation.

2. Write structural formulas for all possible monobromopentanes obtainable from the three isomeric pentanes; name each compound.

3. Write an equation representing the complete combustion of octane. Give evidence that in an automobile engine the gasoline is not converted completely into carbon dioxide and water. What is the poisonous product of incomplete combustion?

4. Represent by equations and structural formulas the following processes:

    a. Cracking of hexane into C_3H_8 and C_3H_6
    b. Isomerization of *n*-pentane to isopentane
    c. Decarboxylation of propionic acid, $CH_3\text{---}CH_2\text{---}COOH$
    d. Hydrogenation of $CH_3\text{---}CH{=}CH\text{---}CH_3$
    e. Chlorination of CH_4; of *n*-C_5H_{12}
    f. Preparation of *n*-hexane by the Wurtz reaction

PROBLEMS

1. Write balanced equations representing four possible reactions which result from heating *n*-decane to a temperature high enough to cause cracking.

2. Outline two procedures for making *n*-pentane from *n*-$C_5H_{11}OH$.

3. How would you proceed to make propane from propyl bromide?

4. Indicate a method for making methane from acetic acid.

5. Starting with C_4H_9Br, C_3H_7Br, and Mg, show by equations how heptane can be prepared. (Use a Grignard reagent.)

6. Why is it impossible to obtain a good yield of 3-chlorohexane by chlorinating *n*-hexane?

7 · THE ALKENE HYDROCARBONS; GEOMETRICAL ISOMERISM

The *alkene* hydrocarbons, like the alkanes, constitute a homologous series of compounds the successive members of which differ in composition by a methylene group ($-CH_2-$). The first member of the series is ethylene, and the higher members are formulated by substituting various alkyl groups for one or more of the hydrogen atoms of ethylene:

$$H_2C=CH_2 \qquad CH_3-CH=CH_2 \qquad RCH=CH_2 \qquad R_2C=CH_2$$

Ethylene
or
ethene

Propylene
or
propene

$$RCH=CHR \qquad R_2C=CR_2$$

Higher alkenes

The general formula for members of the series is C_nH_{2n}. Each member of the series contains a double bond and therefore reacts with the same reagents that act upon ethylene itself. Conversely, any substance which has the chemical properties of an alkene is presumed to have the same functional group, that is, the double bond.

Nomenclature. The lower members of the series were at first referred to as ethylene, propylene, butylene, and amylene. There are, however, three isomeric butylenes and five alkene isomers of the formula C_5H_{10}. Since all members beyond propylene exist in isomeric forms, this system of nomenclature is inadequate. The higher members, particularly those with straight chains, are occasionally named by changing the suffix *ane* of the corresponding alkane to *ylene*. Thus in a general way one refers to hexylenes, heptylenes, and so on. The term *amylene* was derived from a common name for the alcohols of the formula $C_5H_{11}OH$, the amyl alcohols. The amylenes were first prepared from these alcohols.

The lower members of the alkene series are often thought of as substituted ethylenes. For instance, dimethylethylene is easily visualized in two forms, a symmetrical and an unsymmetrical form.

$$CH_3-CH=CH-CH_3 \qquad\qquad (CH_3)_2C=CH_2$$

sym-Dimethylethylene

unsym-Dimethylethylene

This nomenclature recalls the naming of the alkanes as derivatives of methane; it has a real but limited usefulness.

The systematic nomenclature (Geneva system) is based upon the name of the longest continuous chain of carbon atoms present. The

THE COMMON NAMES OF THE LOWER ALKENES

Formula	Common Name	Structure
C_2H_4	Ethylene	$H_2C{=}CH_2$
C_3H_6	Propylene	$CH_3{-}CH{=}CH_2$
C_4H_8	Butylenes	$CH_3{-}CH_2{-}CH{=}CH_2$ $CH_3{-}CH{=}CH{-}CH_3$
	Isobutylene	$(CH_3)_2C{=}CH_2$
C_5H_{10}	Amylenes	$CH_3{-}CH_2{-}CH_2{-}CH{=}CH_2$ $CH_3{-}CH_2{-}CH{=}CH{-}CH_3$
	Isoamylenes	$(CH_3)_2CH{-}CH{=}CH_2$ $(CH_3)_2C{=}CH{-}CH_3$
	Methylethylethylene	$\begin{array}{c} CH_3 \\ \diagdown \\ C_2H_5 \end{array}\!\!\!\diagup\!\!\! C{=}CH_2$

name of the corresponding normal alkane is altered, to indicate the presence of the double bond, by changing the terminal *ane* to *ene*. For example, we have the saturated hydrocarbon pentane, C_5H_{12}, and the corresponding unsaturated compound, pentene, C_5H_{10}. Similarly we have heptane, C_7H_{16}, and heptene, C_7H_{14}. The position of the double bond is shown in the official name by a numeral preceding the name of the carbon chain. The numeral refers to the first doubly linked carbon atom in the reference chain. Numbering normally begins at the end nearest to the double bond.

Propene, $CH_3{-}CH{=}CH_2$, exists in one form only, but there are two possible positions for the double bond in butene and in pentene. There are three hexenes; they correspond to the following formulas:

$$\overset{6}{C}H_3{-}\overset{5}{C}H_2{-}\overset{4}{C}H_2{-}\overset{3}{C}H_2{-}\overset{2}{C}H{=}\overset{1}{C}H_2$$
1-Hexene

$$\overset{6}{C}H_3{-}\overset{5}{C}H_2{-}\overset{4}{C}H_2{-}\overset{3}{C}H{=}\overset{2}{C}H{-}\overset{1}{C}H_3$$
2-Hexene

$$\overset{6}{C}H_3{-}\overset{5}{C}H_2{-}\overset{4}{C}H{=}\overset{3}{C}H{-}\overset{2}{C}H_2{-}\overset{1}{C}H_3$$
3-Hexene

Still other compounds corresponding to the formula C_6H_{12} are known; but they have branched chains, and under the Geneva system they would not be called hexenes.

Groups or atoms substituted for hydrogen are enumerated as they are in an alkane hydrocarbon; for example, a compound which has the structure

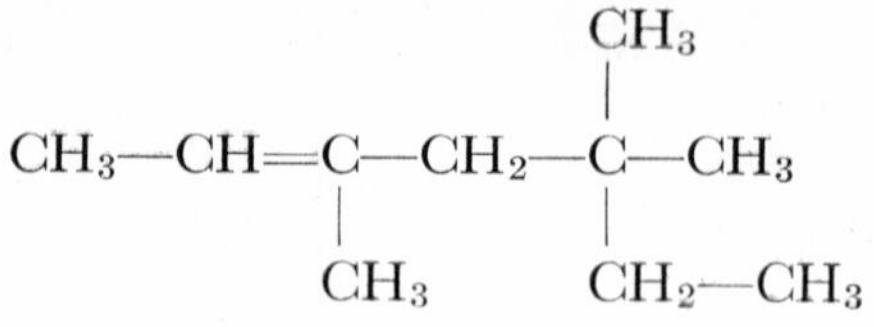

$$CH_3-CH=\underset{\underset{CH_3}{|}}{C}-CH_2-\underset{\underset{CH_2-CH_3}{|}}{\overset{\overset{CH_3}{|}}{C}}-CH_3$$

would be called 3, 5, 5-trimethyl-2-heptene.

THE SYSTEMATIC NAMES AND BOILING POINTS OF SOME ISOMERIC ALKENES			
Formula	Name	Structure	Boiling Point (°C)
C_2H_4	Ethene	$CH_2=CH_2$	− 103.8
C_3H_6	Propene	$CH_3-CH=CH_2$	− 47
C_4H_8	1-Butene	$C_2H_5-CH=CH_2$	− 18
	2-Butene	$CH_3-CH=CH-CH_3$	1.4
	2-Methylpropene	$(CH_3)_2C=CH_2$	− 6
C_5H_{10}	1-Pentene	$CH_3-CH_2-CH_2-CH=CH_2$	40
	2-Pentene	$CH_3-CH_2-CH=CH-CH_3$	36.4
	2-Methyl-1-butene	$H_2C=C(CH_3)-CH_2-CH_3$	32
	3-Methyl-1-butene	$(CH_3)_2CH-CH=CH_2$	20.1
	2-Methyl-2-butene	$(CH_3)_2C=CH-CH_3$	38.4
C_6H_{12}	1-Hexene	$C_4H_9-CH=CH_2$	61.4
C_7H_{14}	1-Heptene	$C_5H_{11}-CH=CH_2$	99
C_8H_{16}	1-Octene	$C_6H_{13}-CH=CH_2$	123
$C_{10}H_{20}$	1-Decene	$C_8H_{17}-CH=CH_2$	172

Properties and uses of the alkenes. Ethylene is a colorless gas which has a faint, sweet odor. It burns with a bright, luminous flame. A mixture of ethylene and air in which the ethylene content is between 4 per cent and 22 per cent is explosive. More than fifty compounds of commercial value are made from ethylene. Among these synthetic products are ethylene glycol, ethyl alcohol, ether, cellosolves, ethyl sulfate, ethylene dibromide, styrene, and dioxane. Ethylene is used to some extent as a general anesthetic for surgery. It is used also to hasten the ripening of bananas, pineapples, lemons, and oranges in storage plants.

Propylene and the butylenes are valuable starting points in the commercial syntheses of alcohols, aldehydes, ketones, ethers, and glycols. They combine with the lower branched-chain alkanes to form aviation gasoline of high octane rating. The alkenes of five carbon atoms or higher are liquids at ordinary pressures and temperatures.

Reactions of the Alkenes

Unsaturated hydrocarbons react in many ways; but the reactions may be classified in five groups: (1) the addition of inorganic reagents, (2) oxidation, (3) alkylation, (4) polymerization, (5) isomerization.

1. **Addition reactions.** Some of the inorganic substances which add to the double bond of a hydrocarbon are shown in the equations below. For the purpose of illustration the alkene is represented by the general formula $R—CH=CH_2$, where R may be any alkyl group. While this formula represents a 1-alkene, similar reactions occur with alkenes in which the double bond is in other positions.

$$R—CH=CH_2 + Cl_2 \longrightarrow R—CHCl—CH_2Cl \tag{1}$$
A 1, 2-dichloroalkane

$$R—CH=CH_2 + Br_2 \longrightarrow R—CHBr—CH_2Br \tag{2}$$
A 1, 2-dibromoalkane

$$R—CH=CH_2 + HOCl \text{ (or } Cl_2 + H_2O)$$
$$\longrightarrow R—CHOH—CH_2Cl \tag{3}$$
A chlorohydrin

$$R—CH=CH_2 + HX \text{ (HCl, HBr, HI)} \xrightarrow{\text{Heat}} R—CHX—CH_3 \tag{4}$$
A secondary alkyl halide

$$R—CH=CH_2 + HOSO_3H \text{ (Conc)} \longrightarrow R—CH—CH_3 \tag{5}$$
$$|$$
$$OSO_3H$$
A sulfuric acid ester

$$R—CH=CH_2 + H_2O \text{ (dil } H_2SO_4) \xrightarrow{\text{Heat}} R—CHOH—CH_3 \tag{6}$$
A secondary alcohol

$$R—CH=CH_2 + H_2 \xrightarrow[\text{Heat}]{\text{Ni}} R—CH_2—CH_3 \tag{7}$$
A saturated hydrocarbon

The utility of these *addition* reactions may be indicated briefly. Reactions (2) and (5) are employed to distinguish saturated from unsaturated hydrocarbons. They are used also to estimate the percentage of saturated and unsaturated hydrocarbons in mixtures containing both types of compounds. Reaction (2) is very rapid and is observed through the disappearance of the color of bromine. Reactions involving the *substitution* of bromine for hydrogen in alkenes and alkanes are usually very slow, and they are always accompanied by the evolution of HBr. A small amount of substitution product may be formed during any addition reaction. Reaction (5), with sulfuric acid, results in *solution* of the alkene hydrocarbon in the acid; alkanes are not appreciably soluble in cold concentrated sulfuric acid.

The products of many addition reactions are commercially valuable. The halides are used as solvents, particularly where there is danger of fire, as in dry cleaning. Ethylene dibromide (CH_2Br—CH_2Br), prepared from ethylene and bromine, is added to gasoline containing the antiknock agent tetraethyl lead. Its purpose is to furnish, after combustion, the bromine necessary to convert the lead into $PbBr_2$. In this form the lead is volatile enough to be eliminated in the engine exhaust. The tetraethyl lead is prepared from C_2H_5Cl, which in turn comes from ethylene and HCl.

The acid esters of sulfuric acid can be hydrolyzed to yield alcohols. The hydrolysis proceeds as follows:

$$R{-}\underset{\underset{\displaystyle O{-}SO_3H}{|}}{CH}{-}CH_3 + H_2O \;\rightleftarrows\; R{-}\underset{\underset{\displaystyle OH}{|}}{CH}{-}CH_3 + H_2SO_4$$

The reaction is reversible; that is, in concentrated acid the alcohol yields the ester, and in dilute acid the alcohol is formed. Equation (6) represents alcohol formation as a hydration of the alkene. The reaction is catalyzed by a dilute acid; water alone does not add to the double bond. Apparently the acid adds to the alkene and is then displaced by water. Since the acid is not consumed in the process but is effective in hastening the addition of the water, it is called a catalyst.

Equation (7) represents catalytic hydrogenation. The reaction is used to convert unsaturated vegetable oils to solid fats. The difference between fats and oils is largely due to the presence of double bonds in molecules of the oils.

When an unsymmetrical reagent like HCl, HBr, HI, HOCl, H_2SO_4, or HOH forms an addition product with an unsymmetrical alkene, two isomeric products may be formed. The addition of HI to propene, for example, might lead to the formation of two iodopropanes, as follows:

$$CH_3{-}CH{=}CH_2 + HI \Big\langle \begin{array}{l} CH_3{-}CHI{-}CH_3 \\ \text{\footnotesize 2-Iodopropane, a secondary halide} \\ CH_3{-}CH_2{-}CH_2I \\ \text{\footnotesize 1-Iodopropane, a primary halide} \end{array}$$

Referring to the reactions of addition given on page 73, one sees that in every case the electropositive part of the addendum is represented as adding to that carbon atom of the double bond which holds the greater number of hydrogen atoms, while the negative part is attached to the carbon atom with the fewer hydrogen atoms (or the greater number of alkyl groups). Hydration (in acid solution) of isobutylene results in the formation of tertiary butyl alcohol, not isobutyl alcohol:

$$(CH_3)_2C{=}CH_2 + H_2O \xrightarrow{\text{Acid}} (CH_3)_2{-}\underset{\underset{\displaystyle OH}{|}}{C}{-}CH_3$$

In 1899 Markownikoff, a Russian chemist, first expressed this generalization, which is known as the *Markownikoff rule*. The rule may be stated as follows: When an unsymmetrical reagent adds to an unsymmetrical alkene, the electronegative part of the addendum is found, for the most part, attached to the carbon atom bearing the smaller number of hydrogen atoms.

This means that *primary* alcohols, halides, and sulfuric acid esters cannot be made directly from alkenes. Under ordinary conditions only *secondary* and *tertiary* alcohols, halides, and esters are made in this way. In 1933 M. S. Kharasch, at The University of Chicago, found a way to obtain primary alkyl bromides from alkenes. He observed that when HBr is added to an alkene in the presence of a peroxide or free oxygen, the orientation rule is reversed:

$$CH_3{-}CH{=}CH_2 + HBr \begin{cases} \nearrow CH_3{-}CHBr{-}CH_3 \\ \text{Normal addition} \\ \searrow CH_3{-}CH_2{-}CH_2Br \\ \text{Peroxide-catalyzed addition} \end{cases}$$

The abnormal, or peroxide-catalyzed, addition occurs with HBr only (not with HCl or HI); but the primary bromide may in turn be converted to a primary chloride, iodide, or alcohol.

Isobutylene, $(CH_3)_2C{=}CH_2$, dissolves readily in 66 per cent sulfuric acid, while 1-butene and 2-butene require 85 per cent acid for rapid solution, and ethylene dissolves readily only in acid more concentrated than 94 per cent. It is evident that, while we write double bonds in all these compounds, and all undergo the same type reactions, the rates and completeness of the reactions may vary considerably.

In the alkenes a bond between two carbon atoms is readily broken; yet in saturated compounds bonds resist rupture. In 1865 Adolf von

Baeyer, a German chemist, sought to account for this difference in behavior by assuming that the formation of a double bond produces a strain in the molecule. If the normal angle between two bonds is $109° 28'$, as demanded by a tetrahedral structure for carbon, there would be a distortion of the bonds from their normal positions in the formation of a double bond. Each bond would be under strain; one of them would rupture easily, but the second would then no longer be under strain and would be stable to the reagents employed in the "addition" reaction. This mechanical analogy has its weakness; but the fact remains that energy (of strain) is lodged in the molecule at the point of the double bond, and is liberated when addition occurs.

2. **Oxidation of the alkenes.** An unsaturated hydrocarbon is rapidly oxidized by permanganate ion; the reaction is catalyzed by dilute alkali. The first product formed is a glycol, but an excess of oxidizing agent may convert the glycol to other oxidation products:

$$3 \text{ R—CH}{=}\text{CH}_2 + 2 \text{ MnO}_4^- + 4 \text{ H}_2\text{O}$$

An alkene

$$\longrightarrow 3 \text{ R—CH—CH}_2 + 2 \text{ MnO}_2 + 2 \text{ OH}^-$$
$$\qquad\qquad \underset{\text{OH}}{|} \quad \underset{\text{OH}}{|}$$

A glycol

The reduction of the permanganate is so easily observed (purple solution to brown precipitate), and the reaction is so rapid at room temperature, that a permanganate solution is used to test for unsaturation in a hydrocarbon. The reagent cannot be used to show the presence of a double bond in an alcohol or an aldehyde, for these compounds, whether saturated or unsaturated, are oxidized rapidly.

Acidic oxidizing agents, such as CrO_3 in acetic acid solution, or dichromic acid, $H_2Cr_2O_7$, generated from $Na_2Cr_2O_7$ and H_2SO_4, react more slowly upon unsaturated hydrocarbons, require higher temperatures, and usually carry the oxidation to the point of rupturing the alkene at the position of the double bond:

$$3 \text{ R—CH}{=}\text{CH—R}' + 4 \text{ Cr}_2\text{O}_7^{--} + 32 \text{ H}^+$$

An alkene

$$\longrightarrow \underbrace{3 \text{ R—COOH} + 3 \text{ R}'\text{—COOH}}_{\text{Lower carboxylic acids}} + 8 \text{ Cr}^{+++} + 16 \text{ H}_2\text{O}$$

This reaction is used at times to prepare carboxylic acids and to determine the structures of unsaturated molecules. For instance, oleic acid, found in fats, has the formula $C_{17}H_{33}$—COOH. Within the radical $C_{17}H_{33}$— there is a double bond; a saturated radical with 17 carbon atoms would be $C_{17}H_{35}$—. The assumption that oleic acid is unsaturated is confirmed by addition of bromine and reduction of permanganate. The acid grouping does not interfere with these reagents, as shown by the fact that saturated acids are inert to them. When oleic acid is oxidized by treatment with chromic acid, two acids are obtained as oxidation products. One proves to be nonylic acid, CH_3—$(CH_2)_7$—$COOH$; the other is azelaic acid, $HOOC$—$(CH_2)_7$—$COOH$. These products account for the original 18 carbon atoms in oleic acid. One of the carboxyl groups was present at the beginning, and the other two must have resulted from oxidation and rupture of the carbon chain at the position of the double bond. Oleic acid, therefore, must be CH_3—$(CH_2)_7$—CH=CH—$(CH_2)_7$—$COOH$. A 1-alkene gives CO_2 as the oxidation product of the terminal carbon atom; the number 2 carbon atom is converted to —$COOH$.

Ozone is another reagent which is used to split a molecule at the point of unsaturation. It is even more reliable than chromic acid, for there are fewer side reactions. When an alkene, dissolved in glacial acetic acid, is treated with ozone, an ozonide is formed:

$$R-CH{=}CH-R' + O_3 \longrightarrow R-\underset{|}{CH}\text{———}\underset{|}{CH}-R'$$

An alkene

$$O-O-O$$

An ozonide

or

$$R-\underset{|}{CH}-O-\underset{|}{CH}-R'$$

$$O\text{————}O$$

The ozonide may have either of the structures written above; those which have been isolated seem to have the second structure. If the ozonide is warmed in alkaline solution, rupture is completed, as indicated by the following equation:

$$R-\underset{|}{CH}-O-\underset{|}{CH}-R' + H_2O \xrightarrow{OH^-} R-C{\stackrel{\displaystyle O}{\diagdown}}_{H} + R'-C{\stackrel{\displaystyle O}{\diagdown}}_{H} + H_2O_2$$

$$O\text{————}O$$

In order to stop further oxidation (by the hydrogen peroxide formed), powdered zinc is often added to remove the peroxide as fast as it is formed. A 1-alkene yields formaldehyde,

$$H-C{\stackrel{\displaystyle H}{\diagdown}}_{O},$$

and some other product; a 2-alkene forms acetaldehyde,

$$CH_3 - C \overset{H}{\underset{O}{\diagdown}},$$

or acetone and other oxidation products. Identification of the products formed reveals the position of the double bond in the original alkene.

Elementary oxygen reacts with ethylene to produce ethylene oxide:

$$2 \; H_2C{=}CH_2 + O_2 \xrightarrow{300°} 2 \; H_2C{-}CH_2$$

Ethylene

$$\underset{\text{Ethylene oxide}}{O}$$

The process is not feasible with the higher alkenes because of other oxidation reactions which occur; but ethylene oxide itself is the starting point in preparing a host of valuable substances, including the rayon solvents, the cellosolves, ethylene glycol, which is used in automobile radiators as an antifreeze, and the ethanolamines, which are employed in the manufacture of brushless shaving creams.

3. **Alkylation.** The alkane hydrocarbons add to the alkenes in the presence of catalysts such as concentrated sulfuric acid, aluminum chloride, or hydrofluoric acid. An alkyl radical adds to one of the unsaturated carbon atoms, and hydrogen adds to the other. The process is called *alkylation*. A large part of aviation gasoline is made in this way from the gaseous butanes and butenes obtained in the cracking of petroleum products and from natural gas. A typical example is given in the following equation:

$$(CH_3)_3CH + H_2C{=}C(CH_3)_2 \xrightarrow[10° C]{H_2SO_4} (CH_3)_3C{-}CH_2{-}CH(CH_3)_2$$

Isobutane   Isobutylene   2, 2, 4-Trimethylpentane or "Isooctane"

The branched-chain alkanes react faster than do the normal alkanes, and isobutylene (2-methyl-1-propene) reacts faster than 1-butene or 2-butene. In commercial practice the normal alkanes are isomerized to branched-chain compounds before they are used in alkylation processes. The products of the alkylation reaction are always branched-chain hydrocarbons, which are the more desirable because of their higher octane rating as fuels.

The product formed in an alkylation process is never a single compound, because each hydrogen of the alkane can react to some degree, isomerization can accompany the addition reaction, and cracking

FIG. 3. A Night View of an Alkylation Unit in a 100-Octane Plant

occurs as well. From isobutane and 2-butene there are obtained three or more of the isomeric octanes as well as isopentane, one or more of the hexanes, and higher-boiling products such as the nonanes and decanes. Fortunately a wide range of hydrocarbon components can be used in the manufacture of gasoline. A mixture seems to be better than any single hydrocarbon.

4. **Polymerization.** Two or more molecules of the same kind may combine to form larger molecules. This sort of addition reaction is called *polymerization*. Many types of unsaturated compounds can be polymerized. Isobutylene affords a typical example:

$$2\ C_4H_8 \xrightarrow[\text{Catalyst}]{} (C_4H_8)_2 \xrightarrow[\text{Catalyst}]{C_4H_8} (C_4H_8)_3 \xrightarrow[\text{Catalyst}]{C_4H_8} (C_4H_8)_n$$

| Monomeric form | Dimeric form | Trimeric form | Polymeric form |

In the absence of a catalyst the polymerization is very slow. Peroxides, sulfuric acid, and phosphoric acid are among the best catalysts. When cold sulfuric acid is used as the catalyst, the dimer (the compound formed from two molecules of the isobutylene) is obtained in good yield. The nature of the polymerization may be clarified by writing the structural formulas:

$$\underset{CH_3}{\overset{CH_3}{>}}\!\!C\underset{\|}{\overset{}{}}\ +\ CH_3\!-\!C\!\!\underset{CH_3}{\overset{CH_2}{<}} \longrightarrow \underset{CH_3}{\overset{CH_3}{>}}\!\!C\underset{CH_3}{\overset{}{-}}CH_2\!-\!C\!\!\underset{CH_3}{\overset{CH_2}{<}}$$

An octene of the structure indicated in the equation constitutes approximately 80 per cent of the yield of dimer. About 20 per cent of the product formed is the isomeric octene $(CH_3)_3C\!-\!CH\!=\!C(CH_3)_2$.

Very high polymers are made from unsaturated hydrocarbons, at low temperatures, through catalysis by hydrofluoric acid (HF) or fluoroboric acid (HBF_4). The polymerization appears to involve only the double bonds, as indicated by the following example:

$$\underset{R}{\overset{R}{|}}C\!=\!CH_2\ +\ \underset{R}{\overset{R}{|}}C\!=\!CH_2\ +\ \underset{R}{\overset{R}{|}}C\!=\!CH_2$$

$$\longrightarrow \cdots \underset{R}{\overset{R}{|}}C\!-\!CH_2\!-\!\underset{R}{\overset{R}{|}}C\!-\!CH_2\!-\!\underset{R}{\overset{R}{|}}C\!-\!CH_2 \cdots$$

The chain elongation may continue until hundreds or even thousands of molecules are united. In the above formulation the dotted lines represent valences to be filled. These can be satisfied by further polymerization, by a coupling of two ends of a chain to form a ring, by addition of catalyst molecules, or by combining with almost any substance which may be present. The process of polymerization is responsible for the drying of unsaturated vegetable oils to form paint films and for the conversion of unsaturated hydrocarbons to synthetic rubber. Not all alkenes polymerize readily, nor are all polymers useful substances, but the reaction is one of common occurrence and is characteristic of unsaturated compounds. Depolymerization is the reverse of polymerization. At elevated temperatures the higher unsaturated hydrocarbons can be broken into simpler ones.

5. **Isomerization.** The position of the double bond in an alkene can be changed. The same types of catalysts which produce alkylation help to establish an equilibrium between the various isomeric forms of an unsaturated hydrocarbon:

$$CH_3-CH_2-CH=CH_2 \underset{}{\overset{\text{Catalyst}}{\rightleftharpoons}} CH_3-CH=CH-CH_3$$

1-Butene (30 per cent)   2-Butene (70 per cent)

This change is achieved by the transfer of hydrogen and a shift of electrons; the carbon framework of the molecule remains unchanged. The shift of a methyl group, as in the isomerization of a *normal* to an *iso* saturated compound, is possible also with the alkenes.

Preparation of the Alkenes

The lower alkenes are found among the gaseous products formed in the cracking of petroleum. Ethene, propene, and the butenes are available from this source as pure substances. In general the alkenes are prepared from alcohols of corresponding structures.

1. **Dehydration of alcohols.** When the vapor of an alcohol is passed over an acidic catalyst such as aluminum oxide, silica, or phosphoric acid on pumice, dehydration takes place:

$$R-CH_2-CH_2OH \xrightarrow[\text{Heat}]{\text{Catalyst}} R-CH=CH_2 + H_2O$$

Secondary alcohols (R_2CHOH) and tertiary alcohols (R_3COH) are dehydrated at lower temperatures than the primary alcohols. A clue to the role of the catalyst is found in the dehydration of an alcohol by sulfuric acid, since the reaction can be made to take place in two steps:

$$CH_3—CH_2—OH + H_2SO_4 \overset{20°}{\rightleftarrows} CH_3—CH_2—O—SO_3H + H_2O \quad (1)$$

$$CH_3—CH_2—O—SO_3H \xrightarrow{170°} CH_2=CH_2 + H_2SO_4 \quad (2)$$

First the acid and alcohol form an ester, in this case ethyl hydrogen sulfate. At about 170° C the ester dissociates to ethylene and sulfuric acid. If the two processes occurred at the same temperature, sulfuric acid would be called a catalyst. It is probable that the surface catalysts (silica and aluminum oxide) form at least small amounts of intermediate compounds which dissociate rapidly to an alkene and water.

2. **Removal of HX from an alkyl halide.** A hydrogen halide (HCl, HBr, or HI) may be removed from an alkyl halide to form a double bond. The reagent usually employed is a strong alkali, such as potassium hydroxide dissolved in alcohol:

$$R—CH_2—CH_2Cl + KOH \xrightarrow{\text{Alcohol}} R—CH=CH_2 + KCl + H_2O$$

Secondary and tertiary halides, such as 2-chloropropane ($(CH_3)_2CHCl$) and tertiary-butyl chloride ($(CH_3)_3CCl$), form the alkenes even with dilute alkali. Some organic halides can lose a molecule of a halogen acid in more than one way. For instance, 2-bromobutane may form either 1-butene or 2-butene:

$$CH_3—\underset{H}{\underset{|}{C}}H—\underset{Br}{\underset{|}{C}}H—\underset{H}{\underset{|}{C}}H_2 \xrightarrow{\text{KOH (alc.)}} \underset{\text{1-Butene}}{CH_3—CH_2—CH=CH_2}$$

$$\xrightarrow{\text{KOH (alc.)}} \underset{\text{2-Butene}}{CH_3—CH=CH—CH_3}$$

The yields depend upon the relative reactivities of the hydrogen atoms which can be removed. In this case more of the 2-butene is formed than of the 1-butene. The organic halides themselves are prepared from alcohols by treatment with a halogen acid or with a phosphorus halide (PCl_3, PBr_3, or PCl_5).

Geometrical Isomerism

We have used the formula $CH_3—CH=CH—CH_3$ for 2-butene. Actually there are two compounds to which this formula must be assigned. One of these compounds boils at 1°, the other at 2.5°. For reasons which will appear later, the one which boils at

1° is called the *cis* isomer, the other the *trans* isomer. That the formula CH_3—CH=CH—CH_3 is correct for both compounds is shown by the following facts:

1. When treated with hydrogen in the presence of a nickel catalyst, both compounds add hydrogen and yield the same saturated hydrocarbon, namely, *n*-butane. Therefore each is a straight-chain compound.

2. Upon treatment with ozone and hydrolysis of the ozonide both yield acetaldehyde, CH_3—CHO. Neither gives formaldehyde, H—CHO, or propionaldehyde, CH_3—CH_2—CHO, or acetone, $(CH_3)_2CO$. The two substances, therefore, are not structural isomers, and neither of them can be CH_3—CH_2—CH=CH_2 or $(CH_3)_2C$=CH_2.

The difference between the two compounds may be explained by considering the spatial geometry of saturated and unsaturated carbon compounds. The carbon atom is tetrahedral in form, and when two carbon atoms are held together by a single bond they are joined point to point, as shown in formula I below. When two carbon atoms are held together by a double bond, the union is edge to edge, as in formulas IIa and IIb.

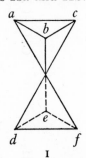 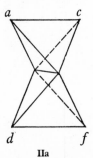 

I   IIa   IIb

In a compound of the type represented by formula I there is very little hindrance to the independent rotations of the two ends of the molecule. If the upper carbon atom is turned, the element or group *a* may be placed directly above *d*, *e*, or *f*. At ordinary temperatures rotation does not occur in doubly bonded compounds. If *a* and *d* are on the same side of the molecule (IIa) when the double bond is established, they remain there. Similarly, if *a* and *d* are on opposite sides (IIb) when the double bond is formed, they remain in that state. It requires heat or some other form of energy to change configuration IIa into IIb or to change IIb into IIa. Compounds corresponding to

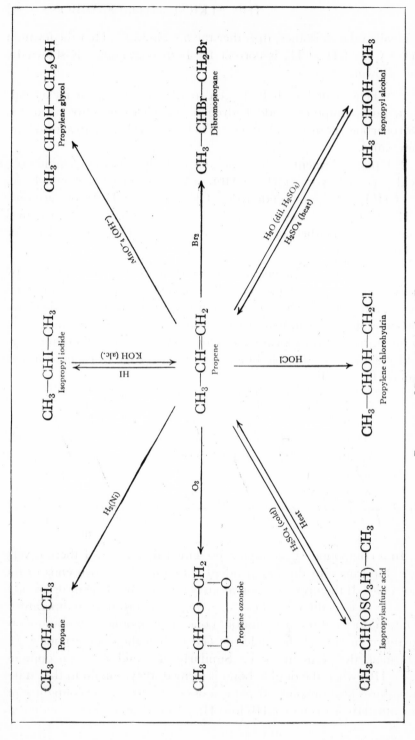

Reactions and Preparation of an Alkene

the two structures IIa and IIb are called *geometrical isomers*. They have the same atoms or groups attached to corresponding carbon atoms and therefore contain the same functional groups. Their chemical properties are similar for that reason. In ordinary structural isomerism the atoms are arranged in different orders. Geometrical isomers are usually convertible into each other by physical means, and they have similar, but not identical, chemical properties. Structural isomers may be chemically alike or very different, and the conversion of one into another is not a simple process.

We can represent geometrical isomers by ordinary formulas of the following type:

$$\begin{array}{ccc} a{-}C{-}b & & b{-}C{-}a \\ \| & \text{and} & \| \\ c{-}C{-}d & & c{-}C{-}d \end{array}$$

The isomers of 2-butene are represented by the formulas

$$\begin{array}{ccc} CH_3{-}C{-}H & & CH_3{-}C{-}H \\ \| & \text{and} & \| \\ CH_3{-}C{-}H & & H{-}C{-}CH_3 \\ \textit{cis-2-Butene} & & \textit{trans-2-Butene} \end{array}$$

The structure in which the similar groups are on the same side of the molecule is called the *cis* form, and the structure in which these are on opposite sides of the molecule is known as the *trans* form. Hundreds of pairs of geometrical isomers are known. The compound $CH_3{-}CH_2{-}CH{=}CH_2$, 1-butene, does not display geometrical isomerism. When one of the doubly linked carbon atoms is attached to two identical atoms or groups, only one configuration is possible.

The rotation about a single bond is nearly frictionless, and the individual parts of a molecule are considered to be rotating freely about such a bond. Double bonds restrict rotational motion, and the molecule is held in one of the two possible positions. If it acquires enough energy from heat or light, it may snap over into the alternate position. Catalysts for the change probably add temporarily to the double bond to produce a single bond which permits rotation.

EXERCISES

1. Write a structural formula for each of the following compounds:

     a. 2-Methyl-3-ethyl-2-hexene
     b. 2, 3, 5-Trimethyl-3-octene
     c. 3-Methyl-2-pentene

2. Name each of the following alkenes:

a. 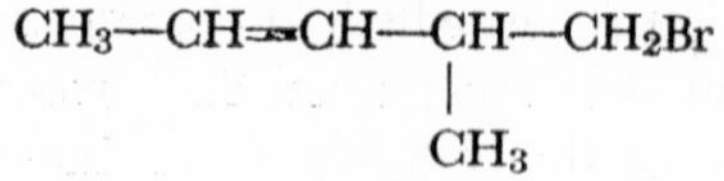 $CH_3-CH=CH-CH-CH_2Br$
$$| \atop CH_3$$

b. 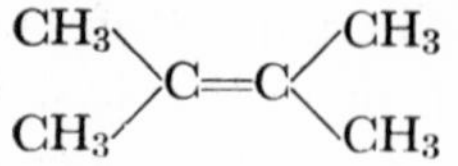 $\underset{CH_3}{\overset{CH_3}{>}}C=C\underset{CH_3}{\overset{CH_3}{<}}$

c. $\underset{CH_3}{\overset{CH_3}{>}}CH-\underset{\underset{CH_3}{|}}{C}=CH-CHCl-CH_3$

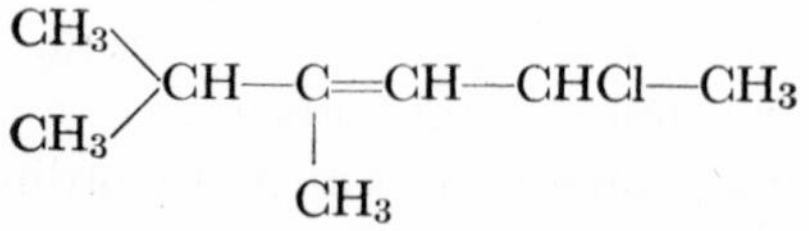

3. Write balanced equations representing the following reactions:

a. The addition of HBr to ethylene; to 1-butene; to 2-butene
b. The hydrogenation of 2-butene
c. The reaction between bromine and 2-methyl-2-pentene
d. The addition of HBr to 1-butene in the presence of hydrogen peroxide

4. Give an example of the application of Markownikoff's rule. State the rule in words.

5. Complete and balance the following equation:

$$CH_3-CH=CH-CH_3 + MnO_4^- + H_2O \longrightarrow \text{a glycol}$$

NOTE. Two equivalents of oxidizing agent are required per mole of alkene.

6. Complete and balance the following equation:

$$CH_3-CH_2-CH=CH-CH_3 + Cr_2O_7^{--} + H^+ \longrightarrow \text{two organic acids}$$

NOTE. Eight equivalents of oxidizing agent are required per mole of alkene.

7. Show how propene may be made from n-propyl alcohol, $CH_3-CH_2-CH_2OH$.

8. How is propene made from isopropyl bromide, $CH_3-CHBr-CH_3$?

9. Write an equation for the hydrolysis of $R-CH_2-O-SO_3H$.

10. Define and illustrate (a) addition reaction, (b) substitution reaction, (c) alkylation, (d) polymerization, (e) isomerization.

11. Write structural formulas for two pentenes which may be formed by treating 2-bromopentane with an alcoholic solution of potassium hydroxide.

12. Which of the following compounds exist in the forms of cis-trans isomers?

a. $CH_3-CH_2-CH=CH_2$
b. $CH_3-CH_2-CH=CH-CH_3$
c. $CH_3-CBr=CH-CH_3$

PROBLEMS

1. Show by balanced equations how the following transformations can be made:

a. $C_3H_7—CH=CH_2 \longrightarrow C_3H_7—CHOH—CH_3$

b. $C_3H_7—CH_2—CH_2OH \longrightarrow C_3H_7—CHOH—CH_3$

c. $C_3H_7—CH_2—CH_2Br \longrightarrow C_3H_7—CHBr—CH_2Br$

2. How many open-chain isomers corresponding to the formula C_6H_{12} exist?

NOTE. Include geometric isomers.

3. How could you prove that two isomeric hexenes have the same carbon skeleton but differ in the position of the double bond?

4. How could you determine the alkene content of a mixture of heptane and heptene?

5. What is the essential process in the "drying" of paint? in the conversion of a salad oil to a solid fat? in the formation of butyl rubber from butylenes?

6. How could you determine whether two isomeric octenes were geometrical or structural isomers?

8 · THE ALKYNE
AND DIENE HYDROCARBONS

Acetylene is the best-known representative of a group of unsaturated hydrocarbons characterized by the presence of a triple bond between carbon atoms. The formula for acetylene is $CH{\equiv}CH$; higher members of the group are represented by the general formulas $R{-}C{\equiv}CH$ and $R{-}C{\equiv}C{-}R$. The Geneva name of any hydrocarbon having the functional group $-C{\equiv}C-$ ends in *yne*, but the lower members of the series are often named as derivatives of acetylene. A few representatives of the acetylene series (alkyne series) are included in the following table.

ALKYNE HYDROCARBONS				
Formula	Systematic Name	Common Name	Melting Point (°C)	Boiling Point (°C)
$CH{\equiv}CH$	Ethyne	Acetylene	− 81.8	− 85
$CH_3{-}C{\equiv}CH$	Propyne	Methylacetylene	− 101.5	− 23.3
$CH_3{-}CH_2{-}C{\equiv}CH$	1-Butyne	Ethylacetylene	− 122.5	8.6
$CH_3{-}C{\equiv}C{-}CH_3$	2-Butyne	Dimethylacetylene	− 24	28
$CH_3{-}CH_2{-}CH_2{-}C{\equiv}CH$	1-Pentyne	*n*-Propylacetylene	− 98	40
$CH_3{-}CH_2{-}C{\equiv}C{-}CH_3$	2-Pentyne	Methylethylacetylene	− 101	55

Preparation of alkynes. Acetylene, the first member of the series, is prepared by the action of water on calcium carbide:

$$CaC_2 + 2\,H_2O \longrightarrow CH{\equiv}CH + Ca(OH)_2$$

The higher members sometimes are prepared by extracting two molecules of a halogen acid from an organic dichloro compound or dibromo compound, in much the same way that an alkene hydrocarbon is made from a monohalogen compound. For example, we may synthesize propyne from *n*-propyl alcohol through the following steps:

$$CH_3{-}CH_2{-}CH_2OH \xrightarrow{1} CH_3{-}CH{=}CH_2$$

$$\xrightarrow{2} CH_3{-}CHBr{-}CH_2Br \xrightarrow{3} CH_3{-}C{\equiv}CH$$

Two bromine atoms are first placed on the two carbon atoms between which the triple bond is to be located. The individual reactions are written as follows:

(1) CH_3—CH_2—CH_2OH $\xrightarrow[\text{Acid catalyst}]{\text{Heat}}$ CH_3—CH=CH_2 + H_2O
1-Propanol   Propene

(2) CH_3—CH=CH_2 + Br_2 ⟶ CH_3—$CHBr$—CH_2Br
   Propene   1, 2-Dibromopropane

(3a) CH_3—$CHBr$—CH_2Br + $NaOH$
   1, 2-Dibromopropane
$\xrightarrow{\text{Alcohol}}$ CH_3—CH=$CHBr$ + $NaBr$ + H_2O
                           1-Bromopropene

(3b) CH_3—CH=$CHBr$ + $NaOH$ $\xrightarrow[\text{Heat}]{\text{Alcohol}}$ CH_3—C≡CH + $NaBr$ + H_2O
   1-Bromopropene   Propyne

A dibromide with the two bromine atoms on the terminal carbon atom would also yield an alkyne hydrocarbon:

C_3H_7—CH_2—$CHBr_2$ + 2 KOH
$\xrightarrow{\text{Alcohol}}$ C_3H_7—C≡CH + 2 KBr + 2 H_2O

Another method for preparing higher alkynes involves the extension of the carbon chain in a compound which is already an alkyne. The available alkyne is first converted to a metallic derivative; then the metal is replaced by an alkyl radical:

$$R-C\equiv CH + Na \xrightarrow{\text{Liquid NH}_3} R-C\equiv CNa + \tfrac{1}{2}H_2 \qquad (1)$$

Sodium dissolved in liquid ammonia is able to displace a hydrogen atom which is attached to a triply bonded carbon atom, and the sodium derivative will react with almost any alkyl halide to form a higher alkyne hydrocarbon. The second phase of the process is accomplished as follows:

$$R-C\equiv C-Na + R'I \longrightarrow R-C\equiv C-R' + NaI \qquad (2)$$

We may start with acetylene itself and replace the two hydrogen atoms in turn:

$$HC\equiv CH \xrightarrow{\text{Na; CH}_3\text{I}} CH_3-C\equiv CH \xrightarrow{\text{Na; C}_4\text{H}_9\text{I}} CH_3-C\equiv C-C_4H_9$$

Reactions of the alkynes. The triple bond adds the same reagents which act upon the alkenes. Of these, chlorine and bromine react rapidly and by a two-stage process:

$$R-C\equiv CH \xrightarrow{\text{Br}_2} R-\underset{\underset{Br}{|}}{C}=\underset{\underset{Br}{|}}{CH} \xrightarrow{\text{Br}_2} R-\underset{\underset{Br}{|}}{\overset{\overset{Br}{|}}{C}}-\underset{\underset{Br}{|}}{\overset{\overset{Br}{|}}{CH}}$$

The halogen acids add slowly to triple bonds; mercury salts catalyze the addition. In general, hydrogen chloride is much slower to react than hydrogen iodide or hydrogen bromide. Acetylene adds HI as follows:

$$HC\equiv CH \xrightarrow{\text{HI}} CH_2=CHI \xrightarrow{\text{HI}} CH_3-CHI_2$$

Acetylene   Vinyl iodide   1, 1-Diiodoethane

A higher alkyne reacts similarly:

$$CH_3-C\equiv CH + 2\,HI \longrightarrow CH_3-CI_2-CH_3$$

Markownikoff's rule, which expresses for alkenes the orientation of an unsymmetrical addendum, applies here as well.

The addition of water, in the presence of a catalyst consisting of a mercury salt and an acid, results in the formation of an aldehyde or a ketone:

$$HC\equiv CH + HOH \xrightarrow{\text{HgSO}_4;\ \text{H}_2\text{SO}_4} \left[H_2C=CHOH \right] \longrightarrow CH_3-C\!\!\big\langle\begin{smallmatrix}H\\O\end{smallmatrix}$$

Acetylene   Acetaldehyde

$$RC\equiv CH + HOH \xrightarrow{\text{HgSO}_4;\ \text{H}_2\text{SO}_4} \left[\begin{smallmatrix}OH\\ |\\ R-C=CH_2\end{smallmatrix} \right] \longrightarrow \begin{smallmatrix}O\\ ||\\ R-C-CH_3\end{smallmatrix}$$

A higher alkyne   A ketone

The addition takes a normal course, but the addition product (which is written within brackets) is unstable and changes immediately to a doubly bonded oxygen derivative (an aldehyde or a ketone). The bracketed intermediate is presumed to exist, but it has not been isolated. This reaction of hydration is used to demonstrate the existence of a triple bond, since the product (a ketone or an aldehyde) is easily identified.

Alkaline permanganate oxidizes the alkynes rapidly, as might be expected from the corresponding oxidation of alkenes; but the products formed are salts of organic acids, not glycols (see page 76). The hydrocarbon is split by oxidation at the point of the triple bond.

$$CH_3-C\equiv C-C_2H_5 + 2\,MnO_4^-$$
$$\longrightarrow CH_3-COO^- + C_2H_5-COO^- + 2\,MnO_2$$

Alkynes which have a hydrogen atom attached to a triply linked carbon atom form silver and copper derivatives. The reaction is carried out with a silver or cuprous salt in an aqueous solution of ammonia:

$$R-C\equiv CH + \overset{+}{Ag}(NH_3)_2 \longrightarrow R-C\equiv CAg + NH_3 + \overset{+}{NH_4}$$

The product, $R-C \equiv CAg$, appears as a solid precipitate. Acetylene yields C_2Ag_2 or C_2Cu_2 (silver or copper acetylide), which in the impure state is explosive when dry. A thorough washing of the precipitate removes some foreign substance, probably vinylacetylene, and the acetylide may then be handled safely even when thoroughly dried. Alkynes of the general formula $R-C \equiv C-R$ do not form acetylides, since they have no hydrogen attached to a triply linked carbon atom.

Acetylene is manufactured in enormous amounts for use as a fuel in acetylene welding and as a raw material for further syntheses. One of its uses is in the manufacture of acetic acid and acetic anhydride. The synthesis of acetic acid proceeds as follows:

$$HC \equiv CH \xrightarrow{H_2O(HgSO_4)} CH_3CHO \xrightarrow[300°]{O_2(MnO)} CH_3COOH$$

The intermediate product, acetaldehyde, is formed by the addition of water to acetylene; the oxidation of the acetaldehyde by air is catalyzed by manganous oxide or by vanadium oxide.

The preparation of acetic anhydride involves the addition of two molecules of acetic acid to one molecule of acetylene. When heated, the addition product dissociates into acetaldehyde and acetic anhydride. The net result of the process is indicated by the following equation:

$$HC \equiv CH + 2\ CH_3-C \overset{O}{\underset{OH}{\big\backslash}} \xrightarrow{Heat} CH_3-C \overset{O}{\underset{H}{\big\backslash}} + CH_3-C \overset{O}{\underset{O}{\big\backslash}}$$
$$CH_3-C \overset{O}{\underset{O}{\big\backslash}}$$

Acetic acid   Acetic anhydride

Vinyl acetate can be made by a process that results in the addition of one molecule of acetic acid to one of acetylene:

$$HC \equiv CH + CH_3-C \overset{O}{\underset{OH}{\big\backslash}} \xrightarrow{HgSO_4} CH_3-C \overset{O}{\underset{O-CH=CH_2}{\big\backslash}}$$

Vinyl acetate (bp 73°)

The ester, vinyl acetate, polymerizes to useful resins.

The manufacture of chloroprene rubber depends upon the use of acetylene as a raw material. The first step is a polymerization of acetylene to a dimer, a reaction similar to the polymerization of an alkene:

$$HC \equiv CH + HC \equiv CH \xrightarrow{CuCl} H_2C = CH-C \equiv CH$$

Vinylacetylene
(colorless liquid)

The common name of the radical $H_2C{=}CH-$ is *vinyl*. Vinylacetylene and hydrogen chloride combine to yield chloroprene, a substance which is used commercially in the preparation of one type of synthetic rubber:

$$H_2C{=}CH-C{\equiv}CH + HCl \longrightarrow H_2C{=}CH-C{=}CH_2$$
$$\underset{\underset{Chloroprene}{Cl}}{|}$$

Cyclic polymers of acetylene. In addition to the linear polymers of acetylene already mentioned, a cyclic tetramer has been prepared. Its formation and structure may be represented as follows:

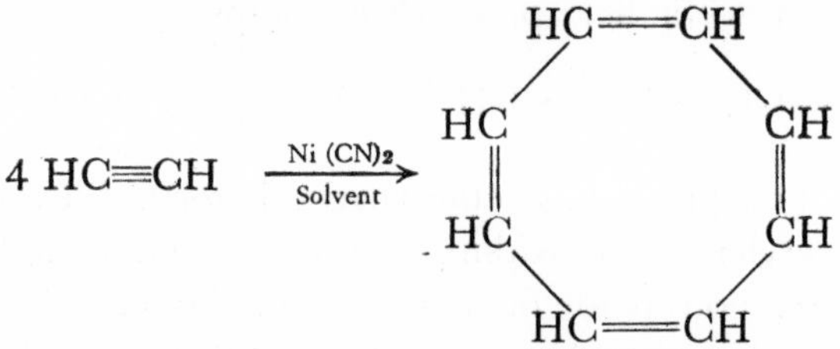

$$4\ HC{\equiv}CH \xrightarrow[\text{Solvent}]{\text{Ni (CN)}_2}$$

Cyclooctatetraene
(Yellow liquid, bp. 143.5°)

Benzene, C_6H_6, is a cyclic trimer of acetylene, but it is not made commercially from acetylene. The natural source of benzene is coal tar, and the synthetic product is made from hexane. The structure of benzene is discussed in another chapter (p. 100).

The Diene Hydrocarbons

Hydrocarbons which contain two double bonds are isomers of the alkynes. Examples of dienes are allene, butadiene, isoprene, and chloroprene:

$$\underset{Allene}{CH_2{=}C{=}CH_2} \qquad\qquad \underset{Butadiene}{CH_2{=}CH-CH{=}CH_2}$$

$$\underset{\substack{|\\ CH_3\\ Isoprene}}{CH_2{=}CH-C{=}CH_2} \qquad\qquad \underset{\substack{|\\ Cl\\ Chloroprene}}{CH_2{=}CH-C{=}CH_2}$$

The suffix *ene* denotes the presence of a double bond; a *diene* has two double bonds. There are corresponding compounds which have three, four, or more double bonds, and they are called trienes, tetraenes, and so on. The dienes of greatest interest are those in which the double bonds are separated by single bonds, as in 1, 3-butadiene.

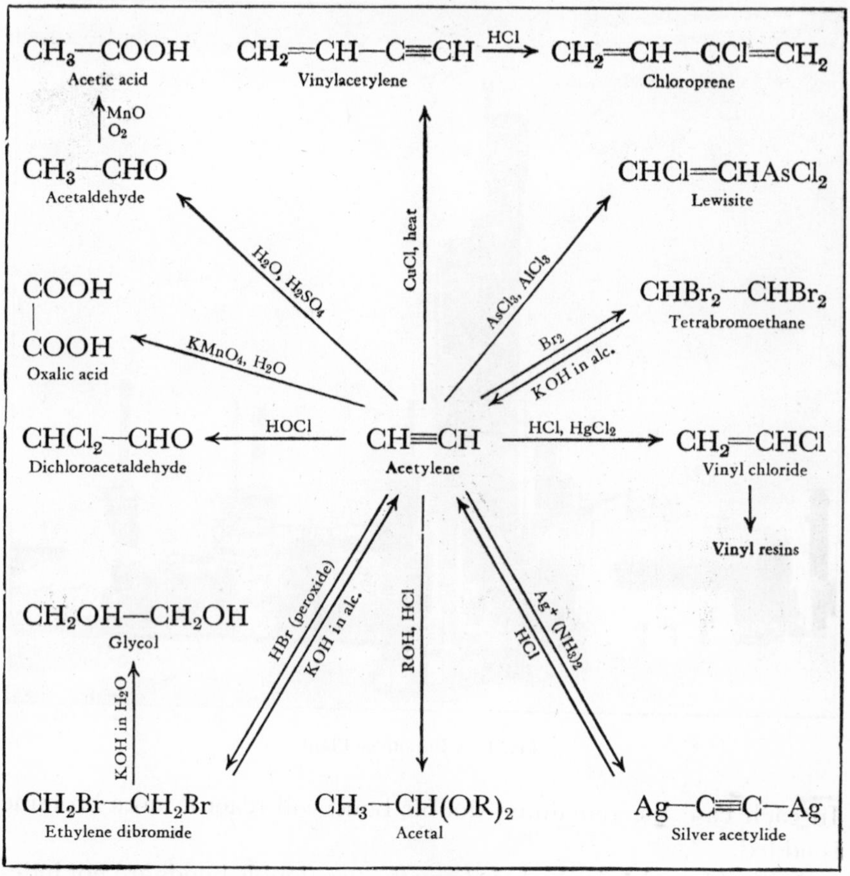

Reactions of an Alkyne

These compounds undergo a reaction known as 1, 4-addition, a reaction which is peculiar to this system. The reaction may be illustrated with reference to 1, 3-pentadiene as follows:

$$\underset{\text{1, 3-Pentadiene}}{CH_3{-}CH{=}CH{-}CH{=}CH_2} + Br_2 \longrightarrow CH_3{-}\underset{\displaystyle Br}{\underset{|}{CH}}{-}CH{=}CH{-}\underset{\displaystyle Br}{\underset{|}{CH_2}}$$

When the double bonds are separated by more than one single bond, addition takes place on adjacent carbon atoms as follows:

$$\underset{\text{1, 4-Pentadiene}}{CH_2{=}CH{-}CH_2{-}CH{=}CH_2} + Br_2$$

$$\longrightarrow \underset{\displaystyle Br}{\underset{|}{CH_2}}{-}\underset{\displaystyle Br}{\underset{|}{CH}}{-}CH_2{-}CH{=}CH_2$$

Standard Oil Company of California

Fig. 4. A Butadiene Plant

In each case the remaining double bond will react if more bromine
is added.

It is evident that in the 1, 3-diene the two double bonds are not independent units; they are in some way related. The terminal positions
of the unsaturated system are the points of greatest reactivity. Such
a system of alternate double and single bonds is called a conjugated
system. More extended conjugated systems are found in the trienes,
tetraenes, and, in general, the polyenes. Compounds in which many
alternate double and single bonds are present as a conjugated system
are usually colored. Carotene, the compound which is responsible for
the yellow color in carrots, contains a conjugated system of eleven
double bonds. Vitamin A (p. 376) has five conjugated double bonds.

1, 3-Butadiene is a colorless gas (bp 1°). It is prepared from ethyl
alcohol or from butane, and it is made in very large amounts for use
in the manufacture of synthetic rubbers. Its usefulness in this connection depends upon its tendency to polymerize and the ease with
which it combines with other unsaturated compounds. The catalysts

most commonly used to promote polymerization are organic peroxides corresponding to the general formula R—O—O—R. Peroxides have a tendency to dissociate into free radicals, and free radicals add to butadiene molecules as follows:

$$RO— + CH_2=CH—CH=CH_2 \longrightarrow RO—CH_2—CH=CH—CH_2—$$

This product is still a radical, and it combines at once with another butadiene molecule:

$$RO—CH_2—CH=CH—CH_2— + CH_2=CH—CH=CH_2$$
$$\longrightarrow RO—CH_2—CH=CH—CH_2—CH_2—CH=CH—CH_2—$$

The process continues until a compound of very high molecular weight has been formed.

Isoprene and chloroprene are dienes in which the double and single bonds constitute conjugated systems. The active positions are at the ends of the conjugated systems, and, like butadiene, they form 1, 4-addition products.

Natural rubber. The rubber which we obtain from the sap of the rubber tree is a polymer of isoprene. The type of chain of isoprene molecules which constitutes a rubber molecule is shown in the following fragment of the formula of rubber:

$$-CH_2—C=CH—CH_2 \vdots CH_2—C=CH—CH_2 \vdots CH_2—C=CH—CH_2-$$
$$\qquad\quad | \qquad\qquad\qquad\quad | \qquad\qquad\qquad\quad |$$
$$\qquad\quad CH_3 \qquad\qquad\qquad CH_3 \qquad\qquad\qquad CH_3$$

Dotted lines are drawn between the isoprene units. The weights of natural rubber molecules vary between 100,000 and 300,000. This means that, in round numbers, from 1500 to 4000 molecules of isoprene must combine to form one of these giant molecules.

Rubber is susceptible to addition reactions, for it contains double bonds. Vulcanization, for example, is a process which is dependent upon the presence of double bonds. In this operation the polymer is heated with sulfur, and the giant molecules become tied together through sulfur atoms which react with the double bonds. These still larger molecules have greater elasticity and strength. The incorporation of carbon black and other fillers in rubber increases the resistance to wear. Not all the double bonds are broken by vulcanization, and the processed rubber is still subject to oxidation by the air. To minimize this oxidation and retard the hardening of the rubber, so-called inhibitors are added.

Synthetic elastimers. Chloroprene, 1, 3-butadiene, styrene, and isobutylene are the principal compounds used in the manufacture of synthetic rubbers, or elastimers. Their polymerization is achieved by emulsifying them in an aqueous soap solution which contains an organic peroxide. The structure of the polymer formed when butadiene is used in this way is similar to the structure indicated above for natural rubber. Some of the hydrocarbon molecules, however, enter the chain by 1, 2-addition and give rise to units of the following structure:

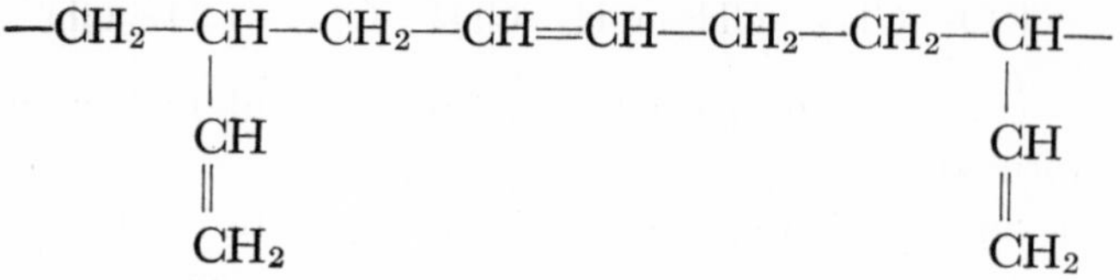

$$—CH_2—CH—CH_2—CH{=}CH—CH_2—CH_2—CH—$$
$$\quad\quad\ \ \ | \quad\quad\quad\quad\quad\quad\quad\quad\quad\quad\quad\quad\quad |$$
$$\quad\quad\ \ \ CH \quad\quad\quad\quad\quad\quad\quad\quad\quad\quad\quad\ CH$$
$$\quad\quad\ \ \ \| \quad\quad\quad\quad\quad\quad\quad\quad\quad\quad\quad\ \|$$
$$\quad\quad\ \ CH_2 \quad\quad\quad\quad\quad\quad\quad\quad\quad\quad CH_2$$

A better rubber for tires is made by allowing 1, 3-butadiene and styrene to polymerize together. Styrene is a colorless liquid which has the formula $C_6H_5—CH{=}CH_2$. In Buna S rubber some styrene molecules are interspersed between butadiene molecules as follows:

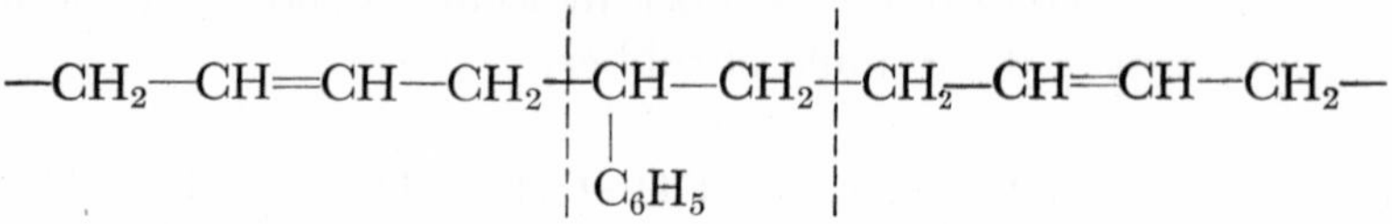

$$—CH_2—CH{=}CH—CH_2{\dashv}CH—CH_2{\dashv}CH_2—CH{=}CH—CH_2—$$
$$\quad\quad\quad\quad\quad\quad\quad\quad\quad\quad | \ |$$
$$\quad\quad\quad\quad\quad\quad\quad\quad\quad C_6H_5$$

A high polymer can be made from isobutylene, $(CH_3)_2C{=}CH_2$, alone. The molecules link together as follows:

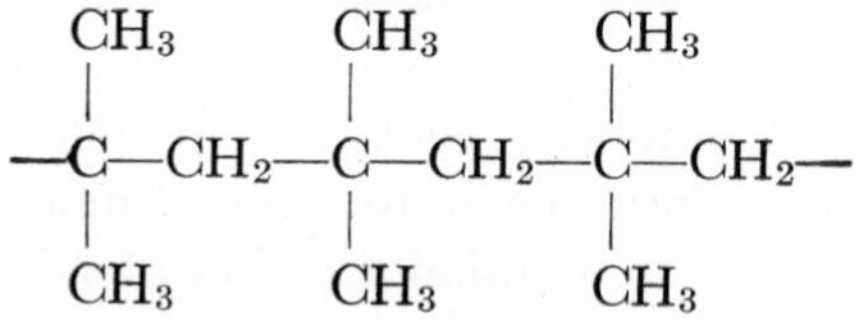

$$\quad\ \ CH_3 \quad\quad\ CH_3 \quad\quad\ CH_3$$
$$\quad\ \ | \quad\quad\quad\ \ | \quad\quad\quad\ \ |$$
$$—C—CH_2—C—CH_2—C—CH_2—$$
$$\quad\ \ | \quad\quad\quad\ \ | \quad\quad\quad\ \ |$$
$$\quad\ \ CH_3 \quad\quad\ CH_3 \quad\quad\ CH_3$$

This elastimer is a saturated hydrocarbon, and it resists oxidation; but for the same reason it cannot be vulcanized, as it contains no double bonds. Vulcanization is necessary to give the product high elasticity, toughness, and strength. If a small quantity of a diene is used with isobutylene as a copolymer, the product is not a fully saturated compound, and it can be vulcanized. The commercial butyl rubbers are copolymers of isobutylene and 1, 3-butadiene.

The free valences which exist at the ends of the growing chains can be satisfied by the addition of groups derived from the peroxide mole-

cules or by addition of any univalent radicals the catalyst and reagents can yield. This sort of addition can occur at any stage; and
since such addition stops the chain reaction, it is obvious that polymers
of various lengths are formed together. In the manufacture of rubber
the conditions must be favorable to continued chain formation, so that
several thousand hydrocarbon molecules will unite before the chain
mechanism is interrupted by a different type of addition.

EXERCISES

1. Write the structural formulas of the following compounds: (a) iso-
propylacetylene, (b) 1-hexyne, (c) 2-chloro-1, 3-butadiene, (d) vinyl bromide,
(e) acetylene, (f) acetaldehyde, (g) acetic acid.

2. Express in equations the preparation of the following compounds.
(Start with coke and any desired inorganic reagents.) (a) $HC\equiv CH$,
(b) CH_3—CHO, (c) CH_3—COOH, (d) $CH_2=CHCl$.

3. Of two substances, one has the formula CH_3—CH_2—$C\equiv CH$ and the
other CH_3—$C\equiv C$—CH_3. How could you tell, by a simple experiment, which
is the former?

4. What is meant by the following terms: (a) polymerization, (b) dimer,
(c) copolymer, (d) elastimer, (e) vulcanization, (f) diene?

5. When water adds to propyne, it is conceivable that either propionaldehyde, CH_3—CH_2—CHO, or acetone, CH_3—CO—CH_3, would be formed.
Which product actually is formed? What rule governs the orientation of the
hydrogen atom and the hydroxyl group in this addition process?

6. Suggest two reagents with which both alkenes and alkynes react rapidly, but with which alkanes react very slowly or not at all.

PROBLEMS

1. Devise a process for converting CH_3—CH_2—CH_2—CH_2Br into
CH_3—CH_2—$C\equiv CH$.

2. How may 1-butyne be prepared from acetylene and ethyl iodide?

3. Write a structural formula for a segment of the polymer which would
be formed if 1, 3-butadiene and isobutylene were used as copolymers and appeared as alternating units in the polymer.

9 · ALICYCLIC AND AROMATIC HYDROCARBONS

The structural units considered so far have been of an open-chain type, consisting of either normal or branched chains. In addition to these we have two types of ring structure. Members of the first class to be considered are called alicyclic compounds; for although they have cyclic, or ring, structures, they resemble in properties the open-chain aliphatic substances. The saturated members are called *cycloalkanes*; the unsaturated ones, *cycloalkenes*.

Cycloalkanes. The first member of the cycloalkane series is cyclopropane, C_3H_6, a colorless gas (mp $-126.6°$; bp $-34.4°$). It is isomeric with propene, CH_3—CH=CH_2, but it does not react with alkaline permanganate. Cyclopropane reacts slowly with bromine and with hydrogen bromide. In these reactions the ring is broken:

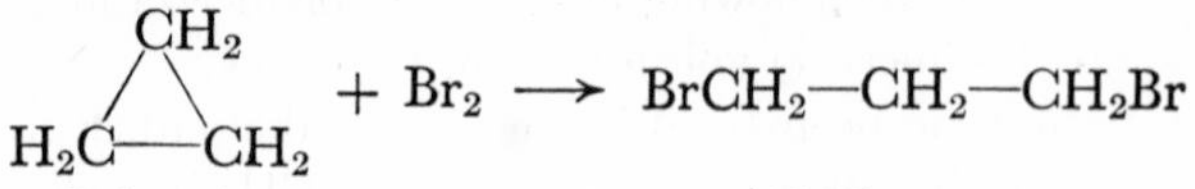

$$\underset{\text{Cyclopropane}}{\begin{array}{c} CH_2 \\ \triangle \\ H_2C\!-\!\!-CH_2 \end{array}} + Br_2 \longrightarrow \underset{\text{1,3-Dibromopropane}}{BrCH_2\text{---}CH_2\text{---}CH_2Br}$$

$$\underset{\text{Cyclopropane}}{\begin{array}{c} CH_2 \\ \triangle \\ H_2C\!-\!\!-CH_2 \end{array}} + HBr \longrightarrow \underset{\text{1-Bromopropane}}{HCH_2\text{---}CH_2\text{---}CH_2Br}$$

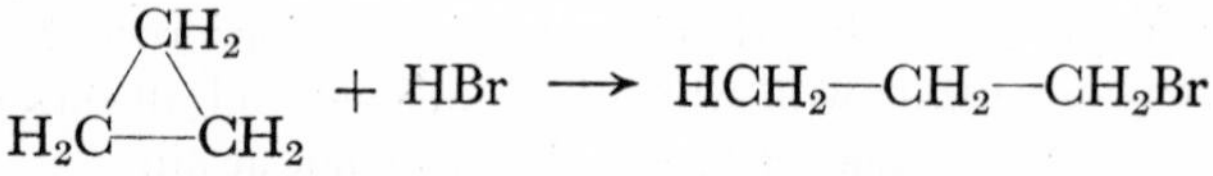

The next member of the series, cyclobutane, and the higher members do not add bromine or hydrogen bromide. They are saturated compounds.

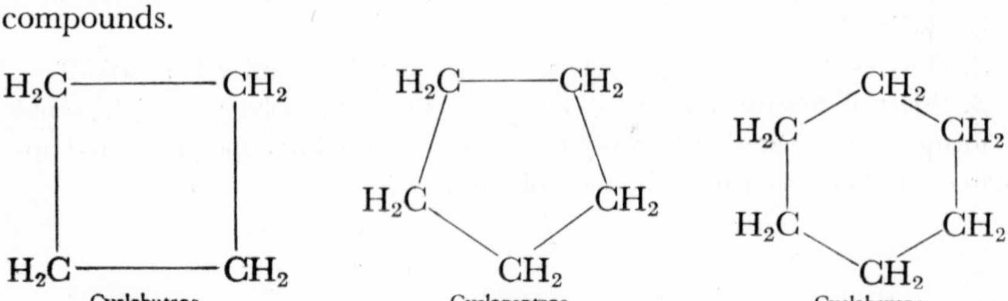

Cyclobutane (bp.13°) Cyclopentane (bp 49.5°) Cyclohexane (bp 81.4°)

In terms of the Baeyer strain theory there is less and less energy in the bonds between the carbon atoms as the bond angle approaches

109° 28', the normal bond angle in open-chain compounds. Rings which contain five carbon atoms, as cyclopentane below, are actually

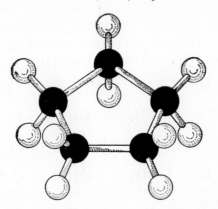

FIG. 5. A Model of the Cyclopentane Molecule

not planar. The pentagonal angle of 108° would impose a slight strain if they were. Moreover, the repulsive forces between the hydrogen atoms, which in ethane are responsible for a slight hindrance to free rotation, also tend to distort the figure from a planar configuration. The cyclopentane ring has an undulatory motion which displaces each of the carbon atoms in turn from a given plane. Cyclohexane and larger rings (rings of thirty methylene groups are known) are puckered or twisted in such a way as to relieve strain.

Cyclopentane and cyclohexane derivatives with aliphatic groups as substituents occur in petroleum; they are called *naphthenes*. Acids derived from them by oxidation are known as *naphthenic acids*; various metallic salts (soaps) of these acids are ingredients of lubricating oils and greases; cobalt salts are used as "driers" in paints to hasten the hardening process.

Cycloalkenes. The cycloalkenes are ring compounds which have one or two double bonds. Their reactions are similar to the reactions of the open-chain unsaturated compounds.

Cyclopentene
(mp − 93°; bp 45°)

Cyclohexene
(mp − 103°; bp 83°)

1, 3-cyclohexadiene
(mp − 96°; bp 80.5°)

Limonene and pinene, isomeric alicyclic hydrocarbons of the formula $C_{10}H_{16}$, are found in lemon oil and pine oil respectively. They are dimers of isoprene, C_5H_8, of which natural rubber is an open-chain polymer, but they are not formed by dimerization of isoprene in the laboratory. The structures are shown below. Of the two rings in pinene the four-membered one is readily ruptured by acids.

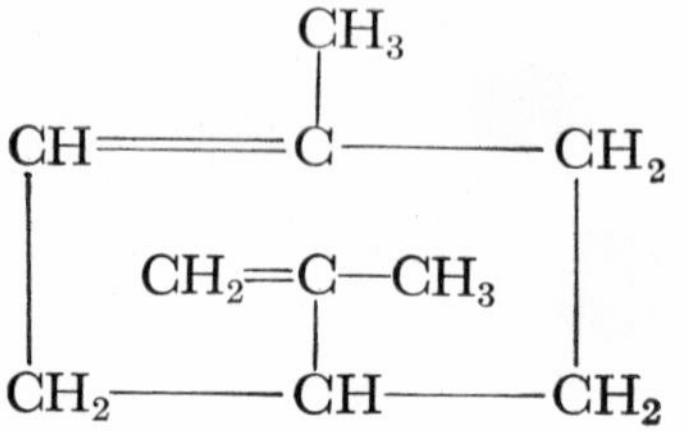

Limonene
(mp − 97°; bp 177°)

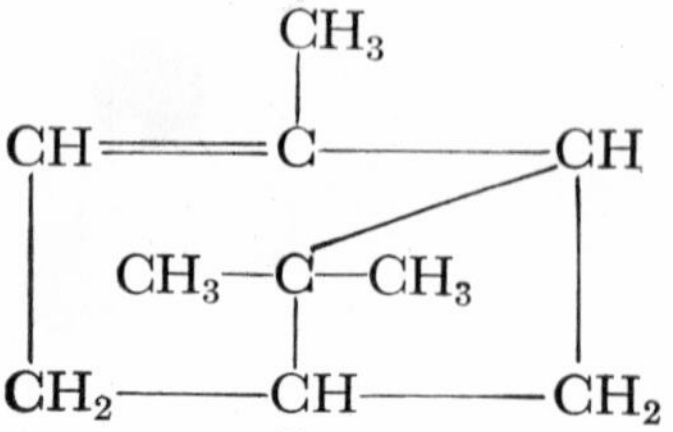

α-Pinene
(mp − 55°; bp 155°)

Aromatic Hydrocarbons

The aromatic hydrocarbons are derivatives of benzene. In structure benzene is a six-membered ring which contains, formally at least, three double bonds:

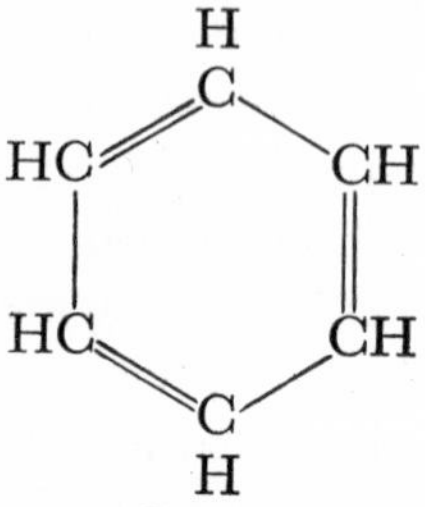

Benzene
(mp 5.4°; bp 80.4°)

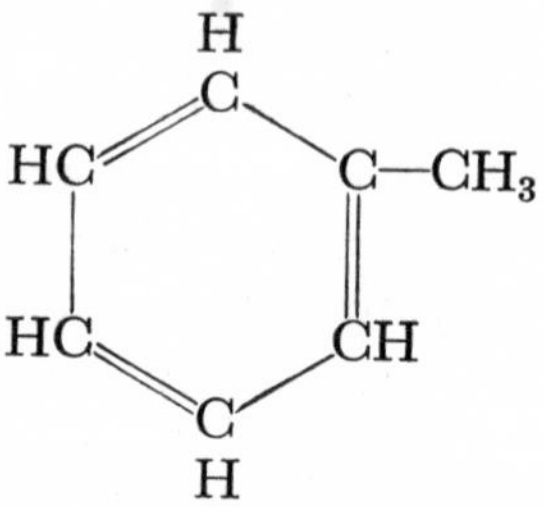

Toluene, or methylbenzene
(mp − 95°; bp 110.8°)

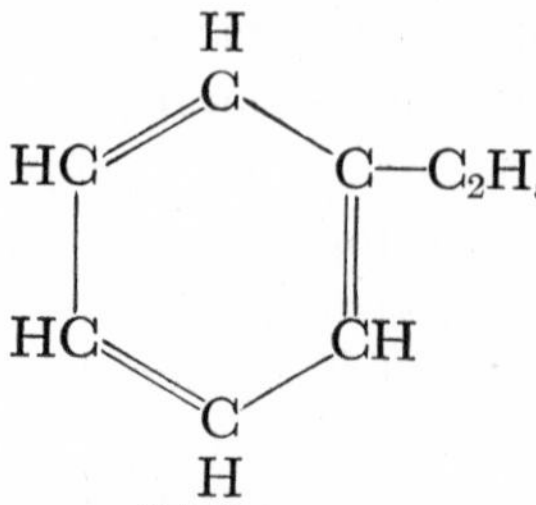

Ethylbenzene
(mp − 94°; bp 136°)

The higher members of the aromatic series of hydrocarbons do not contain more atoms in the ring. They retain the benzene structure; but they have either aliphatic or aromatic groups, attached as side chains. The anomalous character of benzene, which sets it apart from cyclohexene and from cyclohexadiene, is shown by the fact that it does not add bromine in the dark or reduce an alkaline solution of permanganate ions. Benzene adds hydrogen in the presence of platinum or palladium, but even in this reaction it differs from the alkenes. When a mole of any alkene having one double bond adds one mole of hydrogen, between 28,000 and 30,000 calories of heat are liberated; but benzene, with three double bonds, does not liberate three times that amount of heat:

$$3 \ C_6H_{10} + 3 \ H_2 \longrightarrow 3 \ C_6H_{12} + 85{,}800 \text{ cal total}$$
Cyclohexene   Cyclohexane

(28,600 cal per double bond)

$$C_6H_6 + 3 \ H_2 \longrightarrow C_6H_{12} + 49{,}800 \text{ cal total}$$
Benzene   Cyclohexane

(16,600 cal per double bond)

The individual double bonds of benzene are less reactive and under less strain than are isolated double bonds of an alkene. When one of the double bonds in benzene is broken by the addition of hydrogen, less energy is released, on the average, than is evolved in the hydrogenation of ethylene.

The differences between the unsaturation of benzene and that of simple alkenes are so striking that an explanation in terms of structure seems warranted. The three double bonds in benzene are assumed not because of its chemical reactions but because of a desire on the part of chemists to retain the idea that carbon has a valence of four. The tetravalency of carbon is definitely established in connection with the vast majority of the carbon compounds, and we are inclined to assign the same valence to carbon in benzene. If some modification of this valence concept is permitted, the properties and structure of benzene can be reconciled.

The Kekulé formula. A theory presented by Kekulé in 1865 suggested that the positions of the double bonds and single bonds in benzene are not static but interchangeable:

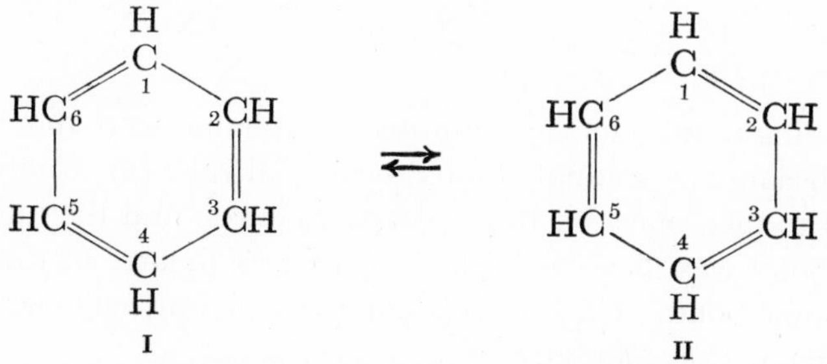

The Kekulé Concept of Oscillating Double Bonds

In this formulation the carbon and hydrogen atoms remain stationary; only the chemical bonds shift position. As we would now express it, the valence electrons shift. Kekulé's theory was supported by the number of isomeric disubstitution products of benzene which could be made. For example, two bromine atoms can be substituted for two hydrogen atoms in benzene, and their relative positions can be determined. It was assumed in Kekulé's time that if the double bonds were not oscillating it should be possible to obtain two dibromo-benzenes in which the two bromine atoms were attached to adjacent

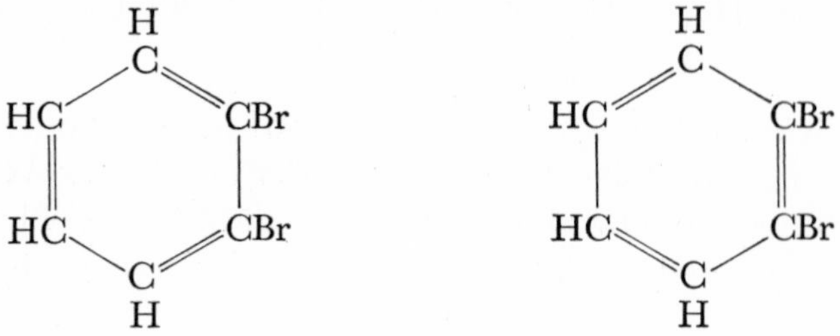

The Kekulé Formulas for Two 1, 2-Dibromobenzenes

carbon atoms. In one of these possible isomers the carbon atoms holding the bromine atoms would be connected by a double bond; in the other, by a single bond. *Experimentally only one 1, 2-dibromobenzene is found.* Kekulé believed that the two compounds existed but could not be separated because of a rapid interchange of the positions of the double and single bonds.

The Thiele formula. A more fruitful concept, which stems from and includes the Kekulé idea, was advanced by Thiele in 1889. Thiele considered the reactivity of a double bond to imply some sort of *partial valence*. This partial, or residual, valence he represented by dotted lines, as follows:

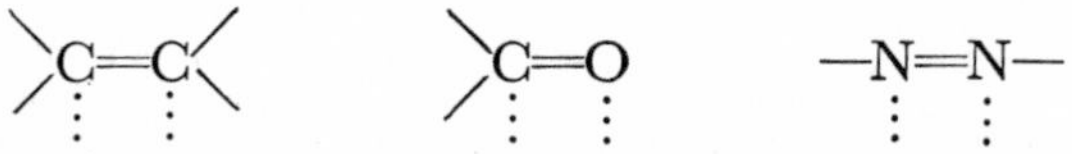

According to this view, unsaturated compounds were thought to be reactive because of residual affinity, or partial valences. Addition was supposed to take place on these partial valences, and the full force of a single bond was then established in the new linkage at the expense of the double bond. Thus the reaction between ethylene and bromine was represented as follows:

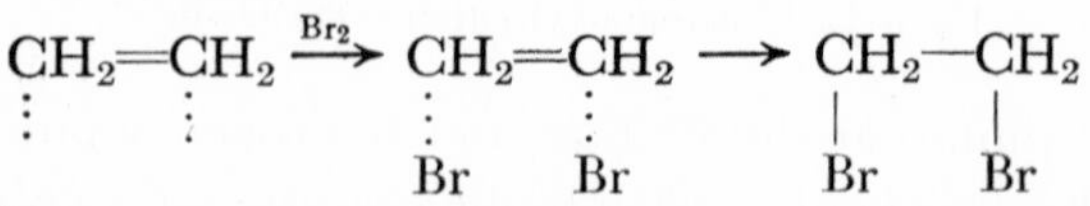

A compound having a pair of double bonds separated by a single bond has been referred to as a *conjugated system* (p. 94). In such cases the residual valences on atoms that are linked together by single bonds may partially satisfy each other, according to Thiele, and become relatively inactive:

$$\overset{1}{C}H_2\!\!=\!\!\overset{2}{C}H\!\!-\!\!\overset{3}{C}H\!\!=\!\!\overset{4}{C}H_2 \quad \text{becomes} \quad \overset{1}{C}H_2\!\!=\!\!\overset{2}{C}H\!\!-\!\!\overset{3}{C}H\!\!=\!\!\overset{4}{C}H_2$$

Carbon atoms 1 and 4 remain active, but the valence requirements of carbon atoms 2 and 3 are to a considerable extent mutually satisfied. Usually, in a compound of this type, addition occurs first on carbon atoms 1 and 4. Carbon atoms 1 and 4 thus become saturated; but 2 and 3 are still unsaturated, and a double bond is established in the 2, 3-position. Further addition may occur on carbon atoms 2 and 3. Thus the saturation of 1, 3-pentadiene by bromine proceeds in steps as follows:

$$CH_3\!\!-\!\!CH\!\!=\!\!CH\!\!-\!\!CH\!\!=\!\!CH_2 \xrightarrow{Br_2} CH_3\!\!-\!\!CHBr\!\!-\!\!CH\!\!=\!\!CH\!\!-\!\!CH_2Br$$

$$\xrightarrow{Br_2} CH_3\!\!-\!\!CHBr\!\!-\!\!CHBr\!\!-\!\!CHBr\!\!-\!\!CH_2Br$$

Extending this concept to benzene, we find in the ring structure a completely conjugated system. In Thiele's formulations of benzene there are no points of major reactivity, and, in harmony with this view, we find experimentally that benzene acts more like a saturated than an unsaturated compound.

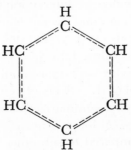

Thiele's Formula of Benzene

Conjugation and resonance. Since the development of the electron theory the idea of conjugation has been broadened and given the name *resonance*. Stated briefly, resonance exists in a molecule if, by shifting the positions of valence electrons with no change in the position of atomic nuclei, more than one stable configuration is possible.

Resonance is evidenced by an increase in stability of the molecule. To write a single structure for benzene one would have to depart from conventional diagrams. The alternative is to write all the conventional formulas and to state that the actual molecule does not correspond to any one of the written structures but is a sort of composite, with the valence electrons lodged not at the extreme positions indicated by the valence theory but at some undetermined points.

Resonance Forms of Benzene · *The actual distribution of valence electrons in benzene does not correspond to either of these forms but is intermediate between the two*

The Kekulé forms of benzene then become resonance forms; but the physical interpretation is not that of a mixture of two substances in equilibrium but of an electron arrangement which is between the two and more stable than either of the two Kekulé forms. The actual configuration is sometimes called a *mesomeric* form, to indicate its intermediate position. The 1, 2-dibromobenzene, described above, is not a pair of isomers in rapid equilibrium but a *single substance*.

Further evidence of resonance interaction **in** aromatic rings is the fact that the carbon-carbon bond distances in benzene are not alternately those of single bonds (1.54 A) and double bonds (1.32 A), but are all of an intermediate value, 1.38 A.

All compounds in which two or more double bonds are present in conjugated position display the effects of resonance to some degree. The physical effects may be summarized as (*a*) higher heats of formation from the elements, (*b*) lower heats of reaction, and (*c*) changes in bond distances, as compared to substances with single or isolated double bonds. Chemical anomalies, such as 1, 4-addition in 1, 3-butadiene and the low reactivity of benzene toward bromine, are observed.

A convenient symbol for benzene, which is commonly used, is a hexagon in which single and double lines alternate as sides; each apex represents one carbon and one hydrogen atom. It is understood that there is a hydrogen atom at each point of the hexagon unless some other atom or group is indicated. For example, bromobenzene, C_6H_5Br, hydroxybenzene, C_6H_5OH, and dimethylbenzene, $C_6H_4(CH_3)_2$, may be written as follows:

Bromobenzene   Hydroxybenzene   Dimethylbenzene

The radical C_6H_5—, derived from benzene by loss of one hydrogen atom, is called the phenyl group or *phenyl radical*. It does not exist in the free state, but it is found in combination with other radicals or with single atoms in a great variety of compounds.

Benzene is a mobile, colorless liquid which crystallizes at 5.5° and boils at 80.4°. It is lighter than water (density $0.8787_4{}^{20}$), sparingly soluble in water but miscible with alcohol and ether. It is an excellent solvent for fats and oils. Benzene was obtained prior to 1949 as a by-product of the coke industry. Since then it has also been produced by the catalytic cracking of those fractions of petroleum which contain methylcyclopentane and cyclohexane.

$$(\text{cyclo})\text{—}C_6H_{12} \xrightarrow[\text{H}_2 \text{ (Heat)}]{\text{Pt—Al}_2\text{O}_3 \cdot \text{SiO}_2} C_6H_6 + 3\,H_2$$

The process is called *platforming* (from the platinum catalyst). Hydrogen gas is introduced with the reactants to assist in maintaining the activity of the catalyst, perhaps by repressing carbonization of the hydrocarbons. Methylcyclopentane is isomerized to cyclohexane.

Reactions of benzene. 1. Chlorine or bromine may be substituted for hydrogen in benzene by direct action of the halogen on the hydrocarbon at the temperature of the laboratory. A small amount of iron in the form of filings, wire, or carpet tacks accelerates the reaction:

$$C_6H_6 + Cl_2 \xrightarrow{\text{Fe}} \underset{\text{Chlorobenzene}}{C_6H_5Cl} + HCl$$

$$C_6H_6 + Br_2 \xrightarrow{\text{Fe}} \underset{\text{Bromobenzene}}{C_6H_5Br} + HBr$$

Further substitution may be accomplished by using an excess of the halogen and prolonging the time of contact of the reagents.

2. Concentrated nitric acid acts upon benzene, replacing a hydrogen atom by the nitro group, —NO_2:

$$C_6H_6 + HONO_2 \longrightarrow \underset{\text{Nitrobenzene}}{C_6H_5NO_2} + H_2O$$

Prolonged treatment with an excess of concentrated nitric acid results in the introduction of two nitro groups, the product being dinitro-benzene, $C_6H_4(NO_2)_2$. Trinitrobenzene is prepared by an indirect method; a very small yield of the compound is obtained by the direct action of nitric acid on benzene.

3. Concentrated sulfuric acid converts benzene into a sulfonic acid:

$$C_6H_6 + H_2SO_4 \longrightarrow C_6H_5SO_3H + H_2O$$
Benzenesulfonic acid

As in the case of nitric acid the reaction can be forced beyond this stage. An excess of hot concentrated sulfuric acid converts benzene into a disulfonic acid or a trisulfonic acid.

These reactions involve substitution of a new atom or group for hydrogen, not addition of the reagent; the aromatic ring remains unchanged. By comparison the alkane hydrocarbons either react more slowly (in the case of the halogens) or are oxidized (by concentrated nitric and sulfuric acids). The alkenes and alkynes give addition reactions with the halogens and sulfuric acid, and are oxidized, sometimes explosively, by strong nitric acid.

In sunlight benzene adds chlorine:

$$C_6H_6 + 3\ Cl_2 \xrightarrow{\text{light}} C_6H_6Cl_6$$
Benzene
hexachloride

The aromatic ring also adds ozone, O_3, to form an ozonide, just as does an alkene. Hydrogenation of benzene takes place with hydrogen under pressure in the presence of finely divided platinum or nickel:

$$C_6H_6 + 3\ H_2 \xrightarrow{\text{Pt or Ni}} C_6H_{12}$$
Cyclohexane

The higher aromatic hydrocarbons contain the nuclei of both aromatic and aliphatic hydrocarbons, and they have the properties of both series of compounds. Ethyl benzene, for example, may be brominated in the ring or in the side chain. When iron is used as a catalyst and the reaction is carried out at the temperature of the laboratory, substitution occurs in the ring:

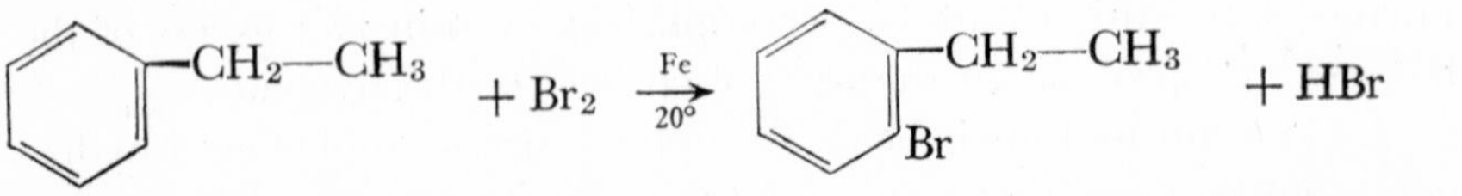

There are five available positions in the ring for attachment of the bromine atom. These positions are not equally active. The structure of the substitution product which is actually formed is described in a later chapter (p. 285).

At a higher temperature and in the absence of iron the side chain is attacked:

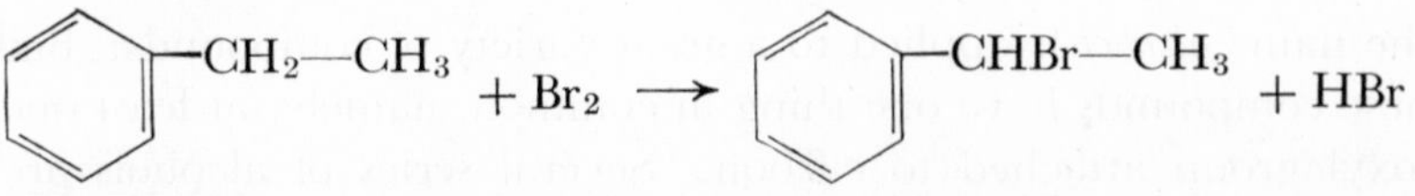

The most active position in the side chain is the one closest to the benzene ring. This is described as the α-position with respect to the cyclic nucleus.

EXERCISES

1. Define the following terms: (a) cycloalkane, (b) cycloalkene, (c) naphthene, (d) side chain.

2. Write a formula which contains a conjugated system of double and single bonds.

3. Write a formula which contains at least two double bonds and two single bonds, but which does not have a conjugated system.

4. Is there a conjugated system in the following formula:

$$CH_3—CH{=}CH—CH_2—CH_2—CH{=}CH—CH_3?$$

5. Write balanced equations for three reactions of benzene.

PROBLEMS

1. Account for the fact that in petroleum five- and six-membered rings are present in greater abundance than three-, four-, and seven-membered rings.

2. Write an equation for a reaction between chlorine and cyclopropane.

3. How many isomers correspond to each of the following molecular formulas: (a) $C_6H_5C_2H_5$, (b) $C_6H_4Br_2$, (c) C_6H_4BrCl?

4. Benzene does not add bromine rapidly. Explain this anomaly on the basis of conjugation between double and single bonds.

10 · THE ALCOHOLS

The name *alcohol* is applied to a great variety of compounds; but all these compounds have one thing in common, namely, at least one hydroxyl group attached to carbon. Several series of alcohols are known. Some of them are saturated compounds; some have double or triple bonds. Some of them have only one hydroxyl group in each molecule; some have two or more hydroxyl groups. The saturated monohydric alcohols correspond to the general formula ROH, in which the symbol R stands for an alkyl radical.

The monohydric alcohols are classified as primary, secondary, or tertiary compounds, the classification being based upon the number of radicals attached to the carbon atom which holds the hydroxyl group. General formulas for the three types of alcohols are written as follows:

$$R-CH_2OH \qquad \underset{R}{\overset{R}{>}}CHOH \qquad \underset{R}{\overset{R}{\underset{R}{-}}}COH$$

Primary alcohol   Secondary alcohol   Tertiary alcohol

The three classes of alcohols differ in several properties, including the following: (*a*) the ease with which they lose water and form alkene hydrocarbons, (*b*) the rates at which they form esters with organic acids, (*c*) the rate of reaction with halogen acids to form alkyl halides, (*d*) the nature of the oxidation products formed when the alcohols are heated with chromic acid.

The alcohols constitute a homologous series which begins with methanol, CH_3OH, and continues by increments of CH_2 to compounds of very high molecular weights. Myricyl alcohol (mp 88°), for example, has the formula $CH_3(CH_2)_{29}CH_2OH$. A few of the simpler members of the series of saturated monohydric alcohols are listed in the table below.

Nomenclature of alcohols. The suffix *ol* is used to designate the presence of a hydroxyl group, just as the suffix *ene* indicates the presence of a double bond. An alcohol is named as a derivative of the hydrocarbon which has the same number of carbon atoms in the longest continuous chain. The final *e* in the name of the corresponding hydrocarbon is changed to *ol*. Thus, an alcohol derived from pentane by substituting a hydroxyl group for a terminal hydrogen atom is called pentanol. The name of a compound having two hydroxyl

SATURATED MONOHYDRIC ALCOHOLS			
Name	Formula	Melting Point	Boiling Point
Methanol (methyl alcohol)	CH_3OH	$-97°$	$64.6°$
Ethanol (ethyl alcohol)	$CH_3—CH_2OH$	$-114°$	$78.5°$
Propyl alcohols			
1-Propanol (n-propyl alcohol)	$CH_3—CH_2—CH_2OH$	$-126°$	$97.8°$
2-Propanol (isopropyl alcohol)	$CH_3—CHOH—CH_3$	$-88.5°$	$82.3°$
Butyl alcohols			
1-Butanol (n-butyl alcohol)	$CH_3—CH_2—CH_2—CH_2OH$	$-90°$	$117.7°$
2-Butanol (methylethylcarbinol)	$CH_3—CH_2—CHOH—CH_3$		$99.5°$
2-Methyl-1-propanol (isobutyl alcohol)	$(CH_3)_2CH—CH_2OH$	$-108°$	$107.3°$
1, 1-Dimethylethanol (tert-butyl alcohol)	$(CH_3)_3COH$	$25°$	$82.3°$
Amyl alcohols			
1-Pentanol (n-amyl alcohol)	$CH_3—(CH_2)_3—CH_2OH$	$-78.5°$	$138°$
2-Pentanol (methylpropylcarbinol)	$CH_3—(CH_2)_2—CHOH—CH_3$		$118°$
3-Pentanol (diethylcarbinol)	$C_2H_5—CHOH—C_2H_5$		$115.6°$
2-Methyl-1-butanol (sec-butylcarbinol)	$C_2H_5—CH(CH_3)—CH_2OH$		$128°$
3-Methyl-1-butanol (isoamyl alcohol)	$(CH_3)_2CH—CH_2—CH_2OH$	$-117°$	$131°$
2-Methyl-2-butanol (dimethylethylcarbinol)	$(CH_3)_2COH—C_2H_5$	$-12°$	$102°$
3-Methyl-2-butanol (methylisopropylcarbinol)	$(CH_3)_2CH—CHOH—CH_3$		$114°$
2, 2-Dimethyl-1-propanol (tert-butylcarbinol)	$(CH_3)_3C—CH_2OH$		$114°$

groups in the molecule would end in *diol*; and the ending *triol* would be assigned to a trihydric alcohol, that is, one which has three hydroxyl groups. Positions of the hydroxyl groups are indicated by numerals immediately preceding the part of the name which indicates the number of carbon atoms in the longest chain. Numbering begins at the end nearest to the hydroxyl group. The following examples will clarify the principle:

$$CH_3—CH—CH_2—CH_2—CH_2OH$$
$$|$$
$$CH_3$$

4-Methyl-1-pentanol

$$CH_3—CHOH—CH_2—CHOH—CH—CH_3$$
$$|$$
$$CH_3$$

5-Methyl-2, 4-hexandiol

If a compound contains a double bond and a hydroxyl group, the position of each functional group must be indicated. In such cases the position of one functional group is shown by a number preceding the name of the carbon chain, and the position of the second group is indicated by a number preceding the suffix relating to that group, as shown in the following example:

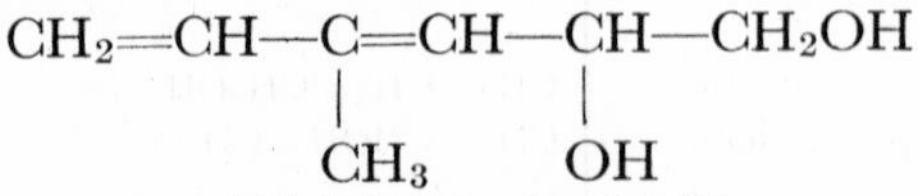

$$CH_2{=}CH{-}C{=}CH{-}CH{-}CH_2OH$$

$$\underset{CH_3}{|} \qquad \underset{OH}{|}$$

3-Methyl-1, 3-hexadiene-5, 6-diol

At one time methyl alcohol, CH_3OH, was called carbinol, and all the simple alcohols were named as derivatives of carbinol. This system is seldom used now, but examples are shown below. The names within parentheses are the official (Geneva) names.

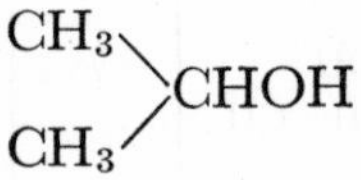

$$\begin{array}{c} CH_3\diagdown \\ \qquad\quad CHOH \\ CH_3\diagup \end{array}$$

Dimethylcarbinol
(2-propanol)

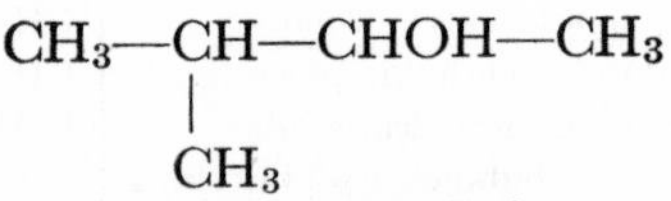

$$CH_3{-}CH{-}CHOH{-}CH_3$$
$$\underset{CH_3}{|}$$

Methylisopropylcarbinol
(3-methyl-2-butanol)

Methyl alcohol. The official name of methyl alcohol, or wood alcohol, is *methanol*. The name indicates the relationship of this compound to methane. Methanol is a colorless liquid which boils at 64.6°, has a burning taste, dissolves in water in all proportions, and is poisonous. Symptoms of poisoning follow the ingestion of less than 15 cc of methanol. Its action upon the central nervous system is similar to that of ethyl alcohol, but it acts specifically upon the optic nerve and in many cases has caused total blindness. Methyl alcohol is manufactured on a large scale, for it has many industrial uses. It is used as a solvent for gums and resins in the manufacture of varnishes, and it is a source of formaldehyde, which, in turn, is a component of Bakelite and of several other useful plastics.

Methyl alcohol is one of the liquids obtained in the destructive distillation of wood. When wood is heated in a deficiency of air it cannot "take fire" and burn, with the production of carbon dioxide and water. Under such conditions gases and liquids escape from the decomposing wood, and a residue of charcoal remains in the still. Among the liquids which escape from the wood are water, methyl alcohol, acetic acid, acetone, and tar. The distillation of wood was the first commercial method developed for the production of methanol, and this accounts for its common name, *wood alcohol*.

A newer process for the synthesis of methanol is the hydrogenation of carbon monoxide. The hydrogenation is accomplished by heating a mixture of carbon monoxide and hydrogen to 450° C under a pressure of about 3000 pounds per square inch while the mixed gases are in contact with a catalyst consisting mainly of zinc chromite:

$$CO + 2\,H_2 \xrightarrow[\;450°\;]{Zn(CrO_2)_2} CH_3OH$$

Ethyl alcohol, CH_3—CH_2OH, is the ordinary alcohol of commerce. It is related to ethane in the same way that methyl alcohol is related to methane, and its official name is *ethanol*. Ethyl alcohol is a very valuable commercial reagent. As a solvent it is surpassed in usefulness only by water, and from it are obtained the ethyl and ethoxy groups found in many synthetic compounds. It is used in the manufacture of drugs, perfumes, flavors, soaps, explosives, dyes, rayons, and a long list of other essential commodities. It rivals petroleum as a source of butadiene for the manufacture of synthetic rubber, and its use in beverages amounts to millions of gallons a year.

Alcohol is commonly regarded as a stimulant; actually its effect upon the central nervous system is that of a depressant. It impairs the higher mental processes, especially those involving memory, training, and self-restraint. As the faculty of self-control is weakened, the individual becomes free from inhibitions; he talks and acts without restraint, and at the same time often without judgment.

Ethyl alcohol is made on a commercial scale from starch, molasses, or sugar by hydrolysis of the starch or sugar to glucose, fermentation of the latter to alcohol and carbon dioxide, and fractional distillation of the resulting solution. The fermentation of fruit juices was an ancient art. Long before the dawn of the Christian Era the cultivation of grapes for the production of wine was an established industry. Through many centuries the art was practiced in a crude way with no understanding of its mechanism, but it was recognized very early that yeast had something to do with it. Leeuwenhoek, in 1683, described the microscopic appearance of yeast, but did not realize that he was dealing with living cells. Yeast was classified as a plant by Tour in 1836. Liebig believed that decomposition of the yeast was a necessary part of the fermentation process. This view was opposed by Berzelius (1843), who advanced the idea of *contact action* and introduced the term *catalysis* to express this type of chemical behavior. Pasteur (1860) connected fermentation with the life processes of the yeast. It was his opinion that yeast, in its growth, utilizes sugar as a food and releases alcohol and carbon dioxide as waste products. This view prevailed until Buchner, in 1897, ground yeast with sand until all the cells had been destroyed and from this lifeless residue extracted a substance which was as good as living yeast for inducing fermentation. This made it evident that some chemical compound produced by yeast, but not the living yeast plant, causes fermentation. Compounds of this sort which are derived from living cells and which catalyze chemical reactions are called *enzymes*. They are complex substances of high molecular weight. Many of the chemical changes which occur in the living body are accomplished under the catalytic influences of specific enzymes.

Wheat, corn, rice, potatoes, and other sources of starch, as well as sugar, can be used in the manufacture of alcohol. When starches are employed, they are first treated with malt to convert them into a sugar called maltose. This conversion is a hydrolysis which is catalyzed by an enzyme called *diastase* or *amylase*. The enzyme is supplied by the malt. Malt is obtained from sprouting barley. The grain is kept warm and moist until it sprouts; it is then subjected to a heat treatment to stop growth, but at a temperature not high enough to destroy the enzymes which are present.

To induce fermentation, yeast is added to a solution of the sugar, either malt sugar (maltose) or cane or beet sugar (sucrose). The yeast in its growth produces an enzyme called *maltase*, which hydrolyzes maltose to glucose. It produces also an enzyme called *invertase*, which hydrolyzes sucrose to glucose and fructose, and still other enzymes which are known collectively as *zymase*. The fermentation of simple sugar molecules is caused by zymase. The main steps in these catalytic processes may be represented in a qualitative way as follows:

$$\underset{\text{Maltose}}{C_{12}H_{22}O_{11}} + H_2O \xrightarrow{\text{Maltase}} \underset{\text{Glucose}}{C_6H_{12}O_6} + \underset{\text{Glucose}}{C_6H_{12}O_6}$$

$$\underset{\text{Sucrose}}{C_{12}H_{22}O_{11}} + H_2O \xrightarrow{\text{Invertase}} \underset{\text{Glucose}}{C_6H_{12}O_6} + \underset{\text{Fructose}}{C_6H_{12}O_6}$$

$$\underset{\substack{\text{Glucose or}\\\text{fructose}}}{C_6H_{12}O_6} \xrightarrow{\text{Zymase}} 2\,\underset{\text{Alcohol}}{C_2H_5OH} + 2\,CO_2$$

The fermentation process, however, is not the simple decomposition which the last equation implies. There are many steps in the fermentation of a sugar, other enzymes are present, and the products formed are not exclusively alcohol and carbon dioxide. By a proper choice of enzymes good yields of acetone, fusel oil (a mixture of amyl alcohols, $C_5H_{11}OH$), glycerol, and butanol can be obtained by fermentation of glucose.

General methods of preparation. Alcohols are made by the following general methods:

1. An alkyl halide is hydrolyzed by heating it with an aqueous solution of a strong base:

$$RX + OH^- \xrightarrow{H_2O} ROH + X^-$$

As a specific example of this reaction we have the production of propyl alcohol from propyl bromide and a hot aqueous solution of sodium hydroxide:

$$C_3H_7Br + NaOH \longrightarrow C_3H_7OH + NaBr$$

Since alkyl halides are usually prepared from alcohols, this process is used only when the halogen atom has been introduced by direct halogenation. A case of this kind is found in the commercial production of alcohols from pentane. A mixture of chloropentanes is hydrolyzed to a mixture of alcohols.

2. Secondary and tertiary alcohols may be made from unsaturated hydrocarbons by treatment with sulfuric acid and hydrolysis of the addition products:

$$R-CH{=}CH_2 + H_2SO_4 \longrightarrow R-\underset{\underset{OSO_3H}{|}}{CH}-CH_3 \tag{1}$$

$$R-\underset{\underset{OSO_3H}{|}}{CH}-CH_3 + H_2O \longrightarrow R-\underset{\underset{OH}{|}}{CH}-CH_3 + H_2SO_4 \tag{2}$$

In breaking the double bond the $-OSO_3H$ group becomes attached to the least hydrogenated carbon atom, and with the exception of ethanol no primary alcohol can be made by this method.

In commercial practice the alkene and steam are passed together over an acidic catalyst:

$$R-CH{=}CH_2 + H_2O \xrightarrow[\text{Heat}]{\text{Catalyst}} R-\underset{\underset{OH}{|}}{CH}-CH_3$$

Since alkenes are by-products of the cracking of petroleum, this procedure is a practical means of producing many alcohols.

3. Aldehydes, ketones, and esters may be reduced to alcohols, some by catalytic hydrogenation, others by the hydrogen produced from metallic sodium and alcohol:

$$\cdot R-\underset{\underset{\text{Aldehyde}}{|}}{\overset{|}{C}}=O + H_2 \xrightarrow{Pt} R-CH_2OH$$

Aldehyde   Primary alcohol

$$R-\underset{\underset{\text{Ketone}}{R}}{\overset{\text{‖}}{C}}=O + H_2 \xrightarrow{Pt} R-\underset{\underset{\text{Secondary alcohol}}{R}}{CHOH}$$

$$R-\underset{\underset{\text{Ester}}{OC_2H_5}}{\overset{\text{‖}}{C}}=O + 4\,Na + 3\,C_2H_5OH \longrightarrow R-CH_2OH + 4\,C_2H_5ONa$$

Ester   Primary alcohol

4. A general method for preparing higher alcohols involves the use of Grignard reagents on aldehydes and ketones. The preparation of these reagents and methods of using them are described elsewhere; see pages 66 and 145.

Reactions of the alcohols. The reactions which may be regarded as characteristic of the alcohols involve the hydroxyl group or the carbon atom to which the hydroxyl group is attached. There are, for example, reactions in which the hydrogen of the OH group is replaced by another atom or by a group of atoms; reactions in which the entire OH group is replaced by another radical or by a single atom; and reactions in which the groups —CHOH— and —CH$_2$OH are oxidized or reduced.

1. Alcohols of low molecular weight react with metallic sodium, with the release of hydrogen and the formation of an alcoholate or alkoxide:

$$C_2H_5OH + Na \longrightarrow C_2H_5ONa + \tfrac{1}{2} H_2$$

Ethyl alcohol   Sodium ethoxide

The alkoxides are colorless solids; they are completely hydrolyzed in water:

$$C_2H_5ONa + H_2O \longrightarrow C_2H_5OH + NaOH$$

2. Alcohols react with concentrated solutions of halogen acids to form alkyl halides and water:

$$C_2H_5OH + HI \rightleftarrows C_2H_5I + H_2O$$

3. Halides of phosphorus convert alcohols into alkyl halides. A specific example of the reaction is found in the preparation of ethyl bromide from ethyl alcohol and phosphorus tribromide:

$$3\ C_2H_5OH + PBr_3 \longrightarrow 3\ C_2H_5Br + H_3PO_3$$

4. Alcohols react with organic acids to form esters and water. The reaction is slow and reversible; a strong inorganic acid will catalyze the reaction and at the same time act as a dehydrating agent to shift the equilibrium and increase the yield of ester. Esters of tertiary alcohols are usually made by other methods.

$$\underset{\text{Acetic acid}}{CH_3{-}COOH} + \underset{\text{Ethanol}}{C_2H_5OH} \underset{}{\overset{H_2SO_4}{\rightleftharpoons}} \underset{\substack{\text{Ethyl acetate}\\\text{(an ester)}}}{CH_3{-}COOC_2H_5} + H_2O$$

5. Concentrated sulfuric acid acts upon an alcohol at room temperature. A primary alcohol forms an ester of sulfuric acid, but secondary and tertiary alcohols are dehydrated to alkenes. The alkene formation is accompanied by polymerization and charring. The following reaction of a primary alcohol is reversible:

$$R{-}CH_2{-}OH + HO{-}SO_3H \rightleftharpoons R{-}CH_2{-}O{-}SO_3H + H_2O$$

Upon dilution with water the acid ester hydrolyzes; the alcohol and sulfuric acid are regenerated.

If the acid ester is heated with an excess of alcohol, alcoholysis takes place, and an ether is formed:

$$R{-}CH_2{-}O{-}SO_3H + R{-}CH_2OH$$
$$\overset{\text{Heat}}{\longrightarrow} R{-}CH_2{-}O{-}CH_2{-}R + H_2SO_4$$

Essentially the two reactions constitute an acid-catalyzed dehydration of an alcohol. The net result may be expressed by a single equation:

$$2\ R{-}CH_2{-}OH \underset{\text{Heat}}{\overset{H_2SO_4}{\longrightarrow}} R{-}CH_2{-}O{-}CH_2{-}R + H_2O$$

In the formation of ethers from most alcohols phosphoric acid is preferred, because at the necessary temperature there is less charring of the alcohol.

If the acid ester is heated alone or with an excess of acid, an alkene is formed:

$$R{-}CH_2{-}CH_2{-}O{-}SO_3H \longrightarrow RCH{=}CH_2 + H_2SO_4$$

This reaction should be reversible; but when sulfuric acid adds to an alkene, the secondary (or tertiary) derivative, not the primary compound, is formed. This makes it possible to convert a primary alcohol into a secondary alcohol. A single equation may be used to represent the result:

$$R-CH_2-CH_2-OH \underset{\text{Heat}}{\overset{\text{Catalyst and heat}}{\rightleftharpoons}} R-CHOH-CH_3$$

The equilibrium favors the secondary (or tertiary) alcohol.

6. The oxidation of an alcohol may be achieved through the use of an oxidizing agent, such as dichromic acid, or by catalytic dehydrogenation. The first product in the case of a primary alcohol is an aldehyde; ketones are produced from secondary alcohols. Typical results are indicated by the following equations:

$$R-CH_2OH \xrightarrow[300°]{\text{Cu-Cr oxides}} R-CHO + H_2$$

$$3R-CH_2OH + Cr_2O_7^{--} + 8H^+ \longrightarrow 3R-CHO + 2Cr^{+++} + 7H_2O$$

$$R_2CHOH \xrightarrow[300°]{\text{Cu-Cr oxides}} R_2C=O + H_2$$

$$3R_2CHOH + Cr_2O_7^{--} + 8H^+ \longrightarrow 3R_2C=O + 2Cr^{+++} + 7H_2O$$

Dehydrogenation of a tertiary alcohol is not possible, for it has no hydrogen atom on the carbinol carbon atom. Oxidizing agents do not attack tertiary alcohols readily; when they do act, a rupture of the carbon structure takes place and acids of fewer carbon atoms and carbon dioxide are formed.

An aldehyde is oxidizable to an acid:

$$3RCHO + Cr_2O_7^{--} + 8H^+ \longrightarrow 3R-CO_2H + 2Cr^{+++} + 4H_2O$$

Control of the temperature and of the relative amounts of alcohol and oxidizing agent permits the preparation of either an aldehyde or an acid from a primary alcohol.

Ethylene glycol (commonly called glycol) is a dihydric alcohol (that is, has two hydroxyl groups). It is a colorless liquid, soluble in water in all proportions, and it has a sweet taste. In cold climates it is used as an antifreeze in automobile radiators. The compound is made from ethylene gas by treatment first with hypochlorous acid and then with aqueous sodium bicarbonate:

$$\begin{array}{c} CH_2 \\ \| \\ CH_2 \\ \text{\small Ethylene} \end{array} + HOCl \longrightarrow \begin{array}{c} CH_2OH \\ | \\ CH_2Cl \\ \text{\small Ethylene chlorohydrin} \end{array}$$

$$\begin{matrix} CH_2OH \\ | \\ CH_2Cl \end{matrix} + H_2O + NaHCO_3 \longrightarrow \begin{matrix} CH_2OH \\ | \\ CH_2OH \end{matrix} + NaCl + H_2O + CO_2$$

Ethylene chlorohydrin   Ethylene glycol

Glycerol, or glycerine, is a sweet, colorless liquid which melts at 17° and boils at 290°. It is completely miscible with water and alcohol, but practically insoluble in chloroform and in ether. The natural animal fats and vegetable oils are esters which yield glycerol and organic acids when hydrolyzed. In the manufacture of soap from fats glycerol is released as a by-product. The fats and oils constitute our natural sources of this compound. Glycerol is a trihydric alcohol and is represented by the formula $CH_2OH—CHOH—CH_2OH$. It is used in many pharmaceutical preparations and in the manufacture of nitroglycerine, the explosive component of dynamite.

Mercaptans. The mercaptans, RSH, are thio alcohols. They may be regarded as ordinary alcohols in which the hydroxyl oxygen atom is replaced by a sulfur atom. The mercaptans are related to hydrogen sulfide in the same way that ordinary alcohols are related to water. Ethyl mercaptan, C_2H_5SH, boils at 36°; the corresponding oxygen compound boils at 78°. Methyl alcohol is a liquid which boils at 64.6°, and the corresponding sulfur compound, methyl mercaptan, CH_3SH, is a gas at the temperature of the laboratory. The mercaptans may be made from alkyl halides by heating the latter, in alcoholic solution, with potassium hydrogen sulfide:

$$C_2H_5I + KSH \longrightarrow C_2H_5SH + KI$$

The mercaptans are characterized by very disagreeable odors, and they can be detected in extremely low concentrations by the sense of smell. A volatile mercaptan is added to natural gas which is to be used for fuel in homes. The mercaptan imparts to the fuel an odor which is quickly detected if a leak develops in the gas line or if a tap is left open.

The mercaptans are somewhat more acidic than the corresponding alcohols; they form metal derivatives very readily. The sodium derivative of ethyl mercaptan (commonly called sodium mercaptide) is made by treating an ether solution of the mercaptan with sodium. Sodium mercaptide, C_2H_5SNa, dissolves in water and hydrolyzes extensively but not completely. Mercury mercaptide, $(C_2H_5S)_2Hg$, is only slightly soluble in water.

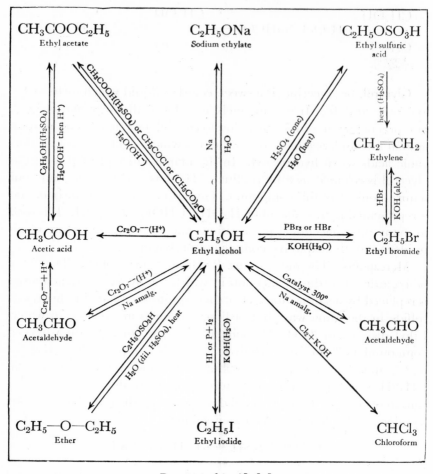

Reactions of an Alcohol

EXAMPLE. Ethanol (ethyl alcohol)

EXERCISES

1. Describe in words, and illustrate, the following terms: (a) primary alcohol, (b) secondary alcohol, (c) tertiary alcohol. Which class of alcohols is not easily oxidized by chromic acid?

2. What are the first oxidation products of primary alcohols? of secondary alcohols?

3. Write structural formulas for three alcohols which have the molecular formula C_4H_9OH, and name them according to the Geneva system and as derivatives of carbinol.

4. Write the structural formulas for (*a*) 3-bromopentanol, (*b*) 5-methyl-2-hexanol, (*c*) methylisobutylcarbinol.

5. What are the major commercial sources of (*a*) methanol? (*b*) ethanol? (*c*) glycerol?

6. How may tertiary butyl alcohol be made from isobutylene?

7. Express in equations the reactions of an alcohol with (*a*) metallic sodium, (*b*) concentrated sulfuric acid (cold), (*c*) concentrated HI (hot).

PROBLEMS

1. Complete and balance the following equations:

$$a.\ C_3H_7OH + PCl_3 \longrightarrow$$
$$b.\ C_4H_9OH + C_2H_5\!\!-\!\!COOH \longrightarrow$$
$$c.\ C_4H_9OH + Na \longrightarrow$$

2. Express in the form of balanced equations a procedure for making a mixture of alcohols from pentane.

3. Why cannot primary alcohols, in general, be made by the acid-catalyzed hydration of the corresponding alkenes? (Refer to the chapter on alkenes and review Markownikoff's rule.)

4. How may a primary alcohol be converted to a secondary alcohol with the same carbon skeleton?

5. Indicate the formation of three products obtainable from a primary alcohol and sulfuric acid.

6. Express in an equation the process by which glucose, $C_6H_{12}O_6$, is converted to ethanol and carbon dioxide.

7. Balance an equation for the oxidation of $C_3H_7\!\!-\!\!CH_2OH$ to $C_3H_7\!\!-\!\!COOH$. Use a mixture of $Na_2Cr_2O_7$ and H_2SO_4 as the oxidizing agent. Calculate the amount of sodium dichromate and of sulfuric acid necessary to oxidize 100 g of the alcohol.

11 · ALIPHATIC ETHERS

Ethers are derivatives of water in which both hydrogen atoms of the water have been replaced by carbon radicals. Alcohols are derivatives of water in which only one of the hydrogen atoms has been replaced by a carbon radical.

$$H—O—H \qquad R—O—H \qquad R—O—R \qquad R—O—R'$$

Water   Alcohol   Simple ether   Mixed ether

The two radicals in an ether may be alike or different. If they are alike, the ether is called a simple ether; if they are different, it is a mixed ether. The alkyl groups in ethers may be primary, secondary, or tertiary.

In addition to the open-chain aliphatic ethers, cyclic ethers are known in which the oxygen atom is a member of the ring structure. Some examples of these are ethylene oxide, dioxane, and trioxane.

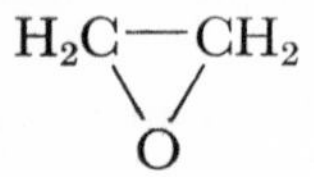

Ethylene oxide
(bp 12°)

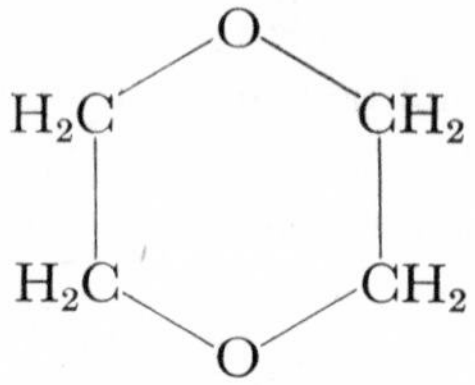

Dioxane
(mp 11.7°; bp 101.5°)

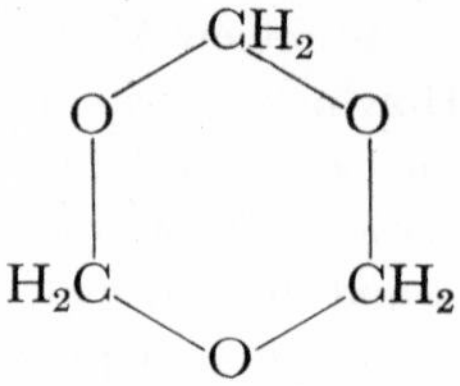

Trioxane
(mp 62°; bp 115°)

The best-known ether is diethyl ether, or, more simply, ethyl ether, $C_2H_5—O—C_2H_5$. Methyl ether and isobutyl ether are, respectively, $CH_3—O—CH_3$ and $(CH_3)_2CH—CH_2—O—CH_2—CH(CH_3)_2$. In naming simple ethers the prefix *di* is usually omitted. The names of some mixed ethers are given in the table on page 122.

Ethers are isomeric with alcohols. Thus the formula C_2H_6O represents either ethanol or dimethyl ether. In spite of this identity in composition and molecular weight the two compounds are very different in chemical and physical properties.

Ethers are more closely related in their properties to hydrocarbons than to alcohols. Ethers and hydrocarbons of comparable structures are much alike with respect to volatility, density, solubility in water, and inertness toward mild oxidizing agents. Alcohols have higher boiling points than their isomeric ethers, and they are more soluble in water. Alcohols are also the more easily oxidized. In Fig. 6 the boiling points of a few members of the three classes of compounds are plotted against the number of carbon, or carbon and oxygen, atoms in the respective kinds of molecules. Only the normal-chain, or straight-chain, compounds are included in the plot; thus the ether, CH_3—CH_2—O—CH_3, the alcohol, CH_3—CH_2—CH_2—OH, and the hydrocarbon, CH_3—CH_2—CH_2—CH_3, are plotted on the abscissa as having four atoms in the chain. The similarity of the hydrocarbons and ethers and their divergence from the alcohols are marked. The

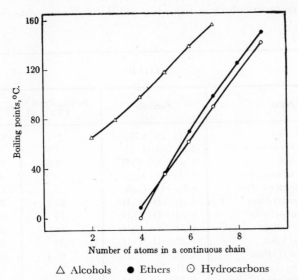

△ Alcohols   ● Ethers   ⊙ Hydrocarbons

FIG. 6. Comparison of the Boiling Points of Alcohols, Ethers, and Hydrocarbons of Approximately Equal Molecular Weights

higher boiling points of the alcohols are due to the fact that the hydroxyl group permits association of alcohol molecules and that this reduces the volatility of the compound. This association of two or more molecules is accomplished through the formation of *hydrogen bonds*. A hydrogen atom can share the attraction of two oxygen atoms simultaneously, as represented by the following formulas:

H—O—H   R—O—H
H—O—H   H—O—R
H—O—H   H—O—R
Associated water molecules   Associated alcohol molecules

Ethers and hydrocarbons cannot form clusters of molecules of this type, because there is no hydroxyl hydrogen present; hydrogen attached to carbon does not engage in such simultaneous attractions. The bond angle in oxygen is essentially the tetrahedral angle, as in carbon. The formulas shown above do not indicate the actual space configurations of these associated molecules. The loose association made possible by the hydrogen bond is not limited to two or three molecules; in water at room temperature the average aggregate contains four to six water molecules.

Except for the two lowest members, the ethers listed in the table below are colorless liquids. Still higher members are waxy solids.

ETHERS

Name	Formula	Boiling Point (°C)	Specific Gravity
Dimethyl ether	CH_3-O-CH_3	−23.7	0.725(0°)
Methyl ethyl ether	$CH_3-O-C_2H_5$	7.9	0.725(0°)
Diethyl ether	$C_2H_5-O-C_2H_5$	34.6	0.714(20°)
Methyl n-propyl ether	$CH_3-O-C_3H_7$	38.9	0.747(0°)
Methyl isopropyl ether	$CH_3-O-C_3H_7$	32.5	0.735(20°)
Ethyl n-propyl ether	$C_2H_5-O-C_3H_7$	61.4	0.732(20°)
Ethyl isopropyl ether	$C_2H_5-O-C_3H_7$	54	0.745(0°)
Di-n-propyl ether	$C_3H_7-O-C_3H_7$	89	0.763(0°)
Diisopropyl ether	$C_3H_7-O-C_3H_7$	69	0.743(0°)
Ethyl n-butyl ether	$C_2H_5-O-C_4H_9$	91.4	0.769(0°)
Ethyl isobutyl ether	$C_2H_5-O-C_4H_9$	80	0.751(20°)
Ethyl tertiary butyl ether	$C_2H_5-O-C_4H_9$	141	0.784(0°)
Di-n-butyl ether	$C_4H_9-O-C_4H_9$	140.9	0.769(20°)
Diisobutyl ether	$C_4H_9-O-C_4H_9$	122.5	0.762(20°)
Diisoamyl ether	$C_5H_{11}-O-C_5H_{11}$	172.2	0.781(15°)
Di-n-amyl ether	$C_5H_{11}-O-C_5H_{11}$	190	0.774(20°)

Ethers are soluble in all proportions in alcohols and in hydrocarbons of similar molecular weight, and they are sparingly soluble in water. Chemically the ethers are inert. They are not attacked by alkalies or dilute acids or by mild oxidizing or reducing agents. Metallic sodium is used in the purification of ethers, because it reacts with water and alcohols but not with the ethers.

Reactions of ethers. 1. Concentrated sulfuric acid dissolves ethers; the lower members are miscible with sulfuric acid in all proportions.

2. Hot aqueous acids slowly hydrolyze ethers:

$$R-O-R + H_2O \xrightarrow{H^+; \text{ heat}} 2 ROH$$

Hydrolysis and solubility in concentrated sulfuric acid serve to distinguish an ether from a hydrocarbon.

3. When stored in contact with air, many ethers slowly absorb oxygen and form explosive peroxides. No ether should be distilled without first testing a portion of it with acidified potassium iodide solution; peroxides liberate iodine, and a yellow-brown color appears. If the test indicates the presence of a peroxide, it would be unsafe to distill the liquid. Removal of the peroxide may be accomplished by shaking the ether with an aqueous solution of ferrous sulfate or by treating the dry ether with metallic sodium.

4. A hot, saturated, aqueous solution of hydrogen iodide gradually converts an ether into alkyl iodides:

$$C_2H_5\text{—}O\text{—}C_3H_7 + 2\ HI \longrightarrow C_2H_5I + C_3H_7I + H_2O$$

This is another reaction which can be used to distinguish an ether from a saturated hydrocarbon. Hydrogen iodide does not react with an alkane.

Preparation of ethers. 1. Some simple ethers are made by heating alcohols with concentrated sulfuric acid. The commercial manufacture of ordinary ether (called ethyl ether or diethyl ether) is accomplished in this way. The reaction goes through two stages, but the net result is expressed by the simple equation

$$\underset{\text{Ethyl alcohol}}{2\ C_2H_5OH} \xrightarrow{H_2SO_4} \underset{\text{Ethyl ether}}{C_2H_5\text{—}O\text{—}C_2H_5} + H_2O$$

The first step in the process is the formation of ethyl sulfuric acid, an oily liquid which can be isolated:

$$C_2H_5OH + H_2SO_4 \longrightarrow \underset{\text{Ethyl sulfuric acid}}{C_2H_5O\text{—}SO_3H} + H_2O \qquad (1)$$

When the ethyl sulfuric acid is heated to about 140° with more alcohol, the second step occurs, and ether distills from the hot mixture:

$$C_2H_5O\text{—}SO_3H + C_2H_5OH \longrightarrow C_2H_5\text{—}O\text{—}C_2H_5 + H_2SO_4 \qquad (2)$$

Phosphoric acid can be substituted for the sulfuric acid.

2. A general method for making both simple and mixed ethers is found in the action of an alkyl halide on an alkoxide. The first step is the preparation of the alkoxide from an alcohol:

$$\underset{\text{An alcohol}}{R\text{—}OH} + Na \longrightarrow \underset{\text{Sodium alkoxide}}{R\text{—}ONa} + \tfrac{1}{2}\ H_2 \qquad (1)$$

In the second step the sodium alkoxide is heated with an alkyl halide:

$$R\text{---}ONa + RX \xrightarrow{\text{Heat}} R\text{---}O\text{---}R + NaX \qquad (2)$$

An ether of the desired structure is made through proper choice of the alcohol used in reaction (1) and of the alkyl halide used in reaction (2). Methyl ethyl ether, $CH_3\text{---}O\text{---}C_2H_5$, for example, may be made by heating together sodium methoxide, CH_3ONa, and ethyl iodide, C_2H_5I, or by heating a mixture of sodium ethoxide, C_2H_5ONa, and methyl iodide, CH_3I.

Methyl ethers of the higher alcohols are prepared from the alcohol, methyl iodide, and silver oxide or from dimethyl sulfate, $(CH_3O)_2SO_2$, the alcohol, and potassium hydroxide solution. These processes will be illustrated later in connection with the methylation of sugars (p. 255).

Ethyl ether is a colorless, volatile liquid which boils at 34.6°. Its vapor forms an explosive mixture with air, and care must be exercised in the use of this compound. Ether is a good solvent for fats and for many other classes of compounds; and since it is only slightly soluble in water, it is used extensively in extraction processes. If an aqueous solution containing a substance which is soluble in ether is shaken with ether, the dissolved substance becomes distributed between the water and ether in proportion to its relative solubilities in the two solvents. When shaking is discontinued, the water and ether form two layers, the light ether forming the top layer. With the aid of a separatory funnel the two layers may be separated, and upon evaporation of the solvent the extracted substance is obtained. Ether dissolves in cold concentrated sulfuric acid and separates from the solution unchanged when the acid is diluted with ice water.

Ether is one of the best general anesthetics known. It was first used in this capacity in 1842. Since then many other compounds with anesthetic properties have been found; among these are chloroform, divinyl ether, ethyl chloride, ethylene, nitrous oxide, and cyclopropane. In high concentrations ether, like other anesthetics, is toxic. The spread in concentration between its narcotic action and its lethal action is great enough for safe usage.

Ethylene oxide is a representative of a group of cyclic ethers, that is, ethers in which there is a closed-chain or ring structure. The compound is made by direct oxidation of ethylene by air or from ethylene chlorohydrin by treatment with a strong base. The oxidation of ethylene is accomplished by mixing the gas with air and passing the mixture over hot, finely divided silver:

$$CH_2 \underset{\underset{350°}{}}{\overset{O_2;\ Ag}{\longrightarrow}} \quad \begin{matrix} CH_2\text{---}CH_2 \\ \diagdown \diagup \\ O \end{matrix}$$

Ethylene
(bp − 103.8°)

Ethylene oxide
(bp 12°)

The preparation from ethylene chlorohydrin is represented by the equation

$$\begin{matrix} CH_2Cl \\ | \\ CH_2OH \end{matrix} + KOH \longrightarrow \begin{matrix} CH_2\text{---}CH_2 \\ \diagdown \diagup \\ O \end{matrix} + KCl + H_2O$$

Ethylene chlorohydrin   Ethylene oxide

Ethylene oxide is a colorless gas. The ring is readily ruptured, a property which is common to all three-membered rings. It combines with water to form ethylene glycol and with ammonia to form ethanolamine:

$$\begin{matrix} CH_2\text{---}CH_2 \\ \diagdown \diagup \\ O \end{matrix} + H_2O \longrightarrow CH_2OH\text{---}CH_2OH$$

Ethylene glycol
(mp − 12.3°; bp 197.2°)

$$\begin{matrix} CH_2\text{---}CH_2 \\ \diagdown \diagup \\ O \end{matrix} + NH_3 \longrightarrow CH_2OH\text{---}CH_2NH_2$$

Ethanolamine
(mp 10.5°; bp 172.2°)

Ethylene oxide combines with alcohols to form compounds known to the trade as *cellosolves*. The cellosolves are glycol ethers. They are used as solvents in the manufacture of some cellulose acetate lacquers:

$$\begin{matrix} CH_2\text{---}CH_2 \\ \diagdown \diagup \\ O \end{matrix} + C_2H_5OH \longrightarrow \begin{matrix} CH_2\text{---}CH_2\text{---}O\text{---}C_2H_5 \\ | \\ OH \end{matrix}$$

Ethylene oxide   Ethylcellosolve

Ethylene oxide forms addition products with the halogen acids. With hydrochloric acid, for example, it yields ethylene chlorohydrin:

$$\begin{matrix} CH_2\text{---}CH_2 \\ \diagdown \diagup \\ O \end{matrix} + HCl \longrightarrow CH_2OH\text{---}CH_2Cl$$

The chlorohydrin is used in the manufacture of many derivatives of ethylene glycol, including amino alcohols, hydroxy ethers, and some plastics.

Dioxane, a cyclic ether, is a useful solvent. It is a colorless liquid (mp 11.7°; bp 101.5°) which dissolves in water in all proportions. Dioxane is made by heating ethylene glycol with a small quantity of concentrated sulfuric acid. Diethylene glycol is formed as an intermediate product:

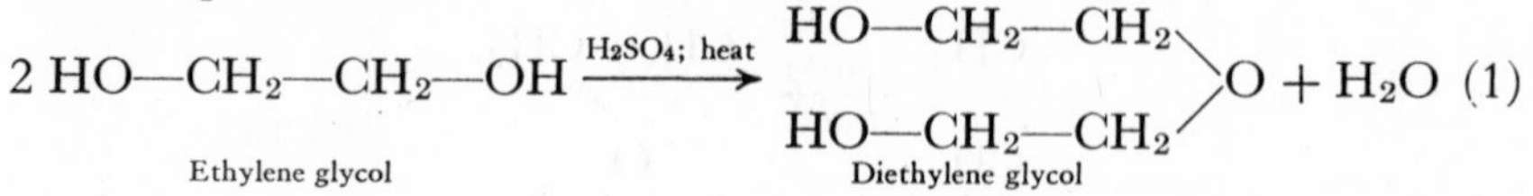

$$2 \text{ HO—CH}_2\text{—CH}_2\text{—OH} \xrightarrow{\text{H}_2\text{SO}_4; \text{ heat}} \begin{array}{c} \text{HO—CH}_2\text{—CH}_2 \\ \\ \text{HO—CH}_2\text{—CH}_2 \end{array}\!\!\!\!\!\text{O} + \text{H}_2\text{O} \quad (1)$$

Ethylene glycol   Diethylene glycol

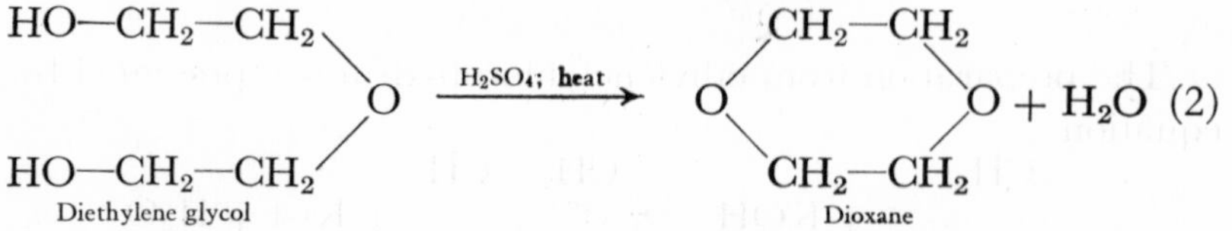

$$\begin{array}{c} \text{HO—CH}_2\text{—CH}_2 \\ \\ \text{HO—CH}_2\text{—CH}_2 \end{array}\!\!\!\!\!\text{O} \xrightarrow{\text{H}_2\text{SO}_4; \text{ heat}} \text{O}\!\!\!\!\!\begin{array}{c} \text{CH}_2\text{—CH}_2 \\ \\ \text{CH}_2\text{—CH}_2 \end{array}\!\!\!\!\!\text{O} + \text{H}_2\text{O} \quad (2)$$

Diethylene glycol   Dioxane

EXERCISES

1. Write the structural formulas of the ethers listed in the table on page 122.

2. Write equations for two methods of making ethyl isopropyl ether.

3. State how one could use such tests as (a) solubility in water, (b) solubility in sulfuric acid, (c) evolution of hydrogen by sodium, (d) reaction with hot concentrated HI, to distinguish from each other the members of the following pairs of compounds:

    a. Ethanol and ethyl ether   *c.* Dioxane and propanol

    b. Pentane and ethyl ether   *d.* Hexane and methanol

4. Write the formulas of (a) dioxane, (b) ethylene oxide, (c) ethyl cellosolve, (d) ethylene glycol.

5. List the major chemical and physical differences between isomeric alcohols and ethers.

6. Rewrite the following reaction in the form of two successive steps:

$$\text{C}_2\text{H}_5\text{OH} \xrightarrow{\text{H}_2\text{SO}_4} \text{C}_2\text{H}_5\text{—O—C}_2\text{H}_5 + \text{H}_2\text{O}$$

PROBLEMS

1. Express in the form of equations two methods of preparing ethylene chlorohydrin from ethylene and any other reagents.

2. What dehydration product of an alcohol other than an ether is commonly produced?

3. Under acidic catalysis propene adds ethanol to form ethyl isopropyl ether, $\text{C}_3\text{H}_7\text{—O—C}_2\text{H}_5$. In a similar way it adds water to form $\text{C}_3\text{H}_7\text{OH}$. Write a structural formula for the ether and one for the alcohol. How would you prepare another ether with the same empirical formula?

4. Why do alcohols boil at temperatures higher than the boiling points of isomeric ethers?

5. Start with ethylene and show how the following compounds may be prepared: (a) ethanol, (b) ethyl ether, (c) ethylene glycol, (d) butyl cellosolve, (e) dioxane.

12 · ALIPHATIC HALOGEN COMPOUNDS

Organic compounds which contain fluorine, chlorine, bromine, or iodine are known as halogen compounds. They are not commonly found in nature; but some of them have commercial uses, and they are made synthetically in large amounts. Halogen atoms are readily replaced by other atoms or by atomic groups, and this property makes halogen compounds useful as sources or as intermediates in the synthetic production of many other types of compounds.

The list of currently used halogen derivatives is a long one; a few examples are given in the table below. Only one member of the group presented there, thyroxine, occurs naturally.

SOME HALOGEN COMPOUNDS

Name	Formula	Use
Methyl chloride	CH_3Cl	Refrigerant; intermediate in the preparation of many reagents
Ethylene dibromide	$BrCH_2$—CH_2Br	Component of leaded gasoline
Chloropicrin	Cl_3CNO_2	Fumigant
Chloretone	Cl_3C—$C(CH_3)_2$	Drug
	OH	
Chloroacetophenone	C_6H_5—CO—CH_2Cl	Lachrymator
Phosgene	$COCl_2$	War gas; drug and dye intermediate
Vinyl chloride	CH_2=$CHCl$	Plastic when polymerized
D.D.T.	$(ClC_6H_4)_2CH$—CCl_3	Insecticide
Mustard gas	$(ClCH_2$—$CH_2)_2S$	War gas (a liquid)
2, 4-Dichlorophenoxy-acetic acid	$Cl_2C_6H_3$—O—CH_2—CO_2H	Weed-killer
Ethylene chlorohydrin	$HOCH_2$—CH_2Cl	Intermediate in synthesis of glycol, divinyl ether, and hydroxy propionic acid
Thyroxine	$C_{15}H_{11}NO_4I_4$	Hormone
Eosin	$C_{20}H_8O_5Br_4$	Ink

Thyroxine is secreted by the thyroid gland, and it acts as a regulator of metabolism. The iodine needed for its production in the thyroid gland is ingested as iodide in the diet; hence the importance of iodized table salt for use in regions where the water and foodstuffs are deficient in iodine.

$$HO-\underset{I}{\overset{I}{\bigcirc}}-O-\underset{I}{\overset{I}{\bigcirc}}-CH_2-\underset{\underset{NH_2}{|}}{CH}-COOH$$

Thyroxine

The table on page 127 includes many types of halogen compounds, but we shall consider in detail at this point only the halogen derivatives of aliphatic hydrocarbons.

Alkyl Halides

The alkyl halides are halogen substitution products of the saturated aliphatic hydrocarbons. The general formula for an alkyl halide is RX, in which R stands for any alkyl radical and X represents any halogen atom. Like the alcohols (p. 108) the alkyl halides may be classified as primary, secondary, and tertiary compounds.

$$R-CH_2X \qquad \underset{R}{\overset{R}{\diagdown}}CHX \qquad \underset{R}{\overset{R}{\diagdown}}CX$$

Primary halide   Secondary halide   Tertiary halide

There are some important differences in the properties of the three types of halides, although in general they react similarly. In a tertiary alkyl halide the halogen atom is held by a carbon which, in turn, is linked to three other carbon atoms; and this condition results in an enhanced activity of the halogen atom in some reactions. Tertiary halides are hydrolyzed much faster than primary and secondary halides. When treated with basic reagents, the tertiary halides yield HX and alkene hydrocarbons more rapidly than do primary or secondary halides. The physical properties of the halides also are modified by changes in structure. Branched-chain compounds boil at temperatures lower than the boiling points of their normal-chain isomers. The character of the halogen also has to be considered in connection with the physical and chemical properties of the alkyl halides; iodine is the most easily replaced halogen atom. The boiling points of halides which contain the same alkyl radical are in the following order:

$$RI > RBr > RCl > RF$$

As indicated in the table (p. 130), methyl chloride, ethyl chloride, and methyl bromide are gases; the higher members included in the table are liquids. Only those of still higher molecular weights (more than fifteen carbon atoms) are solids.

The organic halides, existing as gases or liquids, are in striking contrast to inorganic halide salts. The latter are high-melting solids. This difference means that the cohesive forces between the ions of the salts are strong, while the intermolecular forces between organic halides are weak. The organic halides are sparingly soluble in water; but they are soluble in nonpolar substances, such as ethers and hydrocarbons. There is no ionic dissociation of halide ions from carbon. This is not due to inability of the *halogen* to ionize but to the inability of an *alkyl group* to exist as an ion. Silver nitrate does not instantly produce a precipitate of silver halide when added to an organic halide. In a few cases precipitation occurs in a very short time, but in most cases it requires days or years of contact at room temperature to obtain evidence of reaction.

Preparation of alkyl halides. Several methods are available for making alkyl chlorides, bromides, and iodides. The fluorides are less frequently used and are generally made by different procedures. The most useful synthetic procedures are the following:

1. An alcohol is converted into an alkyl halide by treatment with a halide of phosphorus. Ethyl alcohol may be used to illustrate the method:

$$3\ C_2H_5OH + PCl_3 \longrightarrow 3\ C_2H_5Cl + H_3PO_3$$
$$3\ C_2H_5OH + PBr_3 \longrightarrow 3\ C_2H_5Br + H_3PO_3$$
$$6\ C_2H_5OH + 2\ P + 3\ I_2 \longrightarrow 6\ C_2H_5I + 2\ H_3PO_3$$

A mixture of red phosphorus and crystalline iodine is generally used as a source of phosphorus triiodide.

2. The hydroxyl group of an alcohol may be replaced by halogen through digestion of the alcohol with a saturated solution of a halogen acid:

$$C_2H_5OH + HCl \rightleftarrows C_2H_5Cl + H_2O$$
$$(CH_3)_3COH + HBr \rightleftarrows (CH_3)_3CBr + H_2O$$
$$ROH + HI \rightleftarrows RI + H_2O$$

This type of reaction is reversible. In dilute aqueous acid the equilibrium lies far to the left, but a concentrated solution of the acid or the gaseous hydrogen halide converts a large part of the alcohol into the corresponding alkyl halide. Since the halide boils at a lower temperature than the alcohol, it is often possible to increase the yield by distilling the halide from the solution as fast as it is formed. This procedure prevents the attainment of equilibrium.

ALKYL HALIDES

Alkyl Group	Formula	Chlorides		Bromides		Iodides	
		Boiling Point	Specific Gravity	Boiling Point	Specific Gravity	Boiling Point	Specific Gravity
Methyl	CH_3X	−23.7°	0.952 (0°)	+4.6°	1.732 (0°)	+42.6°	2.293 (18°)
Ethyl	CH_3CH_2X	+12.2°	0.918 (8°)	38°	1.468 (13°)	72.3°	1.944 (14°)
Normal propyl	$CH_3CH_2CH_2X$	46.5°	0.912 (0°)	71°	1.383 (0°)	102.5°	1.786 (0°)
Isopropyl	CH_3CHXCH_3	36.5°	0.882 (0°)	59.6°	1.340 (0°)	89.5°	1.774 (0°)
Normal butyl	$CH_3CH_2CH_2CH_2X$	78°	0.907 (0°)	101.6°	1.305 (0°)	127°	1.643 (0°)
Isobutyl	$(CH_3)_2CHCH_2X$	68.9°	0.895 (0°)	91.5°	1.264 (20°)	120.4°	1.640 (0°)
Secondary butyl	$CH_3CH_2CHXCH_3$	68°	0.871 (20°)	91.3°	1.251 (20°)	117.5°	1.626 (0°)
Tertiary butyl	$(CH_3)_3CX$	51°	0.840 (20°)	73.3°	1.222 (20°)	100°	1.571 (0°)
Normal amyl	$CH_3(CH_2)_3CH_2X$	105.7°	0.901 (0°)	127.9°	1.223 (20°)	156°	1.543 (0°)
Isoamyl	$(CH_3)_2CHCH_2CH_2X$	99.1°	0.893 (20°)	121°	1.215 (20°)	148°	1.510 (20°)
Neopentyl	$(CH_3)_3CCH_2X$		0.879 (0°)		1.225 (0°)		
Active amyl	$(CH_3)(C_2H_5)CHCH_2X$	99°	0.886 (15°)	120°	1.221 (20°)	148°	1.524 (20°)
Normal hexyl	$CH_3(CH_2)_4CH_2X$	134°	0.872 (20°)	156°	1.173 (20°)	180°	1.441 (20°)
Normal heptyl	$CH_3(CH_2)_5CH_2X$	159.5°	0.881 (16°)	179°	1.113 (16°)	203.8°	1.386 (16°)
Normal octyl	$CH_3(CH_2)_6CH_2X$	184.6°	0.880 (16°)	204°	1.116 (16°)	225.5°	1.345 (16°)

Methods 1 and 2 depend upon the availability of alcohols corresponding in structures to the desired halides. They are practical methods, for there are many ways of producing alcohols. On a small scale (especially if the alcohol is expensive) process 1 is employed. Method 2 lends itself to large-scale production.

3. The addition of a halogen acid to an alkene gives rise to an alkyl halide:

$$CH_2{=}CH_2 + HBr \longrightarrow CH_3{-}CH_2Br$$
Ethylene   Ethyl bromide

$$CH_3{-}CH{=}CH_2 + HI \longrightarrow CH_3{-}CHI{-}CH_3$$
Propylene   Isopropyl iodide

The Markownikoff rule places a restriction upon the usefulness of this method. The halogen atom ordinarily becomes attached to the least hydrogenated atom of the hydrocarbon, and this limits the reaction to the production of secondary and tertiary halides. An exception in the case of hydrogen bromide has been mentioned (p. 75).

4. Alkyl chlorides and bromides may be made by direct treatment of saturated hydrocarbons with chlorine or bromine. Iodides are not produced by the direct action of iodine on saturated hydrocarbons.

$$CH_3{-}CH_2{-}CH_3 + Cl_2 \xrightarrow{300°} \begin{cases} CH_3{-}CH_2{-}CH_2Cl + HCl \\ CH_3{-}CHCl{-}CH_3 + HCl \end{cases}$$

The disadvantage of this method lies in the fact that the position of substitution cannot be controlled. There exists also the possibility of placing more than one halogen atom in the same molecule. The method, nevertheless, is used where the mixed products are useful or if they may be easily separated by fractional distillation.

5. Very often an acid is available which has a structure corresponding to that of a desired alkyl bromide; that is, RCOOH is available and RBr is wanted. In such a case the bromide may be made through the action of bromine on the dry silver salt of the acid:

$$RCOOAg + Br_2 \longrightarrow RBr + CO_2 + AgBr$$

Reactions of the alkyl halides. The alkyl halides are valuable as sources from which a great variety of compounds may be prepared. A few of their transformations will be illustrated.

1. Alkyl halides react with strong bases, the products being alcohols or unsaturated hydrocarbons. An *aqueous* solution of potassium hydroxide hydrolyzes the organic halide to an alcohol:

$$CH_3{-}CH_2{-}CH_2Br \xrightarrow{KOH \text{ in water}} CH_3{-}CH_2{-}CH_2OH + KBr$$
n-Propyl bromide   n-Propyl alcohol

An *alcoholic* solution of potassium hydroxide acts upon an alkyl halide with the production of an alkene hydrocarbon if the alkyl halide is so constituted that removal of a halogen atom from one carbon atom and a hydrogen atom from an adjacent carbon atom is possible:

$$CH_3\text{—}CH_2\text{—}CH_2Br \xrightarrow{\text{KOH in alcohol}} CH_3\text{—}CH\text{=}CH_2 + KBr + H_2O$$

n-Propyl bromide   Propene

2. With water, alcohols, and ammonia, reactions occur which are termed respectively hydrolysis, alcoholysis, and ammonolysis.

$$RX + H_2O \rightleftharpoons ROH + HX \qquad \text{(hydrolysis)}$$
An alcohol

$$RX + ROH \rightleftharpoons ROR + HX \qquad \text{(alcoholysis)}$$
An ether

$$RX + 2\,NH_3 \longrightarrow RNH_2 + NH_4X \qquad \text{(ammonolysis)}$$
An amine

The use of the general formula, RX, indicates the possibility of using any alkyl halide in these reactions, but the exact conditions under which the processes occur cannot be generalized. As indicated earlier, primary, secondary, and tertiary halides react at different rates; and chlorides, bromides, and iodides display differences in reactivity. Tertiary halides hydrolyze in water rapidly; in fact, aqueous alkali does not hasten their conversion to alcohols. Primary halides hydrolyze so slowly that the reaction is carried out at high temperatures and alkali is used. Alcoholysis also is slow with primary halides, progressively more rapid with secondary and tertiary halides. Ammonia dissolved in alcohol reacts rapidly with alkyl halides; but since it is definitely basic, the side reaction of alkene formation takes place, particularly with secondary and tertiary halides. The reaction with ammonia takes place in two stages:

$$RX + NH_3 \longrightarrow RNH_3X \qquad (1)$$
$$RNH_3X + NH_3 \rightleftharpoons RNH_2 + NH_4X \qquad (2)$$

3. Sodium ethoxide, C_2H_5ONa, which is prepared from alcohol and metallic sodium, acts upon an alkyl halide to form an ether. Ordinary ether, $C_2H_5OC_2H_5$, may be made in this way:

$$C_2H_5Br + C_2H_5ONa \longrightarrow C_2H_5OC_2H_5 + NaBr$$

The general formula for an ether is ROR, and the general equation for the formation of an ether from an alkyl halide and an alkoxide may be written as follows:

$$R'X + RONa \longrightarrow ROR' + NaX$$

4. When an alkyl halide dissolved in alcohol is mixed with a concentrated aqueous solution of potassium cyanide, and the mixture is heated under a reflux condenser, an alkyl cyanide, or nitrile, is formed:

$$RX + KCN \longrightarrow RCN + KX$$

This reaction proceeds smoothly with primary alkyl halides, but secondary and tertiary halides have a tendency to yield unsaturated hydrocarbons. This is especially true of tertiary halides. Potassium cyanide is basic enough to cause the elimination of the halogen acid, HX. (Compare this result with that caused by alcoholic KOH (p. 132).)

5. Potassium hydrosulfide and alkyl halides yield mercaptans, or thioalcohols:

$$RX + KSH \longrightarrow RSH + KX$$

6. Silver salts of organic acids react with alkyl halides to produce esters:

$$RX + CH_3\text{---}COOAg \longrightarrow CH_3\text{---}COOR + AgX$$

7. Halogen atoms may be substituted for each other by heating alkyl halides with inorganic halides:

$$RCl + KI \longrightarrow RI + KCl$$

Some alkyl fluorides are made in this way.

8. With active metals the alkyl halides form metallic derivatives:

$$2\,RX + 2\,Mg \xrightarrow{\text{Ether}} 2\,RMgX \underset{}{\overset{\text{Ether}}{\rightleftarrows}} R_2Mg + MgX_2$$

$$RX + Li \xrightarrow{\text{Ether}} RLi + LiX$$

Magnesium compounds of the type RMgX are known as Grignard reagents. Ether is used in their formation as a solvent for both the alkyl halides and for the Grignard reagents. Sodium, like lithium, acts upon organic halides; but the product, RNa, immediately reacts with another alkyl halide molecule, as indicated in the discussion of the Wurtz reaction (p. 67). It is interesting to note that while these metals cannot displace hydrogen directly from a hydrocarbon, the hydrocarbon-metal derivative can be produced by a devious path:

$$RH + Cl_2 \longrightarrow RCl + HCl \tag{1}$$
$$RCl + 2\,Li \longrightarrow RLi + LiCl \tag{2}$$

The magnesium and lithium compounds are used in the synthesis of more complex organic compounds.

All but one of the reactions of the halides given above are *substitution reactions*; that is, they are reactions in which the halogen atom is replaced by some other atom or group of atoms. The one exception is alkene formation, which results from elimination of halogen acid from the alkyl halide. Since all the reagents which are used in the substitution reactions are basic to some degree, it is not surprising to find that the two kinds of reaction often proceed simultaneously. For instance, the single reagent sodium hydroxide can produce either an alkene or an alcohol from the same alkyl halide. Such processes are spoken of as competitive reactions, and the ratio of the products depends upon the relative rates of the two processes. These relative rates of reaction may often be influenced by the nature of the solvent and by the temperature. With primary alkyl halides the replacement, or substitution, reaction normally predominates, and from them the corresponding alcohols, amines, ethers, nitriles, mercaptans, esters, and fluorides are readily obtained. With the tertiary compounds alkene formation predominates; only the neutral reagents water, alcohol, and halide salts react with them to give substitution products in good yields. Secondary halides occupy an intermediate position. All three types of alkyl halides form Grignard reagents.

Alkyl iodides react more rapidly than bromides, and the latter more rapidly than chlorides. For this reason the iodides and bromides are preferred, and in some cases necessary, as starting points in synthetic work.

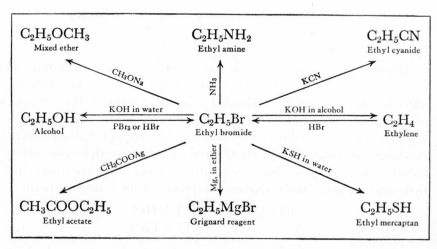

Reactions of a Primary Alkyl Halide

EXERCISES

1. Complete and balance the following equations to show the predominant product.

    a. CH_3—CH_2Cl + KOH (in alcohol) $\longrightarrow$

    b. CH_3—CH_2Cl + KOH (in water) $\longrightarrow$

    c. CH_3—CH_2—CH_2Br + Mg $\xrightarrow{\text{Ether}}$

    d. CH_3—CHBr—CH_3 + KCN $\longrightarrow$

    e. CH_3—CH_2—CHI—CH_3 + KSH $\longrightarrow$

2. Outline a method for making an alkyl halide from each of the following sources:

    a. CH_3—CHOH—CH_3

    b. CH_3—CH=CH—CH_3

    c. CH_3—CH_2—CH_2—CH_3

3. Outline methods for making the transformations indicated below. Assume that all necessary reagents are available.

    a. $C_2H_5OH \longrightarrow C_2H_5NH_2$

    b. CH_3—CH_2—$CH_2Br \longrightarrow CH_3$—CH=$CH_2$

    c. CH_3—$CH_2OH \longrightarrow CH_3$—$CH_2I$

    d. $C_5H_{11}Br \longrightarrow C_{10}H_{22}$

    e. $C_4H_9I \longrightarrow C_4H_9CN$

    f. $C_2H_5OH \longrightarrow C_2H_5OC_2H_5$

4. What evidence is there that organic halides do not ionize?

5. Give the formula and one use for (*a*) methyl chloride, (*b*) ethylene dibromide, (*c*) vinyl chloride, (*d*) carbon tetrachloride, (*e*) chloroform.

PROBLEMS

1. Devise methods for making the compounds listed below from C_2H_5OH and any desired reagents.

    a. C_2H_5Br *d.* C_2H_6

    b. CH_3—O—C_2H_5 *e.* C_2H_5MgI

    c. CH_2Cl—CH_2Cl *f.* CH_3—CH_2—CN

2. Suggest a means of analyzing a mixture of normal C_4H_9Cl and tertiary C_4H_9Cl for the amount of each component in the mixture.

Note. The one reacts much faster than the other, under certain conditions, to give HCl, which may be titrated.

3. Suggest a way of converting CH_3—CH_2—CH_2I into CH_3—CHI—CH_3.

4. Illustrate through the use of balanced equations the term *competitive reactions*.

5. Suggest a means of converting ethylene dibromide, CH_2Br—CH_2Br, into ethylidene bromide, CH_3—$CHBr_2$.

13 · ALIPHATIC ALDEHYDES AND KETONES

The aldehydes and ketones are oxidation products of primary alcohols and secondary alcohols respectively. The simplest aldehyde, formaldehyde, is a gas; all other aldehydes and the ketones are colorless liquids or solids. Many aldehydes and ketones have pleasant odors, and some of them are used in the preparation of flavors and perfumes. Among the well-known natural products which contain fragrant aldehydes are cinnamon, vanilla, almond oil, citronellal, and oil of violets. The odor and flavor of Roquefort cheese are due largely to a ketone (methyl amyl ketone), and camphor is a ketone. Aldehydes and ketones undergo a great variety of reactions and are therefore valuable sources of other types of compounds.

The structural unit which characterizes aldehydes and ketones is the carbonyl group, $> C = O$. In aldehydes the carbonyl group is attached to one hydrogen atom and one carbon radical (formaldehyde, H—CHO, is the only exception). In ketones two carbon radicals are attached to the carbonyl group. The carboxyl group of acids also contains the carbonyl group as an integrated unit. These structures are written in various ways:

Formaldehyde: $\begin{matrix} H \\ \\ H \end{matrix} > C = O$ or H—CHO

Any aldehyde: $\begin{matrix} R \\ \\ H \end{matrix} > C = O$ or $R - C \begin{matrix} \nearrow O \\ \searrow H \end{matrix}$ or R—CHO

Any ketone: $\begin{matrix} R \\ \\ R \end{matrix} > C = O$ or R_2CO or R—CO—R

Any carboxylic acid: RCOOH or $R - C \begin{matrix} \nearrow O \\ \searrow OH \end{matrix}$ or R—CO$_2$H

Preparation of aldehydes and ketones. These compounds are made from alcohols, organic acids, and salts of organic acids, as indicated below.

136

1. A primary alcohol is oxidized to an aldehyde by treatment with potassium dichromate and sulfuric acid:

$$3 \; CH_3\text{—}CH_2OH + Cr_2O_7{}^{--} + 8 \; H^+$$
$$\longrightarrow 3 \; CH_3\text{—}CHO + 2 \; Cr^{+++} + 7 \; H_2O$$

Ethyl alcohol / Acetaldehyde

Only volatile aldehydes, which can escape as fast as formed, are successfully made this way; for continued contact with the oxidizing agent converts the aldehyde into an acid.

A secondary alcohol upon oxidation yields a ketone:

$$3 \; CH_3\text{—}CHOH\text{—}CH_3 + Cr_2O_7{}^{--} + 8 \; H^+$$
$$\longrightarrow 3 \; CH_3\text{—}CO\text{—}CH_3 + 2 \; Cr^{+++} + 7 \; H_2O$$

Isopropyl alcohol / Acetone

A good yield of the ketone can be obtained, because further oxidation is very slow.

2. When a primary or secondary alcohol in the vapor state is passed over hot copper, hydrogen is released, and an aldehyde or ketone is formed:

$$R\text{—}CH_2OH \xrightarrow[300°]{\text{Copper}} R\text{—}CHO + H_2$$

$$\begin{array}{c} R \\ \diagdown \\ R \diagup \end{array} CHOH \xrightarrow[300°]{\text{Copper}} \begin{array}{c} R \\ \diagdown \\ R \diagup \end{array} C\text{=}O + H_2$$

This is the process used in the commercial production of the lower ketones.

3. Aldehydes and some symmetrical ketones may be made by the catalytic pyrolysis (rupture by heat) of carboxylic acids. For the production of a ketone an acid is vaporized and passed over manganese oxide, MnO, at a temperature of 300° or 400°:

$$2 \; RCOOH \xrightarrow{\text{MnO}} R_2CO + H_2O + CO_2$$

To obtain an aldehyde by this method it is necessary to use a mixture of two acids, one of which must be formic acid, HCOOH. An excess of formic acid is used to reduce the chance of ketone formation from the higher acid:

$$\left. \begin{array}{c} R\text{—}COOH \\ H\text{—}COOH \end{array} \right\} \xrightarrow[300°]{\text{MnO}} R\text{—}CHO + H_2O + CO_2$$

It is not expedient to prepare unsymmetrical ketones, R—CO—R′, by the pyrolysis of mixed higher acids.

4. Dry distillation of a salt of a carboxylic acid results in the formation of a ketone. Calcium acetate, for example, yields acetone:

$$(CH_3COO)_2Ca \longrightarrow CH_3-CO-CH_3 + CaCO_3$$

Calcium acetate   Acetone

Calcium, barium, and thorium salts give better yields than do sodium salts. Salts of dicarboxylic acids furnish cyclic ketones:

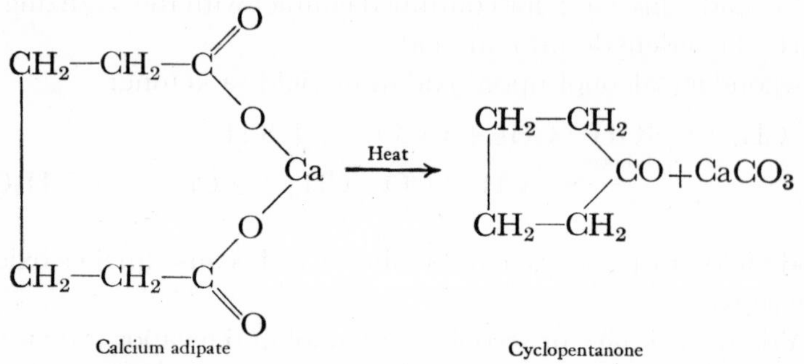

Calcium adipate   Cyclopentanone

A mixture of salts of two different acids, when heated, yields three ketones. If the three ketones are easily separated, this process may be used to prepare unsymmetrical ketones.

5. Ketones react with secondary alcohols if the two reagents are warmed together in contact with aluminum amalgam. An equilibrium is established between the reagents used and the possible products, as indicated by the equation

$$R_2CHOH + R'_2CO \overset{Catalyst}{\rightleftharpoons} R'_2CHOH + R_2CO$$

If an excess of the ketone R'_2CO is used, the equilibrium is displaced to the right, and a good yield of R_2CO may be obtained. The reaction permits the use of an inexpensive ketone, R'_2CO, for the production of a more expensive ketone.

SUMMARY OF PREPARATIVE METHODS		
Intermediate	**Reagent**	**Product**
Primary alcohol	Dichromic acid	Aldehyde (if volatile)
Secondary alcohol	Dichromic acid	Ketone
Primary or secondary alcohol	Cu; 300° (dehydrogenation)	Aldehyde or ketone
Acid (volatile)	MnO; 300°–400°	Ketone (symmetrical)
Formic acid and a higher acid	MnO; 300°–400°	Aldehyde
Ca, Ba, or Th salt of an acid	Heat	Ketone

The outstanding facts so far presented are that aldehydes and ketones may be obtained by the oxidation or dehydrogenation of primary and secondary alcohols respectively or by the pyrolysis of carboxylic acids or salts of these acids.

Nomenclature of aldehydes and ketones. The aldehydes are named from the acids which they produce when oxidized. Formaldehyde, or formic aldehyde, is the member of the series from which formic acid may be derived. Acetaldehyde, or acetic aldehyde, CH_3—CHO, yields acetic acid when oxidized. Ketones are named from the radicals attached to the carbonyl group or, in the case of symmetrical ketones, from the acids which are used to prepare them. Thus, CH_3—CO—CH_3 is dimethyl ketone, or acetone, and CH_3—CO—$CH(CH_3)_2$ is methyl isopropyl ketone.

According to the Geneva system an aldehyde or ketone is named from the hydrocarbon that has the same number of carbon atoms in the longest continuous chain. The final *e* of the hydrocarbon name is changed to *al* to indicate the presence of the aldehyde group or to *one* to indicate a ketone. Thus H—CHO is methanal, CH_3—CHO is ethanal, and so on. In the case of ketones the position of the carbonyl group in the chain must be indicated. A number following the suffix *one*, or immediately preceding the name containing this suffix, indicates that position; for example, CH_3—CH_2—CO—CH_2—CH_3 is pentanone-3 or 3-pentanone, and $(CH_3)_2CH$—CH_2—CH_2—CO—CH_3 is 5-methyl-hexanone-2 or 5-methyl-2-hexanone.

Reactions of Aldehydes and Ketones

The many reactions of aldehydes and ketones may be grouped, for convenience, under three headings: (*a*) reactions which are common to aldehydes and ketones and which can be used to detect the presence of the carbonyl group; (*b*) reactions which can be used to distinguish aldehydes from ketones; (*c*) reactions which are used to convert aldehydes and ketones into useful products of other types.

Among the reagents commonly used for the detection of the carbonyl group are hydroxylamine, phenylhydrazine, and semicarbazide. These reagents act upon aldehydes and ketones in aqueous solution or in alcoholic solution, and the products formed are in most cases solids which are easily crystallized and isolated.

ALDEHYDES

Official Name	Common Name	Formula	Melting Point (°C)	Boiling Point (°C)
Methanal	Formaldehyde	HCHO	− 92	− 21
Ethanal	Acetaldehyde	CH_3CHO	− 123.5	20.2
Propanal	Propionaldehyde	C_2H_5CHO	− 81	48.8
Butanal	Butyraldehyde	C_3H_7CHO	− 99	75.7
2-Methylpropanal	Isobutyraldehyde	C_3H_7CHO	− 65.9	61
Pentanal	Valeraldehyde	C_4H_9CHO	− 91.5	103.4
3-Methylbutyral	Isovaleraldehyde	C_4H_9CHO	− 51	92.5
2, 2-Dimethylpropanal	Trimethylacetaldehyde	C_4H_9CHO	3	75
Hendecanal	Undecylaldehyde	$C_{10}H_{21}CHO$	− 4	117*
Dodecanal	Lauraldehyde	$C_{11}H_{23}CHO$	44.5	184

*At 18 mm pressure.

KETONES
(Normal chains unless otherwise specified)

Official Name	Common Name	Formula	Melting Point (°C)	Boiling Point (°C)
Propanone	Acetone	CH_3COCH_3	− 94.3	56.5
2-Butanone	Methyl ethyl ketone	$CH_3COC_2H_5$	− 86.4	79.6
3-Pentanone	Diethyl ketone	$C_2H_5COC_2H_5$	− 42	101.7
2-Pentanone	Methyl propyl ketone	$CH_3COC_3H_7$	− 77.8	101.8
4-Heptanone	Dipropyl ketone	$C_3H_7COC_3H_7$	− 32.6	143.5
2, 4-Dimethyl-3-pentanone	Diisopropyl ketone	$C_3H_7COC_3H_7$		123.7
6-Undecanone	Dipentyl ketone	$C_5H_{11}COC_5H_{11}$	14.6	226.3
7-Tridecanone	Dihexyl ketone	$C_6H_{13}COC_6H_{13}$	30.5	264
2-Octanone	Methyl hexyl ketone	$CH_3COC_6H_{13}$	− 21.6	172.7
2-Decanone	Methyl octyl ketone	$CH_3COC_8H_{17}$	3.5	211

1. Oxime formation. Hydroxylamine reacts with an aldehyde as follows:

$$R—C{\overset{H}{\underset{O}{}}} + H_2NOH \rightarrow R—C{\overset{H}{\underset{NOH}{}}} + H_2O$$

An aldehyde → An oxime

Ketones react in the same way. In either case the carbonyl oxygen atom is replaced by the group $=NOH$.

Hydroxylamine, H_2NOH, is available only in solution and in the form of its salts. The free compound is unstable. Accordingly the reagent actually used is the hydrochloric acid salt, $H_2NOH \cdot HCl$. To prepare an oxime the aldehyde or ketone is mixed in a solvent with hydroxylamine hydrochloride, and sodium hydroxide is then added to remove HCl and liberate the free hydroxylamine.

2. **Hydrazone formation.** The reaction of phenylhydrazine with a carbonyl group is indicated by the following equation:

$$R\!-\!C\!\!\overset{H}{\underset{O}{\diagdown}} + H_2N\!-\!NH\!-\!C_6H_5 \longrightarrow R\!-\!C\!\!\overset{H}{\underset{N\!-\!NH\!-\!C_6H_5}{\diagdown}} + H_2O$$

An aldehyde   A phenylhydrazone

A ketone reacts in the same way:

$$\underset{\underset{O}{\|}}{R\!-\!C\!-\!R} + H_2N\!-\!NH\!-\!C_6H_5 \longrightarrow \underset{\underset{N\!-\!NH\!-\!C_6H_5}{\|}}{R\!-\!C\!-\!R} + H_2O$$

A ketone   A phenylhydrazone

Phenylhydrazine, $C_6H_5\!-\!NH\!-\!NH_2$, is a high-boiling liquid, oily in appearance, and sparingly soluble in water. It is soluble in dilute acetic acid and is used in that medium. If its hydrochloride salt is used instead of the free base, sodium acetate is added to reduce the concentration of hydrogen ions.

3. **Semicarbazone formation.** Semicarbazide,

$$H_2N\!-\!NH\!-\!CO\!-\!NH_2,$$

is a colorless crystalline compound which dissolves readily in water. A solution of semicarbazide acts upon an aldehyde or ketone to form a crystalline semicarbazone:

$$R\!-\!CHO + H_2N\!-\!NH\!-\!CO\!-\!NH_2$$
$$\longrightarrow R\!-\!CH\!=\!N\!-\!NH\!-\!CO\!-\!NH_2 + H_2O$$

A semicarbazone

4. **Reaction with Fehling's solution.** Aliphatic aldehydes are oxidized by Fehling's solution. Fehling's solution is prepared by adding an alkaline solution of sodium potassium tartrate to a solution of copper sulfate.* Ketones and alcohols are oxidized slowly or not at all

	Grams
*Solution A:	
Water	1000
Copper sulfate (hydrated)	69.3
Solution B:	
Water	1000
Potassium hydroxide	250
Sodium potassium tartrate	346

For use mix equal volumes of A and B. In the presence of tartrate ions copper is not precipitated by the alkali.

by this reagent. By setting a time limit on the reaction it is possible to distinguish an aliphatic aldehyde from a ketone. At 100° visible evidence of reaction appears within five minutes if the substance treated with Fehling's solution is an aldehyde. The test is not entirely reliable; for ketones which have a hydroxyl group in the α-position with respect to the carbonyl group also reduce Fehling's solution promptly. Some of the sugars are α-hydroxy ketones (see page 232).

In the presence of a strong base, cupric and tartrate ions enter into the formation of a blue, soluble, complex ion, $CuC_4H_2O_6^{--}$.

$$Cu^{++} + C_4H_4O_6^{--} + 2\ OH^- \rightleftarrows CuC_4H_2O_6^{--} + 2\ H_2O$$

The formation of this complex ion prevents the precipitation of cupric hydroxide. For the sake of simplicity we shall consider the simple cupric ion, Cu^{++}, as the active agent. When an aldehyde is added to the blue solution and the mixture is warmed, a reddish-yellow precipitate of cuprous oxide appears:

$$R—CHO + 2\ Cu^{++} + 5\ OH^- \longrightarrow R—COO^- + Cu_2O + 3\ H_2O$$

5. **Reaction with Tollens's reagent.** Tollens's solution contains the silver ammonia complex ion, $Ag(NH_3)_2$.* The silver ion, as such or as the complex ion, oxidizes an aldehyde to the salt of the corresponding acid, and a black precipitate consisting of fine particles of metallic silver appears. Very often the silver plates out on the walls of the test tubes, and a beautiful mirror is produced. The reaction proceeds as follows:

$$R—CHO + 2\ Ag(NH_3)_2^+ + 3\ OH^-$$
$$\longrightarrow R—COO^- + 2\ Ag + 4\ NH_3 + 2\ H_2O$$

Ketones fail to reduce silver ions or do so very slowly; aldehydes react promptly. At room temperature reduction is evident within two minutes if an aldehyde is present.

6. **Reaction with Schiff's reagent.** The Schiff reagent, like Fehling's solution and the Tollens reagent, can be used to distinguish aldehydes from ketones. As in the other distinguishing tests a time limit is imposed. Schiff's reagent for aldehydes is prepared from a dye, magenta, which is decolorized by sulfur dioxide. The colorless solution turns

---

*Tollens's reagent is made by adding to a solution of silver nitrate enough dilute sodium hydroxide solution to precipitate the silver in the form of silver oxide. The dark precipitate is then dissolved in the smallest possible quantity of dilute ammonia. An explosive product, which may detonate if one moves the container, develops in Tollens's reagent after this has stood for a few weeks.

red when a trace of aldehyde is added. Only one drop of a suspected aldehyde should be used in making a test, and only two minutes should be allowed for color to appear. The lower ketones and some acetals react with Schiff's reagent, but they do not cause the appearance of a red color within two minutes.

7. **Acetal formation.** Aldehydes react with alcohols to form products known as acetals. Ketones do not react with alcohols in this way.

$$CH_3\text{---}CHO + C_2H_5OH \rightleftarrows CH_3\text{---}CH\overset{OH}{\underset{OC_2H_5}{<}}$$

Hemiacetal (not isolated)

$$CH_3\text{---}CH\overset{OH}{\underset{OC_2H_5}{<}} + C_2H_5OH \rightleftarrows CH_3\text{---}CH\overset{OC_2H_5}{\underset{OC_2H_5}{<}} + H_2O$$

Acetal

The first alcohol molecule breaks the double bond and forms an addition product. The second one forms a condensation product with loss of water. An acid or an acidic salt is needed to catalyze the reaction. In general terms the reaction may be written as follows:

$$R\text{---}CHO + 2\ R'OH \overset{H^+}{\rightleftarrows} R\text{---}CH\overset{OR'}{\underset{OR'}{<}} + H_2O$$

An acetal

In this reaction R' stands for a primary radical; secondary alcohols usually give poor yields of acetals, and tertiary alcohols none. Acetals are readily hydrolyzed in aqueous acidic solutions. They do not reduce Tollens's reagent or Fehling's solution, but they slowly color Schiff's reagent.

8. **Polymerization.** The double bond of an aldehyde permits addition of another molecule of the same kind, and a third molecule may add to form a ring structure.

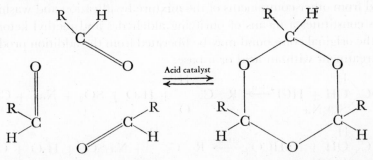

Three Molecules of an Aldehyde   One Molecule of the Cyclic Polymer

The fact that ketones do not polymerize suggests that an alkyl group saturates the carbonyl group more than a hydrogen atom does. In fact, all the reactions of carbonyl derivatives show that the reactivities are in the following order:

$$\begin{matrix} H \\ \quad \end{matrix} C{=}O \; > \; \begin{matrix} R \\ \quad \end{matrix} C{=}O \; > \; \begin{matrix} R \\ \quad \end{matrix} C{=}O$$

9. Formation of cyanohydrins. Aldehydes and ketones combine with hydrocyanic acid to form addition products called cyanohydrins. A trace of base, either sodium hydroxide or an amine, acts as a catalyst:

$$C_2H_5{-}C{<}^H_{O} + HCN \underset{}{\overset{Base}{\rightleftarrows}} C_2H_5{-}C{-}OH{<}^H_{CN}$$

Propanal   Propanal
(propionaldehyde)   cyanohydrin

The cyanohydrins are readily hydrolyzed by hot hydrochloric acid, and this affords a practical method for making α-hydroxy acids.

$$C_2H_5{-}CHOH{-}CN + 2\,H_2O + HCl$$

α-Hydroxybutyronitrile
(propanal cyanohydrin)

$$\longrightarrow C_2H_5{-}CHOH{-}COOH + NH_4Cl$$

α-Hydroxybutyric
acid

This is one of the simpler ways of extending a carbon chain.

10. Bisulfite addition. When an aldehyde is shaken with a saturated solution of sodium bisulfite, an addition product is formed. Ketones having a methyl group attached to the carbonyl group (methyl ketones) also respond to this treatment:

$$R{-}C{<}^H_{O} + NaHSO_3 \rightleftarrows R{-}C{-}OH{<}^H_{SO_3Na}$$

The bisulfite addition product usually precipitates, and it can be freed from other components of the mixture by filtration and washing. This constitutes a means of purifying aldehydes and methyl ketones; for the original compound may be liberated from the addition product by treatment with an acid or a base.

$$R{-}C{-}OH{<}^H_{SO_3Na} + HCl \overset{Heat}{\longrightarrow} R{-}C{<}^H_{O} + H_2O + SO_2 + Na^+ + Cl^-$$

$$R{-}C{-}OH{<}^H_{SO_3Na} + NaHCO_3 \overset{Heat}{\longrightarrow} R{-}C{<}^H_{O} + Na_2SO_3 + H_2O + CO_2$$

11. The Grignard reaction. Alkyl magnesium halides act upon aldehydes and ketones, forming addition products which are easily hydrolyzed to alcohols. Formaldehyde is converted into a primary alcohol, any other aldehyde yields a secondary alcohol, and ketones give rise to tertiary alcohols.

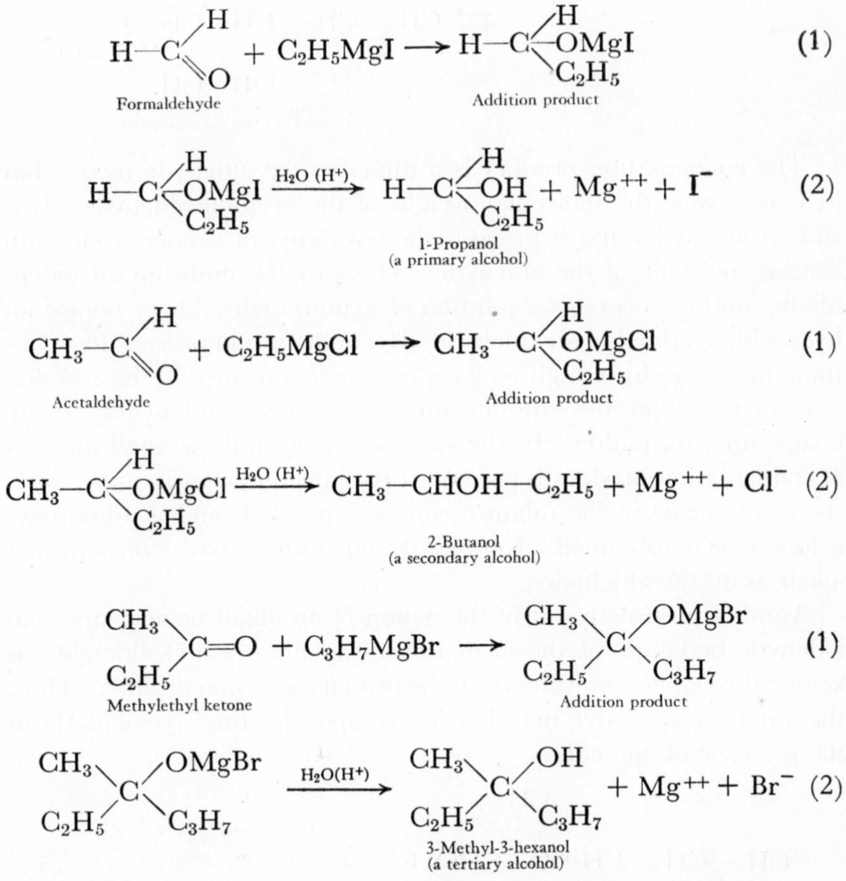

$$H-C{\overset{H}{\underset{O}{}}} + C_2H_5MgI \longrightarrow H-C{\overset{H}{\underset{C_2H_5}{OMgI}}} \qquad (1)$$

Formaldehyde   Addition product

$$H-C{\overset{H}{\underset{C_2H_5}{OMgI}}} \xrightarrow{H_2O\,(H^+)} H-C{\overset{H}{\underset{C_2H_5}{OH}}} + Mg^{++} + I^- \qquad (2)$$

1-Propanol
(a primary alcohol)

$$CH_3-C{\overset{H}{\underset{O}{}}} + C_2H_5MgCl \longrightarrow CH_3-C{\overset{H}{\underset{C_2H_5}{OMgCl}}} \qquad (1)$$

Acetaldehyde   Addition product

$$CH_3-C{\overset{H}{\underset{C_2H_5}{OMgCl}}} \xrightarrow{H_2O\,(H^+)} CH_3-CHOH-C_2H_5 + Mg^{++} + Cl^- \qquad (2)$$

2-Butanol
(a secondary alcohol)

$$\begin{matrix}CH_3 \\ \\ C_2H_5\end{matrix}\!\!>\!C=O + C_3H_7MgBr \longrightarrow \begin{matrix}CH_3 \\ \\ C_2H_5\end{matrix}\!\!>\!C\!\!<\!\begin{matrix}OMgBr \\ \\ C_3H_7\end{matrix} \qquad (1)$$

Methylethyl ketone   Addition product

$$\begin{matrix}CH_3 \\ \\ C_2H_5\end{matrix}\!\!>\!C\!\!<\!\begin{matrix}OMgBr \\ \\ C_3H_7\end{matrix} \xrightarrow{H_2O(H^+)} \begin{matrix}CH_3 \\ \\ C_2H_5\end{matrix}\!\!>\!C\!\!<\!\begin{matrix}OH \\ \\ C_3H_7\end{matrix} + Mg^{++} + Br^- \qquad (2)$$

3-Methyl-3-hexanol
(a tertiary alcohol)

12. The aldol condensation. Aliphatic aldehydes which have hydrogen attached to the α-carbon atom, and a few ketones, are susceptible of the aldol type of condensation. The reaction, which is catalyzed by both alkali and acid, amounts to the addition of one aldehyde molecule to another of the same kind. Hydrogen held by a carbon atom which is adjacent to the carbonyl group is sufficiently active to take part in such an addition reaction; to this extent the addition is similar to cyanohydrin formation. For the purpose of illustration, let us use propionaldehyde, which has hydrogen attached to an α-carbon atom and to a β-carbon atom.

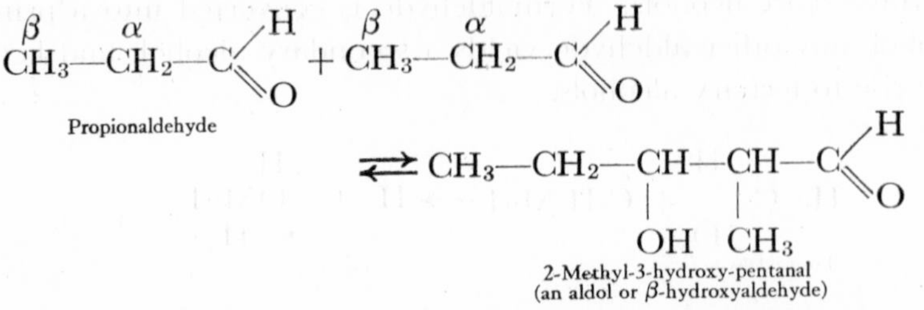

$$\overset{\beta}{CH_3}-\overset{\alpha}{CH_2}-C\overset{H}{\underset{O}{<}} + \overset{\beta}{CH_3}-\overset{\alpha}{CH_2}-C\overset{H}{\underset{O}{<}}$$

Propionaldehyde

$$\rightleftarrows CH_3-CH_2-\underset{\underset{OH}{|}}{CH}-\underset{\underset{CH_3}{|}}{CH}-C\overset{H}{\underset{O}{<}}$$

2-Methyl-3-hydroxy-pentanal
(an aldol or β-hydroxyaldehyde)

The condensation product is a dimer of the aldehyde used; that is, it has twice the molecular weight of the original aldehyde. It is still an aldehyde, and it presents the possibility of condensation with a third molecule of the aldehyde. This process might go on indefinitely; and if a *concentrated* solution of sodium hydroxide or potassium hydroxide is added to an aldehyde, the condensation process does continue until a resin of high molecular weight is formed. The reaction is reversible, and the equilibrium for the lower aldehydes greatly favors aldol formation. In the case of ketones only a small amount of condensation product is present at equilibrium; but in many cases the components of the mixture can be separated, and a 3-hydroxy-ketone can be obtained. Ketones do not resinify with concentrated alkali as do the aldehydes.

Another possible result of the action of an alkali or acid upon an aldehyde or ketone is the formation of an unsaturated aldehyde or ketone through loss of water from the primary addition product. Thus, the aldol shown above may lose water upon heating, particularly in the presence of an acid.

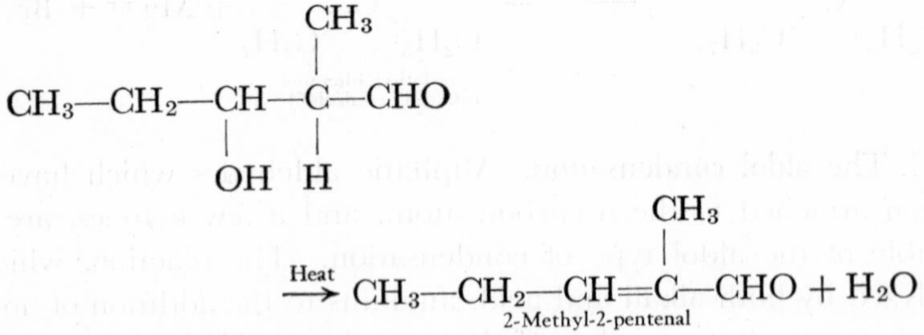

$$CH_3-CH_2-\underset{\underset{OH}{|}}{CH}-\overset{\overset{CH_3}{|}}{\underset{\underset{H}{|}}{C}}-CHO$$

$$\overset{Heat}{\longrightarrow} CH_3-CH_2-CH=\overset{\overset{CH_3}{|}}{C}-CHO + H_2O$$

2-Methyl-2-pentenal

From acetone one can obtain products whose common names are *mesityl oxide*, $CH_3-CH=CH-CO-CH_3$, and *phorone*,

$$(CH_3)_2C=CH-CO-CH=C(CH_3)_2.$$

Alkaline condensing agents are the more suitable if the simple addition product is desired, because acidic agents catalyze the dehydration as well.

The fact that in the aldol condensation only the hydrogen atoms on the carbon atom in the α-position react (not those on carbon atoms farther removed from the carbonyl group) shows that the carbonyl group is responsible for the enhanced reactivity. This is shown also in the halogenation of ketones, which takes place much more rapidly than with hydrocarbons, and in the α-position. The first stage in the chlorination of 3-pentanone is represented by the following equation:

$$CH_3—CH_2—CO—CH_2—CH_3 + Cl_2$$
$$\longrightarrow CH_3—CH_2—CO—CHCl—CH_3 + HCl$$

This halogenation is catalyzed by both acids and bases, and there is reason to believe that aldehydes and ketones undergo a structural change which is promoted by these catalysts. The change is called enolization.

$$\underset{\text{Keto form}}{CH_3—CH_2—\overset{\overset{\displaystyle O}{\|}}{C}—CH_2—CH_3} \underset{\text{Acid or base}}{\rightleftarrows} \underset{\text{Enol form}}{CH_3—CH_2—\overset{\overset{\displaystyle OH}{|}}{C}=CH—CH_3}$$

Tautomeric Change in Structure

The amount of enol present is small, perhaps .01 of 1 per cent or less, and the reverse change from enol to keto is too rapid to permit isolation of the enol. Such a mixture of structural forms, in rapid equilibrium, is called a *tautomeric mixture*; the reversible change is called *tautomerism*; the two forms are called *tautomers*. In most cases it is impossible to separate tautomers, on account of the rapidity of the change from one form to the other. They differ in this respect from ordinary isomers, which do not readily undergo structural changes.

In the aldol condensation and in the halogenation of aldehydes and ketones it is assumed that enolization is the first step. The enol is the active form of the aldehyde or ketone, and the reaction can proceed only as fast as the enol form becomes available.

13. **The haloform reaction.** When ethanol, 2-propanol, acetone, or any methyl ketone is treated in alkaline solution with chlorine, bromine, or iodine, the compound chloroform, $CHCl_3$, bromoform, $CHBr_3$, or iodoform, CHI_3, respectively, is formed. These compounds, CHX_3, are known collectively as the haloforms. We are able to ex-

plain the reactions as follows: The halogens are strong oxidizing agents, and at the same time they rapidly substitute halogen atoms for hydrogen atoms in the α-positions of aldehydes and ketones. In the presence of alkali the actual reactant is probably hypohalite ion:

$$I_2 + 2\,OH^- \longrightarrow IO^- + I^- + 2\,H_2O$$
$$CH_3\!-\!CH_2OH + IO^- \longrightarrow CH_3\!-\!CHO + I^- + H_2O$$
$$CH_3\!-\!CHO + 3\,IO^- \longrightarrow CI_3\!-\!CHO + 3\,OH^-$$

The net change, so far, is the conversion of ethyl alcohol into triiodo-acetaldehyde. This compound, in alkali, undergoes cleavage of the carbon-carbon bond to form iodoform and sodium formate:

$$CI_3\!-\!CHO + NaOH \longrightarrow CHI_3 + HCOONa$$

Similarly a methyl ketone yields a trihaloketone and, by hydrolysis in alkali, produces a haloform:

$$R\!-\!CO\!-\!CX_3 + OH^- \longrightarrow R\!-\!COO^- + CHX_3$$

The higher ketones and aldehydes undergo halogenation on the α-carbon atom, but the resulting substitution products do not undergo hydrolytic cleavage. The haloform reaction thus becomes a test for the structure $CH_3\!-\!CO\!-\!R$ and for methyl carbinols which are oxidizable to this structure.

SUMMARY OF REACTIONS OF ALDEHYDES AND KETONES

I. Reactions in which the carbonyl oxygen is replaced:
1. Formation of oximes, hydrazones, and carbazones
2. Condensation to α-β-unsaturated aldehydes and ketones
3. Acetal formation (aldehydes only)

II. Reactions given by aldehydes and not given by ketones:
1. Oxidation to carboxylic acids of the same number of carbon atoms
2. Reaction with Fehling's, Tollens's, and Schiff's reagents. (Hydroxy ketones are exceptional; see page 142.)
3. Acetal formation
4. Polymerization

III. Addition reactions:
1. Addition of HCN; formation of cyanohydrins
2. Addition of $NaHSO_3$ (aldehydes and lower ketones only)
3. Addition of RMgX; formation of primary, secondary, and tertiary alcohols from $H\!-\!CHO$, $R\!-\!CHO$, and $R\!-\!CO\!-\!R$ respectively
4. The aldol condensation; formation of β-hydroxyaldehydes and β-hydroxyketones

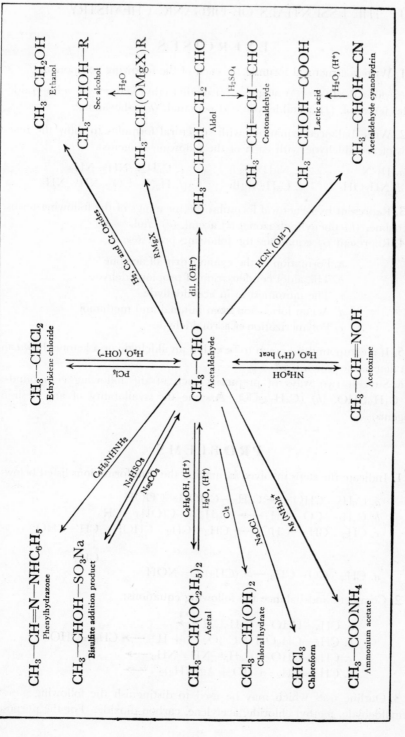

Reactions of an Aldehyde

EXERCISES

1. Write a structural formula for each of the following compounds:

(a) formaldehyde, (b) acetone, (c) methyl ethyl ketone, (d) n-butyralde-hyde, (e) aldol, (f) acetaldehyde, (g) pentanal, (h) 3-hexanone.

2. Write balanced equations with structural formulas to show the reactions of acetaldehyde with each of the following reagents:

a. HCN　　　　　b. NaHSO₃　　　　c. C_6H_5—NH—NH₂
d. NH₂OH　　　　e. C₃H₇MgBr　　　f. H₂N—CO—NH—NH₂

3. Represent by structural formulas the meanings of the following terms:
(a) oxime, (b) phenylhydrazone, (c) acetal, (d) enol.

4. Represent by equations the following processes:

  a. Formation of the cyanohydrin of acetone
  b. The aldol condensation of propionaldehyde
  c. The tautomerism in acetaldehyde
  d. Acetal formation from butanal and methanol
  e. Polymerization of formaldehyde

5. If a compound is known to be either an aldehyde or a ketone, how can you determine which it is?

6. Suggest two ways of preparing each of the following compounds: (a) C_4H_9CHO, (b) $(C_4H_9)_2CO$. Assume the availability of any desired reagents.

PROBLEMS

1. Indicate the steps involved in making the transformations listed below:

  a. C_6H_5—CHO $\longrightarrow$ C_6H_5—CHOH—COOH
  b. C_4H_9—CO—CH₃ $\longrightarrow$ $(C_4H_9)_2$—C(OH)—CH₃
  c. CH₃—CH₂—CHO $\longrightarrow$ CH₃—CH₂—CHOH—CH—CHO
  　　　　　　　　　　　　　　　　　　　　　　　　　　　|
  　　　　　　　　　　　　　　　　　　　　　　　　　　　CH₃

  d. CH₃—CO—CH₃ $\longrightarrow$ $(CH_3)_2C$=NOH

2. Complete and balance the following equations:

  a. CH₃—CHO + C₂H₅OH $\xrightarrow{\text{HCl}}$
  b. CH₃—CH₂OH + $Cr_2O_7^{--}$ + H⁺ $\longrightarrow$ CH₃—CHO
  c. CH₃—CHO + C_6H_5—NH—NH₂ $\longrightarrow$
  d. CH₃—CH₂—CHO + $Ag(NH_3)_2^+$ $\longrightarrow$

3. Outline tests which may be used to distinguish the following gases: formaldehyde, methyl chloride, acetylene, carbon dioxide. For the purpose

consider reactions with Tollens's reagent, bromine in water, and Fehling's solution. Solubility in water and in sodium hydroxide solution may also be used as tests.

4. Which of the following processes are reversible?

a. Bisulfite addition

b. Cyanohydrin formation

c. Aldol condensation

d. Acetal formation

e. Polymerization of an aldehyde

f. Addition of a Grignard reagent

5. Show how C_2H_5MgBr and the appropriate aldehyde or ketone may be used to produce each of the following compounds: (*a*) $C_2H_5CH_2OH$, (*b*) $(C_2H_5)_2CHOH$, (*c*) $(C_2H_5)_3COH$.

6. Outline in equations the formation of iodoform from the alcohol C_2H_5—CHOH—CH_3.

14 · SPECIFIC ALDEHYDES AND KETONES AND THE GENERAL CHARACTER OF CARBONYL REACTIONS

Formaldehyde, HCHO, is a gas under ordinary conditions of temperature and pressure. It is available on the market as a 37 per cent aqueous solution called formalin and in the form of two solid polymers known as paraformaldehyde and trioxymethylene. Paraformaldehyde is a linear polymer containing many formaldehyde units in each molecule:

$$n CH_2O + H_2O \rightleftharpoons HO—CH_2—O—CH_2—O—CH_2—O \cdots CH_2OH$$
$$\text{Paraformaldehyde}$$

Trioxymethylene is a cyclic polymer comprising three formaldehyde molecules:

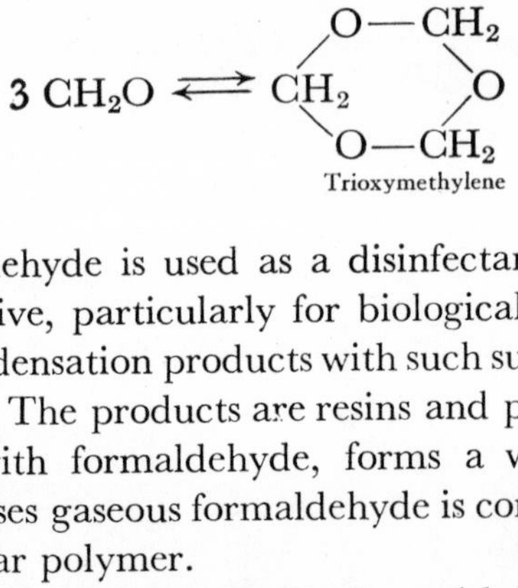

$$3\ CH_2O \rightleftharpoons \begin{array}{c} O—CH_2 \\ CH_2 \qquad O \\ O—CH_2 \end{array}$$
$$\text{Trioxymethylene}$$

Gaseous formaldehyde is used as a disinfectant; in solution it is used as a preservative, particularly for biological specimens. Formaldehyde forms condensation products with such substances as phenols, proteins, and urea. The products are resins and plastics. Casein, the protein of milk, with formaldehyde, forms a water-resistant glue. For all these purposes gaseous formaldehyde is conveniently prepared by heating the linear polymer.

The aldol condensation cannot take place with formaldehyde (there is no α-carbon atom), but the high reactivity of this aldehyde leads to a condensation of another sort. The reaction is catalyzed by $Ca(OH)_2$ and may be represented as follows:

$$CH_2O \xrightarrow{CH_2O} HO—CH_2—CHO \xrightarrow{CH_2O} HO—CH_2—CHOH—CHO \cdots$$

This reaction differs from the polymerization processes mentioned above. It results in the formation of carbon-to-carbon bonds, and the reaction is not reversible. In paraformaldehyde and in trioxymethylene the carbon atoms are linked through oxygen.

Because of the reaction of formaldehyde with proteins the aldehyde cannot be used as an antiseptic, but a number of its derivatives are

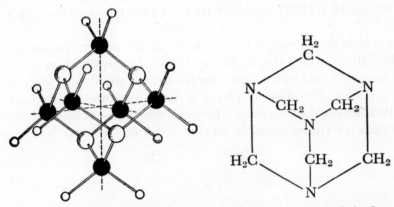

Fig. 7. A Three-Dimensional Model and an Ordinary Structural Formula for the Hexamethylenetetramine Molecule

useful drugs. One in current use is made from formaldehyde and ammonia. It is called hexamethylenetetramine from the formula $(CH_2)_6N_4$. It is a urinary antiseptic, effective perhaps because it hydrolyzes slowly in acidic solutions to yield formaldehyde. To ensure an acidic medium in the bladder and kidneys, ammonium chloride is given with the drug. It is dispensed under the names *urotropin* and *methenamine*. The same substance is used as an accelerator in the vulcanization of rubber.

Methylal is an acetal of formaldehyde and methanol:

$$CH_2O + 2 CH_3OH \xrightarrow{CaCl_2} CH_2(OCH_3)_2 + H_2O$$

Mildly acidic salts, such as calcium chloride, catalyze the reaction. Methylal has been used as a sedative.

Formaldehyde is manufactured by oxidizing methyl alcohol with air; a mixture of the gases is passed over copper or silver gauze at 250°–300°:

$$2 CH_3OH + O_2 \xrightarrow[250°]{Ag} 2 HCHO + 2 H_2O$$

Acetaldehyde, CH_3CHO, is a colorless liquid which boils at 20.2° under atmospheric pressure. It can be made by oxidizing ethyl alcohol with a mixture of sodium dichromate and sulfuric acid, as previously described, or through dehydrogenation of the alcohol. A good commercial method of making acetaldehyde is found in the hydration of acetylene. Mercuric sulfate and dilute sulfuric acid are used as catalysts.

$$HC\equiv CH + HOH \underset{}{\overset{HgSO_4;\ H_2SO_4}{\rightleftarrows}} [H_2C=CHOH] \longrightarrow CH_3-CHO$$

Acetylene   Enol form   Acetaldehyde

The aldehyde is stored in the form of its trimer, paraldehyde, $(CH_3CHO)_3$, which is a liquid (bp 124°). The equilibrium between the monomer and trimer favors the trimer, but distillation, after adding a trace of sulfuric acid, produces the lower boiling compound.

Paraldehyde does not reduce Fehling's solution or Tollens's reagent, nor does it form an oxime in alkaline solution. It colors Schiff's re-

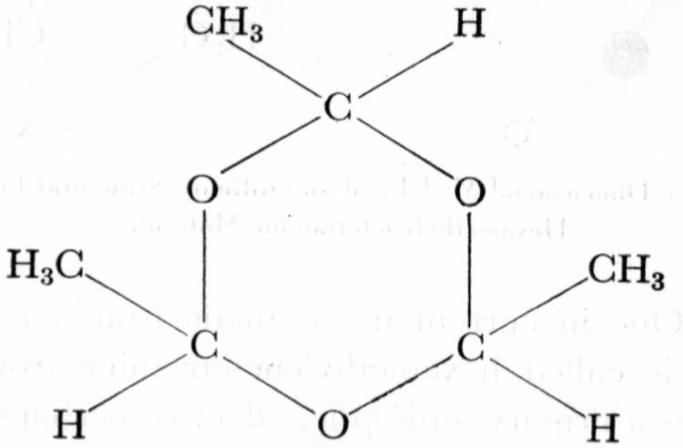

Paraldehyde
(bp 124°)

agent slowly. This shows that the trimer contains no aldehyde group as such and that it depolymerizes slowly or not at all in an alkaline medium. Schiff's reagent is acidic, and the slow coloration of the reagent by paraldehyde depends upon the acid-catalyzed depolymerization of the trimer.

Metaldehyde, $(CH_3CHO)_4$, is another polymer of acetaldehyde. It is a colorless, crystalline solid. Metaldehyde (or metaacetaldehyde) is obtained by passing hydrogen chloride gas into an ethereal solution of acetaldehyde. The compound is employed as a lure in poisons which are used for the extermination of snails.

With ammonia, monomeric acetaldehyde forms a crystalline addition product different in type from that formed with formaldehyde and ammonia:

$$3\ CH_3CHO + 3\ NH_3 \longrightarrow \left[CH_3-CH \Big\langle \begin{matrix} OH \\ NH_2 \end{matrix} \right]_3$$

Acetaldehyde can be recovered from the product through hydrolysis in dilute acid.

Trichloroacetaldehyde, or chloral, is a hypnotic and narcotic of the formula CCl_3—CHO. It is made from ethanol and bleaching powder, $CaOCl_2$, as outlined under the haloform reaction (p. 147). In the presence of water the oily liquid forms a crystalline product, CCl_3—$CH(OH)_2$, called chloral hydrate. This is one of the few stable compounds known in which two hydroxyl groups are attached to the same carbon atom.

In solution with sodium carbonate, acetaldehyde undergoes the aldol condensation. The reaction is reversible, and at equilibrium about 70 per cent of the acetaldehyde is in the form of the condensation product. The aldol, in turn, loses water when heated to 160° and is converted into crotonic aldehyde.

$$2\ CH_3\text{—CHO} \xrightarrow{Na_2CO_3} CH_3\text{—CHOH—CH}_2\text{—CHO}$$

Acetaldehyde
(bp 20.2°)

Acetaldol
(bp 83° at 20 mm)

$$\xrightarrow{Heat} CH_3\text{—CH}{=}\text{CH—CHO} + H_2O$$

Crotonaldehyde
(mp 76.5°; bp 104°)

Acetaldol is used in the vulcanization of rubber, in the manufacture of some perfumes, and as a component of the reagents used in the

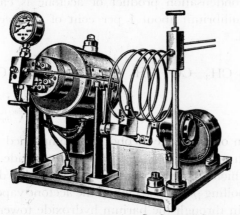

Parr Instrument Company
Fig. 8. Apparatus Used for High-Pressure Catalytic Hydrogenation

flotation process of concentrating ores. Crotonic aldehyde is a liquid of very disagreeable odor. The aldol can be hydrogenated with hydrogen gas (in contact with nickel) to 1, 3-butanediol; crotonic aldehyde, under the same treatment, yields butanal, CH_3—CH_2—CH_2—CHO, and butanol, CH_3—CH_2—CH_2—CH_2OH. These results afford a suggestion, at least, of the multiplicity of products which can be made from acetylene with acetaldehyde as an intermediate. Acetaldehyde is an intermediate product in the fermentation process of converting glucose into alcohol.

Acetone, CH_3—CO—CH_3, a colorless liquid which boils at 56.5°, is produced commercially in several ways: (1) it is one of the products formed in the distillation of wood; (2) it is produced with butanol and ethanol from hydrolyzed starches and sugars by a fermentation process induced by certain bacteria; (3) it is made from calcium acetate by dry distillation of the salt; (4) it is made from acetic acid by passing the vapor of the acid at 450° over a catalyst composed of manganous oxide; (5) it is made from propene by hydration to 2-propanol and dehydrogenation of the latter by heat and a catalyst.

Acetone is soluble in water, alcohol, chloroform, and gasoline. It is used as a solvent in the manufacture of smokeless powders, lacquers, paint-removers, transparent soaps, photographic films, artificial leather, plastics, and numerous other useful products. Acetone is present at a very low concentration in normal blood, and the quantity of acetone in the blood increases in certain types of illness, particularly in diabetes.

The aldol condensation product of acetone is called diacetone alcohol. At equilibrium about 1 per cent of the acetone is in the condensed form.

$$\underset{\substack{\text{Acetone} \\ \text{(bp 56.5°)}}}{\overset{CH_3}{\underset{CH_3}{>}}C{=}O} + \underset{\text{Acetone}}{CH_3{-}CO{-}CH_3} \underset{}{\overset{Ba(OH)_2}{\rightleftharpoons}} \underset{\substack{\text{Diacetone alcohol} \\ \text{(bp 166°)}}}{\overset{CH_3}{\underset{CH_3}{>}}C{-}CH_2{-}\underset{\underset{O}{\|}}{C}{-}CH_3}$$
$$\underset{OH}{}$$

The preparation of diacetone alcohol is accomplished by passing hot acetone through a column of solid barium hydroxide. The equilibrium mixture which emerges from the column is heated to a temperature above the boiling point of acetone; the acetone vapor is condensed and passed again through the barium hydroxide tower. The process is continuous, and the less volatile diacetone alcohol accumulates in the still. Diacetone alcohol can be distilled unchanged if no acid or alkali is present. If an acid is present, dehydration occurs as follows:

$$\underset{\substack{\text{Diacetone alcohol} \\ \text{(mp} - 56°; \text{ bp 166°)}}}{\overset{CH_3}{\underset{CH_3}{>}}\underset{\underset{OH}{|}}{C}{-}CH_2{-}CO{-}CH_3} \rightarrow \underset{\substack{\text{Mesityl oxide} \\ \text{(mp} - 59°; \text{ bp 131°)}}}{\overset{CH_3}{\underset{CH_3}{>}}C{=}CH{-}CO{-}CH_3}$$

Acrolein. An unsaturated aldehyde, acrolein, is obtained from glycerol by dehydration. Acrolein is a volatile liquid; its vapor has an irritating effect upon the eyes. The lachrymatory effect is sometimes experienced when, in cooking, a fat is overheated. The formation of the compound, on a laboratory scale, is represented by the following equation:

$$\underset{\substack{\text{Glycerol (bp 290°)}}}{\overset{\substack{CH_2-CH-CH_2\\ |\quad\ |\quad\ |\\ OH\ \ OH\ \ OH}}{}} \xrightarrow[\text{Acid catalyst}]{\text{Heat}} \underset{\substack{\text{Acrolein (bp 52.5°)}}}{CH_2{=}CH-CHO} + 2\,H_2O$$

The General Character of Carbonyl Reactions

The oxidation state of carbon in aldehydes and ketones is the same as its oxidation state in a dihydric alcohol:

$$R_2C{\overset{\displaystyle OH}{\underset{\displaystyle OH}{\big<}}} \rightleftharpoons R_2C{=}O + H_2O$$

Even though, as a rule, an alcohol with two hydroxyl groups on a single carbon atom cannot be isolated, it must be considered present to some degree in a water solution of any compound which has a carbonyl group. The existence of chloral hydrate, $CCl_3-CH(OH)_2$, and of acetals, $RCH(OR)_2$, is consistent with this view. The acetals are ethers of the corresponding hypothetical alcohols.

The addition of water to the carbonyl group is similar to the addition of HCN, $NaHSO_3$, and RMgX. In each case the negative, or basic, constituent (OH^-, CN^-, SO_3^{--}, or R^-) becomes attached to the carbon atom, while the positive, or acidic, constituent (H^+ or Mg^{++}) finds its way to the oxygen atom. It seems probable that oxime and hydrazone formations start with an addition reaction of the same type, followed by loss of water:

$$R_2C{=}O + H_2NOH \rightleftharpoons \left[R_2C{\overset{\displaystyle OH}{\underset{\displaystyle NHOH}{\big<}}}\right] \rightleftharpoons \underset{\substack{\text{An oxime}}}{R_2C{=}NOH} + H_2O$$

$$R_2C{=}O + H_2N-NH-C_6H_5 \rightleftharpoons \left[R_2C{\overset{\displaystyle OH}{\underset{\displaystyle NH-NH-C_6H_5}{\big<}}}\right]$$

$$\rightleftharpoons \underset{\substack{\text{A hydrazone}}}{R_2C{=}N-NH-C_6H_5} + H_2O$$

The initial addition products, placed within brackets, cannot be isolated because of the rapid dehydration. The reverse reactions—hydrolysis of the oxime and of the hydrazone—take place through the same intermediates. The state of equilibrium is governed by the acidity of the medium. In basic or neutral solutions some H_2NOH and C_6H_5—NH—NH_2 are present, and addition to the aldehyde or ketone occurs; in acid solution these bases are removed as salts ($H_3\overset{+}{N}OH$ and C_6H_5—NH—$\overset{+}{N}H_3$ respectively), and hydrolysis of the condensation product takes place.

The aldol condensation is another example of addition involving the carbonyl group, and in many cases the addition is followed by dehydration. The two processes are outlined as follows:

$$R—CH_2—CHO + R—CH_2—CHO$$
$$\underset{Base}{\rightleftharpoons} R—CH_2—CHOH—CHR—CHO$$
$$\downarrow \overset{Acid;}{Heat}$$
$$R—CH_2—CH{=}CR—CHO + H_2O$$

In some instances dehydration takes place so rapidly that the aldol does not appear at all.

Acetal formation also involves an addition reaction with hemiacetal formation as the first step (p. 143).

EXERCISES

1. Represent by structural formulas the following compounds:

   a. Methylal   d. Acetaldol
   b. Trioxymethylene   e. Diacetone alcohol
   c. Paraldehyde   f. Chloral hydrate

2. By balanced equations indicate methods for making the following compounds:

   a. Formaldehyde from methanol
   b. Acetaldehyde from acetylene
   c. Acetone from propene

3. What are the most generally applicable methods of preparing aldehydes and ketones?

4. What is meant by polymerization of an aldehyde? Do ketones form polymers?

PROBLEMS

1. How could you show that paraldehyde contains no free aldehyde group?

2. Write an equation for each of the steps indicated below:

Ethanol $\longrightarrow$ Acetaldehyde $\longrightarrow$ Acetaldol $\longrightarrow$ 1, 3-butandiol

$$\downarrow$$

1, 3-butadiene

The butadiene prepared by passing ethanol over the proper catalyst is used to manufacture synthetic rubber. Represent by a single equation the over-all reaction: ethanol $\longrightarrow$ butadiene.

3. List the reagents which react with the carbonyl group of a ketone. Which of these reagents form addition products that can be isolated? Which form addition products that immediately lose water?

15 · THE ALIPHATIC MONOBASIC ACIDS

Organic acids have a wide range of properties and uses. Acetic acid is a colorless liquid, soluble in water in all proportions, and sour. Stearic acid, a member of the same homologous series, is a waxlike solid, practically insoluble in water and almost tasteless. But these very different acids have many reactions in common, for each contains the acidic functional group of atoms known as the carboxyl group. The carboxyl group has the structure

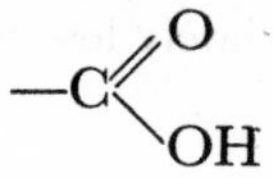

$$-C{\overset{\textstyle O}{\underset{\textstyle OH}{\big\langle}}}$$

Any compound which has this group is called a carboxylic acid; and a general formula for an acid containing one carboxyl group is

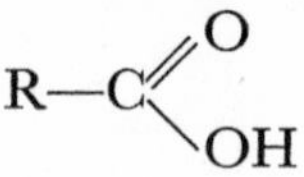

$$R-C{\overset{\textstyle O}{\underset{\textstyle OH}{\big\langle}}}$$

which may be written also as $R-COOH$ or $R-CO_2H$.

Many acids are formed in growing plants. They appear in leaves and in fruits as free acids, as salts, or as esters. Oxalic acid is found in rhubarb; citric acid in lemons, oranges, and grapefruit; malic acid is present in green apples; and salts of tartaric acid are obtained from grapes. Animal fats and vegetable oils are other sources of organic acids. The fats and oils are esters, and from them glycerol and organic acids may be obtained by hydrolysis.

The molecular formula of acetic acid is $C_2H_4O_2$, but only one of the hydrogen atoms ionizes. This is shown by the facts that the sodium salt of the acid has the composition $C_2H_3O_2Na$ and that the equivalent weight of the acid is therefore 60, the same as its molecular weight. Acetic acid is therefore monobasic. The three remaining hydrogen atoms are present in the form of a methyl group. The structural formula of acetic acid is CH_3-COOH.

A few of the acids corresponding to the formula $R-COOH$ are shown in the table below. In the first member of the series R stands for a hydrogen atom. In all other members of the group R represents an alkyl radical.

160

SATURATED MONOBASIC ACIDS					
Acid	Formula	Melting Point (°C)	Boiling Point (°C)	$K_a \times 10^5$	Percentage Ionized in 0.1 N Solution
Formic	HCOOH	8.6	100.7	21.4	4.52
Acetic	CH_3COOH	16.7	118	1.82	1.34
Propionic	CH_3CH_2COOH	− 22.0	141	1.34	1.13
Butyric (normal)	$CH_3CH_2CH_2COOH$	− 7.9	162.5	1.49	1.22
Butyric (iso)	$(CH_3)_2CHCOOH$	− 47	155	1.45	1.20
Valeric (normal)	$CH_3(CH_2)_3COOH$	− 18	186	1.45	1.20
Valeric (iso)	$(CH_3)_2CHCH_2COOH$	− 51	174	1.70	1.29
Methylethylacetic	$(CH_3)(C_2H_5)CHCOOH$	− 80	177	1.69	1.29
Trimethylacetic	$(CH_3)_3CCOOH$	35.5	163.7	0.98	0.99
Caproic (normal)	$CH_3(CH_2)_4COOH$	− 5.2	205.7	1.40	1.18
Palmitic	$CH_3(CH_2)_{14}COOH$	64			
Margaric	$CH_3(CH_2)_{15}COOH$	60.7			
Stearic	$CH_3(CH_2)_{16}COOH$	69.4	383		

A monobasic acid has only one carboxyl group in the molecule. Dibasic acids have two and tribasic acids three carboxyl groups respectively. Familiar examples of polybasic acids are oxalic, tartaric, and citric acids:

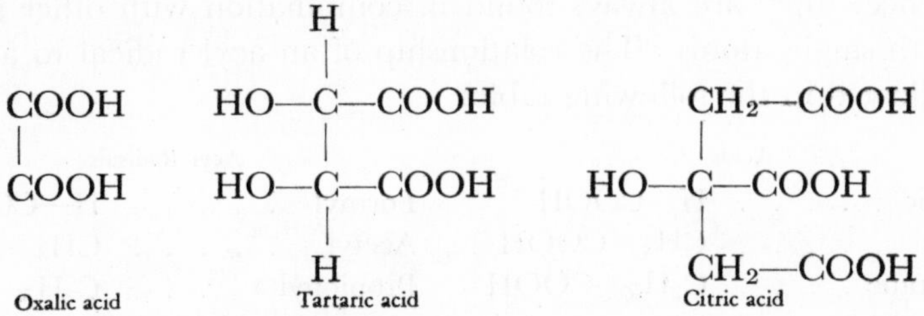

COOH   HO—C—COOH   CH₂—COOH

COOH   HO—C—COOH   HO—C—COOH

              H   CH₂—COOH
Oxalic acid   Tartaric acid   Citric acid

Tartaric acid and citric acid have alcoholic properties as well as acidic properties. They are examples of hydroxy acids. We shall consider the dibasic acids and hydroxy acids in detail later. At this point we shall deal with only the saturated monobasic acids and their derivatives.

Nomenclature of the monobasic acids. The official name of an acid is derived from the name of the longest hydrocarbon chain which contains the carboxyl group. The final *e* of the corresponding hydrocarbon name is changed to *oic*. Common names are usually applied to the acids which are abundant and well known.

The following formulas, common names, and Geneva names are examples:

$$CH_3—COOH$$

Acetic acid
(ethanoic acid)

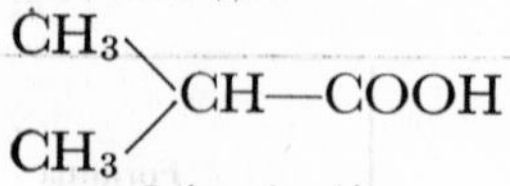

$$CH_3 \diagdown CH—COOH$$
$$CH_3 \diagup$$

Isobutyric acid
(2-methylpropanoic acid)

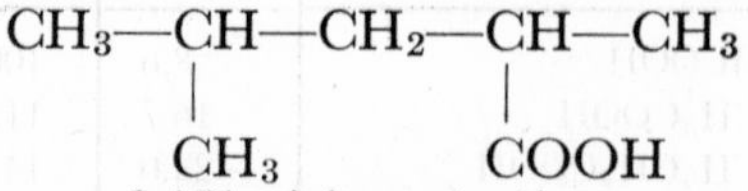

$$CH_3—CH—CH_2—CH—CH_3$$
$$\quad\quad\ |\quad\quad\quad\quad\ |$$
$$\quad\quad CH_3\quad\quad COOH$$

2, 4-Dimethylpentanoic acid

In some cases it is convenient to name an acid as a derivative of acetic acid. Thus the compound $(CH_3)_3C—COOH$ is called trimethyl-acetic acid; its Geneva name is 2, 2-dimethylpropanoic acid. Numbering of the carbon atoms begins with the carboxyl group.

Carboxylic acids, esters, acid chlorides, amides, and acid anhydrides have in common the group

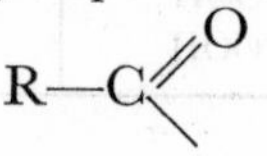

$$R—C \diagup^{\displaystyle O}_{\displaystyle \diagdown}$$

Such a group is called an *acyl radical*. It is the residue which remains when a hydroxyl group is removed from an acid, and it is named by changing the final *ic* in the name of the corresponding acid to *yl*. As in the case of alkyl radicals these groups do not have an independent existence; they are always found in combination with other groups or with single atoms. The relationship of an acyl radical to an acid is indicated in the following table:

Acids		Acyl Radicals	
Formic	H—COOH	Formyl	H—CO—
Acetic	CH₃—COOH	Acetyl	CH₃—CO—
Propionic	C₂H₅—COOH	Propionyl	C₂H₅—CO—

Preparation of acids. Several general methods are available for the synthetic production of acids. The following are the most useful procedures:

1. A primary alcohol may be converted into an acid by treatment with an oxidizing agent such as hot chromic acid or potassium permanganate:

$$3\ R—CH_2OH + 2\ Cr_2O_7^{--} + 16\ H^+$$
$$\longrightarrow 3\ R—COOH + 4\ Cr^{+++} + 11\ H_2O$$

$$3\ R—CH_2OH + 4\ MnO_4^-$$
$$\longrightarrow 3\ R—COO^- + 4\ MnO_2 + OH^- + 4\ H_2O$$

In the latter case a salt of the acid is formed, because the oxidation is carried out in alkaline solution; the organic acid is released from the salt by acidifying the solution with sulfuric acid after the manganese dioxide has been filtered out.

2. Alkyl cyanides are hydrolyzed to acids by treatment with hot hydrochloric acid:

$$C_3H_7CN + 2 H_2O + HCl \longrightarrow C_3H_7COOH + NH_4^+ + Cl^-$$

This method is used mainly for the production of acids in which the carboxyl group is attached to a primary alkyl radical. Attempts to prepare cyanides from secondary and tertiary alkyl halides usually lead to the formation of alkenes. Tertiary butyl bromide, for example, reacts with potassium cyanide as follows:

$$\begin{array}{c} CH_3 \\ \diagdown \\ CH_3 \diagup \end{array} C \begin{array}{c} CH_3 \\ \diagup \\ \diagdown Br \end{array} + KCN \longrightarrow \begin{array}{c} CH_3 \\ \diagdown \\ CH_3 \diagup \end{array} C{=}CH_2 + KBr + HCN$$

3. When carbon dioxide is passed into an ether solution of a Grignard reagent, an addition product is formed, and from the addition product (a magnesium salt) an acid is obtained upon acidification:

$$C_2H_5MgBr + CO_2 \longrightarrow C_2H_5{-}C\diagdown^{\diagup OMgBr}_{\diagdown O} \qquad (1)$$

$$C_2H_5{-}C\diagdown^{\diagup OMgBr}_{\diagdown O} + H^+ \xrightarrow{H_2O} C_2H_5{-}COOH + Mg^{++} + Br^- \qquad (2)$$

Reactions of the Acids

The major reactions of acids are the following: ionization; decarboxylation; formation of anhydrides, acid chlorides, amides, and esters; substitution of a halogen atom for an alpha-hydrogen atom.

1. **Ionization.** The soluble carboxylic acids ionize in dilute aqueous solution $(0.1 \, N)$ to the extent of about 1 per cent. Some of the higher members are so insoluble that they do not yield a sufficiently high concentration of hydrogen ions to have a sour taste or affect litmus paper. The ionization is enhanced by substitution of chlorine, bromine, iodine, cyanide radical, or the hydroxyl group in the α-position.

Ionization is represented by the equation

$$R{-}COOH \rightleftharpoons R{-}COO^- + H^+$$

The equilibrium constant, K_a, called also the dissociation constant, is defined by the equation

$$K_a = \frac{(R—CO_2^-)(H^+)}{(R—CO_2H)}$$

The terms within parentheses stand for the concentrations of the ions and molecules in moles per liter of solution. For the lower fatty acids the numerical value of K_a is approximately 1×10^{-5}. Formic acid, however, is a stronger acid than other members of the series; its dissociation constant is 2.14×10^{-4}. The numerical value of K_a for an acid is obtained by measuring the concentration of hydrogen ion (by means of a hydrogen electrode or glass electrode) in a solution of known normality of the acid. If N is the normality, and there is no salt of the acid present so that $(H^+) = (RCO_2^-)$, and if (H^+) is very small compared to N (the acid is weak), we find that

$$K_a = \frac{(R—COO^-)(H^+)}{(R—COOH)} = \frac{(R—CO_2^-)(H^+)}{(N—(H^+))} \cong \frac{(H^+)^2}{N}$$

If any two of the variables are known the third may be evaluated. Another procedure utilizes a buffer solution which contains a known ratio (perhaps equivalent amounts) of the acid and its salt. In this circumstance (RCO_2^-) is essentially the concentration of the salt and (RCO_2H) that of the acid, so that

$$K_a = \frac{(R—CO_2^-)(H^+)}{(R—CO_2H)} \cong \frac{(Salt)}{(Acid)}(H^+)$$

A solution of a mixture of a weak acid and its salt is called a buffer solution because, upon the addition to it of either a strong acid or a strong base, the (H^+) changes but little. For instance, if 0.01 equivalent of HCl is added to one liter of a solution which is $0.1\ N$ in acetic acid and $0.1\ N$ in sodium acetate, the (H^+) would change from $1.82 \times 10^{-5}\ N$ to $2.22 \times 10^{-5}\ N$, whereas in a liter of pure water the change would be from $1 \times 10^{-7}\ N$ to approximately $1 \times 10^{-2}\ N$ in H^+.

An acid is ionized to a far greater degree than is an alcohol, and some acids are stronger than others. This must be due, as in all variations in equilibria, to factors which affect the relative energy contents of the reactants (acids) and products (anions and proton). Resonance is such a factor, and the alcohol system, in which no resonance is involved, may be taken here as the standard for comparison. Resonance is present in both the undissociated acid and its anion, so it is concluded that, to effect the observed degree of ionization, the resonance stabilization is large in the anion and small in the acid.

$$\left[R—C{\Large\langle}^{O}_{OH} \;>\!\!-\!\!< R—C{\Large\langle}^{O^-}_{O^+H} \right] \rightleftarrows \left[R—C{\Large\langle}^{O}_{O^-} \;>\!\!-\!\!< R—C{\Large\langle}^{O^-}_{O.} \right] + H^+$$

Effect of relative resonance stabilization in an equilibrium

2. **Decarboxylation.** Removal of the carboxyl group of an acid is called decarboxylation. It is often accomplished by heating a salt of the acid with solid sodium hydroxide or with soda lime, which is a mixture of sodium hydroxide and calcium oxide:

$$C_2H_5—COONa + NaOH \xrightarrow{\text{Heat}} C_2H_6 + Na_2CO_3$$

The carboxyl group is replaced by hydrogen. Carbon dioxide may be released from a few acids without resort to the use of their salts and solid sodium hydroxide; malonic acid is an example (p. 189). Aldehydes and ketones may be made by heating salts of carboxylic acids or mixtures of such salts (p. 138). It is not to be expected that every acid will yield a hydrocarbon or a ketone, but in many cases one or the other of these reactions can be used to good advantage.

Decarboxylation of an acid occurs in the alcoholic fermentation of sugar. Pyruvic acid and acetaldehyde are intermediates in the fermentation process. The pyruvic acid is decarboxylated at room temperature under the influence of the enzyme carboxylase.

$$CH_3—\overset{\overset{\displaystyle O}{\|}}{C}—COOH \xrightarrow{\text{Carboxylase}} CH_3—C{\Large\langle}^{O}_{H} + CO_2$$

Pyruvic acid   Acetaldehyde

The release of carbon dioxide from the dry silver salt of an acid is brought about by treatment with bromine. A bromine atom takes the place of the carboxyl group (see page 131).

3. **Formation of acid anhydrides.** Anhydrides of some organic acids can be made by heating the acids alone to temperatures ranging between 300° and 400°, but in general they are prepared indirectly by a process similar to that used in the preparation of mixed ethers. An acid chloride and a salt of an acid are heated together:

$$R—COCl + R—COONa \rightarrow R—\overset{\overset{\displaystyle O}{\|}}{C}—O—\overset{\overset{\displaystyle O}{\|}}{C}—R + NaCl$$

Acid   Salt   Acid
chloride   anhydride

In many syntheses, acid anhydrides are more useful than the acids themselves. For instance, an acetate rayon is manufactured from cellulose and acetic anhydride, whereas acetic acid alone would not suffice. Fortunately there is a less expensive process for manufacturing acetic anhydride than the general method given above (see page 177).

4. **Formation of acid halides.** Acids react with phosphorus halides to form acid halides:

$$3 \ CH_3-C\!\!\!\overset{O}{\underset{OH}{\diagdown}} + PCl_3 \longrightarrow 3 \ CH_3-C\!\!\!\overset{O}{\underset{Cl}{\diagdown}} + H_3PO_3$$

$$CH_3-C\!\!\!\overset{O}{\underset{OH}{\diagdown}} + PCl_5 \longrightarrow CH_3-C\!\!\!\overset{O}{\underset{Cl}{\diagdown}} + POCl_3 + HCl$$

$$3 \ CH_3-C\!\!\!\overset{O}{\underset{OH}{\diagdown}} + PBr_3 \longrightarrow 3 \ CH_3-C\!\!\!\overset{O}{\underset{Br}{\diagdown}} + H_3PO_3$$

Thionyl chloride, $SOCl_2$, a colorless liquid, is a useful reagent for converting acids into acid chlorides. In this reaction the acid chloride is the only liquid product formed; the by-products are gases:

$$CH_3-C\!\!\!\overset{O}{\underset{OH}{\diagdown}} + SOCl_2 \longrightarrow CH_3-C\!\!\!\overset{O}{\underset{Cl}{\diagdown}} + SO_2 + HCl$$

Acid fluorides and acid iodides are not often prepared; the useful reagents in this series of compounds are the chlorides and bromides. Like the alkyl halides, these compounds are of great value as source materials in synthetic work. Unlike the alkyl halides, they have very few direct uses.

5. **Replacement of the hydroxyl group by an amino group.** When the ammonium salt of an acid is heated in the presence of a little of the acid itself, an acid amide is formed. Thus, ammonium acetate yields acetamide:

$$CH_3-CO_2NH_4 \overset{CH_3CO_2H}{\underset{\rightleftharpoons}{}} CH_3-C\!\!\!\overset{O}{\underset{NH_2}{\diagdown}} + H_2O$$

Acetamide

In this way the hydroxyl group of an acid is replaced by the amino group (NH_2). Acid chlorides and acid anhydrides react with ammonia to form acid amides (p. 183).

6. **Ester formation.** Acids react with alcohols to form esters. The reaction is slow, but it may be catalyzed by sulfuric acid. The net change is represented by the following equation:

$$R-C{\overset{O}{\underset{OH}{<}}} + R'OH \overset{H_2SO_4}{\rightleftarrows} R-C{\overset{O}{\underset{OR'}{<}}} + H_2O$$

Acid   Alcohol   Ester

The reaction is reversible, and esters are readily hydrolyzed to acids and alcohols. With one mole of acetic acid and one mole of ethanol, equilibrium is reached when about 70 per cent conversion has taken place. Dehydrating agents improve the yield by removing water. Sulfuric acid has a double role, that of a catalyst to hasten approach to equilibrium and as a reactant with the water.

Esterification takes place in two steps. In the first phase of the reaction an unstable addition product is formed in small amounts between the acid and the alcohol:

$$CH_3-C{\overset{O}{\underset{OH}{<}}} + C_2H_5OH \rightleftarrows \left[CH_3-C{\overset{OC_2H_5}{\underset{OH}{\overset{}{<}}}OH} \right]$$

The second step is the spontaneous decomposition of the addition product:

$$\left[CH_3-C{\overset{OC_2H_5}{\underset{OH}{\overset{}{<}}}OH} \right] \rightleftarrows CH_3-C{\overset{OC_2H_5}{\underset{O}{<}}} + H_2O$$

Ethyl acetate

The unstable intermediate product, which cannot be isolated, is indicated by the formula written within brackets.

Hydrolysis of an ester takes place by the same path in reverse. One consequence of this mechanism is that the acid (not the alcohol) supplies the oxygen atom which eventually is eliminated in the formation of water. The alkyl group is never separated from the oxygen atom to which it is attached in the alcohol. This has been demonstrated experimentally by starting with isotopic oxygen of mass 18 in the alcohol and with ordinary oxygen in the acid; all the oxygen of mass 18 remains in the ester or alcohol, none appears in the water which is formed in the reaction.

Esters are named in the same way that salts are named; that is, they are alkyl acetates, propionates, butyrates, and so on. This should not suggest that esters are ionized; they are nonpolar compounds, completely un-ionized.

7. **Halogenation of acids.** Chlorine and bromine act upon acids, replacing hydrogen atoms in the α-position by halogen atoms. With bromine the reaction proceeds as follows:

$$CH_3-CH_2-COOH + Br_2 \xrightarrow{PBr_3} CH_3-CHBr-COOH$$

Propionic acid α-Bromopropionic acid

The reaction is catalyzed by phosphorus trihalide (in this case by the tribromide). In practice free phosphorus is added, and the tribromide is formed in the reaction mixture. The fact that halogenation takes place only in the α-position reminds one of the activation of the α-position in aldehydes and ketones. The halogenated acids are useful in syntheses for the same reason that alkyl halides are useful: the halogen atom is replaceable by —OH, —OR, —NH$_2$, and —CN groups. To introduce a halogen atom in the β-position a different procedure must be followed.

Individual Acids

Formic acid is the first member of the fatty-acid series. It is a colorless liquid which boils at 100.7° and crystallizes at 8.6°. Formic acid has an irritating odor, and it causes burns if left for a few minutes in contact with the skin. It is found in ants, bees, and some caterpillars; it is present also in some plants, including nettles. The acid is used as a dehairing agent (depilatory) in the tanning industry and as a coagulating agent in the treatment of rubber latex.

When formic acid is heated alone in an autoclave to a temperature of 160°, it is converted into carbon dioxide and hydrogen:

$$H-COOH \longrightarrow CO_2 + H_2$$

When mixed with sulfuric acid and heated, it yields carbon monoxide and water:
$$H-COOH \longrightarrow CO + H_2O$$

This is a good laboratory process for the generation of carbon monoxide.

At a high temperature (above 200°) the sodium salt of formic acid decomposes with the production of sodium oxalate and hydrogen:

$$\begin{array}{ccc} H-COONa & \xrightarrow{\text{Heat}} & \begin{array}{c} COONa \\ | \\ COONa \end{array} + H_2 \\ H-COONa & & \end{array}$$

Sodium formate   Sodium oxalate

Formic acid is easily oxidized—an unusual property for an organic acid. Mercuric chloride oxidizes the acid to carbon dioxide; mercurous chloride is precipitated:

$$H—COOH + 2\ HgCl_2 \longrightarrow 2\ HgCl + CO_2 + 2\ HCl$$

This reaction is used as a qualitative test for formic acid. An alkaline permanganate solution oxidizes the acid to a carbonate:

$$3\ H—COOK + 2\ KMnO_4 + KOH \longrightarrow 3\ K_2CO_3 + 2\ MnO_2 + 2\ H_2O$$

These extraordinary reactions of formic acid are explained by the fact that in this particular acid the carboxyl group is attached to a hydrogen atom, whereas in other acids the carboxyl group is attached to a carbon radical. Formic acid is an aldehyde as well as an acid. A comparison of the formulas makes this point clear:

$$H—C\overset{\displaystyle O}{\underset{\displaystyle OH}{\Big\langle}} \qquad\qquad R—C\overset{\displaystyle O}{\underset{\displaystyle OH}{\Big\langle}}$$

Formic acid   Other acids

CHO and COOH   **No CHO Group**

Sodium formate is prepared commercially by heating sodium hydroxide at temperatures between 150° and 275° with carbon monoxide under pressure of six to ten atmospheres:

$$NaOH + CO \longrightarrow H—COONa$$

The free acid is recovered from the salt by distilling the acid from a mixture of sodium formate and dry sodium hydrogen sulfate:

$$H—COONa + NaHSO_4 \longrightarrow H—COOH + Na_2SO_4$$

Acetic acid, $CH_3—COOH$, is the acid component of vinegar. In this form it was known in ancient times. The souring of wine is caused by the oxidation of alcohol to acetic acid by air, in the presence of certain bacteria. Such a process is called a biological oxidation.

$$\underset{\text{Alcohol}}{CH_3—CH_2OH} + O_2 \xrightarrow{\text{Acetobacter}} \underset{\text{Acetic acid}}{CH_3—COOH} + H_2O$$

Vinegar containing 3 to 6 per cent of acetic acid is made from dilute solutions of alcohol by this method. Beechwood shavings are impregnated with the organisms *Mycoderma aceti*, and a dilute solution of alcohol is allowed to trickle down through the shavings while a current of air moves upward.

Acetic acid is produced, along with methyl alcohol, acetone, and other products, in the distillation of wood. The acetic acid in the distillate is converted into a nonvolatile salt by the addition of lime. Water, methyl alcohol, and acetone are removed from the calcium acetate by distillation, and the solid residue is then treated with the quantity of sulfuric acid calculated to release the acetic acid. The latter is removed from the mixture by vacuum distillation. Another commercial method for making acetic acid was described under the reactions of acetylene (p. 91).

Acetic acid is used in the preparation of vinegar, some dyes, and perfumes and flavors, and as a source of acetone. It is used in the manufacture of airplane lacquers and cellulose acetates, including acetate rayon and cellulose acetate photographic films. Many salts of acetic acid are valuable commercial products. Paris green, for example, is a mixed acetate and arsenite of copper. Basic lead acetate, or white lead, is used in the manufacture of paints.

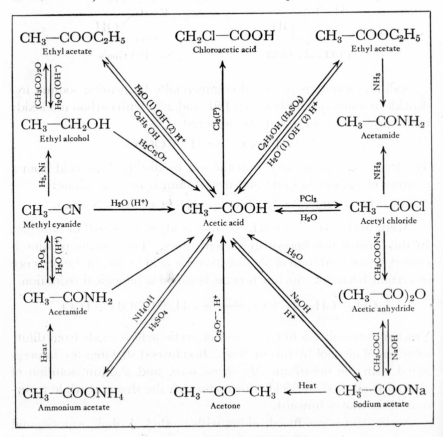

Reactions of a Saturated Acid

Higher acids. Palmitic acid, $C_{15}H_{31}COOH$; stearic acid, $C_{17}H_{35}COOH$; and oleic acid, $C_{17}H_{33}COOH$, are constituents of natural fats and oils. The fats are glyceryl esters of these and a few other acids. Oleic acid is an unsaturated acid; the fats which contain appreciable amounts of it are oils rather than solids. (See fats and soaps, p. 179.)

$$\text{CH}_2\text{OH} \qquad\qquad \text{CH}_2\text{—O—CO—C}_{17}\text{H}_{35}$$
$$|\qquad\qquad\qquad\qquad |$$
$$\text{CHOH} \qquad\qquad \text{CH—O—CO—C}_{17}\text{H}_{35}$$
$$|\qquad\qquad\qquad\qquad |$$
$$\text{CH}_2\text{OH} \qquad\qquad \text{CH}_2\text{—O—CO—C}_{17}\text{H}_{35}$$

Glycerol, a trihydric alcohol   Tristearin, an ester of glycerol and stearic acid

Palmitic acid (mp 64°) is a soft, colorless solid; oleic acid (mp 14°) is an oily liquid. They occur as esters in olive oil. Stearic acid (mp 69°), a white waxlike solid, is obtained by hydrolyzing almost any solid fat; beef tallow is a good source of this compound.

The common names and formulas of some other acids isolated from natural sources are listed for reference.

SOME HIGHER ACIDS			
Name	Formula	Name	Formula
Heptylic	$CH_3—(CH_2)_5—CO_2H$	Pentadecanoic	$CH_3—(CH_2)_{13}CO_2H$
Caprylic	$CH_3—(CH_2)_6—CO_2H$	Arachidic	$CH_3—(CH_2)_{18}CO_2H$
Pelargonic	$CH_3—(CH_2)_7—CO_2H$	Behenic	$CH_3—(CH_2)_{20}—CO_2H$
Capric	$CH_3—(CH_2)_8—CO_2H$	Tetracosanoic	$CH_3—(CH_2)_{22}—CO_2H$
Undecylic	$CH_3—(CH_2)_9—CO_2H$	Carnubic	$C_{23}H_{47}—CO_2H$
Lauric	$CH_3—(CH_2)_{10}—CO_2H$	Cerotinic	$C_{25}H_{51}—CO_2H$
Tridecanoic	$CH_3—(CH_2)_{11}—CO_2H$	Montanic	$C_{27}H_{55}—CO_2H$
Myristic	$CH_3—(CH_2)_{12}—CO_2H$	Melissinic	$C_{30}H_{61}—CO_2H$

EXERCISES

1. Write from memory the formulas of the following compounds: acetic acid, formic acid, isobutyric acid, propionyl chloride, ethyl formate, decanoic acid, hexanoic acid, stearic acid.

2. Write a general structural formula for each of the following types of compounds: carboxylic acid, ester, acid anhydride, acid amide, α-chloro-acid.

3. To what degree, approximately, is a fatty acid ionized in a 0.1 N solution? Is the percentage ionized increased or decreased by dilution of the solution?

4. Complete and balance the following equations:

    a. $n\text{-}C_3H_7OH + n\text{-}C_4H_9COOH \xrightarrow{H_2SO_4}$

    b. $CH_3{-}COOH + CH_2OH \xrightarrow{H_2SO_4}$
                            |
                           CH_2OH

    c. $n\text{-}C_3H_7{-}COOH + PCl_3 \longrightarrow$

    d. $n\text{-}C_4H_9{-}COCl + n\text{-}C_4H_9{-}COONa \longrightarrow$

    e. $CH_3{-}CH_2{-}CH_2{-}COOH + Cl_2 \xrightarrow{P}$

5. Write equations for the preparation of pentanoic acid from each of the following sources:

    a. $CH_3{-}(CH_2)_3{-}CH_2OH$

    b. $CH_3{-}CH_2{-}CH_2{-}CH_2{-}Br$

    c. $n\text{-}C_4H_9{-}COOCH_3$

6. How could you obtain (*a*) $(C_2H_5)_2CO$ and (*b*) C_2H_6 from propionic acid?

7. Illustrate by equations the following terms:

a. Ionization of an acid	*d.* Ester formation
b. Acid anhydride formation	*e.* Acid amide formation
c. Hydrolysis of an ester	*f.* Acid chloride formation

PROBLEMS

1. How would you accomplish the following syntheses?

    a. $C_3H_7{-}COOH \longrightarrow C_3H_7{-}COOC_4H_9$

    b. $C_3H_7{-}COOH \longrightarrow C_3H_7{-}CO{-}NH_2$

    c. $C_3H_7{-}COOH \longrightarrow C_3H_7{-}CO{-}Br$

    d. $C_3H_7{-}COOH \longrightarrow (C_3H_7CO)_2O$

    e. $CH_3{-}CH_2{-}OH \longrightarrow CH_3{-}CH_2{-}COOH$

    f. $CH_3{-}CHO \longrightarrow CH_3{-}CHOH{-}COOH$ (*via* a cyanohydrin)

    g. $CH_3{-}CH_2{-}COOH \longrightarrow CH_3{-}CHOH{-}COOH$ (*via* halogenation)

    h. $C_4H_9{-}COOH \longrightarrow C_4H_9{-}COONa$

2. Formic acid is the only simple carboxylic acid that is easily oxidized by permanganate. Suggest a reason for its exceptional behavior.

3. Outline the process of esterification and of ester hydrolysis and show how they proceed through the same intermediate product.

4. Compare the reactions of (*a*) hydrolysis, (*b*) alcoholysis, and (*c*) ammonolysis of an acid chloride and show in what way they are analogous.

16 · DERIVATIVES
OF THE MONOBASIC ACIDS

Esters, anhydrides, amides, and acyl halides are acid derivatives in which the carboxylic hydroxyl group has been replaced by a different group or by a single atom:

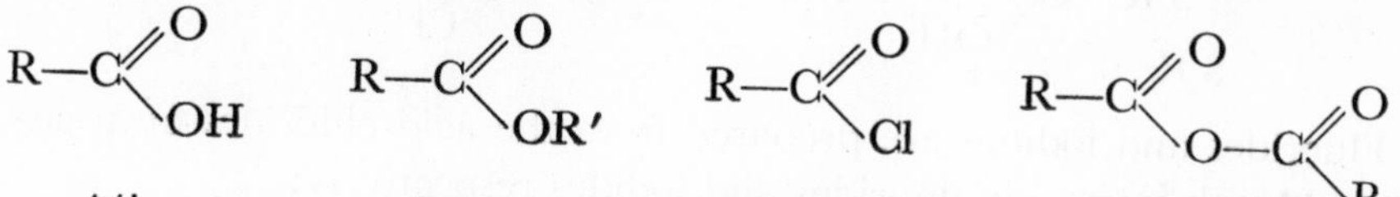

$$R-C\diagup^O_{OH} \qquad R-C\diagup^O_{OR'} \qquad R-C\diagup^O_{Cl} \qquad R-C\diagup^O_{O-C\diagup^O_R}$$

Acid   Ester   Acid chloride   Acid anhydride
                                       (an acyl halide)

Of these classes of compounds the acid chlorides and acid anhydrides are used merely as intermediates in the preparation of other classes of compounds. Esters and amides are found widely distributed in nature, and they are synthesized in large amounts for use in industry and in various arts. Fats, vegetable oils, and waxes are examples of esters which are found in animals and plants. Many other esters are made synthetically for use in the manufacture of plastics. A few esters are used as solvents, and some are employed as perfumes and flavors. The fundamental structure of an acid amide is found in proteins, in many drugs, and in nylon, but these complicated compounds cannot be classed as simple acid amides.

The substances mentioned above are not the only derivatives of acids. Salts of acids are formed by replacement of a hydrogen atom with a metal atom; they will be considered in connection with soaps. Another class of derivatives, one in which the carboxyl group is left intact and substitution is made in some other part of the molecule, will be considered separately.

Acid Halides

The acid halides, or acyl halides, correspond to the general formula

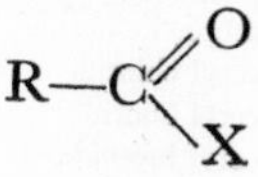

$$R-C\diagup^O_X$$

in which X stands for a halogen atom. Fluorides and iodides may be prepared, but the chlorides and bromides are most commonly used.

173

The lower members of the series are colorless liquids of irritating odor. The higher members take on the physical characteristics of the higher hydrocarbons.

Preparation of acyl halides. The acid chlorides and bromides may be made by treating an acid with a phosphorus halide, PX_3 or PX_5, or through the action of thionyl chloride on an acid (see page 166). The reaction with phosphorus trichloride proceeds as follows:

$$3\ R-C\!\!\begin{smallmatrix}O\\OH\end{smallmatrix} + PCl_3 \longrightarrow 3\ R-C\!\!\begin{smallmatrix}O\\Cl\end{smallmatrix} + H_3PO_3$$

Fluorides and iodides are prepared from the acid chlorides by treatment with inorganic fluorides and iodides respectively:

$$R-C\!\!\begin{smallmatrix}O\\Cl\end{smallmatrix} + KI \longrightarrow R-C\!\!\begin{smallmatrix}O\\I\end{smallmatrix} + KCl$$

Acetyl chloride is required in large amounts commercially, and an inexpensive variation of one of these procedures is used. The reagents are sodium acetate, sulfur dioxide, and chlorine:

$$2\ CH_3CO_2Na + SO_2 + Cl_2 \longrightarrow 2\ CH_3COCl + Na_2SO_4$$

Nomenclature of acyl halides. The data given in the following table illustrate the relationships between the names and formulas of acids and acid halides. In each case the carboxylic hydroxyl group of the acid is replaced by a halogen atom, and the terminal *ic* in the name of the acid is changed to *yl*.

SOME ACID HALIDES				
Acid		**Acid Halide**		
Name	*Formula*	*Name*	*Formula*	*Boiling Point (°C)*
Formic	HCO_2H	Formyl chloride	$CO + HCl$	
Carbonic	$HO-CO_2H$	Carbonyl chloride	$COCl_2$	8.3
Acetic	CH_3CO_2H	Acetyl chloride	CH_3COCl	50.9
		Acetyl fluoride	CH_3COF	20.
		Acetyl bromide	CH_3COBr	76.7
		Acetyl iodide	CH_3COI	106.
Propionic	$CH_3CH_2CO_2H$	Propionyl chloride	CH_3CH_2COCl	80.
Butanoic, or *n*-butyric	$CH_3(CH_2)_2CO_2H$	Butanoyl chloride, or *n*-butyryl	$CH_3(CH_2)_2COCl$	102.

Formyl chloride, HCOCl, is produced in a photochemical reaction between formaldehyde and chlorine, but it dissociates rapidly into carbon monoxide and hydrogen chloride. It cannot be prepared from formic acid and phosphorus trichloride. (See page 329.)

Carbonyl chloride is commonly called phosgene, a name derived from its mode of preparation. Carbon monoxide and chlorine combine in the presence of light to form phosgene. It is highly toxic and was once used in large amounts as a war gas. In spite of its poisonous character it is an important intermediate in many syntheses.

Reactions of acid chlorides. The acid chlorides react readily with compounds in which there is hydrogen attached to oxygen or to nitrogen. Water, alcohol, and ammonia may be used to illustrate this rule:

Hydrolysis: $R—COCl + H_2O \longrightarrow R—\underset{\text{An acid}}{COOH} + HCl$

Alcoholysis: $R—COCl + R'OH \longrightarrow R—\underset{\text{An ester}}{COOR'} + HCl$

Ammonolysis: $R—COCl + 2 NH_3 \longrightarrow R—\underset{\text{An amide}}{CONH_2} + NH_4Cl$

The hydrolysis of an acid chloride is much more rapid than the hydrolysis of an alkyl chloride. In fact, it is dangerous to add acetyl chloride rapidly to water, because of the violence of the reaction; the heat of hydrolysis causes explosion. The higher, more insoluble members of the homologous series react slowly with water and with alcohols. A technique commonly used in esterification of an alcohol with an acid chloride is known as the Schotten-Baumann method. The alcoholysis is carried out in the presence of an aqueous solution of sodium hydroxide or of pyridine. These basic media neutralize the hydrogen chloride formed during esterification and prevent the formation of alkyl chlorides from the alcohol and HCl.

The chlorine atom of an acid chloride may be replaced by fluoride, iodide, cyanide, azide, or carboxylate ion. These reactions of the acid chloride, RCOCl, may be summarized as follows:

Reagent	ZnF_2	AgCN	AgN_3	KI	$R—CO_2Na$
Product	RCOF	RCOCN	$RCON_3$	RCOI	$R—\overset{O}{\overset{\|}{C}}—O—\overset{O}{\overset{\|}{C}}—R$
	Acid fluoride	Acid cyanide	Acid azide	Acid iodide	Acid anhydride

We observe that acid chlorides react usefully (*a*) with water, alcohol, and ammonia and (*b*) with the anions of certain salts.

176 · THE ESSENTIALS OF ORGANIC CHEMISTRY

Acid Anhydrides

Preparation of anhydrides. An acid anhydride is made by heating together the salt of an acid and an acid chloride. Acetic anhydride, a colorless liquid which boils at 140°, is made in this way:

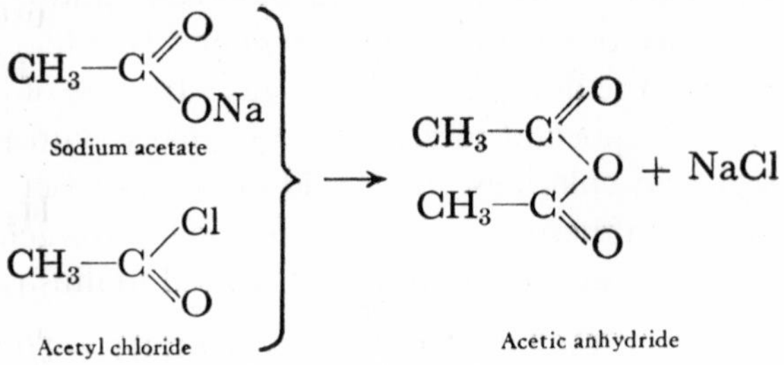

Reactions of anhydrides. Acid anhydrides have the general formula

$$R-\overset{O}{\overset{\|}{C}}-O-\overset{O}{\overset{\|}{C}}-R$$

They undergo hydrolysis, alcoholysis, and ammonolysis, as do the acid halides.

Reaction Type	$R-\overset{O}{\overset{\|}{C}}-O$	$\overset{O}{\overset{\|}{C}}-R$	Products
Hydrolysis	H	OH	Two acids
Ammonolysis	H	NH₂	An acid (or the ammonium salt of an acid) and an amide
Alcoholysis	H	OR	An acid and an ester

In the form of balanced equations these reactions appear as follows:

$$(R-CO)_2O + H_2O \longrightarrow R-COOH + R-COOH$$
$$(R-CO)_2O + 2\,NH_3 \longrightarrow R-CONH_2 + R-COONH_4$$
$$(R-CO)_2O + ROH \longrightarrow R-COOR + R-COOH$$

A strong dehydrating agent will convert an acid into an anhydride. That is, the hydrolysis reaction may be reversed if a reagent like P_2O_5 is used to take up the water and if heat is applied to hasten the dehydration.

Acetic anhydride is used in the esterification of cellulose, which contains hydroxyl groups. The acetylated cellulose is used to manufacture one type of rayon fiber. This is economically feasible because there is a less expensive source of acetic anhydride than the one given above. In the commercial process the anhydride is made from acetylene and acetic acid:

$$HC\equiv CH + 2\ CH_3-COOH \longrightarrow H_3C-CH\begin{cases} O-COCH_3 \\ O-COCH_3 \end{cases}$$

Acetaldehyde diacetate

$$CH_3-CH(O-CO-CH_3)_2 \xrightarrow{\text{Heat}} CH_3-CHO + (CH_3-CO)_2O$$

Acetaldehyde diacetate   Acetaldehyde   Acetic anhydride

The acetaldehyde is oxidized to acetic acid by passing a mixture of air and the aldehyde vapor over hot vanadium oxide.

Esters

Carboxylic acids react with alcohols, in the presence of acidic catalysts, to form esters. The net result of the process is indicated by the equation

$$R-C\!\!\begin{array}{c}O\\\\OH\end{array} + R'OH \underset{}{\overset{H_2SO_4}{\rightleftarrows}} R-C\!\!\begin{array}{c}O\\\\OR'\end{array} + H_2O$$

Acid   Alcohol   Ester   Water

The mechanism of the reaction was outlined on page 167. Acid chlorides and acid anhydrides are better esterifying agents than are acids, because their reactions with alcohols are faster and more complete.

The esters of low molecular weights are liquids characterized by pleasant odors. Many of them are manufactured for use in the preparation of artificial flavors and perfumes. They are valuable also as solvents, and as such they find industrial application in the manufacture of lacquers.

Hydrolysis of an ester in pure water is usually very slow; consequently the conversion of an ester to the corresponding acid and alcohol must be carried out under special conditions. The directions for hydrolysis call for (*a*) use of a catalyst to hasten the reaction, (*b*) establishment of conditions which will force the reaction to completion, (*c*) use of a common solvent for catalyst, water, and ester. The net result of hydrolysis of an ester is indicated as follows:

$$R-COOR' + H_2O \rightleftarrows R-COOH + R'OH$$

For this reaction either hydrogen ion or hydroxyl ion will serve as a catalyst. The latter is the more effective and has the additional advantage that it neutralizes the acid formed in the reaction:

$$R—COOH + OH^- \longrightarrow R—CO_2{}^- + H_2O$$

Thus in alkaline solution the hydrolysis is faster than in water, and the reaction goes to completion. If the acid is to be isolated from an alkaline hydrolysis product, an amount of mineral acid equivalent to the alkali which was used is added after the hydrolysis is complete. Convenient solvents for the higher esters, water, and sodium hydroxide are methanol and ethanol. A very few esters hydrolyze rapidly at room temperature. It is fortunate that some hydrolyses are slow, as otherwise the fats in our bodies could not survive the continued contact with water to which they are subjected.

Ethyl acetate, $CH_3—COOC_2H_5$, made from acetic acid and ethanol, is a colorless liquid which boils at 77° and which is only slightly soluble in water. It has a pleasant, fruity odor. It is employed as a solvent in the extraction of caffeine from coffee.

THE NAMES AND FORMULAS OF SOME ESTERS		
Name	Formula	Occurrence, Use, or Property
Isoamyl acetate	$CH_3—CO_2CH_2CH_2CH(CH_3)_2$	Pear oil and artificial banana oil; lacquer solvent
n-Octyl acetate	$CH_3—CO_2C_8H_{17}$	Odor of oranges
Ethyl butyrate	$CH_3CH_2CH_2CO_2C_2H_5$	Pineapple oil
n-Amyl iso-butyrate	$(CH_3)_2CH—CH_2—CO_2C_5H_9$	Apple odor; flavoring
Cetyl palmitate	$CH_3(CH_2)_{14}CO_2(CH_2)_{15}CH_3$	Spermaceti
Myricyl palmitate	$CH_3(CH_2)_{14}CO_2(CH_2)_{29}CH_3$	Beeswax
Glyceryl esters	$H_2C—O—CO—R$ $\quad\mid$ $HC—O—CO—R$ $\quad\mid$ $H_2C—O—CO—R$	Fats; shortening; salad oils

The toxicity of esters is similar to but less than that of the constituent alcohols; in fact, the toxicity is related to the rate and extent of hydrolysis of the ester. The function of waxes in plant structures such as the skins of grapes and plums seems to be to provide protection against gain or loss of water or against invasion by fungi. Man uses the same waxes to create protective surfaces, as in paints and polishes. When prunes are dipped in lye, the protective coating is ruptured, and the fruit will then dry without spoilage.

Fats and soaps. Hydrolysis of an ester in alkaline solutions is frequently called saponification, because it is this type of reaction which gives rise to soaps. The animal fats and vegetable oils are esters in which the alcohol radical is glycerol and the acids include nearly all members of the fatty series from butyric acid to stearic acid, as well as a number of unsaturated acids, such as oleic acid. Sodium salts of the higher acids are soaps.

The formulas for some fats are shown below:

$$CH_2-O-CO-C_{15}H_{31}$$
$$|$$
$$CH-O-CO-C_{15}H_{31}$$
$$|$$
$$CH_2-O-CO-C_{15}H_{31}$$

Tripalmitin (mp 65°)

$$CH_2-O-CO-C_{17}H_{35}$$
$$|$$
$$CH-O-CO-C_{17}H_{35}$$
$$|$$
$$CH_2-O-CO-C_{17}H_{35}$$

Tristearin (mp 70.8°)

$$CH_2-O-CO-C_{17}H_{33}$$
$$|$$
$$CH-O-CO-C_{17}H_{33}$$
$$|$$
$$CH_2-O-CO-C_{17}H_{33}$$

Triolein (mp − 17°)

$$CH_2-O-CO-C_{17}H_{33}$$
$$|$$
$$CH-O-CO-C_{17}H_{33}$$
$$|$$
$$CH_2-O-CO-C_{17}H_{35}$$

Dioleostearin

When a fat is saponified by treatment with a hot solution of sodium hydroxide, glycerol and sodium salts of the acids are formed. Sodium stearate, sodium palmitate, and sodium oleate are components of most soaps. Potassium salts as well as sodium salts of these acids are used in the manufacture of soaps. Potassium soaps are much softer than the corresponding sodium compounds.

When hydrolysis is complete, sodium chloride is added to "salt out" the soaps. On standing, a crude soap cake forms on the surface, above the aqueous solution of salt, lye, and glycerol. The crude soap is washed, incorporated with other ingredients, such as borax, silicates, resins, perfumes, and glycerol, and pressed into the desired forms.

The saponification of tristearin is represented by the following equation:

$$CH_2-O-CO-C_{17}H_{35} \qquad\qquad CH_2OH$$
$$|$$
$$CH-O-CO-C_{17}H_{35} + 3\ NaOH \longrightarrow CHOH + 3\ C_{17}H_{35}COONa$$
$$|$$
$$CH_2-O-CO-C_{17}H_{35} \qquad\qquad CH_2OH$$

Tristearin (glyceryl tristearate)   Glycerol   Sodium stearate (a soap)

A natural fat is not a pure ester of a single type, and a soap derived from any fat is a mixture of several salts. Butter contains a greater variety of esters of glycerol than does any other fat. The relative quantities of various acids combined with glycerol in several common fats and oils are shown in the following table:

COMPOSITION OF FATS								
Acids	Butter	Lard	Beef Tallow	Olive Oil	Cotton-seed Oil	Linseed Oil	Coconut Oil	Soybean Oil
Butyric	4							
Caproic	2							
Caprylic	2						10	
Capric	2						4	
Lauric	5						51	
Myristic	15	1	3		1		19	
Palmitic	20	28	25	10	21	5	7	8
Stearic	6	9	24	2	2	4	3	5
Oleic	44	57	46	81	30	10	5	29
Linoleic		5	2	7	46	43	1	54
Linolenic						38		4

An inspection of the table shows that cottonseed oil is rich in esters of oleic acid and linoleic acid. These acids have the following structural formulas:

$$CH_3(CH_2)_7CH=CH(CH_2)_7COOH$$
Oleic acid (mp 14°)

$$CH_3(CH_2)_4CH=CH—CH_2—CH=CH(CH_2)_7COOH$$
Linoleic acid (mp − 11°)

The difference between liquid and solid fats, or oils and fats, lies largely in the content of unsaturated acids. When oils are hydrogenated,—that is, subjected to hydrogen gas under pressure in the presence of finely divided nickel,—the double bonds are broken by the addition of hydrogen atoms. Through this addition of hydrogen the oleic and linoleic acids present in the oil are reduced to stearic acid, and the oil becomes a solid. By controlling the degree of hydrogenation one can bring the resulting fat to any desired melting point and hardness up to that of tristearin.

Natural fats have degrees of unsaturation peculiar to their sources, and hence a measurement of unsaturation becomes a means of identifying a fat or of detecting possible adulteration of an oil. Double bonds are broken by the addition of halogens, and a procedure has been devised whereby the amount of iodine absorbed per gram of fat can be measured. This ratio, multiplied by 100, is called the iodine number of the fat. The addition of iodine is carried out in chloroform solution, with mercuric chloride as a catalyst.

$$\text{Iodine number} = \frac{\text{grams of iodine absorbed}}{\text{grams of fat}} \times 100$$

The iodine number of cottonseed oil varies from 111 to 116; that of coconut oil, from 8.5 to 9.0.

Another characteristic of a fat from any particular natural source is a definite ratio between the lower and higher acids in the sample. This ratio determines the Reichert-Meissl number. The lower acids are volatile, and they distill from the mixture when steam is passed through a saponified and acidified fat. The Reichert-Meissl number is the number of milliliters of $0.1\,N$ base required to neutralize the water-soluble, volatile acids obtained from 5 grams of fat. This number for butter is 22 to 30; for oleomargarine, 0.5 to 1.5; for lard, 0.3 to 0.6.

Linseed oil and tung oil are rich in unsaturated components, and they are of particular interest in their capacity to form resinous films as they "dry." This property makes them useful in paints. The drying power is due largely to the presence of the unsaturated linolenic and eleostearic acid components of the glycerides:

$$CH_3(CH_2-CH=CH)_3(CH_2)_7COOH$$
Linolenic acid, or 9, 12, 15-octadecatrienoic acid

$$CH_3-(CH_2)_3-CH=CH-CH=CH-CH=CH-(CH_2)_7COOH$$
Eleostearic acid, or 9, 11, 13-octadecatrienoic acid

The latter, present to a great extent in tung oil, has three double bonds in conjugated positions (alternate double and single bonds). This structure renders the fat very susceptible to polymerization. The so-called "drying" which leads to the formation of an impervious film is a polymerization process.

Raw, or natural, linseed oil dries very slowly, while a sample which has been heated with lead oxide dries rapidly. The polymerization takes place upon exposure to the air, and is catalyzed by peroxides which are formed by interaction of the fat with oxygen of the air. The rate of oxygen absorption is increased by the presence of lead, cobalt, or manganese salts of organic acids. In the paint industry these catalysts are called "driers." The manufacture of paint is not a simple blending of oils and pigments. The quality of the paint film depends not only upon the choice of drying oil but also upon the time and temperature used for incorporation of the drier and upon the nature of the resins employed to give additional plasticity to the paint film.

The properties of soaps depend mainly upon the presence in the molecule of a long hydrocarbon unit in combination with a water-soluble terminal group. Soaps may be described as foam-producing, as dispersing or emulsifying agents, and as detergents or cleansing agents. The water-soluble carboxylate group tends to dissolve in the water, while the hydrocarbon portion of the soap molecule resists solution. When the hydrocarbon chain of a soap molecule is composed of more than nine carbon atoms, the result of the opposing actions is the formation of a film of soap molecules on the surface of the solution or on any solid surface which adsorbs soap molecules.

The detergent action of a soap depends, in part, upon the capacity of the soap film to cover, or wet, a variety of surfaces. Dirt particles adhering to a fabric become covered with soap, just as the cloth itself adsorbs soap; in such circumstances the dirt particles and the fabric no longer adhere to each other. A stain may be removed by soap if the latter is more strongly adsorbed by the cloth than is the stain. A soap solution is not a true solution, because the soap molecules tend to group together in colloidal aggregations. The opalescence of such a solution is due to the scattering of light by these aggregates, or micelles.

Ortho esters. Compounds of the type

$$R-C {\overset{\displaystyle OH}{\underset{\displaystyle OH}{\overset{\displaystyle\diagup}{\underset{\displaystyle\diagdown}{-OH}}}}}$$

(ortho acids) are unknown; attempts to prepare them have always resulted in the formation of ordinary acids and water. On the other hand, esters corresponding to the formula

$$R-C {\overset{\displaystyle OR}{\underset{\displaystyle OR}{\overset{\displaystyle\diagup}{\underset{\displaystyle\diagdown}{-OR}}}}}$$

can be made, and some of them are useful reagents. Ethyl orthoformic ester, for example, is made from chloroform by treatment with sodium ethoxide:

$$H-C {\overset{\displaystyle Cl}{\underset{\displaystyle Cl}{\overset{\diagup}{\underset{\diagdown}{-Cl}}}}} + 3\ C_2H_5ONa \longrightarrow H-C {\overset{\displaystyle OC_2H_5}{\underset{\displaystyle OC_2H_5}{\overset{\diagup}{\underset{\diagdown}{-OC_2H_5}}}}} + 3\ NaCl$$

The ortho esters are readily hydrolyzed by hot dilute acids. The hydrolysis is not catalyzed by hydroxide ions.

Acid Amides

The acid amides are formed by replacing the hydrogen of ammonia by acyl radicals. They are primary, secondary, or tertiary, according to the number of hydrogen atoms replaced.

$$R—CONH_2 \qquad (R—CO)_2NH \qquad (R—CO)_3N$$

Primary amide · Secondary amide · Tertiary amide

The secondary and tertiary compounds are of little importance, and quaternary amides are unknown. With the exception of formamide, a liquid, the primary compounds are colorless solids, and, when pure, they are odorless. The lower members can be distilled under atmospheric pressure without decomposition.

SOME PRIMARY AMIDES			
Name	Formula	Melting Point (°C)	Boiling Point (°C)
Formamide	$H—CONH_2$	2.5	193
Acetamide	$CH_3—CONH_2$	81	222
Propionamide	$C_2H_5—CONH_2$	79	213
Valeramide (n)	$n\text{-}C_4H_9—CONH_2$	106	
Caproamide	$n\text{-}C_5H_{11}—CONH_2$	98	255
Stearamide	$n\text{-}C_{17}H_{35}—CONH_2$	109	

Preparation of amides. Amides of the lower saturated fatty acids may be prepared by thermal dehydration of the ammonium salts of the acids (see page 166).

More generally amides are prepared by the ammonolysis of acid chlorides, acid anhydrides, or esters. Type reactions follow:

$$R—COCl + NH_3 + OH^- \xrightarrow{\text{Cold}} R—CONH_2 + H_2O + Cl^-$$

$$R—COCl + 2NH_3 \xrightarrow{\text{Cold}} R—CONH_2 + NH_4Cl$$

$$(R—CO)_2O + NH_3 + OH^- \xrightarrow{\text{Cold}} R—CONH_2 + RCO_2^- + H_2O$$

$$R—COOR + NH_3 \xrightarrow[\text{Alcohol}]{\text{Heat}} R—CONH_2 + ROH$$

The acid chlorides and acid anhydrides react rapidly. Esters usually require long standing or heat to complete the reaction. If the ester is very insoluble in aqueous ammonia, alcohol is used as a solvent for both the esters and the ammonia gas.

Properties of amides. The essential neutrality of amides toward acids and bases has been mentioned, but the reference was to rapid, ionic reactions. When an amide is heated with an acid or a base, hydrolysis takes place slowly:

$$R\text{—}CO\text{—}NH_2 + H_2O + H^+ \xrightarrow{\text{Heat}} R\text{—}COOH + NH_4^+$$

$$R\text{—}CO\text{—}NH_2 + OH^- \xrightarrow{\text{Heat}} R\text{—}COO^- + NH_3$$

$$R\text{—}CO\text{—}NH_2 + H_2O \xrightarrow{\text{Very slow}} R\text{—}COO^- + NH_4^+$$

This procedure is used in determining the structures of nitrogenous compounds. An organic compound which does not liberate ammonia when added to cold sodium hydroxide, but does form ammonia when heated with the alkali, is presumed to contain the structural unit

$$R\text{—}C{\overset{\displaystyle O}{\underset{\displaystyle NH_2}{<}}}$$

The amides are capable of undergoing many other reactions which, for one purpose or another, are useful. They may be dehydrated by treatment with phosphorus pentoxide. A mixture of an amide and phosphorus pentoxide is heated, and a nitrile distills from the mixture:

$$\underset{\text{An amide}}{RCONH_2} + P_2O_5 \longrightarrow \underset{\text{A nitrile}}{RCN} + 2HPO_3$$

An amide is readily converted into an amine, with loss of one carbon atom, through the Hofmann rearrangement (p. 204).

Acid derivatives and the Grignard reagent. The carboxylic acids give no useful reactions with Grignard reagents. The hydrocarbon corresponding to the Grignard reagent is the product formed when any acid acts upon an alkyl magnesium halide:

$$C_4H_9MgBr + CH_3COOH \longrightarrow C_4H_{10} + Mg{\overset{\displaystyle Br}{\underset{\displaystyle O\text{—}CO\text{—}CH_3}{<}}}$$

Water and the alcohols are sufficiently acidic to produce hydrocarbons from metallic alkyl derivatives. The methyl Grignard reagent, CH_3MgX, is used to test for the presence of very weak acids. Any substance which yields CH_4 when mixed in ether solution with CH_3MgI is presumed to yield hydrogen ions in some degree.

Acid chlorides, on the other hand, react with the Grignard reagent in the same manner as do aldehydes and ketones:

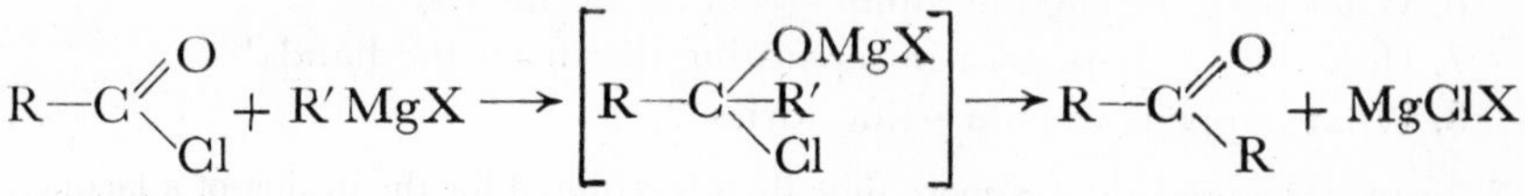

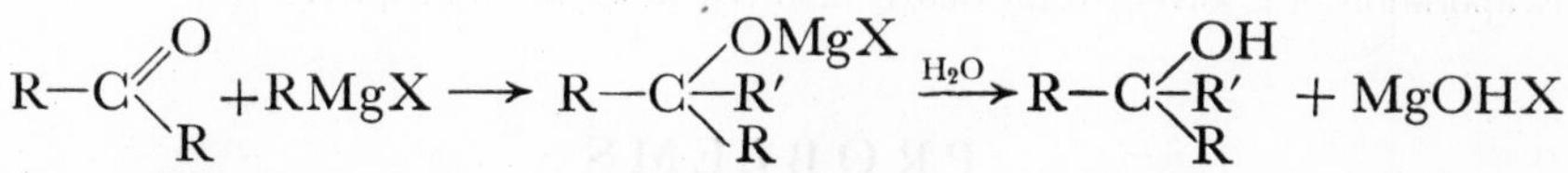

$$R-C{\overset{\displaystyle O}{\underset{\displaystyle Cl}{}}} + R'MgX \longrightarrow \left[R-C{\overset{\displaystyle OMgX}{\underset{\displaystyle Cl}{}}}R' \right] \longrightarrow R-C{\overset{\displaystyle O}{\underset{\displaystyle R}{}}} + MgClX$$

$$R-C{\overset{\displaystyle O}{\underset{\displaystyle R}{}}} + RMgX \longrightarrow R-C{\overset{\displaystyle OMgX}{\underset{\displaystyle R}{}}}R' \xrightarrow{H_2O} R-C{\overset{\displaystyle OH}{\underset{\displaystyle R}{}}}R' + MgOHX$$

Occasionally the reaction can be stopped at the ketone stage; more often a tertiary alcohol is formed through reaction of two molecules of the Grignard reagent.

Esters react in an analogous manner, and tertiary alcohols, rather than ketones, are the usual products.

Lithium alkyls react with acid chlorides to produce ketones:

$$R-C{\overset{\displaystyle O}{\underset{\displaystyle Cl}{}}} + LiR \longrightarrow R-C{\overset{\displaystyle O}{\underset{\displaystyle R}{}}} + LiCl$$

Apparently LiR differs from RMgBr in reacting much more slowly with ketones than with acid chlorides. ·

EXERCISES

1. Complete and balance the following equations:

 a. $C_4H_9COCl + C_3H_7OH + OH^- \longrightarrow$

 b. $\begin{array}{l} CH_2-O-CO-C_{17}H_{35} \\ | \qquad\qquad\qquad\qquad\quad + OH^- \longrightarrow \\ CH_2-O-CO-C_{17}H_{35} \end{array}$

 c. $(CH_3-CO)_2O + C_5H_9OH \longrightarrow$

 d. $C_2H_5COCl + NH_3 \xrightarrow{20°}$

 e. $C_2H_5COOH + NH_3 \xrightarrow{200°}$

 f. $CH_3-CH_2-COOH + PBr_3 \longrightarrow$

2. Write the structural formula of a fat the acid content of which consists of one third (in moles) stearic acid, one third palmitic acid, and one third oleic acid.

3. What type of catalyst is used in the esterification of an alcohol by an acid?

4. In hydrolyzing an ester, which catalyst, H^+ or OH^-, is better?

5. What is the major structural difference between solid fats and vegetable oils? How is an oil converted to a low-melting solid?

6. What does the "iodine number" of an oil measure?

7. How does a soap assist in separating dirt from the hands?

8. What happens when a paint "dries"?

NOTE. The process takes more time than is required for the drying of a lacquer. Evaporation of a solvent is all that is involved in drying a lacquer.

PROBLEMS

1. How could the following syntheses be accomplished?

   a. $C_2H_5COOCH_3 \longrightarrow (C_2H_5)_3COH$
   b. $CH_3CO_2C_2H_5 \longrightarrow CH_3COC_4H_9$ (iso)
   c. $C_6H_5CO_2H \longrightarrow C_6H_5CONH_2$

2. A sample of crude ethyl butyrate was analyzed for butyric acid, esters, and alcohol. A sample weighing 0.500 g was titrated rapidly with 0.1 N alcoholic potassium hydroxide, with the use of phenolphthalein as indicator; 2.3 cc of solution was required. To hydrolyze the ester 50.0 cc of the alkali was then added, and, after boiling, the excess of alkali was neutralized by adding 17.0 cc of 0.1 N acid. What were the percentages of free acid and of ester in the sample?

3. Represent by balanced equations the reactions of a Grignard reagent, C_2H_5MgBr, with (*a*) water, (*b*) ethanol, (*c*) methyl formate, (*d*) methyl acetate, (*e*) acetone.

4. What is an acetylating agent? a methylating agent?

5. Arrange the following in the probable order of their rates of hydrolysis and indicate which is the fastest: esters, ethers, acid anhydrides.

6. How would you determine whether an oil is a higher hydrocarbon or a fat?

17 · ALIPHATIC DIBASIC ACIDS

The Saturated Series

Many naturally occurring acids have two or more carboxyl groups in the molecule. Outstanding examples are oxalic acid, which is present as a potassium salt in rhubarb and other plants; succinic acid, which is present in amber as a constituent of the resin; and tartaric acid, which we obtain from grapes. Dicarboxylic acids are used in the preparation of many of our commercially important synthetic plastics. Our annual production of adipic acid amounts to many thousands of tons. It is used in the manufacture of Nylon.

The more important members of the series of dicarboxylic acids are characterized by a normal (straight) chain of carbon atoms with a carboxyl group at each end of the chain. They are colorless crystalline solids. The compounds having an odd number of carbon atoms are more soluble in water and melt at lower temperatures than those having approximately the same molecular weights but containing an even number of carbon atoms.

ALIPHATIC DIBASIC ACIDS

NAME OF ACID	FORMULA	MELTING POINT	SOLUBILITY IN 100 G OF WATER, 20°	K_{a_1}*
Oxalic	COOH—COOH	189°	8.6	9.5×10^{-2}
Malonic	COOH—CH_2—COOH	135.6°	73.5	1.6×10^{-3}
Succinic	COOH$(CH_2)_2$COOH	185°	5.8	6.8×10^{-5}
Glutaric	COOH$(CH_2)_3$COOH	97.5°	63.9	4.7×10^{-5}
Adipic	COOH$(CH_2)_4$COOH	152°	1.5	3.6×10^{-5}
Pimelic	COOH$(CH_2)_5$COOH	103°	5	3.4×10^{-5}
Suberic	COOH$(CH_2)_6$COOH	140°	0.16	3.0×10^{-5}
Azelaic	COOH$(CH_2)_7$COOH	106.5°	0.24	2.5×10^{-5}
Sebacic	COOH$(CH_2)_8$COOH	127°	0.10	2.3×10^{-5}

*K_{a_1} is the first dissociation constant. The value of K_{a_2} for the second carboxyl group is approximately 5×10^{-6} in all except oxalic acid. For oxalic acid the second dissociation constant is 4.9×10^{-5}. The second dissociation constant is smaller than the first, since the second proton escapes from an anion, whereas the first proton escapes from a neutral molecule.

It will be observed that oxalic acid is a stronger acid than any monocarboxylic acid. Malonic acid also shows the influence of the second carboxyl group upon the degree of ionization of the first. When the two carboxyl groups are separated by two or more carbon atoms, the effect of one group upon the other virtually disappears.

Oxalic acid. Hydrated oxalic acid, $C_2H_2O_4 \cdot 2\ H_2O$, a colorless crystalline solid, melts at 101°, and at that temperature loses the two molecules of water. The anhydrous acid melts and decomposes at 189°. The decomposition products are formic acid and carbon dioxide, or carbon monoxide, carbon dioxide, and water. Formic acid, if formed, is readily decomposed by heat to carbon monoxide and water. Oxalic acid is used in the manufacture of some dyes, and as a mordant in calico printing. It is a component of some ink-removers and bleaching agents. It is classified as a poison.

Oxalic acid is not oxidized by nitric acid or by an alkaline solution of permanganate ions. It is, however, oxidized rapidly and quantitatively by an acidic permanganate solution:

$$5(COOH)_2 + 2\ MnO_4^- + 6\ H^+ \longrightarrow 2\ Mn^{++} + 10\ CO_2 + 8\ H_2O$$

Oxalic acid is made in the laboratory by the action of concentrated nitric acid on sugar at the temperature of a water bath (below 100°). On a commercial scale it is made from sodium formate. When sodium formate is heated, it yields sodium oxalate and hydrogen:

$$\begin{matrix} H—COONa \\ \\ H—COONa \\ \text{Sodium formate} \end{matrix} \xrightarrow{280°} \begin{matrix} COONa \\ | \\ COONa \\ \text{Sodium oxalate} \end{matrix} + H_2$$

The preparation of sodium formate has been described (p. 169).

Since free oxalic acid is soluble in water, is nonvolatile, and cannot be extracted from water with ether, it is prepared from its salts. It is first precipitated in the form of insoluble calcium oxalate, which is dried and weighed. The precipitate is then suspended in water and treated with the calculated amount of sulfuric acid. The calcium sulfate formed is filtered off. The filtrate is then evaporated to small volume, and hydrated oxalic acid crystallizes out.

Malonic acid. Free malonic acid is not an important compound, but its ethyl ester is a very valuable reagent. The preparation of malonic acid from acetic acid illustrates a general method of adding a carboxyl group to a carbon chain. The steps involved in the process are as follows:*

$$CH_3—COOH + Cl_2 \longrightarrow CH_2Cl—COOH + HCl \quad (1)$$

$$CH_2Cl—COOH + KOH \longrightarrow CH_2Cl—COOK + H_2O \quad (2)$$

$$CH_2Cl—COOK + KCN \text{ (fused)} \longrightarrow \begin{matrix} CH_2—COOK \\ | \\ CN \end{matrix} + KCl \quad (3)$$

$$\begin{matrix} CH_2—COOK \\ | \\ CN \end{matrix} + H_2O + KOH \longrightarrow \begin{matrix} CH_2—COOK \\ | \\ COOK \end{matrix} + NH_3 \quad (4)$$

Recovery of malonic acid from its sodium or potassium salt is accomplished by applying the principle previously noted for the preparation of soluble, nonvolatile acids. In this case calcium malonate is precipitated, its suspension in water is treated with oxalic acid, and the less soluble calcium oxalate formed is removed by filtration. The filtrate is then evaporated to dryness.

When malonic acid is heated above its melting point, it decomposes into acetic acid and carbon dioxide; the reaction has been referred to as decarboxylation:

$$COOH—CH_2—COOH \longrightarrow CO_2 + CH_3—COOH$$

At high temperatures decarboxylation is a general reaction, but it takes place at low temperatures with compounds in which two carboxyl groups are attached to the same carbon atom. The loss of carbon dioxide occurs when an aqueous solution of such an acid is heated to the boiling point or when the solid acid is heated to its melting point.

The dibasic acids form acid chlorides, esters, and amides through the same reactions that were discussed in connection with the monobasic acids. Either of the carboxyl groups or both of them may take part in the formation of these derivatives. We shall consider only one of the numerous derivatives of these acids, namely, malonic ester.

*The reaction between chlorine and acetic acid is extremely slow, whereas the chlorinations of acetyl chloride and acetic anhydride are relatively rapid. The practical procedure is to pass chlorine gas into a mixture of acetic acid and red phosphorus. Part of the acetyl chloride, which is first formed, reacts with acetic acid to form acetic anhydride. Chlorine readily replaces hydrogen on the α-carbon atom in either the acid chloride or the anhydride, and from either of these derivatives chloroacetic acid is obtained through interaction with unchanged acetic acid.

Malonic ester. Ethyl alcohol reacts with malonic acid to form ethyl malonate (malonic ester). The reaction is catalyzed by sulfuric acid:

$$\begin{array}{c} COOH \\ | \\ CH_2 \\ | \\ COOH \end{array} + 2\ C_2H_5OH \longrightarrow \begin{array}{c} COOC_2H_5 \\ | \\ CH_2 \\ | \\ COOC_2H_5 \end{array} + 2\ H_2O \qquad (1)$$

Malonic acid (crystalline solid)   Malonic ester (colorless liquid)

Sodium cyanoacetate is another source of malonic ester:

$$\begin{array}{c} CN \\ | \\ CH_2 \\ | \\ COONa \end{array} + 2\ C_2H_5OH \xrightarrow{\ 2\ HCl\ (dry)\ } \begin{array}{c} COOC_2H_5 \\ | \\ CH_2 \\ | \\ COOC_2H_5 \end{array} + NaCl + NH_4Cl$$

Sodium cyanoacetate   Malonic ester

This ester affords a valuable starting point for the synthesis of the higher monocarboxylic acids. The ester is first converted to a sodium derivative by treatment in alcohol solution with either metallic sodium or sodium ethoxide:

$$\begin{array}{c} COOC_2H_5 \\ | \\ HCH \\ | \\ COOC_2H_5 \end{array} + \overset{+}{Na}\ \overset{-}{O}C_2H_5 \rightleftharpoons \overset{+}{Na} \left[\begin{array}{c} COOC_2H_5 \\ | \\ CH \\ | \\ COOC_2H_5 \end{array} \right]^{-} + HOC_2H_5$$

In this reaction the ester behaves as a very weak acid, comparable to ethanol in dissociation as an acid, but weaker than water and stronger than acetylene. It is to be remembered that alkanes and alkenes exhibit no dissociation of a proton. The reason for the dissociation here is that the anion of ethyl malonate is stabilized by resonance, since the negative charge may be placed upon the carbonyl oxygen atom of either ester group, as well as upon the methylenic carbon atom. The result is the apparent replacement of the proton by sodium ion. This metallic derivative, like the alkyl magnesium halides (Grignard reagents) and sodium or lithium alkyl derivatives, supplies an anion in its reaction with alkyl halides (see pages 68 and 69).

An alkyl halide acts upon sodiomalonic ester to replace the sodium with an alkyl radical:

$$CH_3I + Na—\underset{\underset{\textstyle COOR}{|}}{\overset{\overset{\textstyle COOR}{|}}{C}}—H \longrightarrow CH_3—\underset{\underset{\textstyle COOR}{|}}{\overset{\overset{\textstyle COOR}{|}}{C}}—H + NaI \qquad (4)$$

The ester is converted to the free acid by hydrolysis:

$$CH_3—\underset{\underset{\textstyle COOC_2H_5}{|}}{\overset{\overset{\textstyle COOC_2H_5}{|}}{C}}—H + 2\,H_2O \xrightarrow{OH^-,\ then\ H^+} CH_3—\underset{\underset{\textstyle COOH}{|}}{\overset{\overset{\textstyle COOH}{|}}{C}}—H + 2\,C_2H_5OH \quad (5)$$

Methylmalonic acid

The product formed in equation (5) has two carboxyl groups attached to the same carbon atom. When heated it yields propionic acid and carbon dioxide:

$$CH_3—\underset{\underset{\textstyle COOH}{|}}{\overset{\overset{\textstyle COOH}{|}}{C}}—H \xrightarrow{Heat} CH_3—CH_2—COOH + CO_2 \qquad (6)$$

If in equation (4) we had used ethyl iodide instead of methyl iodide, the product formed in (6) would be the next higher monobasic acid, namely, butyric acid. This provides a method for making any acid corresponding to the general formula $R—CH_2—COOH$.

Instead of hydrolyzing the ester formed in equation (4) we may replace the remaining hydrogen atom of the methylene group with sodium:

$$CH_3—\underset{\underset{\textstyle COOR}{|}}{\overset{\overset{\textstyle COOR}{|}}{C}}—H + Na \longrightarrow CH_3—\underset{\underset{\textstyle COOR}{|}}{\overset{\overset{\textstyle COOR}{|}}{C}}—Na + \tfrac{1}{2}H_2 \qquad (7)$$

The sodium atom in the new product may be replaced with an alkyl radical, as in equation (4). By hydrolyzing the resulting dialkylmalonic ester to the dibasic acid and then heating the latter to 100°–150° C, monobasic acids of the type $R_1R_2CH—CO_2H$ may be prepared.

Succinic acid. The third member of this series of acids, succinic acid, $HOOC—(CH_2)_2—COOH$, is found in many plants and fruits such as grapes, rhubarb, and beets. It is a product of bacterial decomposition and fermentation. Together with other four-carbon acids, namely, tartaric, malic, maleic, fumaric, and aspartic, it plays a part in plant metabolism. These acids are convertible into each other. The fossil resin, amber, contains succinic acid as a polyester of high molecular weight. A synthesis of succinic acid starts with ethylene dichloride:

$$\begin{array}{c} CH_2Cl \\ | \\ CH_2Cl \end{array} \xrightarrow{2KCN} \begin{array}{c} CH_2CN \\ | \\ CH_2CN \end{array} \xrightarrow{4H_2O(H^+)} \begin{array}{c} CH_2COOH \\ | \\ CH_2COOH \end{array} + 2NH_4^+$$

Of particular interest is the readiness with which succinic acid is converted into its cyclic anhydride (see page 195).

$$\begin{array}{c} CH_2—COOH \\ | \\ CH_2—COOH \end{array} \xrightarrow{\text{Heat}} \begin{array}{c} CH_2—C \\ | \\ CH_2—C \end{array}\!\!\!\begin{array}{c} \diagup^O \\ \diagdown O \\ \diagdown_O \end{array} + H_2O$$

Succinic acid   Succinic anhydride
(mp 185°)   (mp 119.6°; bp 261°)

Such an intramolecular reaction of bifunctional molecules is faster than the corresponding reaction between different molecules if the product is a five- or six-membered ring; ring formation is also favored in reversible reactions (see page 215).

Adipic acid. Hexanedioic acid, $HOOC—(CH_2)_4—COOH$, or adipic acid, is a colorless crystalline compound which melts at 152°. It is slightly soluble in water but very soluble in ethanol. The acid is observed among the products of vegetable metabolism, and among the products formed in the oxidation of unsaturated fats.

A textile fiber, Nylon, is a polyamide made by heating adipic acid and hexamethylene diamine, $H_2N—(CH_2)_6—NH_2$, under pressure.

$$\begin{array}{c} CO\lceil OH \\ | \\ (CH_2)_4 \\ | \\ COOH \end{array} + \begin{array}{c} H_2\rceil N—CH_2 \\ | \\ (CH_2)_4 \\ | \\ CH_2—NH_2 \end{array} \xrightarrow[-H_2O]{\text{Heat}} \left[\begin{array}{cc} CO—NH—CH_2 \\ | \quad\quad | \\ (CH_2)_4 \quad (CH_2)_4 \\ | \quad\quad | \\ HO\lfloor—CO \quad CH_2—NH \end{array} \right]_n H$$

Adipic acid   Hexamethylene diamine   Structural unit of Nylon

These bifunctional reactants were chosen to minimize the chance of ring formation and thereby favor the formation of a linear polyamide of high molecular weight. Of equal importance was the requirement that the reactants be available in large quantities, and this was satisfied by the development of processes which start with the raw materials cyclohexane, benzene, and butadiene. Cyclohexane, obtained from petroleum, is first oxidized to a mixture of cyclohexanol and cyclohexanone by passing oxygen gas into the liquid in the presence of cobalt naphthenates. The reaction mechanism of this step is that of a radical-chain. The alcohol may then be oxidized to the ketone by oxygen over a silver catalyst and the ketone oxidized in turn to adipic acid by nitric acid; or the mixture of alcohol and ketone may be oxidized to adipic acid directly by nitric acid.

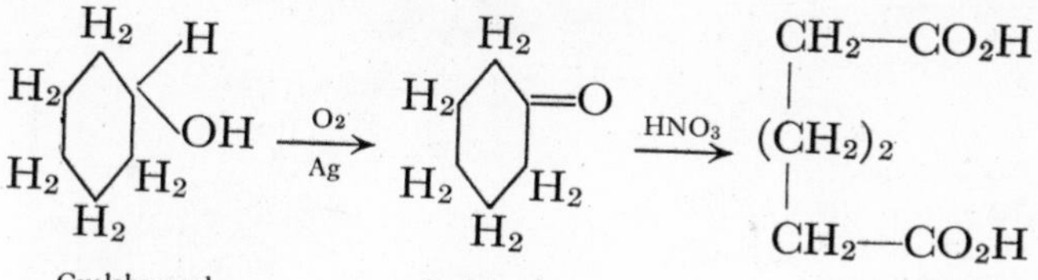

Cyclohexanol   Cyclohexanone   Adipic acid

When benzene is the starting point, phenol is first made by the usual steps (see page 296); the phenol is then hydrogenated to cyclohexanol and the latter oxidized as described above.

The hexamethylene diamine used in the production of Nylon is obtained by the hydrogenation of adiponitrile, $N\equiv C-(CH_2)_4-C\equiv N$. The latter is made in two ways. First, from the chlorine addition products of 1, 3-butadiene through the following sequence of reactions:

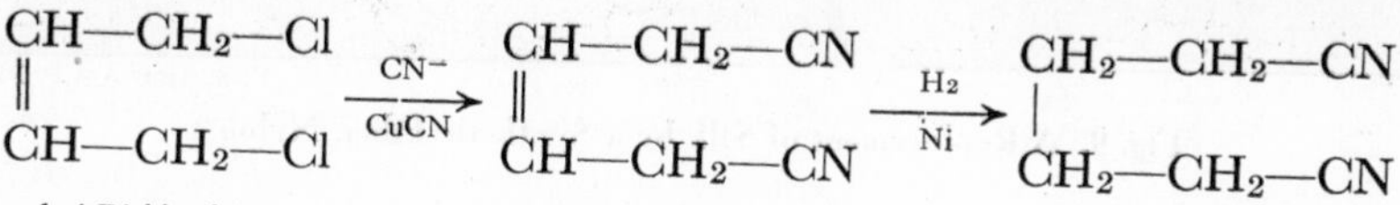

1, 4-Dichlorobutenes   1, 4-Dicyanobutenes   Adiponitrile

Second, from adipic acid by the following steps:

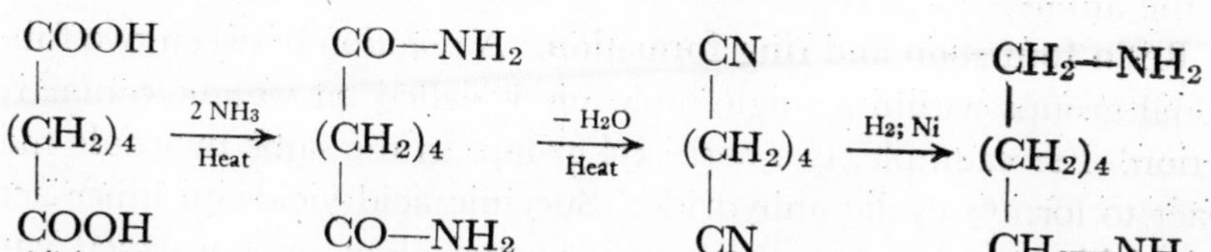

Adipic acid   Adipic acid diamide   Adiponitrile   Hexamethylene diamine

U. S. Army A.A.F. Photo

Fig. 9. A Replacement of Silk by a Synthetic Fiber, Nylon

The first step, amide formation, is followed by dehydration of the amide to the corresponding nitrile, and finally the nitrile is reduced to the amine.

Resin formation and ring formation. A reaction between two functional groups within a single molecule is called an *intra*molecular reaction. For example, two carboxyl groups in the same molecule may react to form a cyclic anhydride. Succinic acid yields an inner acid anhydride readily when the acid is heated alone or is warmed with acetic anhydride. Glutaric acid also forms an inner acid anhydride in good yield; but adipic acid and higher dicarboxylic acids, upon dehydration, give decreasing yields of cyclic anhydrides and increasing amounts of resinous substances of high molecular weight. Apparently in all cases two types of reaction, *intra*molecular and *inter*molecular, compete with each other.

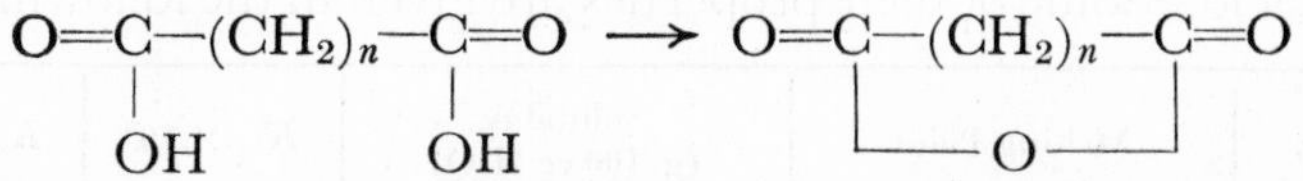

$$O\!\!=\!\!\underset{OH}{\overset{\ \ }{C}}\!\!-\!\!(CH_2)_n\!\!-\!\!\underset{OH}{\overset{\ \ }{C}}\!\!=\!\!O \longrightarrow O\!\!=\!\!\overset{\ \ }{C}\!\!-\!\!(CH_2)_n\!\!-\!\!\overset{\ \ }{C}\!\!=\!\!O$$

Formation of a cyclic anhydride predominates when $n = 2$ or 3. The ring formed contains 5 or 6 atoms

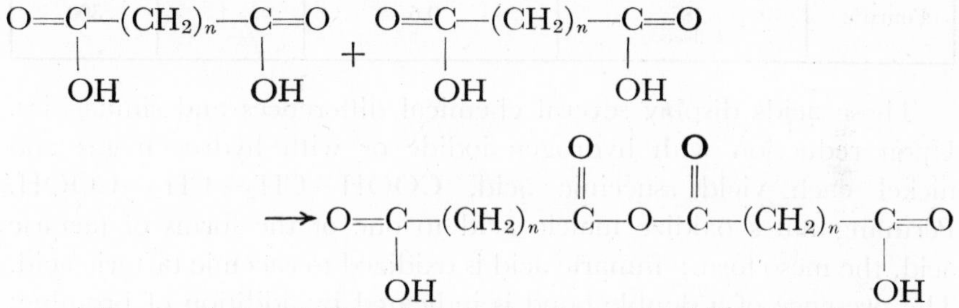

$$O\!\!=\!\!\underset{OH}{\overset{\ \ }{C}}\!\!-\!\!(CH_2)_n\!\!-\!\!\underset{OH}{\overset{\ \ }{C}}\!\!=\!\!O \ + \ O\!\!=\!\!\underset{OH}{\overset{\ \ }{C}}\!\!-\!\!(CH_2)_n\!\!-\!\!\underset{OH}{\overset{\ \ }{C}}\!\!=\!\!O$$

$$\longrightarrow O\!\!=\!\!\underset{OH}{\overset{\ \ }{C}}\!\!-\!\!(CH_2)_n\!\!-\!\!\overset{\overset{\displaystyle O}{\|}}{C}\!\!-\!\!O\!\!-\!\!\overset{\overset{\displaystyle O}{\|}}{C}\!\!-\!\!(CH_2)_n\!\!-\!\!\underset{OH}{\overset{\ \ }{C}}\!\!=\!\!O$$

Formation of a linear anhydride predominates when n is greater than 3. The condensation can continue, and substances of high molecular weights may be formed

Salts of many dibasic acids yield cyclic ketones when heated. The yields are good when ketones having five or six atoms in the ring can be formed. Resins of high molecular weight are formed from salts of dibasic acids in which the carboxyl groups are far apart. Salts of adipic acid and pimelic acid yield ketones as follows:

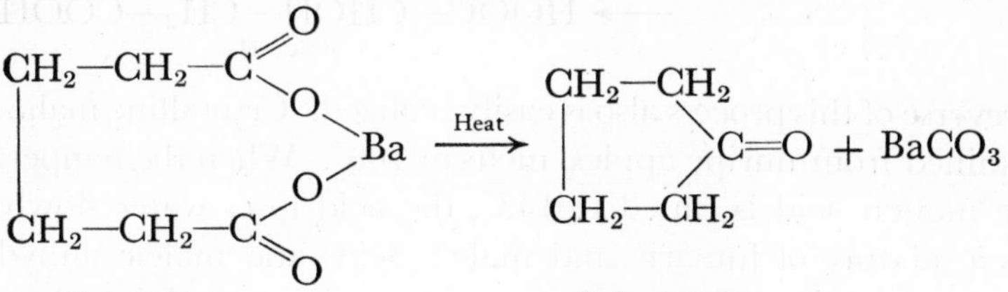

Barium adipate → Cyclopentanone (bp 129°–130°) + BaCO₃

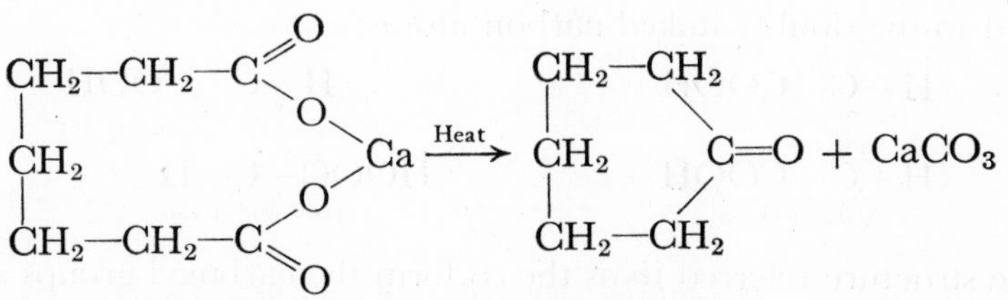

Calcium pimelate → Cyclohexanone (bp 155°–156°) + CaCO₃

Unsaturated Dibasic Acids

Maleic and fumaric acids. The simplest structure for an unsaturated dicarboxylic acid is COOH—CH=CH—COOH, and this formula has been assigned to two different compounds, namely, maleic acid and fumaric acid. Some of their properties are given in the following table:

	Melting Point	Solubility (g/100 cc H_2O)	$K_{a_1} \times 10^3$	$K_{a_2} \times 10^7$
Maleic	130°	50	13	2
Fumaric	287° (sublimes)	0.6	1	300

These acids display several chemical differences and similarities. Upon reduction with hydrogen iodide or with hydrogen gas and nickel each yields succinic acid, COOH—CH_2—CH_2—COOH. Permanganates oxidize maleic acid to one of the forms of tartaric acid, the meso form; fumaric acid is oxidized to racemic tartaric acid. The presence of a double bond is indicated by addition of bromine; but, like other α-β-unsaturated acids, these compounds add bromine slowly as compared with the rate of addition to an alkene hydrocarbon. Either maleic or fumaric acid can be converted into malic acid by hydration. This is accomplished by treatment with hot, dilute sulfuric acid, which acts as a catalyst:

HOOC—CH=CH—COOH + H_2O
Fumaric, or maleic acid H_2SO_4
$\xrightarrow{\quad}$ HOOC—CHOH—CH_2—COOH
Malic acid

The reverse of this process also is easily realized. Crystalline malic acid, as obtained from unripe apples, melts at 100°. When the temperature of the molten acid is raised to 145°, the acid loses water slowly and yields a mixture of fumaric and maleic acids and maleic anhydride.

The structural difference between fumaric acid and maleic acid is represented by different spatial arrangements of the groups attached to the doubly linked carbon atoms:

H—C—COOH   H—C—COOH
‖   ‖
H—C—COOH   HOOC—C—H
Maleic acid (cis)   Fumaric acid (trans)

In the structure referred to as the *cis* form the carboxyl groups are on the same side of the molecule; in the *trans* form they are on opposite sides of the molecule. If the double bond were an axis of rotation, an equilibrium would be established between the two forms. The fact that they exist separately implies a hindrance to rotation. This type of stereoisomerism is called *geometric* or *cis-trans* isomerism, to distinguish it from other types of space isomerism.

Maleic acid is assigned the *cis* structure because it readily forms an inner acid anhydride. Anhydride formation within a single molecule could not occur if the carboxyl groups were not on the same side of the molecule.

$$
\begin{array}{c}
\text{HC}\!-\!\text{COOH} \\
\| \\
\text{HC}\!-\!\text{COOH}
\end{array}
\quad\xrightarrow{\text{Heat}}\quad
\begin{array}{c}
\text{HC}\!-\!\text{C} \diagup\!\!\!\diagdown{}^{\text{O}} \\
\| \qquad\quad \text{O} \;+\; \text{H}_2\text{O} \\
\text{HC}\!-\!\text{C} \diagdown_{\text{O}}
\end{array}
$$

The reaction is reversible, and slow, at a temperature of 150°.

Fumaric acid does not form an anhydride unless it is heated to a temperature of 200° or higher; and at this temperature it yields, in addition to products of decarboxylation, the same anhydride which is obtained from maleic acid. In other words, at temperatures above 200° the rotation of one half of the molecule with respect to the other becomes rapid, and ring closure can take place.*

The conversion of maleic acid into fumaric acid can be accomplished at room temperature under the catalytic influence of hydrobromic acid. The rearrangement is reversible and equilibrium is established, with the major part of the mixture in the form of fumaric acid. Another evidence that fumaric acid is more stable than maleic acid is found in the fact that the heat released when maleic acid is burned is greater than the heat of combustion of fumaric acid.

Since it is possible to convert maleic acid into fumaric acid, and since the reverse process also is possible, we must reconsider the assignment of the *cis* structure to the acid which forms the anhydride. The behavior of the anhydride itself settles the question. In pure water (with no catalyst) and at room temperature the anhydride hydrolyzes to maleic acid exclusively, and in pure water at room temperature the free acids do not undergo the rearrangement. We are convinced, therefore, that maleic acid has the *cis* structure.

---

*The resistance to rotation about the single bond in ethane is only 3000 cal; and while this is detectable by physical measurement of heat capacities, it is not enough to prevent a methyl group from spinning with respect to the rest of the molecule. For rotation to occur about a double bond approximately 40,000 cal of energy are needed. A double bond hinders rotation but does not prevent it.

EXERCISES

1. Write from memory the names and formulas of the first six dicarboxylic acids of the normal series.

2. How would you prepare the following compounds?

a. Malonic acid from chloroacetic acid

b. Succinic acid from ethylene bromide

c. Malic acid from fumaric acid

d. Tartaric acid from fumaric acid. (See page 221 for the structure of tartaric acid)

3. What is the structural formula of ethyl malonate? How does it react with metallic sodium and with sodium ethoxide? Are these reactions given by esters of acetic acid and of succinic acid?

4. Outline the use of sodiomalonic ester in the preparation of isobutylacetic acid.

5. What is the structural difference between maleic and fumaric acids? How may one determine which formula belongs to maleic acid?

6. Which of the dicarboxylic acids referred to in Exercise 1 yield cyclic anhydrides? Which lose CO_2 at or below 150°?

7. Write the formula of adipic acid and of hexamethylene diamine (1, 6-diaminohexane). Show how, through amide formation, these substances form linear molecules of high molecular weight.

PROBLEMS

1. What evidence is there that a double bond restricts rotation of one part of a molecule with respect to the remainder of the molecule?

2. Show how acetic acid may be used as a source of each of the following compounds. Assume the availability of any desired reagents.

a. $H_2C(COOC_2H_5)_2$ *c.* $(CH_3)_2CH—CH_2—COOH$

b. $(C_2H_5)_2CHCOOH$ *d.* $(CH_3)(C_2H_5)CH—COOH$

3. Write an equation for each step in the synthesis of a mixture of maleic and fumaric acids from ethyl alcohol. A possible course is as follows: ethanol, ethylene, ethylene dibromide, ethylene dicyanide, succinic acid, monobromosuccinic acid, fumaric and maleic acids.

4. Explain why resins and plastics are made from substances containing two or more functional groups. Illustrate your answer by outlining the synthesis of Nylon from phenol.

5. Oleic acid, upon oxidation, breaks into two acids, the point of rupture being the double bond. The new products are azelaic acid and *n*-nonylic acid. Write the full structure of oleic acid, to show the position of its double bond, and state the reason for placing the double bond in the specified position.

18 · ALIPHATIC AMINES

The amines are derivatives of ammonia, just as alcohols and ethers are derivatives of water. They are classified according to the number of hydrogen atoms of ammonia which have been substituted by alkyl groups. Thus a primary amine, RNH_2, is a monosubstituted ammonia, and the NH_2 group is called the *amino* group. A secondary amine, R_2NH, is a disubstituted ammonia. A tertiary amine, R_3N, is a trisubstituted ammonia; its nitrogen atom no longer holds a proton.

Physical properties of amines. The simplest member of this class of compounds is methyl amine, CH_3NH_2. It is a gas under ordinary conditions, its boiling point being $-6.5°$. Its odor resembles the odor of ammonia. The salt which it forms with hydrochloric acid is a white solid, soluble in alcohol and in water. Dimethyl amine, $(CH_3)_2NH$, also is a very low-boiling liquid of similar properties. Trimethyl amine, $(CH_3)_3N$, boils at $3.5°$, and its vapor at low concentrations has the odor of decayed fish; in fact, it is a product of the putrefaction of fish meal.

The amines of intermediate molecular weights are liquids. Their solubilities in water decrease with increasing molecular weight. A branched-chain amine has a lower boiling point than an isomeric normal compound. The liquid and gaseous amines are very soluble in alcohol and in ether. The solid amines become increasingly like paraffin waxes in properties as the molecular weights increase.

BOILING POINTS OF A FEW AMINES			
NAME	MONO-	DI-	TRI-
Methylamine	$-6.5°$	$7.4°$	$3.5°$
Ethylamine	$16.6°$	$56°$	$89.5°$
Normal propylamine	$48.7°$	$110.7°$	$156°$
Isopropylamine	$34°$	$84°$	—
Normal butylamine	$78°$	$161°$	$214°$
Isobutylamine	$68°$	$138.8°$	$191.5°$
Secondary butylamine	$63°$	$132°$	—
Tertiary butylamine	$43.8°$	—	—
Normal amylamine	$104°$	—	—
Isoamylamine	$95°$	$190°$	$237°$

Nomenclature of amines. In naming the primary amines the prefix *mono-* is generally omitted. If the substituents in a secondary or tertiary amine are identical, the prefix *di-* or *tri-* is used. Thus we have ethylamine, $C_2H_5NH_2$; diethylamine, $(C_2H_5)_2NH$; triethylamine, $(C_2H_5)_3N$. If different alkyl groups are present in the same molecule, each group is designated by name; for example,

$$CH_3 \diagdown \atop C_2H_5 \diagup N-H \qquad\qquad CH_3 \diagdown \atop CH_3 \diagup N-C_2H_5$$

Methylethylamine   Dimethylethylamine

In applying the Geneva nomenclature the amino, or NH_2, group is considered a substituent in a hydrocarbon chain. The compound $CH_3-CH_2-CH-NH_2$ would be named 2-aminobutane. It is com-
$|$
CH_3
monly called secondary butylamine. It is a primary amine. The term *secondary* used in the common name applies to the butyl radical. A secondary amine, such as ethylisopropylamine,

$$CH_3 \diagdown \atop CH_3 \diagup CH-N \diagup^{H} \diagdown_{CH_2-CH_3},$$

is named, according to the Geneva plan, 2-(ethylamino) propane. The choice of the Geneva system or the nomenclature based upon ammonia substitution depends upon which name more readily suggests the molecular structure.

Ammonia and the amines as bases. When ammonia dissolves in water, two things occur, namely, hydration and ionization. Ammonia becomes hydrated (combined with water) through the establishment of a hydrogen bond. A hydrogen bond is formed through the mutual attraction of a proton and two other atoms. This may be written to show the role of the valence electrons of ammonia and water, as follows:

$$H:\overset{H}{\underset{H}{N}}: + H:\overset{..}{\underset{..}{O}}:H \rightleftarrows H:\overset{H}{\underset{H}{N}}:H:\overset{..}{\underset{..}{O}}:H \rightleftarrows H:\overset{H}{\underset{H}{N}}:H^+ + :\overset{..}{\underset{..}{O}}:H^-$$

The hydrated ammonia, called ammonium hydroxide, ionizes to a slight extent. Ammonia is correspondingly a weak base; it removes hydrogen ions from water to a small degree and forms hydroxide ions. The ratio of hydrated to unhydrated ammonia in a solution is not known.

Ammonia takes a hydrogen ion from an acid to form a salt:

$$NH_3 + HCl \longrightarrow NH_4^+ + Cl^-$$

Aqueous ammonia may form ammonium chloride in either of two ways: (a) the one given above, in which hydrogen ion from the acid adds to a molecule of ammonia, or (b) through reaction of the acid with ammonium hydroxide:

$$NH_4OH + HCl \longrightarrow NH_4^+ + Cl^- + H_2O$$

When dry ammonia and dry hydrogen chloride are brought together, with dry ether as a solvent, ammonium chloride precipitates. Water apparently is not required for interaction of ammonia with an acid.

The electronic structure of an amine shows four electron pairs about the nitrogen atom, one pair being unshared as in the case of ammonia. This unshared electron pair has a strong tendency to acquire and hold a proton. A salt is formed by addition of an acid to an amine, and the formula of the salt may be written in either of two forms:

$$C_2H_5NH_2 + HCl \longrightarrow \begin{cases} C_2H_5NH_3^+ + Cl^- & (1) \\ \text{or } C_2H_5NH_2 \cdot HCl & (2) \end{cases}$$

The salt is actually ionized, but it is often convenient to use the alternative formula (2). The first is analogous to the formula $NH_4^+ + Cl^-$ for ammonium chloride, and the second corresponds to the formula $NH_3 \cdot HCl$. We may write these formulas also as $C_2H_5NH_3Cl$ and NH_4Cl.

The behavior of an amine in water is represented by the equation

$$RNH_2 + H_2O \rightleftarrows RNH_3^+ + OH^-,$$

and the dissociation constant, K_b, is defined by the equation

$$K_b = \frac{(RNH_3^+)(OH^-)}{(RNH_2)}$$

The quantities in parentheses are concentrations of the respective substances in moles per liter of solution. To evaluate K_b, the concentration of the hydroxide ion is measured with the aid of colored indicators or by other means, and the total base present is determined by titration with a standard acid solution. The constants for a few amines are given in the following table:

DISSOCIATION CONSTANTS OF AMINES			
NAME	FORMULA	K_b	MOLES OF OH– PER LITER IN A 0.1 M SOLUTION
Ammonia	NH_3	1.9×10^{-5}	1.4×10^{-3}
Methylamine	CH_3NH_2	5×10^{-4}	6.9×10^{-3}
Dimethylamine	$(CH_3)_2NH$	7.4×10^{-4}	8.6×10^{-3}
Trimethylamine	$(CH_3)_3N$	7.4×10^{-5}	2.7×10^{-3}
Ethylamine	$C_2H_5NH_2$	5.6×10^{-4}	7.2×10^{-3}
Diethylamine	$(C_2H_5)_2NH$	1.3×10^{-3}	1.1×10^{-2}
Triethylamine	$(C_2H_5)_3N$	6.4×10^{-4}	8×10^{-3}

In water solution the amines are somewhat stronger bases than ammonia, and the secondary bases are stronger than either the primary or the tertiary compounds.

Preparation of Amines

1. **From alkyl halides.** Hofmann prepared a mixture of primary, secondary, and tertiary amines by heating an alkyl halide, such as ethyl iodide, with ammonia in alcohol solution. Because of the volatility of the ammonia the heating was done in a sealed tube. The formation of the primary amine salt may be represented as follows:

$$C_2H_5I + NH_3 \longrightarrow C_2H_5NH_3I \text{ (or } C_2H_5NH_2 \cdot HI) \qquad (1)$$

The ethylammonium iodide reacts with the excess of ammonia present, and an equilibrium is established between ethylammonium ions, ethylamine, ammonia, and ammonium ions:

$$C_2H_5NH_3I + NH_3 \rightleftarrows C_2H_5NH_2 + NH_4^+ + I^- \qquad (2)$$

The ethylamine released, as indicated by equation (2), competes with ammonia in reacting with the remaining alkyl halide molecules to form a secondary amine salt, in this case diethylammonium iodide:

$$C_2H_5I + C_2H_5NH_2 \longrightarrow (C_2H_5)_2NH_2I \qquad (3)$$

This salt, in turn, is partly converted to the free base by ammonia:

$$(C_2H_5)_2NH_2I + NH_3 \rightleftarrows (C_2H_5)_2NH + NH_4I \qquad (4)$$

In the same way some of the diethylamine reacts to form triethyl-amine:

$$C_2H_5I + (C_2H_5)_2NH \longrightarrow (C_2H_5)_3NHI \tag{5}$$

$$(C_2H_5)_3NHI + NH_3 \rightleftarrows (C_2H_5)_3N + NH_4^+ + I^- \tag{6}$$

The tertiary amine may also combine with the alkyl halide. If it does, the product formed is a quaternary ammonium salt:

$$C_2H_5I + (C_2H_5)_3N \longrightarrow (C_2H_5)_4NI \tag{7}$$

When all the alkyl halide has reacted, there is present a mixture of salts. The amines are obtained from the salts by adding aqueous alkali equivalent to the iodide ion present and distilling the mixture.

$$\left.\begin{matrix} NH_4I \\ RNH_3I \\ R_2NH_2I \\ R_3NHI \end{matrix}\right\} + NaOH \longrightarrow \left\{\begin{matrix} NH_3 \\ RNH_2 \\ R_2NH \\ R_3N \end{matrix}\right. + NaI + H_2O$$

The quantity of quaternary salt present is usually negligible if an excess of ammonia is used.

The Hofmann method therefore normally leads to the production of a mixture of primary, secondary, and tertiary amines. The method would be useless if it were not possible to separate the components of the mixture. The separation is usually accomplished by fractional distillation, but chemical methods are available (see page 207).

2. **Hydrolysis of isocyanates.** Isocyanates are hydrolyzed in alkaline solution to primary amines. The isocyanates are made from potassium cyanate and alkyl halides, or from acid amides through the Hofmann rearrangement, as shown on page 204. The hydrolysis of an isocyanate is represented by the following equation:

$$RNCO + 2\,OH^- \longrightarrow RNH_2 + CO_3^{--}$$

3. **Reduction of nitriles.** Primary amines may be made by reducing alkyl cyanides. The required cyanide (nitrile) is obtained through the action of potassium cyanide on an alkyl halide (p. 133) or from an acid amide by dehydration with P_2O_5 (p. 184). The reduction of the nitrile is accomplished through catalytic hydrogenation:

$$RCN + 2\,H_2 \xrightarrow{Pt} RCH_2NH_2$$

4. Gabriel's synthesis. A method based upon the use of potassium phthalimide, $C_6H_4(CO)_2NK$, as first outlined by Gabriel, leads to primary amines. It is really a variation of Hofmann's method, in which two of the three hydrogen atoms of ammonia are temporarily replaced by the phthalic acid residue. The third position is alkylated by treatment with an alkyl halide, and the protecting groups are then removed by hydrolysis. The reactions are as follows:

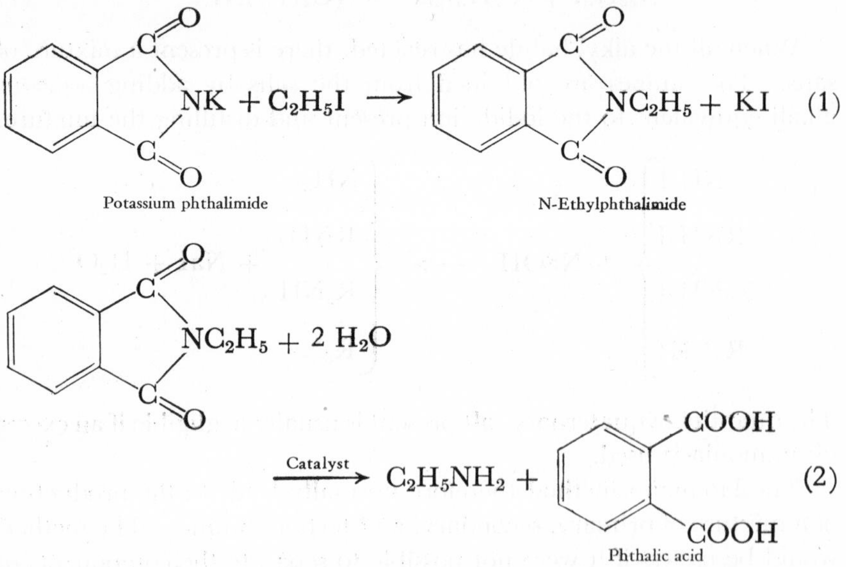

Potassium phthalimide   N-Ethylphthalimide

$$\text{NK} + C_2H_5I \longrightarrow \text{NC}_2H_5 + KI \quad (1)$$

$$\text{NC}_2H_5 + 2\ H_2O \xrightarrow{\ \text{Catalyst}\ } C_2H_5NH_2 + \begin{matrix}\text{COOH}\\\text{COOH}\end{matrix} \quad (2)$$

Phthalic acid

If an acid is used to catalyze reaction (2), a salt of the amine is formed; if a base is used to catalyze the hydrolysis, a salt of phthalic acid is produced.

5. The Hofmann rearrangement. The most general method of preparing primary amines depends upon the Hofmann rearrangement of acid amides. Unlike some of the preceding methods, it is applicable to tertiary and secondary, as well as to primary, alkyl radicals. An acid amide is converted into an isocyanate by treatment with a warm alkaline solution of bromine. Since isocyanates are hydrolyzed rapidly by aqueous alkali, this affords a means of converting amides into amines:

$$\underset{\text{Amide}}{RCONH_2} + Br_2 + 2\ KOH \longrightarrow \underset{\text{Isocyanate}}{RNCO} + 2\ KBr + 2\ H_2O$$

$$\underset{\text{Isocyanate}}{RNCO} + 2\ KOH \longrightarrow \underset{\text{Amine}}{RNH_2} + K_2CO_3$$

In the amide the radical, R, is attached to carbon. In the iso-cyanate the same radical is attached to nitrogen. Such a shift of a radical from one position to another within a molecule is called a re-arrangement. With acetamide as an example the course of the re-arrangement may be outlined as follows:

The first step is the formation of a bromoamide:

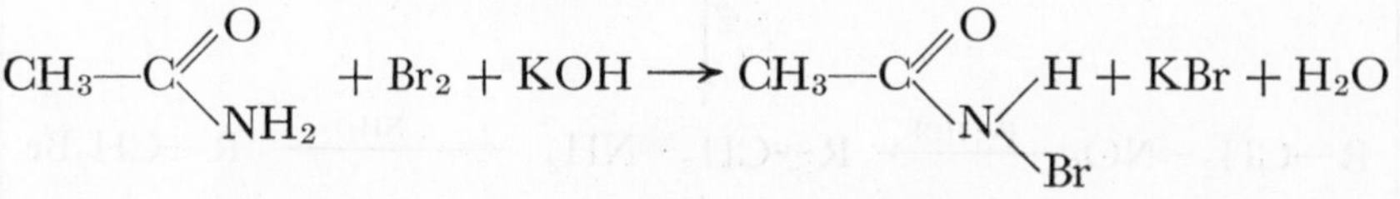

$$CH_3-C\begin{smallmatrix}O\\NH_2\end{smallmatrix} + Br_2 + KOH \longrightarrow CH_3-C\begin{smallmatrix}O\\N\end{smallmatrix}\begin{smallmatrix}H\\Br\end{smallmatrix} + KBr + H_2O$$

The bromoamide (in this case N-bromoacetamide) is a stable com-pound and can be isolated. It is not ordinarily isolated; for as a rule the desired product is an amine, and no special care is used to stop the reaction at this stage.

The second stage involves the rearrangement

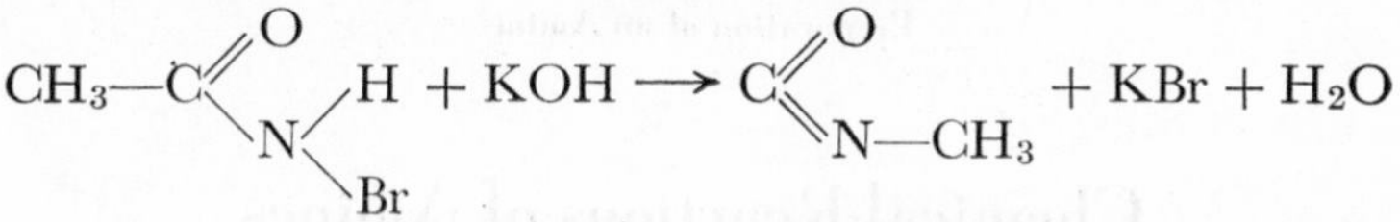

$$CH_3-C\begin{smallmatrix}O\\N\\Br\end{smallmatrix}H + KOH \longrightarrow C\begin{smallmatrix}O\\N-CH_3\end{smallmatrix} + KBr + H_2O$$

N-Bromoacetamide   Methyl isocyanate

Finally the isocyanate is hydrolyzed to an amine:

$$CH_3-N{=}C{=}O + 2\ KOH \longrightarrow CH_3-NH_2 + K_2CO_3$$

Methyl isocyanate   Methyl amine

The Hofmann rearrangement furnishes a method for decarboxyla-tion, or removal of a carboxylic carbon atom. The over-all reaction may be written as follows:

$$R-CONH_2 + Br_2 + 4\ NaOH$$
$$\longrightarrow RNH_2 + Na_2CO_3 + 2\ NaBr + 2\ H_2O$$

6. **The reduction of nitro compounds.** Primary amines can be made from nitro compounds by reduction. Various reducing agents are used, of which metallic iron in contact with an aqueous solution of an acid is one of the best:

$$R-NO_2 + 2\ Fe + 7\ HCl \longrightarrow RNH_2 \cdot HCl + 2\ FeCl_3 + 2\ H_2O$$

An aliphatic nitro compound may be prepared from an alkyl halide and sodium nitrite. Some of the lower members are available through a high-temperature reaction between nitric acid vapor and the vapor of a hydrocarbon. Nitropropane and nitrobutane may be made in this way. By a combination of these methods some of the lower amines are manufactured economically.

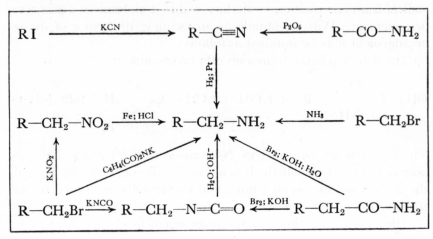

Preparation of an Amine

Chemical Reactions of Amines

1. **Salt formation.** The capacity of amines to neutralize acids has been discussed (p. 201). The salts of primary, secondary, and tertiary amines are salts of weak bases, and accordingly they are hydrolyzed to a slight extent in water:

$$R_3NHCl + H_2O \rightleftarrows R_3NHOH + HCl$$

The quaternary salts, however, are not hydrolyzed, nor do they react with cold, dilute sodium hydroxide. They are apparently salts of strong bases.

$$\underbrace{\begin{array}{ccc} H & H & R \\ | & | & | \\ R-N-HOH & R-N-HOH & R-N-HOH \\ | & | & | \\ H & R & R \end{array}}_{\text{Weakly basic amine hydrates}} \quad \underbrace{\begin{array}{c} R \\ |+ \\ R-N-R \quad OH^- \\ | \\ R \end{array}}_{\text{Strong base}}$$

2. **Alkylation.** Amines form addition products with alkyl halides:

$$RNH_2 + RX \longrightarrow R_2NH_2X$$
$$R_2NH + RX \longrightarrow R_3NHX$$
$$R_3N + RX \longrightarrow R_4NX$$

The product in each case is an ionized salt. If in the positive ion of the salt there is a hydrogen atom attached to the nitrogen atom, a molecule of halogen acid can be removed by treatment with a base:

$$R_2NH_2X + NaOH \longrightarrow R_2NH + NaX + H_2O$$

In this way secondary amines are made from primary amines, and tertiary amines are made from secondary amines. (See the Hofmann reaction, p. 202.)

3. Acylation. Primary and secondary amines react with acid chlorides and form amides. The reaction is carried out usually in the presence of an inorganic base, such as sodium carbonate or sodium hydroxide, which takes up the hydrogen chloride formed in the reaction:

$$RNH_2 + R'{-}COCl + NaOH \longrightarrow R'{-}CONHR + NaCl + H_2O$$
$$R_2NH + R'{-}COCl + NaOH \longrightarrow R'{-}CONR_2 + NaCl + H_2O$$

Tertiary amines do not react with acid chlorides; they do not have a hydrogen atom which is replaceable by the acyl group. Acid anhydrides, with primary and secondary amines, also form amides:

$$RNH_2 + (CH_3CO)_2O \longrightarrow CH_3CONHR + CH_3CO_2H$$

4. Reactions with nitrous acid. Nitrous acid, or a mixture of sodium nitrite and hydrochloric acid, acts upon a primary amine with the release of nitrogen gas. Secondary amines with nitrous acid yield nitrosoamines. Tertiary amines form salts only.

$$\underset{\substack{\text{Primary} \\ \text{amine}}}{RNH_2} + HNO_2 \longrightarrow \underset{\text{Alcohol}}{ROH} + N_2 + H_2O$$

$$\underset{\substack{\text{Secondary} \\ \text{amine}}}{R_2NH} + HNO_2 \longrightarrow \underset{\text{Nitrosoamine}}{R_2N{-}NO} + H_2O$$

Salts of the primary and secondary amines react with nitrous acid in a similar way:

$$CH_3NH_2 \cdot HCl + HNO_2 \longrightarrow CH_3OH + N_2 + H_2O + HCl$$

5. The Hinsberg reaction. The Hinsberg separation of primary, secondary, and tertiary amines involves a special case of acid amide formation. Hinsberg observed that when a mixture of amines is treated with benzenesulfonyl chloride, $C_6H_5SO_2Cl$, the product formed with the primary amine is soluble in aqueous alkali, while that formed with the secondary amine is insoluble, and the tertiary amine fails to react. Benzenesulfonyl chloride is a colorless, oily liquid. Chlorides made from other aromatic sulfonic acids, such as toluenesulfonic acid, $CH_3C_6H_4SO_3H$, serve as well.

$$C_6H_5SO_2Cl + \begin{cases} RNH_2 \xrightarrow{\text{OH}^-} \underset{\text{Soluble in alkali}}{C_6H_5SO_2NHR} + Cl^- + H_2O & (1) \\[2em] R_2NH \xrightarrow{\text{OH}^-} \underset{\text{Insoluble in alkali}}{C_6H_5SO_2NR_2} + Cl^- + H_2O & (2) \\[2em] R_3N \longrightarrow \text{No reaction} & (3) \end{cases}$$

The amides of benzenesulfonic acid, $C_6H_5SO_3H$, are sufficiently acidic to form salts in dilute alkali if there is at least one hydrogen atom attached to the nitrogen atom. Hence the alkaline reaction mixture consists of a solution of the primary amine product and a suspension of the secondary amine product. Any tertiary amine present may be removed by distillation with steam. The suspension is then filtered, and the alkaline filtrate is acidified to precipitate the primary sulfonamide. The sulfonamides are then separately hydrolyzed to obtain the original amines.

$$C_6H_5SO_2NHR + H^+ + H_2O \longrightarrow C_6H_5SO_3H + RNH_3^+$$
$$C_6H_5SO_2NR_2 + H^+ + H_2O \longrightarrow C_6H_5SO_3H + R_2NH_2^+$$

After the amides have been hydrolyzed, the free amines are obtained by rendering the solutions alkaline and distilling the amines with steam or extracting them with ether.

EXERCISES

1. Write structural formulas for the following compounds and state in each case whether the compound is a primary, secondary, or tertiary amine, or a quaternary ammonium compound:

a. Isopropylamine   d. Methylethylamine
b. Ter-butylamine   e. Tetramethylammonium chloride
c. Dimethyl-n-propylamine   f. Isoamyl amine

2. Write equations for the reactions of ammonia and of methylamine with each of the following reagents: (a) water, (b) hydrochloric acid, (c) sulfuric acid, (d) acetic acid.

3. Write the reactions which would take place if mixtures of ethylamine, diethylamine, and triethylamine were treated with (a) propionyl chloride, (b) benzenesulfonyl chloride, (c) nitrous acid.

4. Represent by balanced equations each of the following processes:

a. Gabriel's synthesis of a primary amine
b. The alkylation of ammonia by methyl iodide
c. The catalytic reduction of a nitrile to a primary amine
d. The reduction of a nitro compound by iron and hydrochloric acid
e. The alkylation of trimethylamine by ethyl iodide

SUMMARY OF METHODS FOR MAKING AMINES

A. **Primary amines**
  1. Hofmann rearrangement of amides
  2. Gabriel phthalimide synthesis
  3. Reduction of nitriles
  4. Reduction of nitro compounds
  5. Dehydration and reduction of amides
  6. Hofmann synthesis of mixed amines from alkyl halides

B. **Secondary amines**
  1. Hofmann alkylation of ammonia followed by the Hinsberg separation
  2. Alkylation of primary amines and subsequent separation of the mixed products

C. **Tertiary amines**
  1. Alkylation of secondary amines
  2. Alkylation of ammonia and subsequent application of the Hinsberg reaction

---

SUMMARY OF THE REACTIONS OF AMINES

A. **Salt formation**

B. **Alkylation by alkyl halides**

C. **Acylation by acid chlorides and acid anhydrides**
  1. Of primary and secondary amines (not of tertiary amines)
  2. Hinsberg identification and separation of amines through the use of benzenesulfonyl chloride

D. **Nitrous acid**
  1. Destruction of primary amine with evolution of N_2
  2. Nitrosoamine formation with secondary amines
  3. No reaction with tertiary amines

PROBLEMS

1. Show by equations the preparation of isoamylamine,

$$(CH_3)_2CH—CH_2—CH_2—NH_2,$$

by each of the following methods:

        a. Reduction of a nitrile
        b. Reduction of a nitro compound
        c. The Hofmann rearrangement of an amide
        d. Gabriel's phthalimide reaction

2. What volume of nitrogen at 18° and 740 mm may be obtained from nitrous acid and 1.4 g of amylamine hydrochloride?

3. How could you take advantage of differences in solubilities in water, acids, and bases to separate the following?

        a. A higher amine from an ether
        b. An amide from an amine
        c. An acid from a nitrile
        d. The benzenesulfonamides and tertiary amine derived from a mixture of primary, secondary, and tertiary amines

4. How may the following syntheses be accomplished? Supply the reagents and specify the necessary conditions.

a. $C_3H_7COOH \longrightarrow C_3H_7OH$ *d.* $C_3H_7COOH \longrightarrow C_3H_7CONHCH_3$
b. $C_4H_9OH \longrightarrow C_4H_9CH_2NH_2$ *e.* $CH_3COOH \longrightarrow H_2NCH_2COOH$
c. $C_2H_5COOH \longrightarrow C_2H_5NH_2$ *f.* $C_2H_5NH_2 \longrightarrow C_2H_5OH$

5. What volume of 0.1 N hydrochloric acid would be required to neutralize 15 grams of diethylamine?

19 · HYDROXY ACIDS AND STEREOISOMERISM

The hydroxy acids display some of the properties of alcohols as well as the properties of acids; they have the two functional groups —OH and —COOH. In some respects they are quite unlike the fatty acids. The hydroxyl group has the effect of making these acids less volatile and more soluble in water than corresponding members of the fatty series. As a result the hydroxy acids are not easily distilled, they do not precipitate when aqueous solutions of their salts are acidified, and they are not extracted from water by ether. In other words, it is difficult to isolate and purify them.

Many hydroxy acids, or salts of these acids, are found in living tissues of plants and animals. Malic acid in green apples, citric

TYPES OF HYDROXY ACIDS

Acid	Formula	Occurrence
α-Hydroxy acids		
Glycolic	$CH_2OH-COOH$	Unripe grapes and tomatoes
Lactic	$CH_3-CHOH-COOH$	Sour milk, wine, cheese
Malic	$\begin{array}{l}CHOH-COOH\\ \mid\\ CH_2-COOH\end{array}$	Unripe fruits, especially green apples and gooseberries
Citric	$\begin{array}{l}CH_2-COOH\\ \mid\quad OH\\ C\\ \mid\quad COOH\\ CH_2-COOH\end{array}$	Lemons, oranges, grapefruit
Tartaric	$\begin{array}{l}CHOH-COOH\\ \mid\\ CHOH-COOH\end{array}$	Grapes
β-Hydroxy acids		
Hydroxypropionic	CH_2OH-CH_2-COOH	Synthetic
Hydroxybutyric	$CH_3-CHOH-CH_2-COOH$	Urine of diabetics
γ-Hydroxy acids		
Hydroxybutyric	$CH_2OH-CH_2-CH_2-COOH$	Synthetic
Polyhydroxy acids		
Gluconic	$CH_2OH-(CHOH)_4-COOH$	Oxidation product of glucose

acid in lemons, and β-hydroxybutyric acid in the urine of persons suffering with diabetes are examples of the production of hydroxy acids in life processes.

The types of hydroxy acids which are commonly encountered are illustrated in the table on page 211. It will be observed that the position of the hydroxyl group varies with respect to the carboxyl group, and that there may be more than one alcohol group or more than one carboxyl group in a single molecule.

Lactic acid, or α-hydroxypropionic acid, is obtained from sour milk or from the fermented juice of sugar beets. It appears in muscle tissue during exercise, as one of the oxidation products of glycogen. Lactic acid is available commercially in the form of a sirupy liquid consisting of 85 per cent acid and 15 per cent water. The pure acid (obtained from an aqueous solution through vacuum distillation) boils at 83° under 1 mm pressure.

The lactic acid found in muscles is dextrorotatory (see page 216), while that produced in most fermentation processes is racemic, a mixture in equal amounts of the dextro and levo forms.

Lactic acid is made commercially by fermentation of glucose. An enzyme produced in the growth of certain bacteria induces the reaction. (A different enzyme converts glucose into alcohol.) Lactic fermentation is represented by the following equation:

$$\underset{\text{Glucose}}{C_6H_{12}O_6} \xrightarrow{\text{Enzyme}} 2\ \underset{\text{Lactic acid}}{CH_3\text{---}CHOH\text{---}COOH}$$

Monobasic Hydroxy Acids

Synthesis of α-hydroxy acids. It is not possible to replace a hydrogen atom in a fatty acid directly by a hydroxyl group, but the exchange can be accomplished indirectly. The following methods are commonly employed:

1. When a saturated acid is treated with chlorine gas, in the presence of phosphorus as a catalyst, chlorination occurs in the α-position. The α-chloro-acid produced in this way is hydrolyzed by heating it with an aqueous solution of potassium hydroxide:

$$R\text{---}CH_2\text{---}COOH + Cl_2 \xrightarrow{\text{(P)}} R\text{---}CHCl\text{---}COOH + HCl \quad (1)$$

$$R\text{---}CHCl\text{---}COOH + KOH \xrightarrow{H_2O} R\text{---}CHOH\text{---}COOH + KCl \quad (2)$$

2. Cyanohydrins (formed from aldehydes and ketones with hydrocyanic acid) hydrolyze in strong acid solutions and produce α-hydroxy acids:

$$R—CH\!\!\begin{array}{c}{}^{OH}\\{}_{CN}\end{array} + 2\,H_2O + HCl \longrightarrow R—CH\!\!\begin{array}{c}{}^{OH}\\{}_{COOH}\end{array} + NH_4Cl$$

Synthesis of β-hydroxy acids. The β-hydroxy acids may be made from β-halogen-substituted acids by hydrolysis, or from unsaturated hydrocarbons by treatment, successively, with hypochlorous acid, potassium cyanide, and a hot solution of a strong acid or base.

1. Hydrolysis of a salt of a β-halogen acid proceeds as follows:

$$R—CHCl—CH_2—COO^- + KOH \longrightarrow$$
$$R—CHOH—CH_2—COO^- + KCl$$

2. The cyanide synthesis of a β-hydroxy acid is accomplished by adding hypochlorous acid to an unsaturated hydrocarbon, then replacing the halogen with the cyanide group, and finally hydrolyzing the cyanide:

$$R—CH\!=\!CH_2 + HOCl \longrightarrow R—CHOH—CH_2Cl \qquad (1)$$
$$R—CHOH—CH_2Cl + KCN \longrightarrow \qquad\qquad (2)$$
$$R—CHOH—CH_2—CN + KCl$$
$$R—CHOH—CH_2—CN + H_2O \xrightarrow{OH^-}$$
$$R—CHOH—CH_2—COO^- + NH_3 \quad (3)$$

The synthesis of acids in which the hydroxyl group is farther away from the carboxyl group can be accomplished, but no general procedure is available. Special devices are used to obtain products of desired structures.

Reactions of hydroxy acids. The α-hydroxy acids are stronger acids than the fatty acids, but they are nevertheless to be classed as weak acids. They are about 5 per cent ionized in 0.1 N solution. The β-hydroxy acids are only slightly stronger than the fatty acids. The effect of the hydroxyl group in increasing the acidity of the carboxyl group is appreciable only when the hydroxyl is in the α-position.

The product formed when a hydroxy acid is heated is an ester. Water is lost by interaction between the two functional groups, —OH and —COOH, either *intra*molecularly or *inter*molecularly. The course of the reaction (that is, whether it takes place within a single molecule or between two different molecules) is determined by the position of the hydroxyl group with respect to the carboxyl group. When an α-hydroxy acid is heated to the temperature required for elimination of water, the alcoholic hydroxyl group of one molecule reacts with the carboxyl group of another molecule of the acid, and a cyclic ester, called a lactide, is formed:

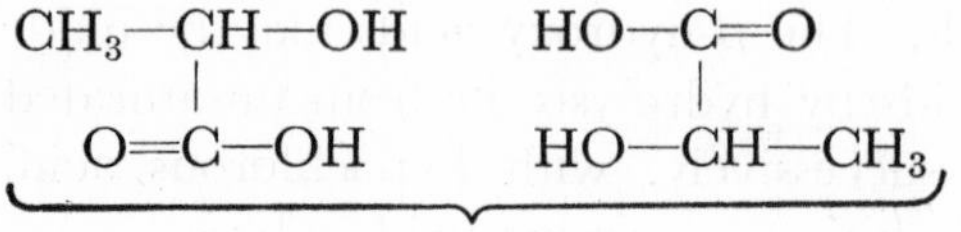

$$CH_3-CH-OH \qquad HO-C{=}O$$
$$\qquad | \qquad\qquad\qquad |$$
$$\quad O{=}C-OH \qquad HO-CH-CH_3$$

I

α-Hydroxypropionic acid
(lactic acid) $\xrightarrow{-H_2O}$ $CH_3-CH{-}{-}{-}O{-}{-}{-}C{=}O$
$\qquad\qquad\qquad\qquad\qquad | \qquad\qquad\qquad |$
$\qquad\qquad\qquad\qquad O{=}C-OH \quad HO-CH-CH_3$

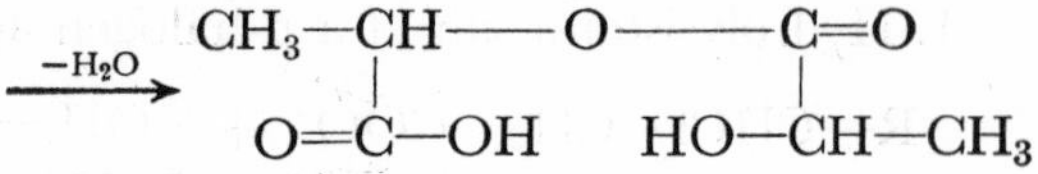

II

Lactyllactic acid

$$CH_3-CH{-}{-}{-}O{-}{-}{-}C{=}O \quad \xrightarrow{-H_2O} \quad CH_3-CH-O-C{=}O$$
$$\qquad | \qquad\qquad\qquad | \qquad\qquad\qquad\qquad\qquad | \qquad\qquad |$$
$$\quad O{=}C-OH \quad HO-CH-CH_3 \qquad\qquad O{=}C{-}{-}{-}O-CH-CH_3$$

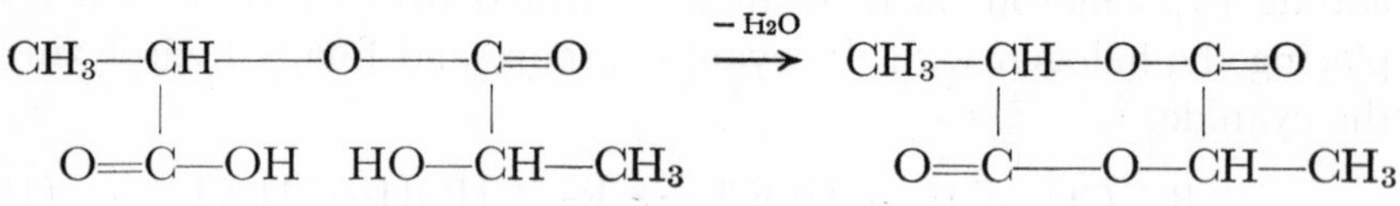

II   **III**

Lactide (a cyclic ester)

Instead of closing the ring by removal of water, as indicated in the second step above, a third molecule of the acid may react with the free carboxyl group in formula II to form a linear ester containing three acid units; and the process may continue until resinous products of high molecular weights have been produced. Mixed products (cyclic and linear esters) usually are obtained in a process of this kind.

In the presence of hot, dilute sulfuric acid the α-hydroxy acids yield formic acid and an aldehyde or a ketone:

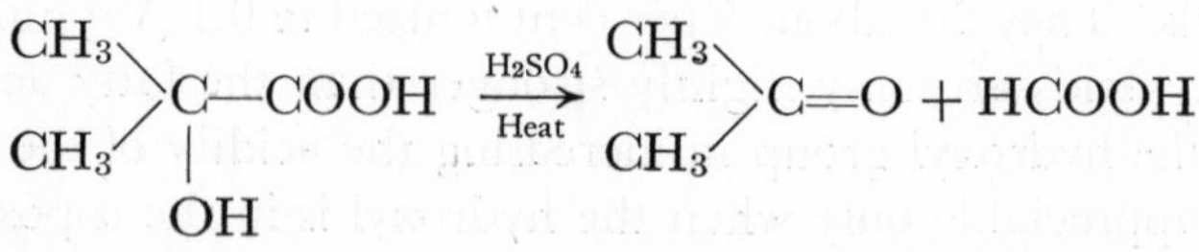

$$\begin{array}{c} CH_3 \\ \diagdown \\ \diagup \\ CH_3 \end{array}\!\!\!C{-}COOH \xrightarrow[\text{Heat}]{H_2SO_4} \begin{array}{c} CH_3 \\ \diagdown \\ \diagup \\ CH_3 \end{array}\!\!\!C{=}O + HCOOH$$
$$\qquad\qquad |$$
$$\qquad\qquad OH$$

Oxidizing agents such as permanganic acid and lead tetraacetate degrade these acids in much the same way, except that carbonic acid instead of formic acid is produced. The interest in the process lies in the fact that we have here a way to split off one carbon atom from an α-hydroxy acid under mild conditions, and identification of the resulting fragments often enables us to establish the structure of the original substance.

When β-hydroxy acids are heated, unsaturated acids are formed:

$$CH_3—CHOH—CH_2—COOH \longrightarrow CH_3—CH=CH—COOH + H_2O$$

β-Hydroxybutyric acid   Crotonic acid

This dehydration is promoted by acid or alkali, but in many cases heat alone is effective. The reaction takes place under milder conditions than does the formation of an alkene from a simple alcohol, because the hydrogen atom involved in forming water is activated by the adjacent carboxyl group. The α-hydroxy acids do not yield unsaturated acids; for ester formation, as indicated above, takes precedence over other possible reactions.

The γ-hydroxy acids and δ-hydroxy acids are characterized by ease and completeness of ring closure. Five-membered rings and six-membered rings form very readily. A cyclic ester produced from a single molecule by ring closure is called a *lactone*. The name distinguishes this type of compound from an open-chain ester derived from two separate molecules.

$$R—\underset{\underset{\displaystyle OH}{|}}{CH}—CH_2—CH_2—COOH \rightleftarrows R—\underset{\underset{\displaystyle \Big\lfloor\!\!\underline{\qquad O \qquad}\!\!\Big\rfloor}{|}}{CH}—CH_2—CH_2—C=O + H_2O$$

A γ-hydroxy acid   A γ-lactone

$$R—\underset{\underset{\displaystyle OH}{|}}{CH}—(CH_2)_3—COOH \rightleftarrows R—\underset{\underset{\displaystyle \Big\lfloor\!\!\underline{\qquad O \qquad}\!\!\Big\rfloor}{|}}{CH}—(CH_2)_3—C=O + H_2O$$

A δ-hydroxy acid   A δ-lactone

Acids in which the hydroxyl group is still further from the carboxyl group tend to yield resins or polymers rather than monomeric lactones, although some lactones with fifteen or more atoms in the ring are known.

Stereoisomerism

Most hydroxy acids exhibit a type of isomerism which is different from the types we have so far considered. Lactic acid will be used as an example. In this acid the α-carbon atom is attached to four *different* atoms or groups. If we represent this carbon atom as a tetrahedron, it becomes obvious that there are two different ways of attaching the four different groups.

$$COOH \qquad COOH \qquad COOH \qquad COOH$$

$$H \longleftarrow OH \quad HO \longleftarrow H \qquad H-C-OH \quad HO-C-H$$

$$CH_3 \qquad CH_3 \qquad CH_3 \qquad CH_3$$

Spatial, or Stereoisomeric, Representation of   Projection Representation of the
the Lactic Acids   Lactic Acids

Each of the two forms is asymmetric and, in molecular structure, each is the mirror image of the other. Because of the latter relationship such isomers are called enantiomorphic isomers; and because they contain the same groups arranged differently in space they are classified with geometric isomers under the general term stereoisomers.

Enantiomorphic isomers occur in pairs. The members of each pair differ from each other in only one physical property—one known as optical activity, which is exhibited only by asymmetric objects. Similarly, in chemical reactions enantiomorphs behave identically unless the other reagent is asymmetric.

Optical activity. By optical activity is meant the capacity of a substance to rotate the plane of transmitted plane-polarized light. It is a measure of the very small difference in the indexes of refraction of the substance for right- and left-handed circularly polarized light. Two enantiomorphs rotate the plane of polarization in opposite directions, but to the same degree; they are frequently referred to as optical isomers.

Plane polarized light is produced by passing a beam of ordinary light (the waves of which are in all possible planes) through a doubly refracting substance such as Iceland spar (a transparent crystal of

Fig. 10. A Nicol Prism

calcite, $CaCO_3$). The transmitted light emerges in two beams, in each of which the waves are in a single plane. A prism of calcite can be so constructed that only one of the plane-polarized beams emerges with the direction of the original beam (a Nicol prism). If, now, a second prism is placed in the emergent beam, the polarized light will pass through or be cut off, according to whether the two prisms have their axes in the same plane or in planes at right angles to each other. The first prism is called a polarizer and is stationary; the second may be rotated, and is called the analyzer. By interposing a solution between the two prisms in an instrument called a polarimeter the effect of the solution upon the plane of polarization may be observed. The position of the analyzer is set, originally, to extinguish the light with nothing but air or distilled water between the two prisms. A tube having glass ends and containing the solution to be examined is then placed between the prisms. If the light still fails to get through, the substance in the tube is said to be optically inactive. If the position of the analyzer has to be changed to cause extinction of the light, the solution is said to be optically active.

| Coaxial; Light Transmitted | Axes Crossed; Opaque | Optically Active Substance Interposed; Analyzer Turned to Opaque Position |

The angle of rotation required for extinction of the light is a measure of the activity. It varies with the amount of substance interposed, the wave length of the light, the temperature, and the solvent used.

One member of a pair of optical isomers rotates the plane of polarized light to the right; the other rotates it to the left and to the same degree. Rotation to the right is called *dextro* rotation; it is designated by the letter *d* or by a plus sign. Rotation to the left, *levo* rotation, is indicated by the letter *l* or by a minus sign. A mixture of dextro and levo isomers in equal amounts is optically inactive; each compensates the action of the other. The separation of such a mixture into its components requires special techniques, because the chemical properties of the isomers are identical. It often happens that in nature only one of the two isomers of an optically active compound is produced; and before life processes can be fully explained, the reason for this and the path by which it is accomplished must be understood.

When an asymmetric molecule is produced by a synthetic process in the laboratory, the *dextro* and *levo* forms appear in equal amounts.

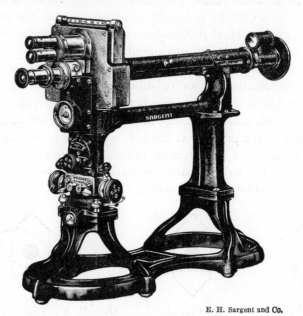

E. H. Sargent and Co.

Fig. 11. A Polarimeter

Such a mixture is said to be *racemic*. The *d* and *l* forms are there; but they compensate each other in their action on plane-polarized light, and the mixture is optically inactive. As an example, let us consider the addition of HCN to acetaldehyde. Through this addition the carbon atom of the aldehyde group becomes asymmetric:

$$CH_3-C=O + HCN$$

$$
\begin{array}{c}
\qquad \qquad H \\
\qquad \qquad | \\
CH_3-C-OH \\
\qquad \qquad | \\
\qquad \qquad CN \\
\\
\qquad \qquad H \\
\qquad \qquad | \\
CH_3-C-CN \\
\qquad \qquad | \\
\qquad \qquad OH
\end{array}
$$

Racemic lactonitrile

In breaking the double bond of the carbonyl group there are equal chances of producing the dextro and the levo forms of the cyanohydrin, and the two forms are produced in equal quantities.

TYPES OF ISOMERISM	
Name	Differences
A. Structural isomerism	
1. Different functional groups	1. All properties different
2. The same functional groups arranged in a different order	2. Chemical properties similar but not identical; physical properties different
B. Stereoisomerism	
1. Geometric, or cis-trans; the same groups held in different positions by a double bond or by a ring	1. Chemical properties similar in part; physical properties different
2. Optical isomerism	2. Isomers occur in pairs; members of each pair different in one optical property

Polybasic Hydroxy Acids

Malic acid. Hydroxysuccinic acid, or malic acid, is especially abundant in unripe apples, gooseberries, and the berries of the mountain ash. It may be extracted from these natural sources, or it may be made by hydrolysis of bromosuccinic acid or by hydration of maleic acid.

$$\begin{array}{ccc}
\underset{\text{Maleic acid}}{\begin{array}{l}\text{CH—COOH}\\ \| \\ \text{CH—COOH}\end{array}} & \xrightarrow[\text{H}_2\text{O}]{\text{H}_2\text{SO}_4} & \underset{\text{Malic acid}}{\begin{array}{l}\text{CHOH—COOH}\\ | \\ \text{CH}_2\text{—COOH}\end{array}} & \underset{\text{H}_2\text{O}}{\overset{\text{Ag}_2\text{O}}{\longleftarrow}} & \underset{\text{Bromosuccinic acid}}{\begin{array}{l}\text{CHBr—COOH}\\ | \\ \text{CH}_2\text{—COOH}\end{array}}
\end{array}$$

Maleic acid is obtained by oxidation of benzene, and bromosuccinic acid may be prepared by direct bromination of succinic acid or by addition of hydrogen bromide to maleic acid.

Malic acid, as obtained from fruits, is levorotatory. Synthetic malic acid is a mixture of dextro and levo forms. Both the synthetic and the naturally occurring acids are reduced by hot hydriodic acid to succinic acid. This proves that they have the same carbon skeleton.

The two possible arrangements in space and corresponding plane projections are as follows:

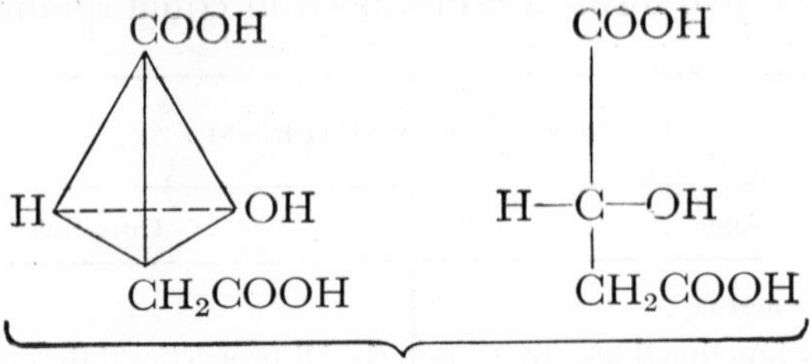

$$
\begin{array}{cc}
\text{COOH} & \text{COOH} \\
\triangle & | \\
H \leftarrow\!-\!-\!\!\to OH & H\!-\!C\!-\!OH \\
\text{CH}_2\text{COOH} & \text{CH}_2\text{COOH}
\end{array}
$$

Dextromalic acid
(*d*-malic acid)

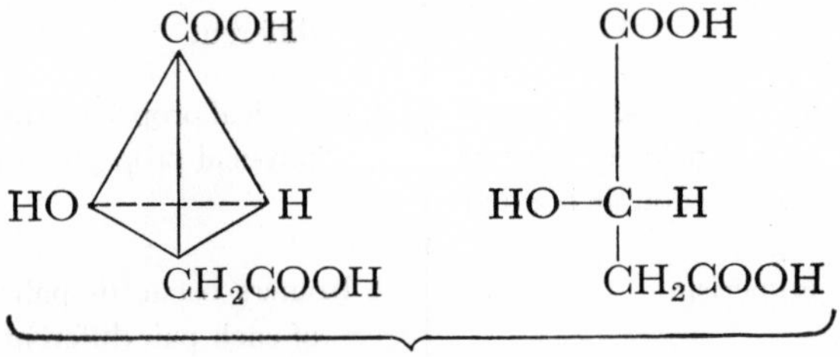

$$
\begin{array}{cc}
\text{COOH} & \text{COOH} \\
\triangle & | \\
HO \leftarrow\!-\!-\!\!\to H & HO\!-\!C\!-\!H \\
\text{CH}_2\text{COOH} & \text{CH}_2\text{COOH}
\end{array}
$$

Levomalic acid
(*l*-malic acid)

One form is arbitrarily chosen as representing the dextro acid. The other configuration represents the levo form. If one views the molecule from the nearest apex of the tetrahedron, he sees the H, COOH, and OH groups on a circle, and in that order the course from one to another in the upper formula is clockwise. The same groups are arranged counterclockwise in the levorotatory molecule.

Tartaric acids. Acid potassium tartrate crystallizes in wine vats in a crude form called argol. Commercially it is known as cream of tartar, and it is used in some baking powders, as the acidic constituent, to liberate carbon dioxide. The salt is dextrorotatory.

Free tartaric acid is very soluble in water and is nonvolatile, so that its preparation involves precipitation of a lead or calcium salt and subsequent removal of the metal with sulfuric acid. Upon evaporation of a solution the acid crystallizes. Actually there are three forms of tartaric acid: one dextrorotatory, another levorotatory, and the third optically inactive. They are called, respectively, dextrotartaric acid, levotartaric acid, and mesotartaric acid. In addition, there is racemic tartaric acid, which is an optically inactive mixture of the dextro and levo forms.

Each of these substances, in anhydrous form, has the molecular weight and composition indicated by the formula $C_4H_6O_6$. Each is a dibasic acid; each reacts with acetic anhydride to give a diacetyl derivative, $C_4H_4O_6(OCCH_3)_2$. Vigorous reduction with hydriodic acid converts each of these acids into succinic acid. Structurally each must therefore be represented by the formula

$$COOH—CHOH—CHOH—COOH$$

Their differences are due to different arrangements in space of the constituent groups.

Structures of the tartaric acids. Our conception of a carbon atom is that of a symmetrical tetrahedron having the capacity to hold an atom or group on each apex. In such a model, asymmetry results when four different atoms or groups are attached to the same carbon atom. When two or more similar groups are held by a carbon atom a plane of symmetry exists in the molecule, and the compound is not optically active.

On the basis of a tetrahedral carbon atom there are three stereo structures possible for tartaric acid. Two of them are optically active, and a mixture of these two compounds, in equal amounts, is racemic tartaric acid. The third compound, mesotartaric acid, is optically inactive and cannot be resolved into active components. It contains the two asymmetric carbon atoms, but the arrangements of the groups around the two asymmetric centers are opposite in configuration. The upper carbon atom in the diagram has the arrangement assigned to the dextro acid; the lower one corresponds to the levo acid. As a result this tartaric acid is *internally* compensated. The racemic acid is inactive, because it is *externally* compensated; it is a mixture.

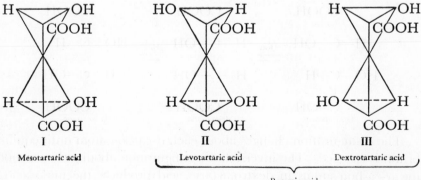

I — Mesotartaric acid

II — Levotartaric acid

III — Dextrotartaric acid

Racemic acid

The plane projections of these models are represented as follows:

$$
\begin{array}{ccc}
\text{COOH} & \text{COOH} & \text{COOH} \\
| & | & | \\
\text{H—C—OH} & \text{HO—C—H} & \text{H—C—OH} \\
| & | & | \\
\text{H—C—OH} & \text{H—C—OH} & \text{HO—C—H} \\
| & | & | \\
\text{COOH} & \text{COOH} & \text{COOH} \\
\text{I} & \text{II} & \text{III} \\
\text{Mesotartaric acid} & \text{Levotartaric acid} & \text{Dextrotartaric acid}
\end{array}
$$

The physical properties of the tartaric acids are given in the table below. In solution the racemic acid is a simple mixture of dextro and levo acids; but the two acids enter into the formation of single crystals, giving rise to a molecular aggregation which has properties different from the properties of the separate components.

THE TARTARIC ACIDS				
	Dextro-tartaric (d-Tartaric)	Levo-tartaric (l-Tartaric)	Racemic Tartaric (dl-Tartaric)	Meso-Tartaric (i-Tartaric)
Solubility in 100 g water at 20°	139	139	20.6	125
Melting point	170°	170°	206°	140°
H_2O of crystallization	None	None	1 H_2O	1 H_2O

Inversion of tartaric acid. When dextrotartaric acid is heated in aqueous solution, it slowly changes into a mixture of racemic and mesotartaric acids. If crystallization occurs before this process is complete, then the three acids, dextro, racemic, and meso, will be obtained.

$$
\begin{array}{ccccc}
\text{COOH} & & \text{COOH} & & \text{COOH} \\
| & & | & & | \\
\text{H—C—OH} & \overset{\text{Heat}}{\rightleftharpoons} & \text{H—C—OH} & \overset{\text{Heat}}{\rightleftharpoons} & \text{HO—C—H} \\
| & & | & & | \\
\text{HO—C—H} & & \text{H—C—OH} & & \text{H—C—OH} \\
| & & | & & | \\
\text{COOH} & & \text{COOH} & & \text{COOH} \\
\text{Dextrotartaric} & & \text{Mesotartaric} & & \text{Levotartaric}
\end{array}
$$

The configuration changes about each α-carbon atom until equilibrium is reached. The inversion of configuration about either one of the α-carbon atoms in dextrotartaric acid produces the meso acid, and inversion about both α-carbon atoms converts the compound to the levo acid. At equilibrium equal amounts of dextro and levo acids are present; and since this mixture is the racemic acid, the change from an optically active compound to a racemic mixture is called *racemization*.

Resolution of racemic acids. Pasteur noticed (1848) that the crystals of salts of dextrotartaric acid possess hemihedral facets and are unsymmetrical. It occurred to him that if there were any connection between optical activity in solution and asymmetry in crystal form, inactive racemic acid or its salts would not display asymmetry in the crystalline state. Upon examination of large crystals of sodium ammonium racemate he found the same facets and dissymmetry that were present in crystals of the active acids; but he observed that the crystal mass contained two kinds of crystals, one of which was the mirror image of the other. He separated the two kinds of crystals, dissolved them separately, and tested the solutions for optical activity. One solution rotated the plane of polarization of the transmitted light to the right, the other to the left. A solution made by dissolving the two kinds of crystals together, in equal quantities, was inactive. In this way he proved that racemic tartaric acid is a mixture of dextro and levo forms. The meso acid could not be separated, or resolved, into different kinds of crystals.

Pasteur found three ways in which the components of racemic tartaric acid could be separated. First, the crystals of the sodium ammonium salts of the two acids are mirror images of each other; they could be separated by mechanical means. Second, he found microorganisms which would consume one form of the acid preferentially. The other form could then be isolated. This method resulted in the loss of one form of the acid and only partial recovery of the other. Third, he found that an optically active base acts upon a racemic mixture of the acids to form salts which differ in solubility. The two salts could be separated by fractional crystallization, and the optically active organic base could then be removed from each salt by treatment with hydrochloric acid.

The third method has proved to be one of very general application. Nature has supplied several optically active bases, including strychnine, brucine, and cinchonine; and some optically active acids, including malic, tartaric, and camphoric acids. We may formulate the resolution of a racemic mixture, in general terms, as follows: Let $\overset{+}{A}$ be any dextrorotatory acid and $\overset{-}{A}$ its mirror image; and let $\overset{-}{B}$ stand for a levorotatory base such as strychnine. When $\bar{\mathbf{B}}$ is added to the solution of $\overset{+}{\mathbf{A}}$ and $\bar{\mathbf{A}}$, two salts are formed, namely, $\overset{+}{\mathbf{A}}\bar{\mathbf{B}}$ and $\bar{\mathbf{A}}\bar{\mathbf{B}}$. These are not mirror images; they differ in solubility and can be separated. The free acids $\overset{+}{\mathbf{A}}$ and $\bar{\mathbf{A}}$ are released from the separated salts by treatment with hydrochloric acid.

Synthesis of tartaric acid. The tartaric acids have been synthesized by the oxidation of maleic acid and fumaric acid. The reaction is similar to the oxidation of an alkene hydrocarbon to a glycol.

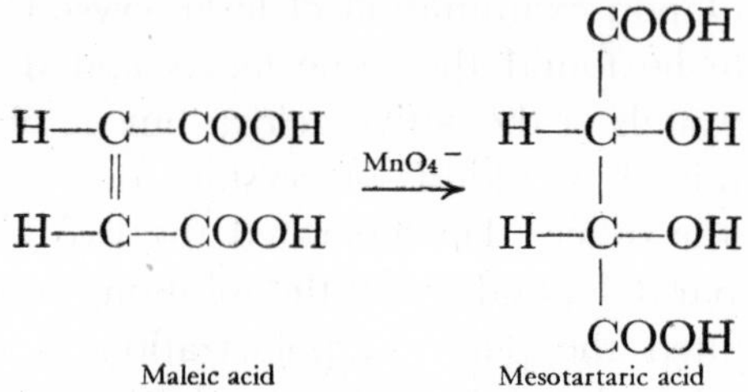

Maleic acid   Mesotartaric acid

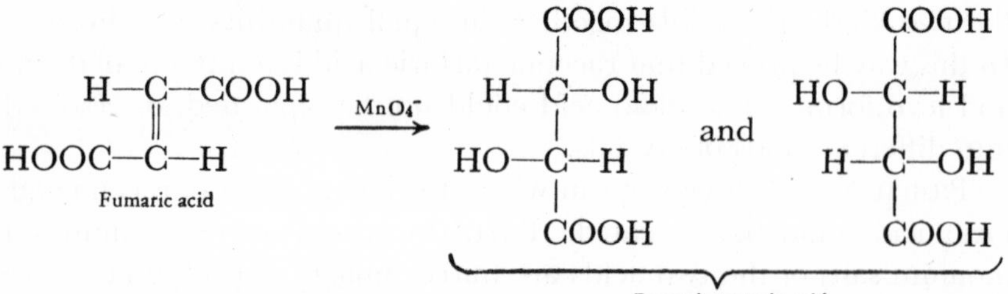

Fumaric acid   and   Racemic tartaric acid

There are equal chances for breaking the individual bonds in the double bonds of maleic and fumaric acids. In the former case mesotartaric acid is formed by breaking either bond; in the latter case d-tartaric acid is formed when one bond breaks, and l-tartaric acid is produced if the other bond breaks.

Citric acid. A crystalline tribasic acid, $C_6H_8O_7$, known as citric acid, is obtained from lemons and other citrus fruits. The structure of the molecule is represented by the following formula:

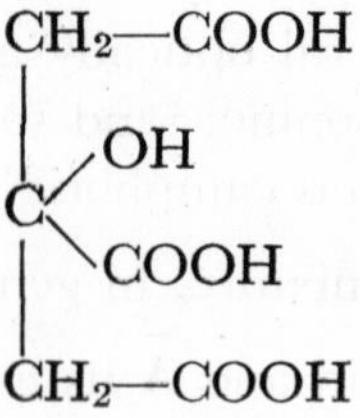

The presence of an alcoholic hydroxyl group is indicated by the fact that the triethyl ester of citric acid reacts with acetyl chloride to form an acetyl derivative of the ester. The primary product obtained from citric acid by oxidation is acetone dicarboxylic acid,

$$HOOC—CH_2—CO—CH_2—COOH$$

This places the hydroxyl group upon the third carbon atom of the pentane chain. The conclusion is supported by synthetic methods of making citric acid.

EXERCISES

1. Represent by structural formulas the stereoisomeric forms of the following acids: (a) lactic, (b) malic, (c) tartaric.

2. Name an acid which is commonly found in each of the following sources: (a) sour milk, (b) wine, (c) green apples, (d) lemons.

3. What is meant respectively by α-, β-, and γ-substituted acids? Illustrate each.

4. When some hydroxy acids undergo self-esterification, a lactone is formed; in other cases resinous esters of high molecular weights are formed. Explain this difference in the behavior of different acids.

5. What is meant by each of the following phrases: (a) stereoisomer, (b) optical activity, (c) plane-polarized light, (d) racemic mixture, (e) meso-isomer? Illustrate each case by formulas or diagrams.

6. Outline the three methods used by Pasteur to separate the optically active components of a racemic acid.

7. Which of the following compounds could exhibit optical activity?

a. $CH_3—CHBr—CHBr—COOH$ d. $CH_3—CH=CH—COOH$

b. $CH_3—CHBr—CHCl—CH_3$ e. $(CH_3)_2CHOH$

c. $CH_3—CBr_2—CH_2Cl$ f. $CH_3—CHOH—C_2H_5$

PROBLEMS

1. Represent by structural formulas and balanced equations the following processes:

a. Lactone formation from a γ-hydroxy acid

b. Racemization of an optically active lactic acid

c. Formation of a β-hydroxy acid from an α, β-unsaturated acid

d. The conversion of propionaldehyde to α-hydroxybutyric acid by way of a cyanohydrin

e. The addition of water to an α, β-unsaturated acid

f. The oxidation of maleic and fumaric acids to meso and racemic tartaric acids respectively

20 · KETO ACIDS AND TAUTOMERISM

The keto acids are characterized by the presence of a carbonyl group in addition to a carboxyl group. In the better-known members of this group the carbonyl group is in the α-position or the β-position with respect to the carboxyl. Glyoxylic acid is an aldehyde as well as an acid. All other members of the series included in the table below are ketones and acids.

KETO ACIDS		
Common Name	Geneva Name	Formula
Glyoxylic acid	Oxoethanoic acid	$H—CO—COOH$
Pyruvic acid	2-Oxopropanoic acid	$CH_3—CO—COOH$
Mesoxalic acid	Oxopropanedioic acid	$HOOC—CO—COOH$
Acetoacetic acid	3-Oxobutanoic acid	$CH_3—CO—CH_2—COOH$
Benzoylacetic acid	3-Oxo-3-phenylpropanoic acid	$C_6H_5—CO—CH_2—COOH$

Glyoxylic acid is found in the leaves and green fruits of many plants. It is isolated from these sources in the form of a hydrate,

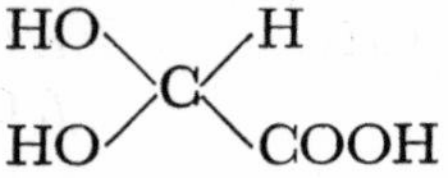

$$\underset{HO}{\overset{HO}{>}}C\underset{COOH}{\overset{H}{<}}$$

The name, *glyoxylic acid* (or, as it is often written, *glyoxalic acid*), implies a relationship to glycolic acid and to oxalic acid. The relationship is shown by the following structural formulas:

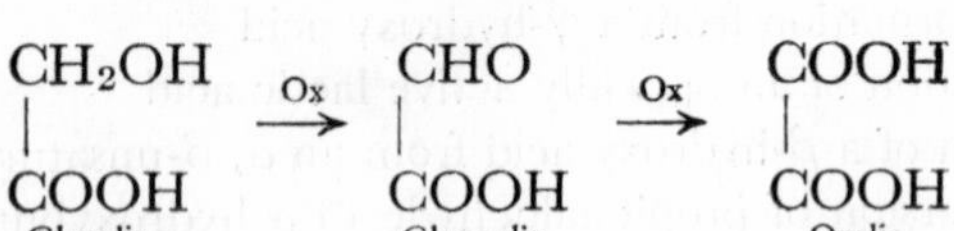

$$\underset{\substack{COOH \\ \text{Glycolic} \\ \text{acid}}}{\overset{CH_2OH}{|}} \xrightarrow{Ox} \underset{\substack{COOH \\ \text{Glyoxylic} \\ \text{acid}}}{\overset{CHO}{|}} \xrightarrow{Ox} \underset{\substack{COOH \\ \text{Oxalic} \\ \text{acid}}}{\overset{COOH}{|}}$$

The α-keto acids are formed in nature from α-hydroxy acids and from α-amino acids. Several methods are available for their synthetic

226

production. Pyruvic acid, for example, is obtained when tartaric acid is decomposed by heat:

$$
\begin{array}{ccc}
\text{COOH} & \text{COOH} & \\
| & | & \\
\text{CHOH} & \text{CH}_2 & \text{CH}_3 \\
| \quad \xrightarrow[\text{Heat}]{-\text{H}_2\text{O}} & | \quad \xrightarrow[\text{Heat}]{-\text{CO}_2} & | \\
\text{CHOH} & \text{CO} & \text{CO} \\
| & | & | \\
\text{COOH} & \text{COOH} & \text{COOH} \\
\text{Tartaric acid} & \text{Oxalacetic acid} & \text{Pyruvic acid} \\
\text{(mp 170°)} & & \text{(mp 13.6°; bp 165°)}
\end{array}
$$

The first step is an intramolecular oxidation-reduction which is characteristic of glycols; the second is decarboxylation, which takes place readily upon heating a β-keto acid.

The next higher member of the series of α-keto acids is made from propionyl chloride by the following series of reactions:

$$\text{CH}_3\text{—CH}_2\text{—COCl} + \text{KCN} \longrightarrow \text{CH}_3\text{—CH}_2\text{—CO—CN} \quad (1)$$
$$\text{Propionyl chloride} \qquad\qquad\qquad \text{Propionyl cyanide}$$

$$\text{CH}_3\text{—CH}_2\text{—CO—CN} + 2\,\text{H}_2\text{O}$$
$$\xrightarrow{\text{HCl}} \text{CH}_3\text{—CH}_2\text{—CO—COOH} + \text{NH}_4\text{Cl}$$
$$\alpha\text{-Keto butyric acid}$$

Acetoacetic ester. The most important β-keto acid is acetoacetic acid, which is best known in the form of its esters. The ethyl ester is a colorless liquid (bp 181°) which is sparingly soluble in water. It is a mixture of two structural isomers which change rapidly from one into the other. The two labile forms are called tautomers. In any sample of the substance the two kinds of molecules are normally present in a state of equilibrium.

One structure is known as the *keto* form ($\sim$ 92 per cent) and the other as the *enol* form ($\sim$ 8 per cent). The rapid conversion of one form into the other is an example of *keto-enol-tautomerism*:

$$
\begin{array}{cc}
\overset{\text{O}}{\underset{\text{Keto form}}{\text{CH}_3\text{—C—CH}_2\text{—COOC}_2\text{H}_5}} & \rightleftharpoons \quad \overset{\text{OH}}{\underset{\text{Enol form}}{\text{CH}_3\text{—C}=\text{CH—COOC}_2\text{H}_5}}
\end{array}
$$

The first, or keto structure, represents the compound as a ketone; the second, known as the enol structure, represents it as an unsaturated alcohol. If a reagent which reacts with the enol form only is added to the ester, the equilibrium is disturbed as the enol is removed, and the keto form is progressively changed to the enol. The entire quantity therefore acts as if it were an enol. On the other hand, if a reagent is used that removes the keto form, the shift occurs in the opposite direction, and the entire sample behaves as if it were a ketone.

Acetoacetic ester is prepared by the condensation of ethyl acetate. The reaction occurs when ethyl acetate is warmed with sodium ethoxide (or with metallic sodium and a trace of alcohol). The ethoxide ion, $C_2H_5O^-$, is a catalyst for the reaction. The first step in the formation of acetoacetic ester is a condensation of the aldol type occurring between two molecules of ethyl acetate. This is followed immediately by the elimination of a molecule of alcohol.

$$CH_3-C\overset{O}{\underset{OC_2H_5}{\big<}} + CH_3-C\overset{O}{\underset{OC_2H_5}{\big<}} \xrightarrow{NaOR} \left[CH_3-\underset{\underset{OC_2H_5}{\big|}}{\overset{\overset{OH}{\big|}}{C}}-CH_2-C\overset{O}{\underset{OC_2H_5}{\big<}} \right]$$

$$\left[CH_3-\underset{\underset{OC_2H_5}{\big|}}{\overset{\overset{OH}{\big|}}{C}}-CH_2-C\overset{O}{\underset{OC_2H_5}{\big<}} \right] \longrightarrow CH_3-\overset{\overset{O}{\|}}{C}-CH_2-C\overset{O}{\underset{OC_2H_5}{\big<}} + C_2H_5OH$$

The keto and enol forms can be separated by distillation from a quartz vessel, but not from a glass vessel. The enol form is more volatile than the keto form.* The change from one form to the other is slow if no catalyst is present, but very rapid in the presence of either an acid or a base. A glass surface is sufficiently basic to accelerate the change; and when a glass distilling apparatus is used, the distillate is an equilibrium mixture of the two forms.

A determination of the enol content of the mixture is made by the rapid addition of a standardized solution of bromine. The enol form

*It seems anomalous that the enol form, which shows a high acidity and presumably contains a hydroxyl group, should boil at a lower temperature than its ketonic isomer. Actually the hydroxyl group is present; but instead of associating through a hydrogen bond with other molecules, and thus reducing its volatility, it forms a hydrogen bond *intra*molecularly.

$$\overset{O-H\cdots O}{\underset{CH_3-C=C-C-OC_2H_5}{\big| \qquad \|}}$$

Enolic structure with hydrogen bond

Cyclic structures of this sort are called chelate forms. Because of this chelation the enol form of acetoacetic ester is probably less associated than is the keto form.

decolorizes bromine at once by an addition reaction which is followed by loss of HBr:

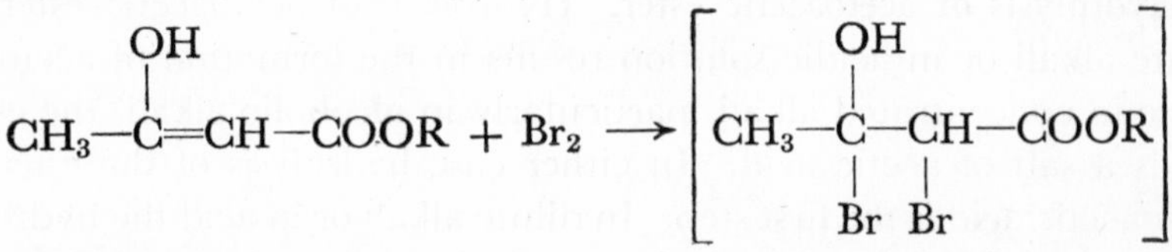

$$CH_3-\underset{\underset{}{\overset{|}{OH}}}{C}=CH-COOR + Br_2 \longrightarrow \left[CH_3-\underset{\underset{Br\ Br}{|\ \ |}}{\overset{\overset{OH}{|}}{C}}-CH-COOR \right]$$

A compound with a hydroxyl group and a halogen atom attached to the same carbon atom is unstable; it immediately yields a molecule of hydrogen halide:

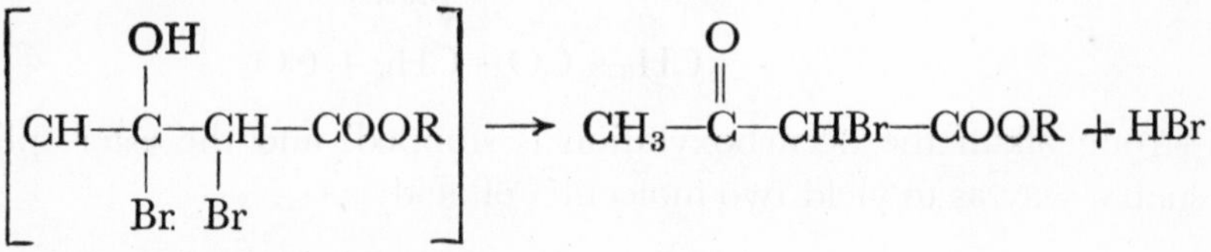

$$\left[CH-\underset{\underset{Br\ Br}{|\ \ |}}{\overset{\overset{OH}{|}}{C}}-CH-COOR \right] \longrightarrow CH_3-\underset{\overset{||}{O}}{C}-CHBr-COOR + HBr$$

The keto form acts on bromine only as rapidly as the tautomeric change to the enol form occurs. The amount of bromine which is immediately decolorized is a measure of the quantity of enol present.

Tautomerism involves a shift of a hydrogen atom and a simultaneous change in the position of a double bond. The hydrogen atom which is involved actually dissociates as a hydrogen ion to an appreciable degree. A β-keto ester is definitely, but weakly, acidic.

Sodium acts upon acetoacetic ester with the liberation of hydrogen and the formation of a sodium derivative of the ester. The sodium compound is usually represented as a derivative of the enol form of the ester:

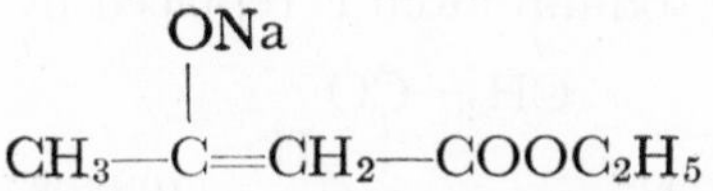

$$CH_3-\underset{\underset{}{\overset{|}{ONa}}}{C}=CH_2-COOC_2H_5$$

The same derivative may be made from sodium ethoxide and the ester. In this respect this β-keto ester is similar to malonic ester.

Malonic ester	$C_2H_5O\!-\!\underset{\overset{||}{O}}{C}-CH_2-\underset{\overset{||}{O}}{C}\!-\!OC_2H_5$	Trace of enol
Acetoacetic ester	$CH_3\!-\!\underset{\overset{||}{O}}{C}-CH_2-\underset{\overset{||}{O}}{C}\!-\!OC_2H_5$	8 per cent enol

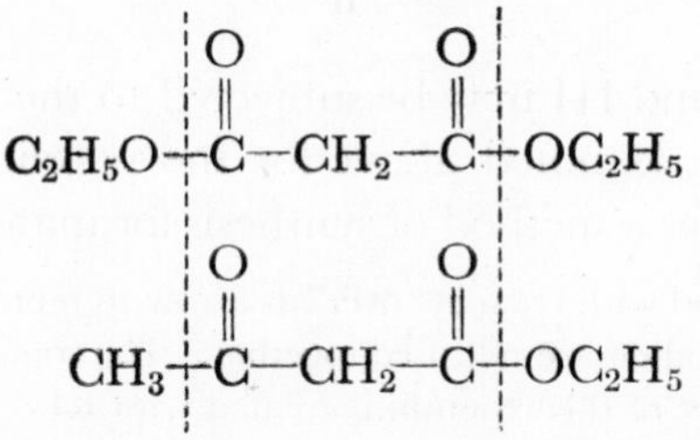

Both compounds possess an active methylene group; both form sodium derivatives; both sodium derivatives react with alkyl halides.

Hydrolysis of acetoacetic ester. Hydrolysis of acetoacetic ester in dilute alkali or in acidic solution results in the formation of acetone, while in concentrated alkali, particularly in alcoholic alkali, the ester yields a salt of acetic acid. In either case hydrolysis of the ester to acetoacetic acid is the first step. In dilute alkali or in acid the hydrolysis is followed by decarboxylation:

$$CH_3—CO—CH_2—COOC_2H_5 + H_2O \xrightarrow{Heat}$$
$$CH_3—CO—CH_2—COOH + C_2H_5OH$$
$$\downarrow Heat$$
$$CH_3—CO—CH_3 + CO_2$$

In strong alkali the decarboxylation is stopped, and the ester splits in such a way as to yield two molecules of acid:

$$CH_3—CO—CH_2—COOC_2H_5 + OH^- \xrightarrow{Heat}$$
$$CH_3—CO—CH_2—CO_2^- + C_2H_5OH$$
$$Heat \downarrow OH^-$$
$$CH_3—CO_2^- + CH_3—CO_2^- \xrightarrow{2H^+} 2\ CH_3COOH$$

These reactions are referred to as ketonic and acidic splitting of the β-keto ester.

Acetoacetic ester synthesis of ketones and acids. The hydrogen atoms of the methylene group in acetoacetic ester may be replaced by alkyl groups. The course of the reaction is identical with that of malonic ester (p.191). First a sodium derivative of the ester is prepared, and then the sodium atom is replaced by the alkyl group:

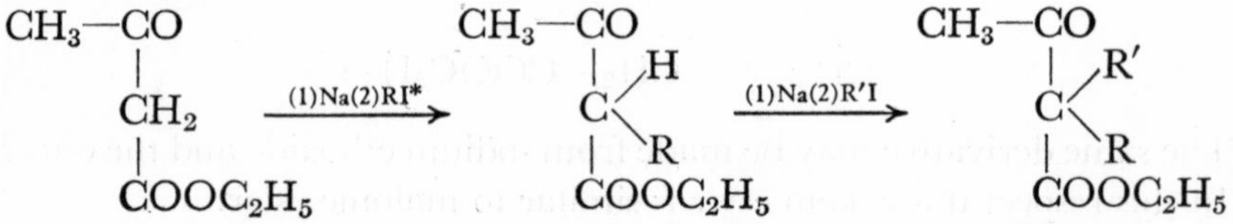

CH₃—CO	CH₃—CO	CH₃—CO
CH₂ $\xrightarrow{(1)Na(2)RI*}$	C⟨H,R $\xrightarrow{(1)Na(2)R'I}$	C⟨R',R
COOC₂H₅	COOC₂H₅	COOC₂H₅
I	II	III

The products II and III may be subjected to the ketone splitting or to the acid splitting, as noted above for the parent compound, and the procedure becomes a method of synthesis for many ketones and acids.

*Numbers are used with reagents over an arrow to represent successive steps. Sodium and the alkyl iodide are not used together. The compound is treated first with Na: then the product of this reaction is treated with RI.

KETONIC AND ACIDIC SPLITTING OF B-KETO ESTERS		
Substituted Acetoacetic Esters	Products of Hydrolysis	
	Ketones	Acids
CH_3—CO—CHR—$COOC_2H_5$	CH_3—CO—CH_2R	RCH_2—COOH + CH_3COOH
CH_3—CO—CRR′—$COOC_2H_5$	CH_3—CO—CHRR′	RĆH—COOH + CH_3COOH

EXERCISES

1. Represent by balanced equations the decarboxylation of the following acids: (a) malonic, (b) acetoacetic, (c) pyruvic, (d) oxalic.

NOTE. The temperatures at which these reactions occur are in the order (b) < (a) < (d) < (c); yet pyruvic acid is converted to acetaldehyde (during fermentation) by enzymes at room temperature.

2. Show by an equation the relationship of lactic acid to pyruvic acid. (They are oxidation-reduction products of each other.)

3. How does tautomerism differ from isomerism?

4. If only a small percentage of a substance is enolic, how is it possible for the substance to react as if it were all enolic?

5. Show by equations how ketones of the type R—CH_2—CO—CH_3 and acids of the type R—CH_2—COOH can be prepared from acetoacetic ester.

PROBLEMS

1. How may the enol content of a tautomeric mixture be determined quantitatively?

2. Enolic esters of the type R—C(OH)=CH—COOR and unsaturated esters such as CH_3—CH=CH—CH_2—COOR decolorize bromine very rapidly. Suggest a way of ascertaining which type of compound is present when the compound is known to be one of the two.

3. How may the following compounds be prepared from acetoacetic ester?

a. CH_3—CO—CH_2—$C(CH_3)_3$ c. $(CH_3)_2CH$—CO—CH_3

b. $(CH_3)_2CH$—CH_2—CH_2—COOH   d. C_6H_5—CH_2—CH_2—COOH

21 · THE CARBOHYDRATES

Sugars, starches, and celluloses are called carbohydrates. They are composed of carbon, hydrogen, and oxygen, and the general formula $C_nH_{2n}O_n$ applies to nearly all members of the group. By the term *sugar* we refer to the crystalline, soluble carbohydrates which have a sweet taste. They are comparatively simple compounds, and their molecular weights are known with precision. The starches and celluloses are carbohydrates of very high molecular weights; they are only slightly soluble in water, and they are tasteless.

Sugars

The best-known sugar, but not the simplest, is sucrose, $C_{12}H_{22}O_{11}$. It is obtained from sugar cane, sugar beets, and the sap of the sugar maple. Cane sugar was at one time called saccharose. The name is not in common use at present, but a word derived from it, namely, saccharide, has a prominent place in the literature relating to the sugars. Some sugars which are articles of commerce are listed in the table below.

SOME COMMON SUGARS	
Name of Sugar	Occurrence
Sucrose	Sugar cane; sugar beets; sap of sugar maple
Lactose (milk sugar)	Milk
Maltose (malt sugar)	Fermentation product of grains; hydrolysis product of starch
Glucose (grape sugar)	Grapes and other fruits; hydrolysis product of starch, maltose, sucrose, and some other carbohydrates
Invert sugar	Hydrolysis product of sucrose; natural occurrence in honey. It is a mixture of glucose and fructose

Structural differences among the sugars. An examination of the structures of glucose and fructose reveals that one is a polyhydroxy aldehyde and the other is a polyhydroxy ketone. Arabinose and ribose, like glucose and mannose, are aldehydes. Arabinose and ribose are pentoses; that is, they are sugars which have five carbon atoms in the molecule. Glucose and mannose are hexoses; they have

232

six carbon atoms in the molecule. The sugars differ from each other not only in the number of carbon atoms per molecule but also in the spatial arrangements of atoms and groups around the asymmetric carbon atoms. Formulas of two of the isomeric pentoses are written as follows:

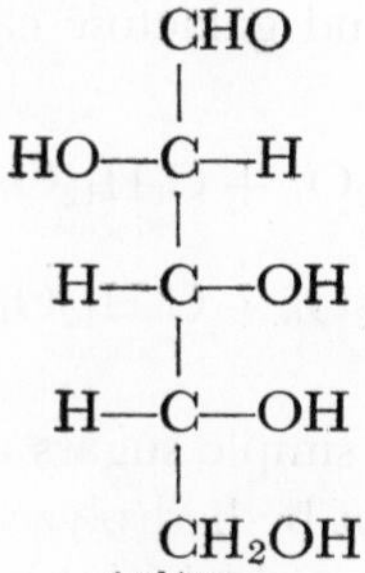

```
        CHO                      CHO
         |                        |
   HO—C—H                   HO—C—H
         |                        |
    H—C—OH                  HO—C—H
         |                        |
    H—C—OH                  HO—C—H
         |                        |
      CH₂OH                    CH₂OH
     Arabinose                  Ribose
```

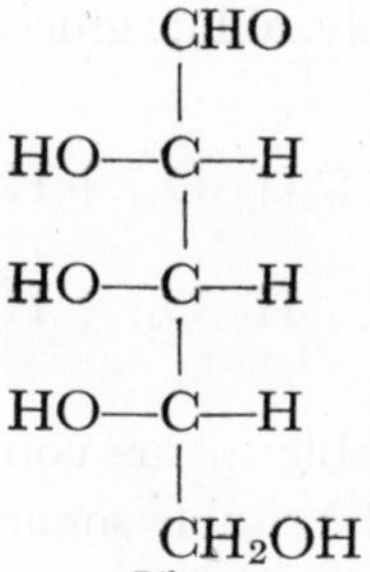

A complete list of the pentoses is given on page 260. Formulas of three of the hexoses (sugars with six carbon atoms in the molecule) are shown here:

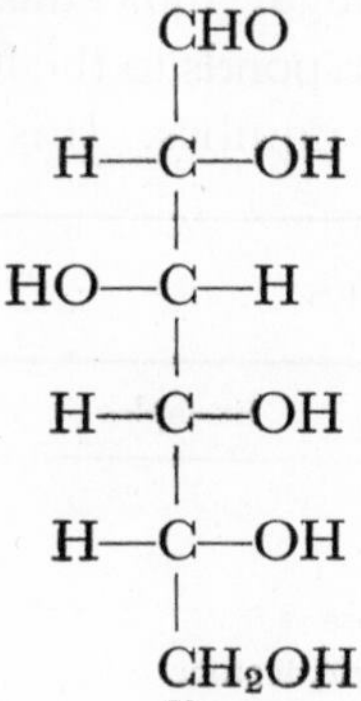

```
      CHO            CH₂OH            CHO
       |               |              |
  H—C—OH            C=O         HO—C—H
       |               |              |
 HO—C—H          HO—C—H        HO—C—H
       |               |              |
  H—C—OH          H—C—OH        H—C—OH
       |               |              |
  H—C—OH          H—C—OH        H—C—OH
       |               |              |
     CH₂OH          CH₂OH          CH₂OH
    Glucose         Fructose        Mannose
```

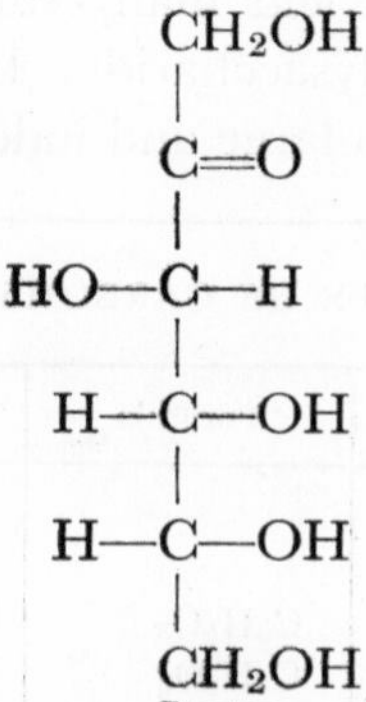

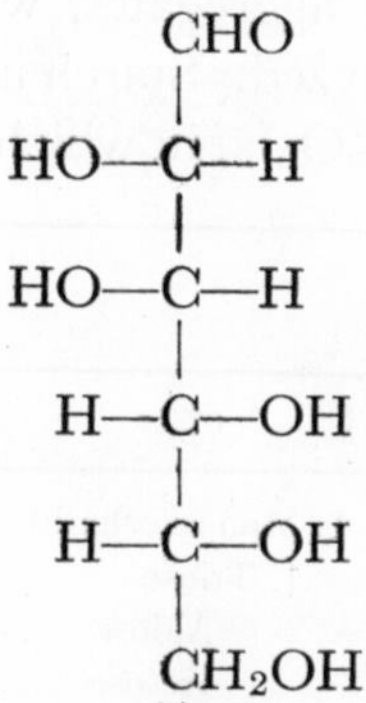

The number of sugars corresponding to a given structure is determined by the number of asymmetric centers present in the molecule. Two arrangements are possible for each asymmetric center, so that each additional asymmetric carbon atom doubles the number of isomers. In the formula for arabinose as written above, there are three such centers, and there are 2^3, or 8, stereoisomers which correspond to the formula $C_5H_{10}O_5$. Each of them contains a chain of five carbon atoms, an aldehyde group, and four hydroxyl groups. In glucose, as shown above, there are four asymmetric carbon atoms, and there are 2^4, or 16, ways in which the five hydroxyl groups can be arranged. We shall see later that the above formulas must be modified to account for the existence of more than eight pentoses and more than sixteen hexoses.

Classification of sugars. Simple sugars differ from the more complex ones in that they cannot be broken down by hydrolysis into compounds of fewer carbon atoms. Cane sugar, milk sugar, and malt sugar are all hydrolyzable; glucose, fructose, and galactose cannot be hydrolyzed.

$$\underset{\text{Sucrose}}{C_{12}H_{22}O_{11}} + H_2O \xrightarrow{H^+} \underset{\text{Glucose}}{C_6H_{12}O_6} + \underset{\text{Fructose}}{C_6H_{12}O_6}$$

$$\underset{\text{Lactose}}{C_{12}H_{22}O_{11}} + H_2O \xrightarrow{H^+} \underset{\text{Glucose}}{C_6H_{12}O_6} + \underset{\text{Galactose}}{C_6H_{12}O_6}$$

Hydrolyzable sugars composed of two simple sugars are called *disaccharides*; the simple sugars which cannot be hydrolyzed are termed *monosaccharides*. If a monosaccharide is an aldehyde, it is called an *aldose*; if it is a ketone, it is called a *ketose*. Higher aggregates, such as *trisaccharides* and *tetrasaccharides* are known; they contain three and four monosaccharide residues respectively. *Polysaccharides* are still higher aggregates, which yield many simple sugar molecules when hydrolyzed. Starch is a polysaccharide. It corresponds to the formula $(C_6H_{10}O_5)_n$, in which n is a large and indefinite number. It is classed

CLASSES OF CARBOHYDRATES		
Class	Formula	Examples
A. Monosaccharides		
1. Triose		
Aldose	$C_3H_6O_3$	Glycerose
Ketose	$C_3H_6O_3$	Dihydroxyacetone
2. Tetroses		
Aldoses	$C_4H_8O_4$	Erythrose, threose
3. Pentoses		
Aldoses	$C_5H_{10}O_5$	Arabinose, xylose, lyxose, ribose
4. Hexoses		
Aldoses	$C_6H_{12}O_6$	Glucose, mannose, galactose, allose, altrose, talose, gulose, idose
Ketoses	$C_6H_{12}O_6$	Fructose, sorbose
5. Heptoses	$C_7H_{14}O_7$	Mannoheptose, glucoheptose
B. Disaccharides	$C_{12}H_{22}O_{11}$	Sucrose, lactose, maltose, cellobiose
C. Trisaccharides	$C_{18}H_{32}O_{16}$	Raffinose, gentianose
D. Polysaccharides		
1. Pentosans	$(C_5H_8O_4)_n$	Araban, xylan
2. Hexosans	$(C_6H_{10}O_5)_n$	Starch, glycogen, dextrin, cellulose, inulin

as a carbohydrate, but not as a sugar, because it is neither crystalline nor sweet.

The monosaccharides correspond to the general formula $C_nH_{2n}O_n$. In the sugars known as *pentoses* n is 5, the formula being $C_5H_{10}O_5$. Most of them are *aldopentoses*, that is, aldehydes. The sugars known as *hexoses* have the formula $C_6H_{12}O_6$. Only a few are ketones, or *ketohexoses*. Monosaccharides ranging from $C_3H_6O_3$ to $C_{10}H_{20}O_{10}$ have been synthesized in the laboratory.

Structural relationships of the sugars. The lower monosaccharides of three and four carbon atoms can hardly be classified as sugars because they are noncrystallizable sirups. Yet they constitute a basis for the naming of the whole series of sugars. Examples are dihydroxyacetone and glycerose.

$$
\begin{array}{ccc}
\text{CH}_2\text{OH} & \text{CHO} & \text{CHO} \\
| & | & | \\
\text{C}{=}\text{O} & \text{H}{-}\text{C}{-}\text{OH} & \text{HO}{-}\text{C}{-}\text{H} \\
| & | & | \\
\text{CH}_2\text{OH} & \text{CH}_2\text{OH} & \text{CH}_2\text{OH} \\
\text{Dihydroxyacetone} & \textit{d-}\text{Glycerose} & \textit{l-}\text{Glycerose} \\
\end{array}
$$

Ketotriose	Aldotrioses

Glycerose is a derivative of the trihydric alcohol, glycerol. It has only one asymmetric center and therefore exists in only two stereoisomeric forms. By common agreement the dextrorotatory form is written as above, arbitrarily, with the hydroxyl group on the right of the asymmetric carbon atom, hydrogen on the left, the aldehyde group above, and the primary alcohol group below the asymmetric carbon atom. All the naturally occurring hexoses and nearly all pentoses obtained from natural sources have the same configuration as d-glycerose in so far as the asymmetric carbon atom next to the primary alcohol group is concerned. On this basis they are classified as members of the d-series of sugars. Half the possible pentoses and half the possible hexoses belong to the d-series; the other half have the configuration of l-glycerose at this point in the molecule and are said to belong to the l-series of sugars. (See page 260.)

Not all sugars of the d-series are dextrorotatory. This makes it necessary to employ a system of naming which indicates both the structural relationship of a sugar to one of the glyceroses and also the measured rotation of the compound. For instance, the fructose which is found in honey is levorotatory, but the arrangement of the H, OH and CH_2OH groups about its terminal asymmetric carbon atom is the same as the corresponding arrangement found in d-glycerose. Both these facts are indicated in the name d- $(-)$ *fructose*. Naturally occurring glucose is d- $(+)$ glucose. The $(-)$ and $(+)$ signs mean levo and dextro rotation respectively, while the d indicates that both sugars belong to the d-series and are related to the arbitarily chosen d-glycerose. This dual notation is confined to the sugars. In connection with other classes of compounds d and l indicate dextro and levo optical rotation respectively. When a sugar is referred to without specification of its rotation,—that is, merely as glucose or galactose,—the reference is to the naturally occurring sugar.

Reactions of the sugars. The principal reactions of the sugars will be considered in the next chapter, but a few chemical characteristics of the group should be mentioned here. The sugars which are aldehydes reduce Fehling's solution and Tollens's reagent as would be anticipated, but the ketone sugars also reduce these reagents. The α-hydroxy ketones in general are easily oxidized, and the reagents which are used to distinguish aldehydes from simple unsubstituted ketones are untrustworthy when applied to hydroxy ketones. Both aldoses and ketoses add HCN; they react with hydroxylamine and phenylhydrazine to form oximes and hydrazones, and they react with acetic anhydride to form esters.

Oxidation of an aldose leads to the formation of an acid which has the same number of carbon atoms. The case of glucose may be used in illustration:

$$
\underset{\substack{\text{Saccharic acid}}}{\begin{array}{c} COOH \\ | \\ (CHOH)_4 \\ | \\ COOH \end{array}} \xleftarrow{\;HNO_3\;} \underset{\substack{\text{Glucose}}}{\begin{array}{c} CHO \\ | \\ (CHOH)_4 \\ | \\ CH_2OH \end{array}} \xrightarrow{\;Br_2,\ H_2O\;} \underset{\substack{\text{Gluconic acid}}}{\begin{array}{c} COOH \\ | \\ (CHOH)_4 \\ | \\ CH_2OH \end{array}}
$$

The aldehyde group alone or the aldehyde and primary alcohol groups may be oxidized as indicated. A more drastic oxidation results in the formation of acids of lower molecular weights. Oxalic acid is formed in good yield when glucose is heated with concentrated nitric acid. Oxidation of the primary alcohol group with retention of the aldehyde group cannot be accomplished directly by laboratory methods. It is done in living cells, and it can be accomplished through an indirect course in the laboratory. To do this the aldehyde group is first converted into a derivative which resists oxidation. The primary alcohol group is then oxidized to carboxyl, and finally the aldehyde group is regenerated. The result (but not the mechanism) is formulated as follows:

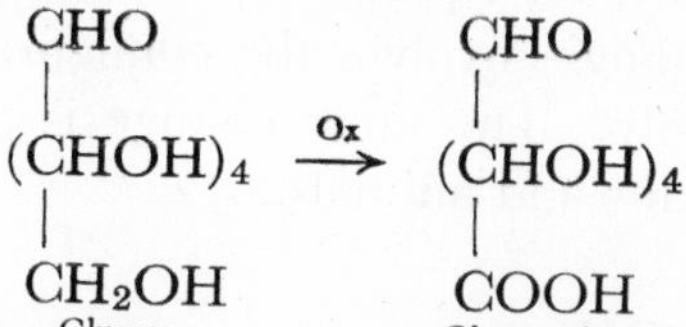

$$
\begin{array}{ccc}
\text{CHO} & & \text{CHO} \\
| & & | \\
(\text{CHOH})_4 & \xrightarrow{\text{Ox}} & (\text{CHOH})_4 \\
| & & | \\
\text{CH}_2\text{OH} & & \text{COOH} \\
\text{Glucose} & & \text{Glucuronic acid}
\end{array}
$$

Glucuronic acid is a product of animal metabolism, and it is found in the urine combined with compounds which if free would be toxic. Apparently glucuronic acid functions as an agent to protect the organisms from poisons by combining with toxic substances and converting them into harmless products which can be eliminated from the system through the kidneys.

Glucuronic acid is found in plants in a type of polysaccharide called hemicellulose. One type of hemicellulose, xylan, consists exclusively of xylose units, just as ordinary starch is composed of glucose units. Decarboxylation of glucuronic acid results in the formation of xylose:

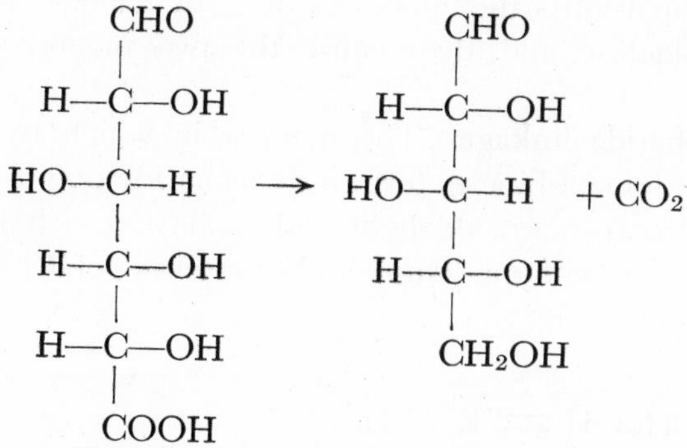

$$
\begin{array}{ccc}
\text{CHO} & & \text{CHO} \\
| & & | \\
\text{H—C—OH} & & \text{H—C—OH} \\
| & & | \\
\text{HO—C—H} & \longrightarrow & \text{HO—C—H} \quad + \text{CO}_2 \\
| & & | \\
\text{H—C—OH} & & \text{H—C—OH} \\
| & & | \\
\text{H—C—OH} & & \text{CH}_2\text{OH} \\
| & & \\
\text{COOH} & & \\
\text{Glucuronic acid} & & \text{Xylose}
\end{array}
$$

Xylose is the main source of furfuraldehyde, which is obtained commercially from corn husks and other cellulose materials. Furfuraldehyde is used in the manufacture of plastics and as a solvent.

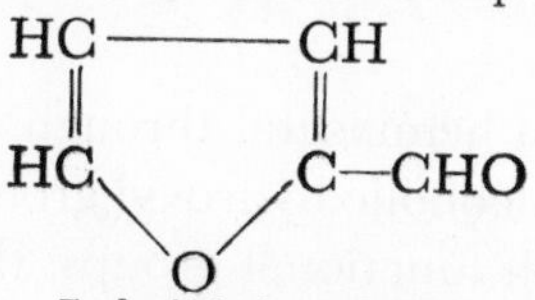

$$
\begin{array}{c}
\text{HC} \underline{\hspace{1cm}} \text{CH} \\
\| \qquad \| \\
\text{HC} \diagdown \qquad \diagup \text{C—CHO} \\
\text{O}
\end{array}
$$

Furfuraldehyde, or furfural
(mp − 36°; bp 162°)

It appears probable that, in living plants, xylan is derived from cellulose through oxidation and subsequent decarboxylation.

Glucose, mannose, and fructose are mutually interconvertible. When an alkaline solution of any one of these sugars is allowed to stand for several hours, an equilibrium mixture of the three sugars is produced. The change involves the configuration about the first two carbon atoms only. The same change is produced by certain enzymes in living plants and animals.

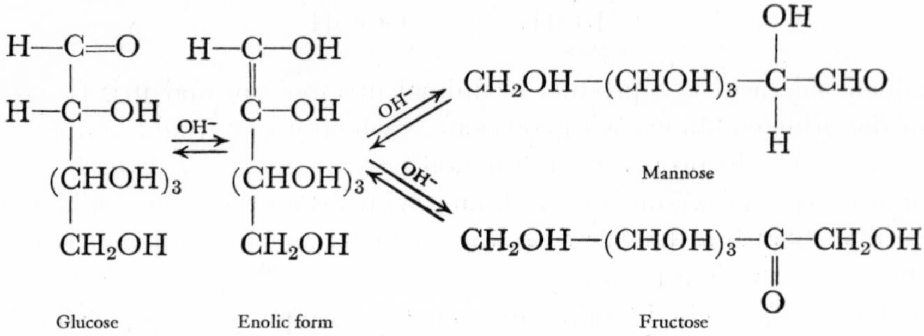

$$H—C{=}O \quad H—C—OH$$
$$H—C—OH \underset{OH^-}{\overset{OH^-}{\rightleftarrows}} C—OH$$
$$(CHOH)_3 \quad (CHOH)_3$$
$$CH_2OH \quad CH_2OH$$

Glucose   Enolic form

$$CH_2OH—(CHOH)_3—\overset{\displaystyle OH}{\underset{\displaystyle H}{C}}—CHO$$

Mannose

$$CH_2OH—(CHOH)_3—\underset{\displaystyle O}{\overset{\displaystyle \|}{C}}—CH_2OH$$

Fructose

The mammary glands take glucose from the blood stream and convert it into milk sugar, a disaccharide composed of glucose and galactose. Apparently the gland is able to change some of the glucose to galactose and then cause the two monosaccharides to combine.

The disaccharide linkage. The manner in which two monosaccharide molecules combine to form a disaccharide may be illustrated by a reaction between any aldehyde and an alcohol such as methanol. An aldehyde reacts with methanol, in the presence of HCl as a catalyst, to yield an acetal:

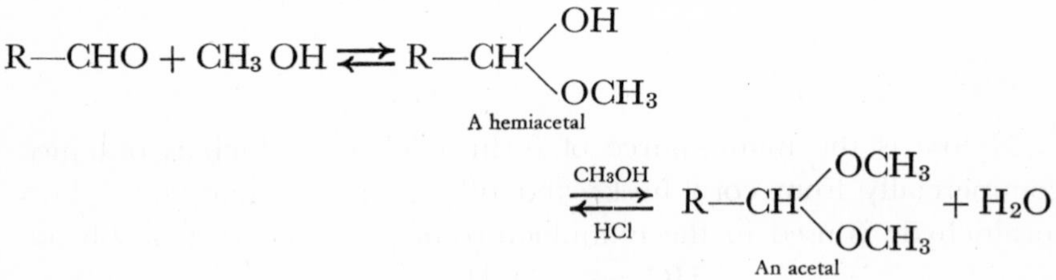

$$R—CHO + CH_3OH \rightleftarrows R—CH\overset{\displaystyle OH}{\underset{\displaystyle OCH_3}{<}}$$

A hemiacetal

$$\underset{HCl}{\overset{CH_3OH}{\rightleftarrows}} \quad R—CH\overset{\displaystyle OCH_3}{\underset{\displaystyle OCH_3}{<}} + H_2O$$

An acetal

Similarly glucose forms a hemiacetal through a reaction between the aldehyde group and an alcoholic hydroxyl group; but a single glucose molecule can supply both functional groups, the aldehyde group and the hydroxyl group. The alcoholic group on carbon atom 4 or 5 is favorably located for reaction with the terminal aldehyde group. The hemiacetal formed in this way may then react with another alcohol molecule to form an acetal. The second alcohol may be an ordinary alcohol like methanol or it may be another simple sugar.

$$
\begin{array}{lll}
\text{HC}^1\!\!=\!\!\text{O} & \text{H--C}^1\text{-----OH} & \text{H--C}^1\text{-----OCH}_3 \\
\text{H--C}^2\text{--OH} & \text{H--C}^2\text{--OH} & \text{H--C}^2\text{--OH} \\
\text{HO--C}^3\text{--H} \rightleftharpoons \text{HO--C}^3\text{--H} \quad\text{O} \underset{\text{HCl}}{\overset{\text{CH}_3\text{OH}}{\rightleftharpoons}} \text{HO--C}^3\text{--H} \quad\text{O} + \text{H}_2\text{O} \\
\text{H--C}^4\text{--OH} & \text{H--C}^4\text{--OH} & \text{H--C}^4\text{--OH} \\
\text{H--C}^5\text{--OH} & \text{H--C}^5\text{------} & \text{H--C}^5\text{------} \\
\text{C}^6\text{H}_2\text{OH} & \text{C}^6\text{H}_2\text{OH} & \text{C}^6\text{H}_2\text{OH}
\end{array}
$$

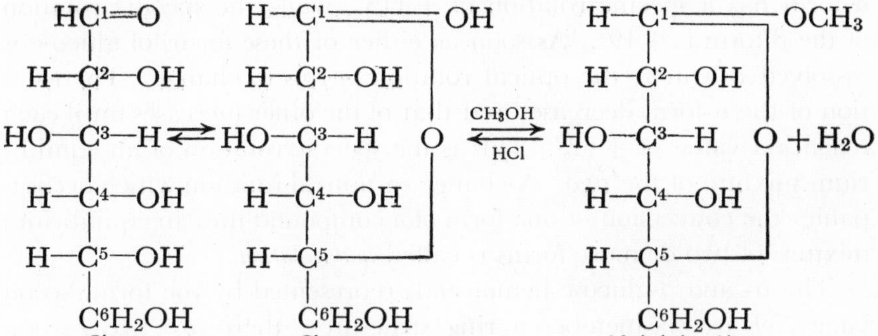

Glucose (aldehyde form)　　Glucose (hemiacetal form)　　Methyl glucoside (an acetal)

If the second stage of the reaction shown above were completed with a molecule of glucose instead of methyl alcohol, the acetal formed would be a disaccharide (see the formulas of sucrose and lactose, pp. 241 and 245).

Mutarotation. Hemiacetal formation is rapid and reversible, and a solution of a monosaccharide consists of an equilibrium mixture of the aldehyde and hemiacetal forms. In solution most of the sugar is actually in the hemiacetal form. There are two hemiacetal forms of the sugar, because the aldehyde carbon atom (number 1) becomes asymmetric in the process of forming the hemiacetal, and two ring structures can be produced. The two isomers are designated as α and β sugars.

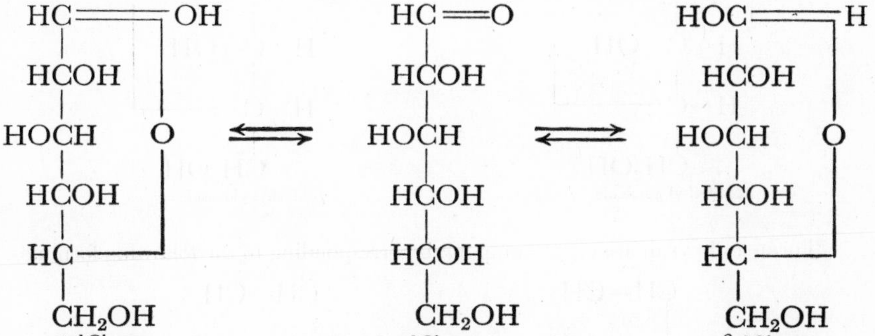

$$
\begin{array}{lll}
\text{HC-----OH} & \text{HC}\!\!=\!\!\text{O} & \text{HOC-----H} \\
\text{HCOH} & \text{HCOH} & \text{HCOH} \\
\text{HOCH} \quad\text{O} \rightleftharpoons \text{HOCH} \rightleftharpoons \text{HOCH} \quad\text{O} \\
\text{HCOH} & \text{HCOH} & \text{HCOH} \\
\text{HC------} & \text{HCOH} & \text{HC------} \\
\text{CH}_2\text{OH} & \text{CH}_2\text{OH} & \text{CH}_2\text{OH}
\end{array}
$$

α-*d*-Glucose (a hemiacetal)　　*d*-Glucose (aldehyde form)　　β-*d*-Glucose (a hemiacetal)

In the α-form of a sugar hemiacetal the first two hydroxyl groups (at the aldehyde end of the chain) are on the same side of the molecule; in the β-form these two hydroxyl groups are on opposite sides of the molecule. Two crystalline forms of *d*-glucose are actually known, one being obtained by crystallizing the sugar from water, the other by crystallizing it from pyridine. They differ in optical activity: the α-form has a specific rotation of $+113°$, while the specific rotation of the β-form is $+19°$. As soon as either of these forms of glucose is dissolved in water, the optical rotation begins to change. The rotation of the α-form decreases and that of the other increases until each reaches a value of $+52°$. This is the specific rotation of an equilibrium mixture of the two. A change in optical rotation which accompanies the conversion of one form of a compound into an equilibrium mixture of two or more forms is called *mutarotation*.

The α- and β-glucose hemiacetals represented by the formulas on page 239 are six-membered ring structures; there are five carbon atoms and one oxygen atom in each ring. This is similar to the structure of *pyran*, and the two forms of glucose are often called α-glucopyranose and β-glucopyranose. An acetal which contains the same ring is called a pyranoside. Similarly, if the hemiacetal contains a five-membered ring, as in *furan*, it is called a furanose, and an acetal derived from it is a furanoside.*

Glycosides. The sugar acetals are called glycosides. Specific compounds of this type are given names which indicate the particular al-

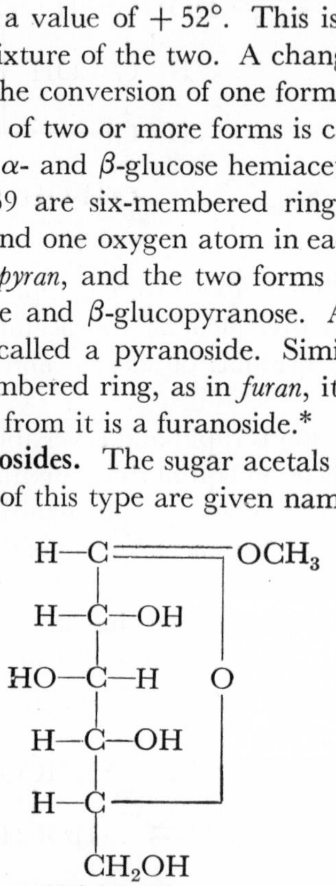

α-Methyl glucoside   β-Methyl glucoside

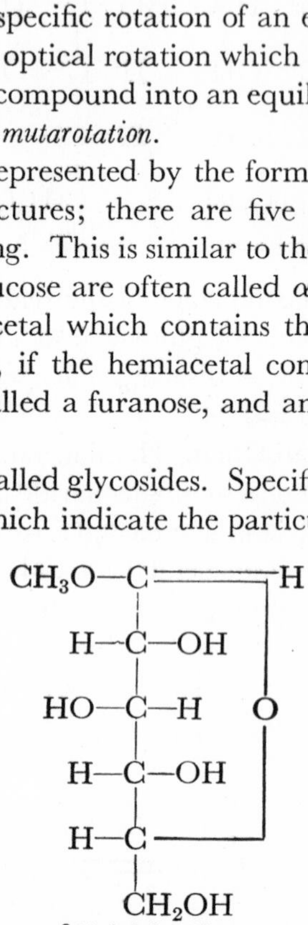

*Furan and pyran are cyclic compounds corresponding to the following formulas:

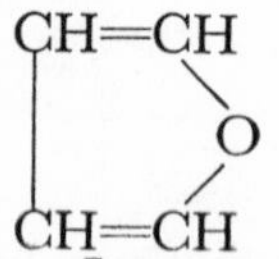

Furan 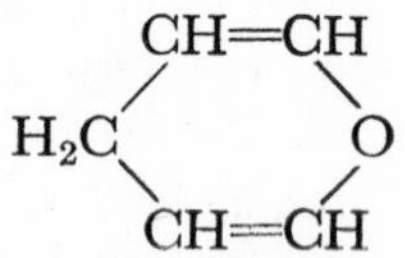   Pyran

Furan (furfuran) is a colorless liquid. It boils at 32° and is insoluble in water. Pyran has not been isolated in the free state, but many derivatives of the compound are known.

cohol and sugar involved in the formation of the acetal. Thus the methyl derivative of glucose is methyl glucoside, and the corresponding derivative of fructose is methyl fructoside; both are methyl glycosides. When hydrogen chloride gas is passed into a solution of glucose in methyl alcohol, two methyl glucosides are formed. They correspond to the α- and β-glucose hemiacetals.

The glycosides do not display mutarotation; they are permanent, stable structures. They do not reduce Tollens's reagent or Fehling's solution. They can be hydrolyzed, and the sugars released from glycosides by hydrolysis are reducing sugars. Carbohydrate derivatives which do not reduce Tollens's and Fehling's reagents are called nonreducing sugars. The structural implication of the test with Fehling's solution is that nonreducing sugars are glycosides, while reducing sugars are hemiacetals, in equilibrium with the free aldehyde form.

Aldehyde Hemiacetal

Reducing forms of a sugar

A glycoside

Nonreducing

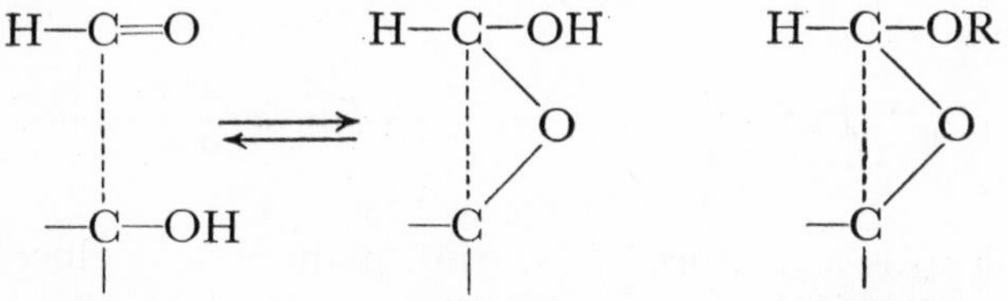

Cane sugar, an anhydride of glucose and fructose, is a nonreducing sugar. Therefore the hemiacetal hydroxyl groups of both units (glucose and fructose) have been used in effecting the union.

Glucose unit Fructose unit

Sucrose

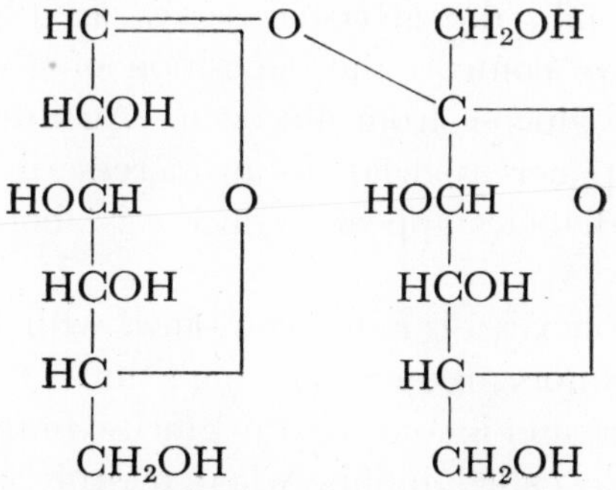

The differences in the α- and β-configurations are biologically important. An α-glycoside is hydrolyzed by the enzyme *maltase*, from malt, while a β-glycoside is hydrolyzed by the enzyme *emulsin*, which is widely distributed in plants. The hydrolysis of a β-glycoside is not catalyzed by maltase, and emulsin does not promote the hydrolysis of an α-glycoside. In starch the combined glucose units are in α-configurations, while in cellulose they are present in the β-form.

Specific Carbohydrates

Glucose. Ripe grapes contain large quantities of glucose; the polysaccharides starch, glycogen, and cellulose are composed entirely of glucose units; sucrose, lactose, and many other glucosides are combinations of glucose with other sugars. The main commercial source of glucose is starch, from which the sugar is obtained by hydrolysis:

$$(C_6H_{10}O_5)_n \xrightarrow[H_2O]{H^+} \text{dextrins} \xrightarrow[H_2O]{H^+} \text{maltose} \xrightarrow[H_2O]{H^+} \text{glucose}$$

Corn sirup is a mixture of dextrins, maltose, and glucose derived from corn starch by hydrolysis. Pure crystalline glucose can be obtained from the mixture, but the sirup finds direct use in the preparation of jams, jellies, sirups, and candies. Normally glucose is present in the blood to the extent of one tenth of 1 per cent. If the blood sugar rises above this value, the liver withdraws the excess from circulation and converts it into glycogen, or animal starch. Should consumption of the glucose by muscular activity cause the blood-sugar content to fall, the glycogen serves as a source of supply. The enzyme *insulin* controls the deposition of glucose as glycogen and the release of glucose from glycogen. An insufficient supply of insulin (from the pancreas) leads to an increase in blood sugar, and the symptoms of diabetes appear. Glucose is about half as sweet as sucrose.

Fructose, a ketohexose, is found combined with glucose in sucrose. Fructose is levorotatory, reduces Fehling's and Tollens's solutions, is fermented by yeast, and is converted to glucose in the liver. A starch-like polysaccharide called inulin, when hydrolyzed, yields fructose only. Inulin is found in dahlia roots, dandelions. and the Jerusalem artichoke.

NATURALLY OCCURRING CARBOHYDRATES

Common Name	Scientific Name	Formula	Occurrence
	l-Arabinose	$C_5H_{10}O_5$	Constituent of gum arabic; combined in pectin
	d-Xylose	$C_5H_{10}O_5$	Combined in wood, straw, corn cobs, hulls
	d-Ribose	$C_5H_{10}O_5$	Combined with noncarbohydrate substances
Grape sugar, or dextrose	d-Glucose	$C_6H_{12}O_6$	Grapes, constituent of other sugars, starches, and cellulose
Fruit sugar	d-Fructose, or levulose	$C_6H_{12}O_6$	Honey and fruits, constituent of sucrose and inulin
	d-Mannose	$C_6H_{12}O_6$	Combined with noncarbohydrate substances
	d-Galactose	$C_6H_{12}O_6$	Constituent of lactose
Cane sugar Beet sugar Maple sugar	Sucrose	$C_{12}H_{22}O_{11}$	Cane, beet, and sap of maple tree
Milk sugar	Lactose	$C_{12}H_{22}O_{11}$	Milk
Malt sugar	Maltose	$C_{12}H_{22}O_{11}$	From action of malt enzymes on starch
Starch (insoluble)	Amylopectin	$(C_6H_{10}O_5)_n$	Grains, roots, tubers
Starch (soluble)	Amylose	$(C_6H_{10}O_5)_n$	Grains
Liver starch	Glycogen	$(C_6H_{10}O_5)_n$	Liver and muscles
Wood and vegetable fiber	Cellulose	$(C_6H_{10}O_5)_n$	Wood, cotton, flax fiber
	Inulin	$(C_6H_{10}O_5)_n$	Dahlia and artichoke tubers

Invert sugar is hydrolyzed sucrose and therefore a mixture of glucose and fructose.

$$C_{12}H_{22}O_{11} + H_2O \xrightarrow{\text{Acid or invertase}} C_6H_{12}O_6 + C_6H_{12}O_6$$

Sucrose ($[\alpha]_D = +66.4°$) — Glucose ($[\alpha]_D = +52.5°$) — Fructose ($[\alpha]_D = -92°$)

The optical rotation of a cane-sugar solution changes from dextro to levo upon hydrolysis; hence the term *invert sugar* for the mixture. Honey is largely invert sugar.

Lactose is present in milk to the extent of 2.5 to 3 per cent. The percentage is somewhat higher (up to 5 per cent) in human milk. Lactose is a reducing sugar; only one of the two hemiacetal hydroxyl groups in the components (glucose and galactose molecules) is involved in glycoside formation.

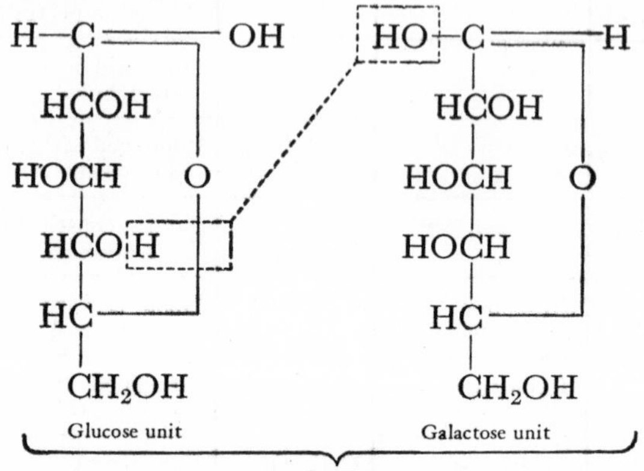

Lactose

It can be shown that it is the glucose half of the molecule which reduces Fehling's solution. Lactose shows mutarotation and can be obtained in two forms.

The ring structures for glucose and galactose as written above in the formula for lactose are not accurate representations of the sugar molecules. The tetrahedral bond angles make the six-membered rings assume the form of hexagons. The glucose molecule is more accurately pictured as follows:

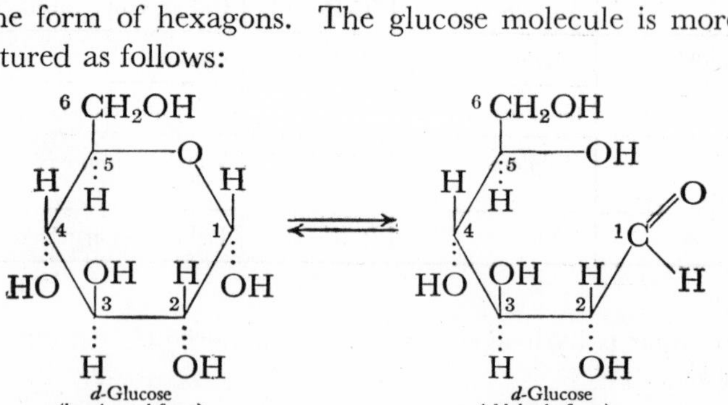

d-Glucose (hemiacetal form) — *d*-Glucose (aldehyde form)

There is a carbon atom (not shown in the formula) at each corner of the hexagon. The numbering of the carbon atoms corresponds to the numbering shown in the formulas on page 239. The solid lines extend above the plane of the ring, and dotted lines are below the plane of the ring. In the formulas on page 239 the atoms and groups on the right-hand side of the chain correspond to the atoms and groups below the plane of the hexagon. The formula for galactose may be written in a similar form, and the formula for lactose would then appear as two hexagons connected through an oxygen atom. When glucose and galactose combine, with loss of water, the water molecules are derived from the hydroxyl group on carbon (1) in the galactose unit and on carbon (4) in the glucose unit.

Starches are white, granular, insoluble substances found in wheat, rye, corn, potatoes, rice, and other plant products. They are represented by the formula $(C_6H_{10}O_5)_n$. The starch grains from different vegetable sources differ in size and form, but they are composed of the same fundamental materials. An outer coating of the granule bursts when starch is heated in water, and a water-soluble starch called amylose is released. The insoluble portion (about 80–90 per cent) is called amylopectin. Amylose is responsible for the blue color a starch solution gives with iodine; amylopectin with iodine gives a red-violet color. Amylose is hydrolyzed completely to maltose by the enzyme amylase, while amylopectin is only partially hydrolyzed by that enzyme. The diastase of malt is a mixture of enzymes that hydrolyzes starch completely to maltose. The maltose, in turn, is hydrolyzed to glucose in the presence of the enzyme *maltase*. A dilute, hot solution of acid also causes the hydrolysis of starch. Corn starch is converted by acidic hydrolysis to corn sirup, which is largely glucose. The digestion of starch follows the same course. An enzyme *ptyalin*, from the saliva and stomach, carries the hydrolysis of starch to the maltose stage, and the hydrolysis is completed in the intestinal tract under the influence of the enzyme maltase. The reverse process takes place in the liver and muscles when glucose is converted to animal starch, or glycogen.

The molecular weight of amylose ranges from 10,000 to 50,000; the higher figure represents about 300 glucose units. The glucosidic connections may be pictured as follows:

End group

The hydroxyl groups on carbon atoms number 1 and 4 of glucose hemiacetal are the ones used to link the glucose residues in the formation of starch. In amylose the chain of molecules is continuous, probably arranged like a spiral or spring; in amylopectin there are side chains, each consisting of about fifteen glucose units. These are attached to about every ninth glucose unit of the main chain. The molecular weight of amylopectin may be as high as 1,000,000, a value corresponding to 6000 glucose units. These differences in structure between amylose and amylopectin account for their different solubilities, their different colors with iodine, and the fact that different enzymes are required to hydrolyze them.

Glycogen. An amorphous carbohydrate of high molecular weight, $(C_6H_{10}O_5)_n$, known as glycogen or animal starch, is found in the liver and in all muscle cells of the body. Glycogen, like ordinary vegetable starch, yields but one monosaccharide, namely, glucose, when subjected to hydrolysis. In the living cells of animals the formation of glycogen from glucose occurs rapidly after a meal which is rich in carbohydrates. The reverse process, the regeneration of glucose from glycogen, occurs with equal readiness when the sugar content of the blood falls below the normal concentration. The pancreas is one of the sugar-regulating organs of the body, and disorders of the pancreas are often accompanied by an excess of sugar or a lack of sugar in the blood. Either condition may cause serious illness. Injection of insulin (derived from the pancreas) is a common treatment for diabetes, a disorder which appears when metabolism of the blood sugar fails and glucose in the blood reaches an abnormally high level.

Glycogen is structurally similar to amylopectin. It is not a single chain of glucose residues; it consists of a large number of shorter chains, joined together through glycosidic linkages, but not end to end.

The conversion of glucose to glycogen, and the reverse, is not simple dehydration and hydrolysis. The enzymes which produce the reversible change are accompanied by a source of phosphoric acid. The polymerization and depolymerization entail the formation of phosphoric esters of glucose.

Cellulose, $(C_6H_{10}O_5)_n$, constitutes the principal building material of the cell walls of plants. Like starch, it is a glucoside. On hydrolysis cellulose yields a disaccharide called cellobiose, and finally glucose, whereas starch hydrolyzes to maltose and then to glucose. Cellobiose is hydrolyzed by emulsin and not by maltase; it is a β-glucoside.

The chain length of cellulose is of the order of 1500 to 2000 glucose units, and the molecular weight varies from 300,000 to 500,000. The fibrous character of cellulose indicates a long chain structure. The strong cohesion of cellulose molecules results in extreme insolubility in water.

Cellulose in plants is associated with hemicellulose, lignins, resins, and inorganic substances. Pure cellulose is isolated by dissolving the resins in various solvents, then removing the lignins (noncarbohydrate materials) and hemicellulose by successive treatments with chlorine, sodium bisulfite, and dilute sodium hydroxide. The residue which survives these extractions is known as α-cellulose. Cotton is almost pure α-cellulose; wood celluloses are of shorter fibers and are less homogeneous, but they have the same composition as α-cellulose.

Cellulose is resistant to hydrolysis, and it cannot be utilized as a food by carnivorous animals. Snails and ruminating animals depend upon microorganisms in their digestive tracts to make cellulose available to them. Wood has been hydrolyzed by chemical treatment and converted into glucose.

Rayons are made of wood and other cellulose fibers. Fibers that are too short to be spun directly into threads may be used. In all cases the process depends upon converting the cellulose into a material which will dissolve, and which can be reprecipitated in the form of fine threads. In one method a copper hydroxide solution in ammonia (Schweitzer's reagent) is used. This reagent dissolves cellulose, and the cellulose is recovered in the form of threads when the solution is forced through fine holes into an acid bath. A *viscose* rayon is made by treating cellulose with sodium hydroxide and carbon disulfide, whereupon a product known as sodium cellulose xanthate is formed. From this dilute acids precipitate a thread of xanthic acid, which in turn loses carbon disulfide to regenerate the cellulose. If by ROH we represent one of the alcohol groups in cellulose, we may write for the process

$$\text{ROH} \xrightarrow{\text{NaOH}} \text{RONa} \xrightarrow{\text{CS}_2} \text{RO}-\text{C}\overset{S}{\underset{SNa}{<}}$$

$$\xrightarrow{\text{H}^+} \text{RO}-\text{C}\overset{S}{\underset{SH}{<}} \longrightarrow \text{ROH} + \text{CS}_2.$$

Cellophane is made by mixing viscose with a plasticizer and extruding the mixture in the form of a sheet.

Nitrated cellulose is used in the manufacture of smokeless powder, lacquers, and pyroxylin. Gun cotton is a fully nitrated cellulose. The three free hydroxyl groups present in each glucose unit are available for a reaction with nitric acid. The type reaction may be written as follows:

$$ROH + HONO_2 \xrightarrow{H_2SO_4} RONO_2 + H_2O$$

Specific reaction:

$$[C_6H_7O_2(OH)_3]_n + 3nHNO_3 \longrightarrow [C_6H_7O_2(ONO_2)_3]_n + 3nH_2O$$
Cellulose   Gun cotton

In making pyroxylin the nitration is carried only to the dinitrate stage. The product is soluble in an alcohol-ether mixture, and such solutions are marketed under the name *collodion*. Pyroxylin with camphor as a plasticizer forms celluloid; dissolved in butyl acetate, and with pigments and plasticizers added, it finds use as a lacquer.

Cellulose acetate is prepared from cellulose and glacial acetic acid, acetic anhydride, and sulfuric acid. The diacetate is soluble in acetone. The acetylation is liable to proceed to the triacetate stage, but a partial hydrolysis of the latter permits the desired diacetate to be manufactured. To produce a fiber of this composition an acetone solution of the compound is forced through a fine nozzle into warm air. The acetone evaporates, and fine threads of the synthetic textile are obtained. Cellulose diacetate finds wide use as a plastic. Combined with plasticizers it can be heated and injected into a mold; in sheets it is used in place of glass. By the use of mixed organic acids for esterification, mixed cellulose esters with a wide range of properties are prepared.

Cellulose ethers, prepared from alkyl chlorides, sodium hydroxide, and cellulose, constitute another class of useful plastics:

$$[C_6H_9O_4(OH)]_n \xrightarrow{NaOH} [C_6H_9O_4(ONa)]_n \xrightarrow{RCl} [C_6H_9O_4(OR)]_n$$
Cellulose   Cellulose ether

In all these products the degree of complexity of the cellulose molecule may be retained or the cellulose, through hydrolysis, may be degraded to smaller molecules. The variety of products in terms of hardness, solubility, softening point, wear resistance, brittleness, fiber strength, and so on is almost unlimited. Cellulose is a naturally occurring polymer of high molecular weight and of useful molecular shape. Its functional group is hydroxyl, which lends itself to many transformations. Yet for many purposes the plastics, resins, and fibers derived from synthetic polymers have superseded the cellulose derivatives.

EXERCISES

1. Illustrate by formulas and equations the terms (*a*) monosaccharide, (*b*) aldopentose, (*c*) ketohexose, (*d*) disaccharide, (*e*) polysaccharide.

2. How many stereoisomers exist corresponding to the formulas CH_2OH—$CHOH$—CHO and CH_2OH—$CHOH$—$CHOH$—CHO? Write the projection formulas for all isomers in each case.

3. Give the names of two naturally occurring aldopentoses, three aldohexoses, and one ketohexose.

4. The carbohydrates, like other alcohols, form acetates with acetic anhydride. What is the formula of the triacetate of cellulose, if cellulose has the formula $[C_6H_7O_2(OH)_3]_n$?

5. As an aldehyde a sugar reacts with (1) hydroxylamine to form an oxime, (2) with one of its own hydroxyl groups to form a hemiacetal, and (3) with a different alcohol to form a glycoside. Represent these reactions by equations and structural formulas. Use glucose as the sugar in each case.

6. What is meant by the mutarotation of a freshly prepared solution of a sugar? What change in structure accompanies the phenomenon?

7. What are the ultimate hydrolysis products of each of the following carbohydrates: (*a*) sucrose (cane and beet sugar)? (*b*) maltose? (*c*) lactose? (*d*) starch? (*e*) glycogen? (*f*) cellulose?

22 · REACTIONS AND STRUCTURES
OF THE MONOSACCHARIDES

The reactions of the simple sugars are, in part, those to be expected of aldehydes, ketones, and alcohols; but some deviations from the simple type reactions are to be expected because of the presence in the same molecule of two functional groups. One example of such variation has already been presented, the formation of cyclic hemiacetals. Another example is found in the reduction of Tollens's reagent and Fehling's solution by hydroxy ketones. A third example will be found in the reactions of phenylhydrazine with the monosaccharides.

Reactions of the Sugars

1. **Oxidation by Fehling's and Tollens's reagents.** Some carbohydrates precipitate metallic silver from Tollens's solution, and cuprous oxide (Cu_2O) from Fehling's solution; other carbohydrates fail to reduce these reagents. Sugars which reduce Fehling's solution and Tollens's reagent are called reducing sugars; the others are nonreducing sugars. Sucrose is a nonreducing sugar, while its isomers, lactose and maltose, are reducing sugars. All the unsubstituted monosaccharides are reducing sugars. It often happens that we find in nature a glucose derivative of unknown structure, and as a preliminary step in a study of the compound we apply the ordinary aldehyde tests. If the compound does not reduce Fehling's solution, we know at once that some substituting group, which we may designate as **B**, renders the hemiacetal system of the sugar inactive because the reducing action is associated with that part of the molecule. The substituting group, **B**, could occupy any other position in the molecule without modifying the capacity of the sugar to reduce Fehling's solution.

A glucose derivative which acts as a reducing agent must be represented as an ether, not as a glucoside. In lactose, which is composed of glucose and galactose, one hexose unit is glycosidic and nonreducing; the other has a hemiacetal structure. Lactose is a reducing sugar. It can be shown that glucose is the reducing unit; hence lactose is a galactoside, not a glucoside.

250

$$\begin{array}{c}
\text{H--C}\!\!=\!\!\!=\!\!\text{OB} \\
| \\
\text{H--C--OH} \\
| \\
\text{HO--C--H} \qquad \Big|\;\text{O} \\
| \\
\text{H--C--OH} \\
| \\
\text{H--C} \\
| \\
\text{CH}_2\text{OH}
\end{array}
\qquad
\begin{array}{c}
\text{H--C}\!\!=\!\!\!=\!\!\text{OH} \\
| \\
\text{H--C--OH} \\
| \\
\text{HO--C--H} \qquad \Big|\;\text{O} \\
| \\
\text{H--C--OB} \\
| \\
\text{H--C} \\
| \\
\text{CH}_2\text{OH}
\end{array}
\qquad
\begin{array}{c}
\text{H--C}\!\!=\!\!\!=\!\!\text{OH} \\
| \\
\text{H--C--OH} \\
| \\
\text{HO--C--H} \qquad \Big|\;\text{O} \\
| \\
\text{H--C--OH} \\
| \\
\text{H--C} \\
| \\
\text{CH}_2\text{OB}
\end{array}$$

A Nonreducing Glucose Derivative   **Reducing Glucose Derivatives**

2. Oxidation by other reagents. Oxidation of aldoses to monocarboxylic acids and dicarboxylic acids has already been mentioned (p. 236), as well as the biological oxidation to "uronic" acids (as in glucuronic acid). Ketoses, on oxidation, yield acids of shorter carbon chains. In alkaline solution oxidation and enolization of a ketone proceed simultaneously, with the result that alkaline permanganate, which attacks double bonds, converts a hexose into acids of two, three, four, and five carbon atoms. The way an aldehyde or a ketone is ruptured may be indicated as follows:

$$
\begin{array}{c}
| \\
\text{C}\!\!=\!\!\text{O} \\
| \\
\text{H--C--OH} \\
|
\end{array}
\;\underset{}{\overset{\text{OH}^-}{\rightleftharpoons}}\;
\begin{array}{c}
| \\
\text{C--OH} \\
\| \\
\text{C--OH} \\
|
\end{array}
\;\overset{\text{Ox.}}{\longrightarrow}\;
\begin{array}{c}
| \\
\text{COOH} \\
\\
\text{COOH} \\
|
\end{array}
$$

Aldehyde or   Enol or   Acids of lower
ketone   "enediol"   molecular weight

The acids corresponding to the sugars form lactones readily:

$$
\begin{array}{c}
\text{COOH} \\
| \\
\text{H--C--OH} \\
| \\
\text{HO--C--H} \\
| \\
\text{H--C--OH} \\
| \\
\text{H--C--OH} \\
| \\
\text{CH}_2\text{OH}
\end{array}
\quad\underset{\text{Heat}}{\overset{}{\rightleftharpoons}}\quad
\begin{array}{c}
\text{O}\!\!=\!\!\text{C} \\
| \\
\text{H--C--OH} \\
| \\
\text{HO--C--H} \qquad \Big|\;\text{O} \\
| \\
\text{H--C} \\
| \\
\text{H--C--OH} \\
| \\
\text{CH}_2\text{OH}
\end{array}
\quad + \text{H}_2\text{O}
$$

Gluconic acid   Gluconolactone

The carboxyl group may react with a hydroxyl group in the γ or the δ position to form a five-membered ring or a six-membered ring. The more stable lactone is the one formed with the γ-carbinol group.

3. **Addition of HCN.** The addition of HCN to a monosaccharide produces two cyanohydrins. In the formulas written below, the part of the molecule which remains unchanged is blocked out.

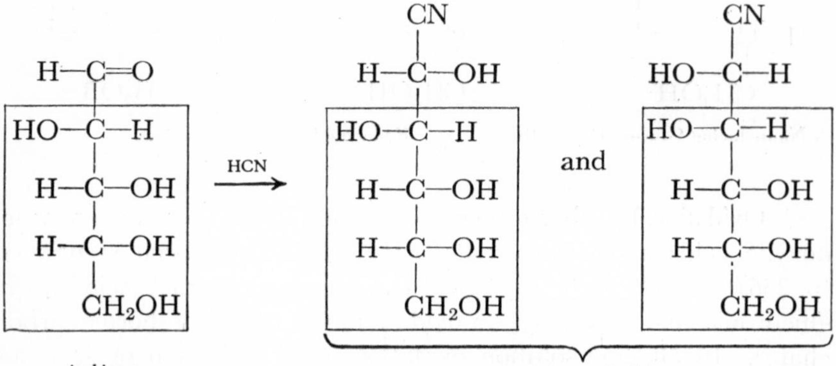

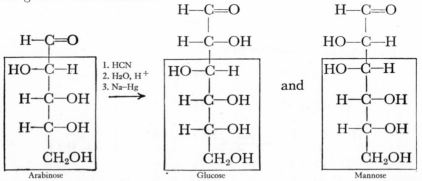

Arabinose   Isomeric cyanohydrins

The carbon atom of the original CHO group is rendered asymmetric by the addition of HCN, and two configurations are possible. The CN groups of the two cyanohydrins can be hydrolyzed to carboxyl groups by hot hydrochloric acid, and the resulting hydroxy acids form lactones spontaneously. Lactones are reduced to aldehydes by sodium amalgam. In this way two hexoses are made from a pentose. The hexoses corresponding to the two cyanohydrins shown above are glucose and mannose:

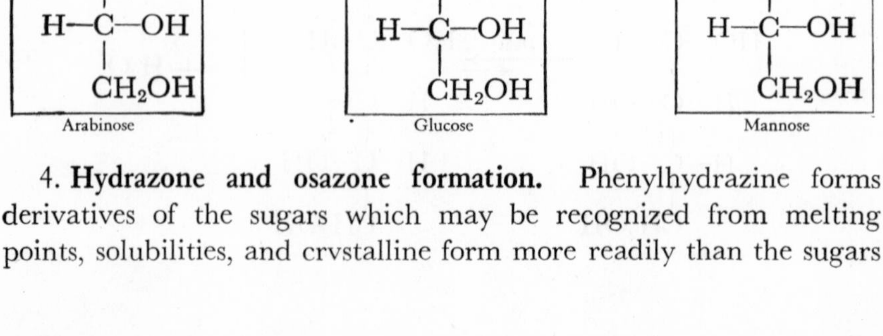

4. **Hydrazone and osazone formation.** Phenylhydrazine forms derivatives of the sugars which may be recognized from melting points, solubilities, and crystalline form more readily than the sugars

themselves can be identified. These derivatives are called osazones. The first product formed from a sugar and phenylhydrazine is a hydrazone:

$$
\begin{array}{ccc}
\begin{array}{l}
\text{CHO} \\
| \\
\text{CHOH} \\
| \\
(\text{CHOH})_3 \\
| \\
\text{CH}_2\text{OH} \\
\text{An aldose}
\end{array}
&
\xrightarrow{\text{C}_6\text{H}_5\text{NHNH}_2}
&
\begin{array}{l}
\text{CH}{=}\text{N}{-}\text{NH}{-}\text{C}_6\text{H}_5 \\
| \\
\text{CHOH} \\
| \\
(\text{CHOH})_3 \qquad\qquad +\,\text{H}_2\text{O} \\
| \\
\text{CH}_2\text{OH} \\
\text{A hydrazone}
\end{array}
\end{array}
$$

In the presence of an excess of the reagent the hydrazone is oxidized to a ketohydrazone, and a molecule of phenylhydrazine is reduced simultaneously to aniline and ammonia:

$$
\begin{array}{ccc}
\begin{array}{l}
\text{CH}{=}\text{N}{-}\text{NH}{-}\text{C}_6\text{H}_5 \\
| \\
\text{CHOH} \\
| \\
(\text{CHOH})_3 \\
| \\
\text{CH}_2\text{OH}
\end{array}
&
\xrightarrow{\text{C}_6\text{H}_5\text{NHNH}_2}
&
\begin{array}{l}
\text{CH}{=}\text{N}{-}\text{NH}{-}\text{C}_6\text{H}_5 \\
| \\
\text{C}{=}\text{O} \\
| \qquad\qquad +\,\text{C}_6\text{H}_5\text{NH}_2 + \text{NH}_3 \\
(\text{CHOH})_3 \\
| \\
\text{CH}_2\text{OH}
\end{array}
\end{array}
$$

A third molecule of phenylhydrazine then acts upon this ketone, with the production of a yellow, crystalline, insoluble osazone:

$$
\begin{array}{ccc}
\begin{array}{l}
\text{CH}{=}\text{N}{-}\text{NH}{-}\text{C}_6\text{H}_5 \\
| \\
\text{C}{=}\text{O} \\
| \\
(\text{CHOH})_3 \\
| \\
\text{CH}_2\text{OH}
\end{array}
&
\xrightarrow{\text{C}_6\text{H}_5\text{NHNH}_2}
&
\begin{array}{l}
\text{CH}{=}\text{N}{-}\text{NH}{-}\text{C}_6\text{H}_5 \\
| \\
\text{C}{=}\text{N}{-}\text{NH}{-}\text{C}_6\text{H}_5 \\
| \qquad\qquad\qquad +\,\text{H}_2\text{O} \\
(\text{CHOH})_3 \\
| \\
\text{CH}_2\text{OH} \\
\text{An osazone}
\end{array}
\end{array}
$$

Glucose, fructose, and mannose give the same osazone, which proves that they differ only in configuration about the first and second carbon atoms in the chain. Isomeric sugars which give different osazones must differ at other points in the molecules.

5. **Reduction of monosaccharides.** The sugars are easily reduced to the corresponding polyhydric alcohols. Either metallic sodium in alcohol, or hydrogen gas in contact with platinum or palladium,

may be used to accomplish this reduction. Glucose is reduced to sorbitol:

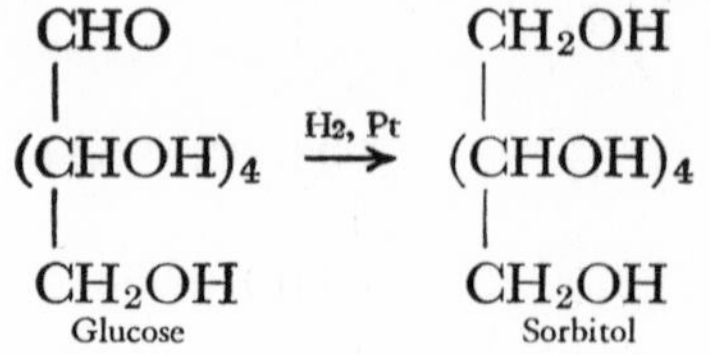

$$\begin{array}{ccc}
CHO & & CH_2OH \\
| & & | \\
(CHOH)_4 & \xrightarrow{H_2,\ Pt} & (CHOH)_4 \\
| & & | \\
CH_2OH & & CH_2OH \\
\text{Glucose} & & \text{Sorbitol}
\end{array}$$

In alkaline media sorbitol reduction is accompanied by tautomerism; and when sodium in alcohol is used as the reducing agent, glucose yields a mixture of mannitol and sorbitol. These alcohols differ in configuration about carbon number two. Mannitol is found in many plants. It is the main constituent of manna, the dried juice of various species of manna plants; it is obtained from mannose by reduction.

6. **Formation of hemiacetals and glycosides.** The reactions leading to the formation of hemiacetals and glycosides from monosaccharides were considered in the preceding chapter (pp. 238 and 240).

7. **Acetylation.** When a sugar is warmed with acetic anhydride and acetic acid, the hydroxyl groups are esterified. The complete acetylation of glucose results in the formation of a pentaacetyl derivative:

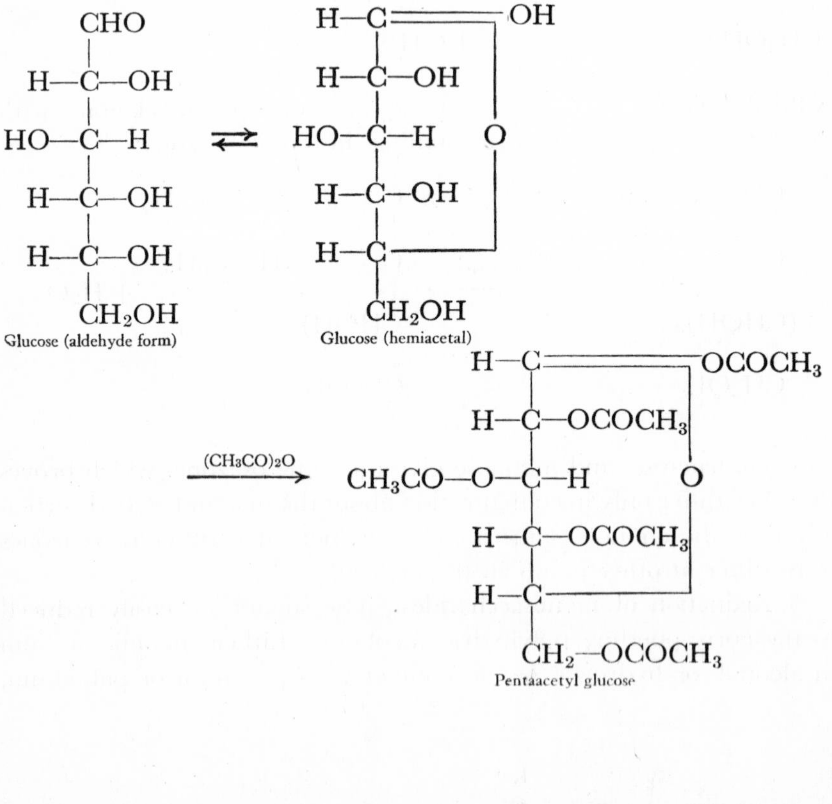

Glucose (aldehyde form) ⇌ Glucose (hemiacetal) →(CH₃CO)₂O→ Pentaacetyl glucose

Sucrose yields an octaacetyl derivative. The number of acetyl groups which can be introduced into a carbohydrate by treatment with acetic anhydride or acetyl chloride corresponds to the number of hydroxyl groups in the carbohydrate molecule.

Alkylation. When a hexose (such as glucose) is warmed with methanol and hydrogen chloride, an acetal is formed. Only one methyl group is introduced into the sugar molecule in this way; only one of the five hydroxyl groups reacts with the alcohol. The hydroxyl group which reacts is the one which is formed as a result of the hemiacetal ring formation, and the methylated sugar formed in this way does not display mutarotation and does not reduce Fehling's solution.

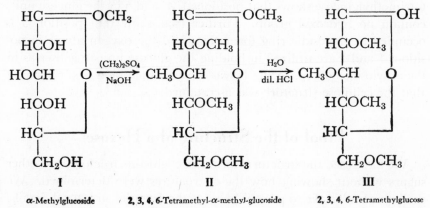

Glucose (hemiacetal form)   Methyl glucoside (an acetal)

Further methylation of the sugar can be achieved by using methyl sulfate in alkaline solution as the alkylating agent; and when the pentamethyl derivative, formed in this way, is heated with a dilute acid solution, only one of the five methyl groups is removed by hydrolysis. This is the glucosidic methyl group, the one formed in the acetal type of union. These facts are summarized by the following formulas:

I   II   III

α-Methylglucoside   2, 3, 4, 6-Tetramethyl-α-methyl-glucoside   2, 3, 4, 6-Tetramethylglucose

In solution the α-hemiacetal form of the methylated sugar, III, is in equilibrium with the aldehyde form, IV, and the β-form, V, as shown below:

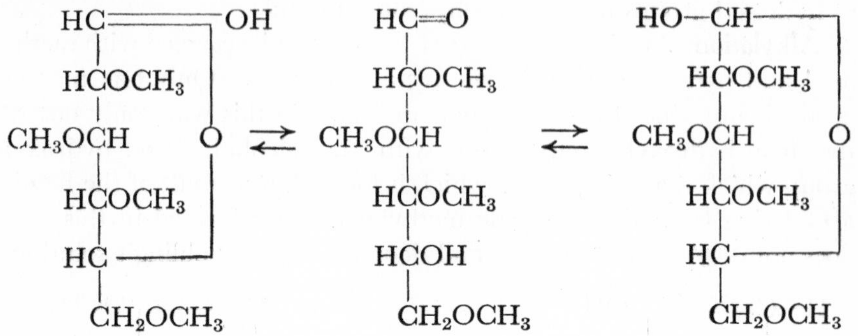

$$
\begin{array}{ccc}
\text{HC}\!\!=\!\!\!-\text{OH} & \text{HC}\!\!=\!\!\text{O} & \text{HO}\!-\!\text{CH}\!-\!\!\! \\
| \quad\quad\; | & | & | \quad\quad\quad | \\
\text{HCOCH}_3 \;\; | & \text{HCOCH}_3 & \text{HCOCH}_3 \\
| \quad\quad\; | & | & | \quad\quad\quad | \\
\text{CH}_3\text{OCH} \quad\; \text{O} & \rightleftarrows \;\; \text{CH}_3\text{OCH} \;\; \rightleftarrows & \text{CH}_3\text{OCH} \quad\; \text{O} \\
| \quad\quad\; | & | & | \quad\quad\quad | \\
\text{HCOCH}_3 \;\; | & \text{HCOCH}_3 & \text{HCOCH}_3 \\
| \quad\quad\; | & | & | \quad\quad\quad | \\
\text{HC}\!-\!\!\!-\!\!\!| & \text{HCOH} & \text{HC}\!-\!\!\!-\!\! \\
| & | & | \\
\text{CH}_2\text{OCH}_3 & \text{CH}_2\text{OCH}_3 & \text{CH}_2\text{OCH}_3 \\
\text{III} & \text{IV} & \text{V}
\end{array}
$$

The unsubstituted hydroxyl group in formula IV marks the position at which the ring in the original glucoside, I, was closed. This position can be determined experimentally; for the group HCOH in formula IV is readily oxidized to a ketone group, and further oxidation converts it to a carboxyl group by rupturing the carbon chain at this point. Treatment with nitric acid, for instance, converts the tetramethylglucose (prepared as described above) into trimethoxyglutaric acid, carbon dioxide, and water, indicating that in the original monomethylglucoside carbon atoms 1 and 5 were linked to each other through the oxygen atom.

Cellulose is alkylated by treatment with concentrated sodium hydroxide and ethyl chloride or methyl chloride. The fact that fully methylated cellulose, upon acidic hydrolysis, produces largely 2, 3, 6-trimethylglucose shows that positions 1, 4, and 5 in the glucose units contain no hydroxyl group. Further facts show that position 5 is occupied in glucosidic ring formation, and the oxygen atoms in positions 1 and 4 are utilized in holding the glucose units together as in the amylose chain (p. 245). It was through such facts and reasoning that the cellulose structure was ascertained.

Proof of the Structure of a Hexose

We have used the structural formulas of glucose, fructose, and other sugars without showing how these structures were determined. We shall now undertake to present proof of the essential structural details.

Let us review the facts we have already learned about the sugars and correlate these facts with the structures which, up to this point, we have assumed to be correct.

A molecular formula is established easily through a consideration of the percentage composition of a compound and its molecular weight. It is a far more difficult task to determine the structural arrangement of the atoms within the molecule. Analyses of glucose, fructose, mannose, and a number of other sugars show that they all have the same composition, namely, carbon 40.00 per cent, hydrogen 6.66 per cent, and oxygen 53.33 per cent. The empirical formula is, then, $(CH_2O)_x$. The molecular weight is obtained from measurements of the freezing points of solutions of these sugars. It is found that each of these sugars has a molecular weight of 180. Each member of this large group of sugars must therefore have the same formula, namely, $(CH_2O)_6$ or $C_6H_{12}O_6$. They are isomers. They differ in melting points, solubilities, sweetness, optical activity, and other properties; these differences are due to different arrangements of the atoms in the molecules.

To determine the molecular structure of any one of these sugars we must apply logical reasoning to a variety of experimental facts. Let us deal with glucose as a representative of the simple sugars.

1. To obtain a survey of the carbon skeleton it is first observed that glucose cannot be hydrolyzed by heating it with a dilute acid or base; it does not yield by hydrolysis any substance of fewer than six carbon atoms per molecule. Therefore the carbon atoms are joined together in either a straight chain, a branched chain, or a ring, with no ether, ester, or acetal bonds. By converting glucose to some substance of known carbon skeleton the arrangement of the carbon atoms can be ascertained. Digestion of almost any aliphatic carbon-oxygen compound with concentrated hydriodic acid in the presence of phosphorus reduces the compound to either a hydrocarbon or an organic iodide. Glucose reacts in part as follows:

$C_{10}H_{12}O_6$ + 13 HI (conc)
Glucose

$$\xrightarrow{300°} CH_3—CH_2—CH_2—CH_2—CHI—CH_3 + 6\ I_2 + 6\ H_2O$$
2-Iodohexane

The iodine produced reacts with the phosphorus and water, and HI is regenerated.

$$6\ I_2 + 4\ P + 12\ H_2O \longrightarrow 12\ HI + 4\ H_3PO_3$$

The product obtained from glucose in this reduction (2-iodohexane) has a normal carbon chain (it can be reduced to normal hexane);

therefore the six carbon atoms of glucose are in a continuous chain (straight chain).

2. The chemical reactions of glucose serve to detect the presence of its functional groups. The sugar is neutral; therefore there is no carboxyl group. In the absence of ether, ester and acetal linkages, and carboxyl groups there remain only hydroxyl, ketone, and aldehyde groups to consider in accounting for the oxygen atoms. Glucose forms an oxime and a phenylhydrazone; it adds one molecule of HCN to form a cyanohydrin. These are reactions of the carbonyl group; that is, glucose is an aldehyde or a ketone.

The usual differentiation between aldehydes and ketones depends upon reduction of Fehling's solution and Tollens's reagent and the coloration of Schiff's reagent. The last is not given by glucose; and the first two reagents are of no value in this case because hydroxy ketones as well as aldehydes precipitate cuprous oxide and metallic silver from Fehling's and Tollens's solutions respectively. These reagents serve only to distinguish simple aldehydes from simple ketones.

Glucose can be oxidized by bromine water to an acid of six carbon atoms. The acid corresponds to the formula $C_6H_{12}O_7$. Only an aldehyde or a primary alcohol can yield an acid upon oxidation without rupture of the carbon chain. An alcohol upon oxidation *loses* two hydrogen atoms, while an aldehyde merely *adds* one oxygen atom. The type reactions are as follows:

$$R—CH_2OH \xrightarrow{Ox.} R—COOH + H_2O$$

$$R—CHO \xrightarrow{Ox.} R—COOH$$

Glucose is therefore an aldehyde, not a ketone. The fact that glucose easily reduces Fehling's and Tollens's solutions is consistent with this conclusion.

The five oxygen atoms so far unaccounted for in glucose are present as hydroxyl groups. This is shown by acetylation with acetic anhydride. In each hydroxyl group the hydrogen atom is replaced by an acetyl group. A simple alcohol reacts with acetic anhydride as follows:

$$ROH + (CH_3CO)_2O \longrightarrow R—O—CO—CH_3 + CH_3COOH$$

Glucose reacts in the same way, and the formula of the fully acetylated product is found to be $C_{16}H_{22}O_{11}$.

$$C_6H_{12}O_6 + 5(CH_3CO)_2O \longrightarrow C_{16}H_{22}O_{11} + 5\ CH_3COOH$$

Five acetyl groups replace five hydrogen atoms.

3. The simplest structure which conforms to the facts so far established is CH_2OH—$CHOH$—$CHOH$—$CHOH$—$CHOH$—CHO. If any two of the five hydroxyl groups were attached to a single carbon atom, water would be easily lost, and a second carbonyl group would be formed. This is not the case, as shown by the fact that glucose reacts with only one molecule of HCN. The five hydroxyl groups are distributed evenly between the five carbon atoms, and the tetravalence of the carbon atoms is completed by attachment of the necessary hydrogen atoms.

4. Nitric acid oxidizes glucose to saccharic acid, a dibasic acid having the composition and molecular weight represented by the formula $C_6H_{10}O_8$. It will be recalled that the milder oxidizing agent, bromine water, produced a monobasic acid, $C_6H_{12}O_7$. The two groups which can be oxidized to carboxyl without rupture of a carbon chain are the aldehyde group, CHO, and the primary alcohol group, CH_2OH. Bromine water oxidizes the aldehyde group; nitric acid converts both groups to COOH.

The formula for glucose is thus established as shown above. We should have arrived at the same result if we had dealt with mannose or galactose. There are, in fact, sixteen sugars to which this formula would be assigned. The properties which differentiate the members of this group of sixteen sugars are determined by the arrangements in space of the hydrogen atoms and hydroxyl groups around the four asymmetric carbon atoms.

Stereochemistry

The possible arrangements of the hydrogen atoms and hydroxyl groups around asymmetric centers are indicated in the table on page 260. The simplest aldose, glycerose, has only one asymmetric center, and it exists in two forms:

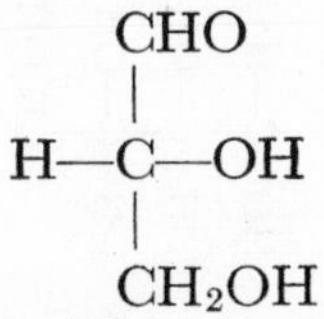

$$
\begin{array}{cc}
\text{CHO} & \text{CHO} \\
| & | \\
\text{H—C—OH} & \text{HO—C—H} \\
| & | \\
\text{CH}_2\text{OH} & \text{CH}_2\text{OH} \\
\textit{d}\text{-Glycerose} & \textit{l}\text{-Glycerose}
\end{array}
$$

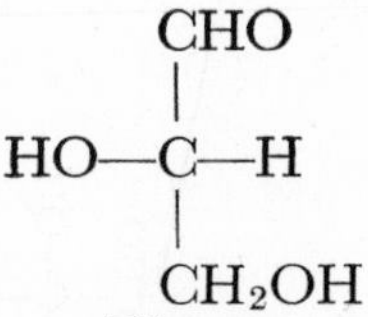

Four tetroses can be made from the two glyceroses by the cyanohydrin synthesis (p. 252). They are d- and l-threose and d- and l-erythrose. Each additional —CHOH— group permits two new arrangements

d AND *l* SERIES OF SUGARS

The configurations of the *d* and *l* glyceroses
are assigned arbitrarily.

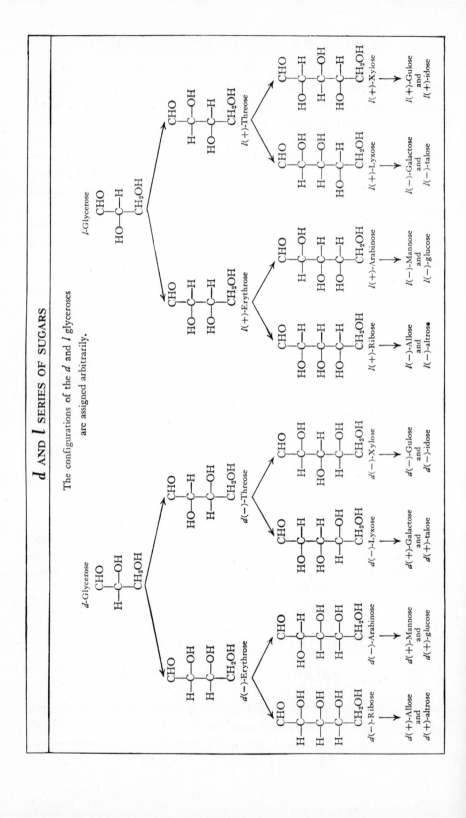

from the corresponding lower aldose, as indicated in the chart. If n is the number of asymmetric centers in an aldose, the number of optical isomers is 2^n. These exist in pairs of mirror images. Thus there are eight pairs of aldohexoses, or sixteen stereoisomers. The stereo configurations of several naturally occurring sugars have been given (pp. 233, 241, 244, 260).

Proof of the stereochemical structure of each individual sugar involves the study of many additional reactions. It is beyond the scope of this course to establish the orientation of the atoms and groups attached to each asymmetric carbon atom. The existence of more than one crystalline form of each of the sixteen hexoses, as illustrated by α-d-glucose and β-d-glucose (p. 239), is not accounted for in the chart on page 260. The phenomenon of mutarotation, which is exhibited by all reducing sugars, makes necessary a revision of the formulas as they appear in the chart. The possibility of forming cyclic hemiacetals in which the aldehydic carbon becomes an asymmetric atom increases the number of isomeric forms of the sugars.

Stereoisomers which are mirror images of each other exist in pairs called enantiomorphic forms or optical isomers. Examples of the structural relationship between such pairs have been found in d- and l-tartaric acid, d- and l-glucose, d-and l-galactose, and so on. Meso-tartaric acid, on the other hand, is a stereoisomer of d-tartaric acid and of l-tartaric acid, but it is not a mirror image of either of them. Meso-tartaric acid and d-tartaric acid are not enantiomorphic compounds. They present a type of space isomerism to which the name *diastereo-isomerism* has been applied. Diastereoisomers are isomers of the optical type (they contain asymmetric centers), but they are not mirror images of each other. Enantiomorphic isomers differ in only one property, namely, optical activity; but diastereoisomers differ to some extent in all properties.

EXERCISES

1. Represent by structural formulas the following: (a) α-methylglucoside, (b) β-methylglucoside.

NOTE. Assume a pyranose, or 1, 5-oxide, ring.

2. What is meant by a reducing sugar: (a) in terms of experimental results? (b) in terms of structure? Write the structures of two methyl derivatives of glucose, one reducing and one nonreducing.

3. Complete and balance equations for the formation of the phenylosazone of (*a*) glucose, (*b*) fructose, (*c*) mannose. If these three sugars form the same osazone, how do the structures of the free sugars differ?

4. Summarize the arguments which lead to the conclusion that an aldohexose has the formula $CH_2OH—(CHOH)_4—CHO$. State how nonreducing methylglycosides force a revision of this structure.

5. Some rayons are acetyl and alkyl derivatives of cellulose. State how such rayons are made.

6. By what chemical tests could you distinguish between a solution of glucose and a solution of sucrose?

PROBLEMS

1. Express in equations a method of preparing glucose from arabinose.

2. Explain the fact that two cyanohydrins are formed from a monosaccharide and HCN.

3. A carboxylic acid which is represented by the empirical formula $C_3H_6O_4$ reacts with acetic anhydride to yield an acid of the formula $C_7H_{10}O_6$. How many hydroxyl groups are there in each molecule of the original acid? Write a possible structural formula for each of the acids.

4. If a hexose is largely in the hemiacetal form, how do you account for the completeness of oxime and hydrazone formation, and for complete oxidation by Fehling's solution?

23 · PROTEINS AND AMINO ACIDS

Proteins constitute the major part of the solid matter in the skin, muscle, blood, hair, and nails of animal organisms. In smaller quantities they are found also in plants. All living cells of both plants and animals contain proteins.

Composition of proteins. The proteins obtained from different sources differ widely in chemical and physical properties, but they are very much alike in elementary composition. All proteins contain nitrogen, carbon, hydrogen, and oxygen. Sulfur, phosphorus, and a few other elements are found in many proteins. Analyses of hundreds of protein substances have indicated compositions between the limits shown below.

	Percentage		Percentage
Carbon	51–55	Sulfur	0–3
Oxygen	20–24	Phosphorus	0–1
Nitrogen	15–18	Other elements	0–1
Hydrogen	5–7		

The proteins fall into two general groups: (1) the insoluble, fibrous substances which form the major part of wool, silk, hair, nails, feathers, and connective tissues; (2) proteins which are soluble in either water, alcohol-water mixtures, dilute acids, dilute alkalies, or salt solutions. The soluble group includes egg albumin, the albumin and globulin of blood serum, the casein of milk, and proteins found in the germs of wheat, rice, barley, and corn. The proteins are complex substances, varying in molecular weight from 17,000 to several million.

The study of proteins has been hampered by difficulty in purification of the compounds, and difficulty also in determining when purification has been achieved. Substances of high molecular weight do not crystallize readily, and the ordinary criterion of purity—a sharp melting point—can seldom be applied. In a crude sample the protein may be mixed with other types of substances, or may even be a mixture of several proteins which differ slightly in composition and properties. In some cases substances which appear to be impurities may turn out to be necessary adjuncts to the proteins as far as their biological functions are concerned. For instance, some enzymes are combinations of specific proteins and vitamins. Fortunately, it is not necessary to purify a compound to the point where we are certain that there is only one kind of molecule present before proceeding to study its composition. Some information as to its real nature is often necessary before systematic methods of purification can be devised.

The general mode of attack on the problem of protein chemistry follows the pattern used in the case of the polysaccharides. A moderately pure sample is subjected to hydrolysis in either acidic or basic solution. By this procedure many compounds of high molecular weight are broken down to simpler substances, or even to one simple substance. If the building blocks produced in this way can be separated and recognized, the next problem is to determine how they were put together in the original complex mass. In 1820 Braconnot subjected gelatin to hydrolysis in dilute sulfuric acid, and he isolated glycine, a substance which was identified later as aminoacetic acid, H_2N-CH_2-COOH. This was the first amino acid obtained from a protein by hydrolysis. A polysaccharide, when hydrolyzed, usually yields a single simple sugar. A protein, when hydrolyzed, yields a great variety of simple amino acids. A comparison of the results of hydrolysis in the two cases may be indicated as follows:

$$\text{Starch} \xrightarrow{H_2O} \text{dextrins} \xrightarrow{H_2O} \text{maltose} \xrightarrow{H_2O} \text{glucose}$$

$$\text{Protein} \xrightarrow{H_2O} \text{proteans} \xrightarrow{H_2O} \text{proteoses} \xrightarrow{H_2O} \text{peptones} \xrightarrow{H_2O} \text{polypep-}$$
$$\text{tides} \xrightarrow{H_2O} \text{dipeptides} \xrightarrow{H_2O} \text{amino acids}$$

Twenty-four amino acids have been definitely identified as components of proteins; nine other amino acids have been reported as members of the group; and still others may be added to the list as studies in this field are continued.

Amino Acids Isolated from Proteins

GROUP I. AMINO ACIDS HAVING AN EQUAL NUMBER OF ACIDIC AND BASIC GROUPS. WEAKLY AMPHOTERIC COMPOUNDS

A. Aliphatic Acyclic Acids

1. *Glycine:* CH_2NH_2-COOH

2. *Alanine:* CH_3-CHNH_2-COOH

3. *Valine:*
$$\begin{matrix} CH_3 \\ \diagdown \\ \diagup \\ CH_3 \end{matrix} CH-CHNH_2-COOH$$

4. *Leucine:*
$$\begin{matrix} CH_3 \\ \diagdown \\ \diagup \\ CH_3 \end{matrix} CH-CH_2-CHNH_2-COOH$$

5. *Norleucine:* CH_3—CH_2—CH_2—CH_2—$CHNH_2$—$COOH$

6. *Isoleucine:* $\begin{matrix} CH_3 \\ \diagdown \\ \diagup \\ C_2H_5 \end{matrix}$ CH—$CHNH_2$—$COOH$

7. *Serine:* CH_2OH—$CHNH_2$—$COOH$

8. *Cysteine:* CH_2SH—$CHNH_2$—$COOH$

9. *Threonine:* CH_3—$CHOH$—$CHNH_2$—$COOH$

10. *Cystine:*
$$\begin{matrix} CH_2-S-S-CH_2 \\ | \qquad\qquad | \\ CHNH_2 \qquad CHNH_2 \\ | \qquad\qquad | \\ COOH \qquad COOH \end{matrix}$$

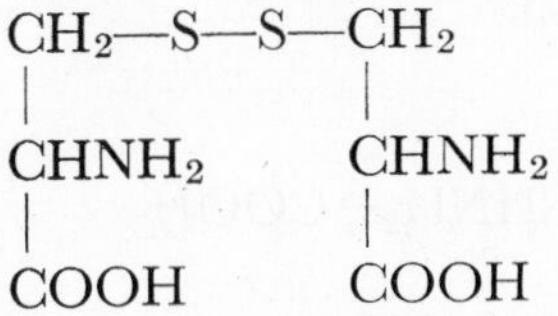

11. *Methionine:* CH_3—S—CH_2—CH_2—$CHNH_2$—$COOH$

B. Aromatic Derivatives of Alanine

12. *Phenylalanine:* C_6H_5—CH_2—$CHNH_2$—$COOH$

13. *Tyrosine:* p-HO—C_6H_4—CH_2—$CHNH_2$—$COOH$

14. *Tryptophan:*
$$\begin{matrix} C-CH_2-CHNH_2-COOH \\ \diagup\diagdown \\ C_6H_4 \qquad CH \\ \diagdown\diagup \\ NH \end{matrix}$$

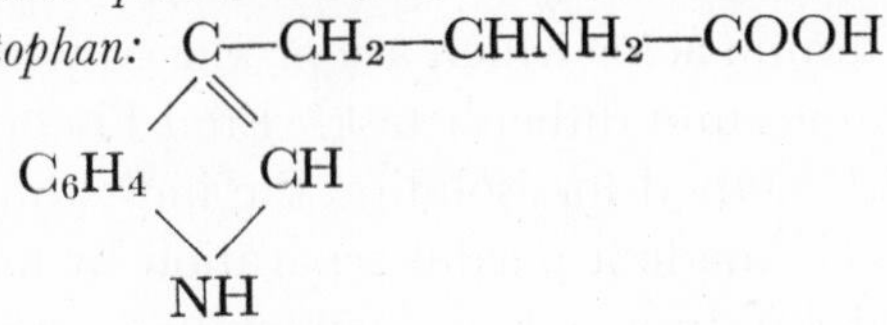

15. *Thyroxine:* HO—⬡—O—⬡—CH_2—$CHNH_2$—$COOH$ (with I substituents)

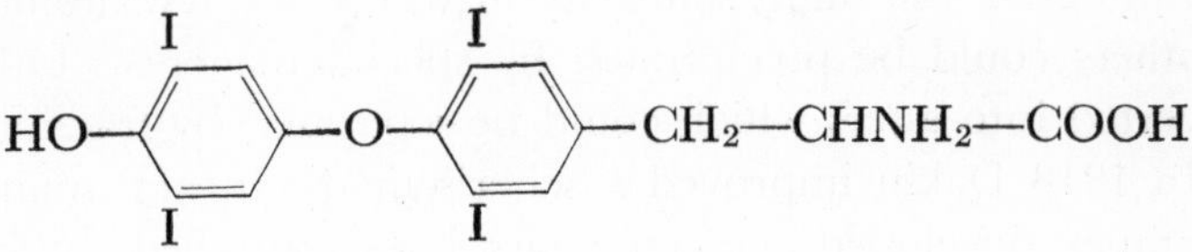

16. *Iodogorgoic acid:* HO—⬡—CH_2—$CHNH_2$—$COOH$ (with I substituents)

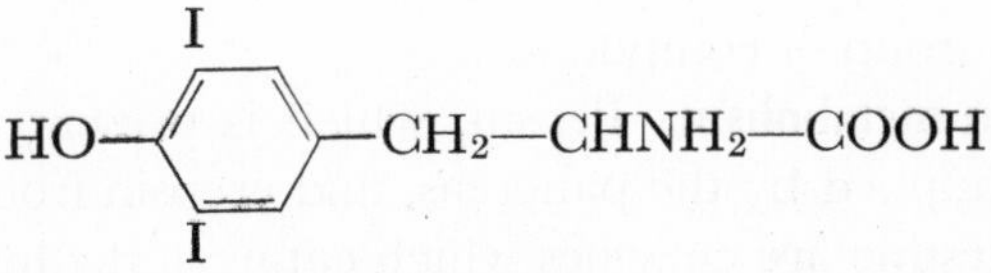

C. Pyrrolidine Carboxylic Acids. Heterocyclic Secondary Amines

17. *Proline:*
$$\begin{matrix} CH_2-CH_2 \\ | \qquad\quad | \\ CH_2 \quad CH-COOH \\ \diagdown\;\diagup \\ NH \end{matrix}$$

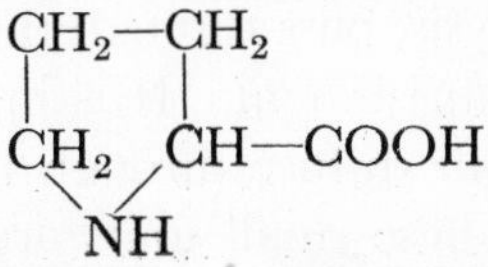

18. *Hydroxyproline:*
$$\begin{matrix} CH_2-CHOH \\ | \qquad\quad | \\ CH_2 \quad CH-COOH \\ \diagdown\;\diagup \\ NH \end{matrix}$$

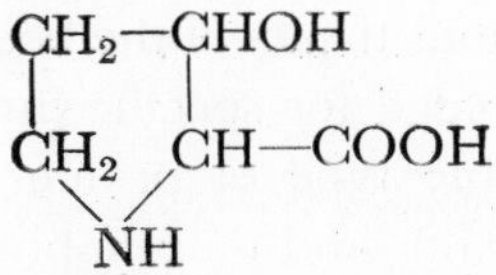

GROUP II. AMINO ACIDS HAVING FEWER ACIDIC THAN BASIC GROUPS.
PREDOMINANTLY BASIC

19. *Arginine:* $HN\!=\!C\Big\langle\begin{array}{l}NH_2\\ NH\!-\!CH_2\!-\!CH_2\!-\!CH_2\!-\!CHNH_2\!-\!COOH\end{array}$

20. *Lysine:* $H_2N\!-\!CH_2\!-\!CH_2\!-\!CH_2\!-\!CH_2\!-\!CHNH_2\!-\!COOH$

21. *Histidine:*

$$\begin{array}{c}CH\\ \diagup\;\diagdown\\ N\quad\;NH\\ |\qquad\;|\\ CH\!=\!C\!-\!CH_2\!-\!CHNH_2\!-\!COOH\end{array}$$

GROUP III. AMINO ACIDS HAVING FEWER BASIC THAN ACIDIC GROUPS.
PREDOMINANTLY ACIDIC

22. *Aspartic acid:* $COOH\!-\!CH_2\!-\!CHNH_2\!-\!COOH$

23. *Glutamic acid:* $COOH\!-\!CH_2\!-\!CH_2\!-\!CHNH_2\!-\!COOH$

24. *β-Hydroxyglutamic acid:* $COOH\!-\!CH_2\!-\!CHOH\!-\!CHNH_2\!-\!COOH$

The separation of the amino acids which are produced when a protein is hydrolyzed is a tedious and difficult task. Emil Fischer (1901) devised the first successful method for isolating the individual amino acids from the mixture. He made a partial separation by taking advantage of the slight solubility in water of a few amino acids. A few others could be precipitated by special reagents. Others were converted into esters which could be separated by fractional distillation. In 1918 Dakin improved Fischer's method; and many special techniques, developed in recent years, have simplified investigations of this complex group of compounds.

Protein metabolism. Pepsin, which is present in the gastric juice, trypsin supplied by the pancreas, and erepsin from the mucous lining of the intestine are enzymes which catalyze the hydrolysis of proteins. As a result of the continued action of these enzymes most of the proteins of our diet are broken into simple amino acid fragments. Proteins like keratin, which resist hydrolysis, pass through the alimentary tract without contributing to our nourishment. It is in the form of amino acids that the protein materials diffuse through the intestinal wall and enter the blood stream. These small units are withdrawn from the blood by the various tissues of the body and are used to build the particular proteins needed for specific functions. The process of tearing apart any available type of protein, delivering the simple segments to the blood stream, and reassembling these parts in such a way as to build muscle, lung tissue, skin, hair, or nerve is an amazing series of chemical transformations. It is not yet within the power of the chemist to duplicate these processes in the laboratory.

The living animal organism cannot synthesize all the needed amino acids from nonprotein materials, such as carbohydrates, fatty acids, hydroxy acids, keto acids, and ammonia derivatives. The required building blocks, however, are produced in the vegetable world, and they are obtained by man directly through a vegetable diet or indirectly through the use of meat from herbivorous animals. Proteins which contain all the needed amino acids are rare, if they exist at all. Casein of milk comes very close to that category. An amino acid which cannot be synthesized by an animal, and hence must be supplied in the diet, is called an essential amino acid. The list of essential amino acids for rats and dogs includes lysine, tryptophan, histidine, valine, methionine, phenylalanine, leucine, isoleucine, threonine, and arginine. Apparently the others may be synthesized in the tissues of these experimental animals.

Many proteins have been given names which indicate their sources. In the table below, some common members of the group are listed:

SOME COMMON PROTEINS

Name of Protein	Occurrence	Name of Protein	Occurrence
Albumins		Scleroproteins	
Serum albumin	Blood serum	(albuminoids)	
Leucosine . .	Wheat germ	Keratin . . .	Horn, hair, wool
Myogen . . .	Muscle	Fibroin . . .	Silk
Ovalbumin . .	Egg	Elastin . . .	Ligaments
Lactalbumin .	Milk	Collagen . . .	Glue, gelatin
Globulins		Nucleoprotein	Cell nuclei, thymus,
Serum globulin	Blood serum		pancreas, spleen
Myosin . . .	Muscle	Glycoproteins	
Thyroglobulin	Thyroid	Mucin	Saliva
Edestin . . .	Egg yolk	Mucoids	Bone, tendons
Glutelins . . .		Phosphoproteins	
Glutenin . . .	Wheat	Vitelline	Egg yolk
Oryzenin . . .	Rice	Casein	Milk
Prolamines . . .		Hemoglobins	Blood
Gliadin . . .	Wheat	Lecithoproteins	Cytoplasm, all mem-
Hordein . . .	Barley		branes
Zein	Corn	Lipoproteins .	Cell membranes
Histones			
Globin	Hemoglobin		
Protamines . .	Sperm, eggs		

Classification of proteins. An arbitrary classification of proteins based upon analyses and physical properties is given below. Methods of separating from each other proteins of different types are implied in this system of classification.

GROUP I. SIMPLE PROTEINS

Hydrolysis products consist of amino acids only.

1. *Albumins.* Soluble in water and dilute salt solution.

2. *Globulins.* Insoluble in water. Soluble in dilute neutral salt solutions.

3. *Glutelins.* Insoluble in water and insoluble in neutral salt solutions. Soluble in dilute solutions of acids and bases.

4. *Prolamines.* Soluble in 70–80 per cent alcohol; insoluble in absolute alcohol, water, and neutral salt solutions.

5. *Albuminoids.* Insoluble in water, salt solution, dilute acids, and bases.

6. *Histones.* Basic proteins. Soluble in water and dilute acids. Insoluble in dilute ammonia. Form precipitates with solutions of other proteins. Coagulate when heated. Coagulum soluble in very dilute acids.

7. *Protamines.* Simple basic polypeptides, not coagulated by heat. Soluble in water, dilute acids, and ammonia. Basic amino acids predominate in hydrolysis products.

GROUP II. CONJUGATED PROTEINS

Hydrolysis products consist of amino acids and at least one other type of molecule, called a prosthetic group.

1. *Nucleoproteins.* Protein molecules combined with a nucleic acid.

2. *Glycoproteins.* Proteins combined with a carbohydrate not included in nucleic acid.

3. *Phosphoproteins.* Proteins containing phosphorus not included in nucleic acid or in lecithins.

4. *Hemoglobins.* Proteins combined with hemin.

5. *Lecithoproteins.* Proteins combined with lecithins.

6. *Lipoproteins.* Proteins combined with fatty acids.

GROUP III. DERIVED PROTEINS

Cleavage products of more complex proteins.

1. *Proteans.* Insoluble in water. First products of hydrolytic cleavage.

2. *Metaproteins.* Products formed by further action of acids, alkalies, or enzymes. Soluble in dilute acids and alkalies. Insoluble in neutral solvents.

3. *Coagulated proteins.* Insoluble products formed by the action of heat or alcohol on protein solutions.

4. *Proteoses.* Soluble hydrolysis products of proteins. Not coagulated by heat. Precipitated by saturating the solution with ammonium sulfate.

5. *Peptones.* Hydrolysis products. Soluble in water. Not coagulated by heat. Not precipitated by ammonium sulfate.

6. *Peptides.* Definite compounds of known structure, consisting of two or more amino acids united through the amino and the carboxyl groups.

Amino Acids

Properties of amino acids. The amino acids are colorless, crystalline solids. They possess the basic amino group and the acidic carboxyl group. These groups neutralize each other, and the so-called amino acids exist mainly in the form of intramolecular salts. An equilibrium exists between the free acid and the salt, as shown by the following formulas:

$$
\begin{array}{ccc}
\overset{\text{H}}{\underset{\underset{\text{NH}_2}{|}}{\overset{|}{\text{R—C—COOH}}}} & \rightleftharpoons & \overset{\text{H}}{\underset{\underset{\text{NH}_3^+}{|}}{\overset{|}{\text{R—C—COO}^-}}}
\end{array}
$$

Amino acid (un-ionized form)   Intramolecular salt (a dipolar compound)

A compound carrying a positive charge and a negative charge in the same molecule is said to be dipolar; it is sometimes called a zwitter ion. As a matter of convenience and established custom we shall write the formulas of amino acids in the un-ionized (nonpolar form) unless ionization is involved in the problem at hand.

Amino acids with one amino and one carboxyl group are nearly neutral, but they react with strong acids and strong bases. They are therefore to be classified as amphoteric substances. This behavior is indicated by the following equilibria:

$$
\underset{\underset{\text{NH}_3^+}{|}}{\text{R—CH—COOH}} \overset{\text{H}^+}{\underset{}{\rightleftharpoons}}
\left\{
\begin{array}{c}
\underset{\underset{\text{NH}_3^+}{|}}{\text{R—CH—COO}^-} \\
\updownarrow \\
\underset{\underset{\text{NH}_2}{|}}{\text{R—CH—COOH}}
\end{array}
\right\}
\overset{\text{OH}^-}{\underset{}{\rightleftharpoons}}
\underset{\underset{\text{NH}_2}{|}}{\text{R—CH—COO}^-}
$$

Cation present in acid   Amino acid   Anion present in base

An amino acid is acidic or basic if it does not contain the same number of carboxyl and amino groups. (See table, p. 264.)

All naturally occurring amino acids, except glycine, are optically active. Some are dextrorotatory and some are levorotatory. The spatial arrangement of the groups about the α-carbon atom, however, is the same in all these amino acids, regardless of the direction of rotation. Their configuration is related to dextrorotatory lactic acid.

$$CH_3$$
$$|$$
$$H-C-NH_2$$
$$|$$
$$COOH$$

Alanine

$$CH_3$$
$$|$$
$$H-C-OH$$
$$|$$
$$COOH$$

Lactic acid
(dextrorotatory form)

Reaction with nitrous acid. The amino acids react quantitatively with nitrous acid; the amino group is replaced by hydroxyl, and nitrogen gas is evolved. Sodium nitrite and acetic acid are used as a source of the required nitrous acid.

$$R-\underset{\underset{NH_2}{|}}{CH}-COOH + HNO_2 \longrightarrow R-\underset{\underset{OH}{|}}{CH}-COOH + N_2 + H_2O$$

The volume of nitrogen released per mole of amino acid indicates the number of amino groups present. This analytical procedure can be applied to proteins or to any other class of compounds in which there is an NH_2 group. It is known as the Van Slyke method of determining amino nitrogen.

Methods of making amino acids. The amino acids included in the list on pages 264–266 are found in proteins, and can be released from these natural sources by hydrolysis. In many cases, however, it is simpler to prepare amino acids through synthetic processes. The following methods are useful for this purpose:

1. The ordinary saturated acids (members of the acetic acid series) are readily chlorinated in the α-position (p. 168), and an amino group may be substituted for the chlorine atom by treatment with ammonia (p. 132) or through the agency of potassium phthalimide (p. 204). Glycine, alanine, and valine have been prepared from the corresponding α-chloroacids. An example follows:

$$CH_3-CHCl-COOH \xrightarrow{2\,NH_3} CH_3-CH(NH_2)-COOH + NH_4Cl$$

2. The malonic ester synthesis has been used with success in the preparation of many amino acids. The amino acids listed below have

been made from malonic ester, sodium, and the specified halide. For details concerning the steps in a malonic ester synthesis see page 190.

Amino Acid	Halide Used
Phenylalanine . . $C_6H_5CH_2$—$CH(NH_2)CO_2H$	C_6H_5—CH_2—Cl
Methionine . . . $CH_3S(CH_2)_2CH(NH_2)CO_2H$	CH_3S—CH_2—CH_2Cl
Norleucine . . . $CH_3(CH_2)_3CH(NH_2)CO_2H$	n-C_4H_9Br
Isoleucine . . . $CH_3CH_2CH(CH_3)CH(NH_2)CO_2H$	$C_2H_5CH(CH_3)Br$
Leucine . . . . $(CH_3)_2CHCH_2CH(NH_2)CO_2H$	iso-C_4H_9Br

If we indicate the halide by **RX**, the reactions may be written as follows:

$$H_2C(COOC_2H_5)_2 \xrightarrow{Na} NaHC(COOC_2H_5)_2$$

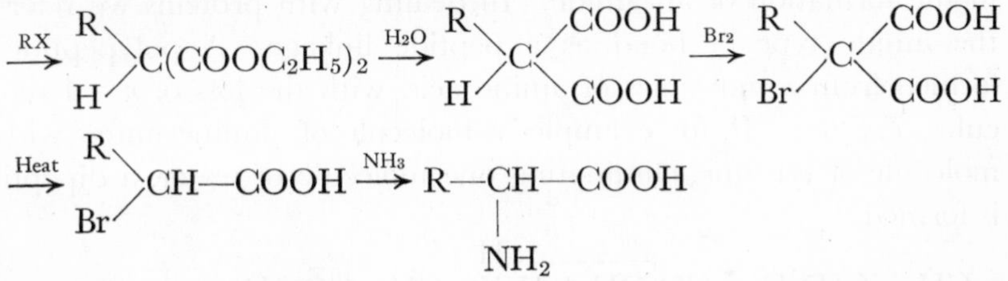

$$\xrightarrow{RX} \begin{matrix} R \\ \diagdown \\ H \diagup \end{matrix} C(COOC_2H_5)_2 \xrightarrow{H_2O} \begin{matrix} R \\ \diagdown \\ H \diagup \end{matrix} C \begin{matrix} \diagup COOH \\ \diagdown COOH \end{matrix} \xrightarrow{Br_2} \begin{matrix} R \\ \diagdown \\ Br \diagup \end{matrix} C \begin{matrix} \diagup COOH \\ \diagdown COOH \end{matrix}$$

$$\xrightarrow{Heat} \begin{matrix} R \\ \diagdown \\ Br \diagup \end{matrix} CH—COOH \xrightarrow{NH_3} R—CH—COOH$$
$$\underset{NH_2}{|}$$

3. Strecker's synthesis. The first step in a method devised by Strecker is the formation of an aldehyde ammonia. The latter is converted into an amino nitrile, and the nitrile in turn is hydrolyzed to the corresponding acid. The three steps are indicated by the following equations:

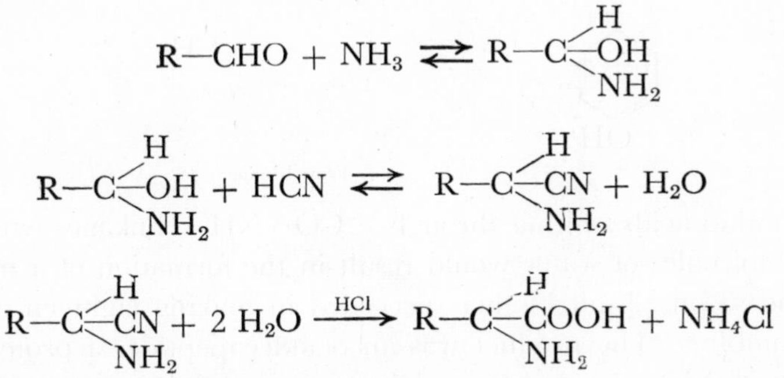

$$R—CHO + NH_3 \rightleftarrows R—C\overset{H}{\underset{NH_2}{\diagdown}}OH \qquad (1)$$

$$R—C\overset{H}{\underset{NH_2}{\diagdown}}OH + HCN \rightleftarrows R—C\overset{H}{\underset{NH_2}{\diagdown}}CN + H_2O \qquad (2)$$

$$R—C\overset{H}{\underset{NH_2}{\diagdown}}CN + 2 H_2O \xrightarrow{HCl} R—C\overset{H}{\underset{NH_2}{\diagdown}}COOH + NH_4Cl \qquad (3)$$

Alanine, glycine, and serine have been made in this way from the aldehydes CH_3CHO, HCHO, and CH_2OHCHO respectively.

All amino acids which are found in proteins have been synthesized, and the racemic mixtures produced by synthetic methods have been resolved into the optically active forms. In the preparation of the complex amino acids, however, it has been necessary to supplement the simple processes, described above, with many special devices.

Protein Structure

The simple proteins are polypeptides of high molecular weights. A polypeptide is a compound in which several amino acids are combined, the union in each case being established through the amino group of one molecule and the carboxyl group of another. The union is a result of loss of a molecule of water which is derived from the two functional groups. It is the same type of linkage that is established in the formation of an amide. In dealing with proteins we refer to the amide type of bond as a peptide linkage. A polypeptide is formed from n molecules of amino acid with the loss of $n - 1$ molecules of water. If, for example, a molecule of alanine unites with a molecule of tyrosine, eliminating one molecule of water, a dipeptide is formed:

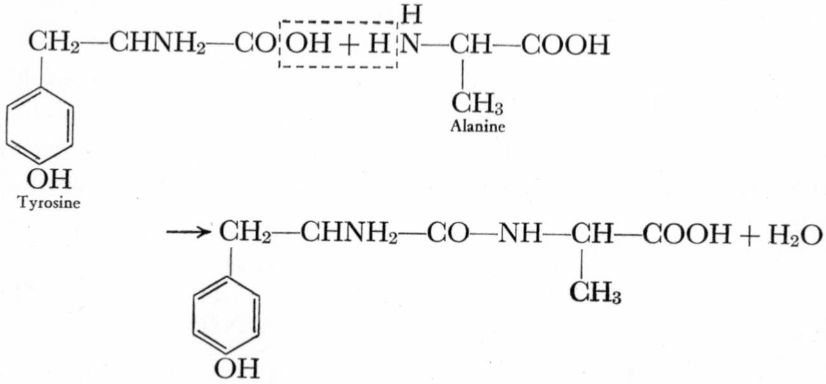

$$CH_2—CHNH_2—CO\overline{|OH + H|}N—CH—COOH$$

$$\underset{Tyrosine}{\underset{OH}{\bigcirc}} \qquad \underset{Alanine}{\overset{|}{CH_3}}$$

$$\longrightarrow CH_2—CHNH_2—CO—NH—CH—COOH + H_2O$$

$$\underset{OH}{\bigcirc} \qquad \overset{|}{CH_3}$$

Tyrosylalanine

Three amino acids uniting through —CO—NH— linkages with loss of two molecules of water would result in the formation of a tripeptide, and so on. Emil Fischer succeeded in making eighteen amino acids combine. The product was an octadecapeptide, a proteinlike substance having a molecular weight of more than 1200.

A segment of a simple protein molecule may be represented as follows:

In this formula each R stands for the residue of an amino acid beyond the α-carbon atom. The carbon of the carboxyl group and the α-carbon to which nitrogen is attached are included in the structure. This sort of structure, with proper substitutions for R, if continued to give a molecular weight of about 17,000 or more, would represent a possible simple protein.

In protein molecules the amino acids can be arranged in an enormous number of permutations. Some progress is being made in determining the order of arrangement of these units in specific compounds. The shape of a molecule determines to some extent its properties, and physical methods are being developed to reveal the shapes of large molecules. The electron microscope is useful in such investigations.

Egg albumin, when heated, is converted into an insoluble mass (coagulated), with no change in chemical composition. The alteration in properties is apparently due to changes in molecular structure. Acids coagulate albumin at ordinary temperatures; alcohol has a similar effect on many proteins. An irreversible change in properties of a protein caused by heat or by an acid or alcohol is called *denaturation*.

PARTIAL LIST OF PERCENTAGES OF AMINO ACIDS IN SOME PROTEINS

	Casein (Milk)	Gelatin	Egg Albumin	Gliadin (Wheat)	Hemo- globin	Zein (Corn)
Alanine	1.9	8.7	2.2	2.0	4.2	9.8
Arginine	5.2	9.1	6.0	3.2	3.1	1.8
Aspartic acid	4.1	3.4	6.2	0.8	6.4	1.8
Cystine	0.3	0.2	0.8	2.4	0.5	1.8
Glutamic acid	21.8	5.8	13.3	43.7	3.5	31.3
Glycine	0.4	25.5				
Histidine	2.6	0.9	2.3	2.1	7.4	1.2
Hydroxyproline	0.2	14.1			1.0	
Leucine	9.7	7.1	10.7	6.6	29.0	25.0
Lysine	7.6	5.9	3.8	0.6	8.0	
Phenylalanine	3.9	1.4	5.1	2.3	4.2	7.6
Proline	8.0	9.5	3.6	13.2	2.1	9.0
Serine	0.5	0.4			0.6	1.0
Tryptophan	2.2		1.2	0.8	2.6	0.2
Tyrosine	6.5		4.0	3.1	1.3	5.9
Valine	7.9		2.5	3.3		1.9

National Dairy Products Corporation

Fig. 12. A Dress Made from the Casein of Milk

The biological activity of a denatured protein is usually quite different from that of the original compound.

Methods of polypeptide synthesis. Simple acid amides are made by treating an acid chloride, an ester, or an acid anhydride with ammonia or with an amine. In some cases a free carboxylic acid can be converted into an amide by condensation with ammonia or an amine. In amino acids both functional groups which are involved in the formation of an amide are present in the same molecule, and special procedures are necessary to force the reaction to take place between separate molecules. One method is to start with an acid in which there is a chlorine atom, instead of an amino group, in the α-position. The chlorine atom is replaced by an amino group after a peptide linkage has been formed with another amino acid. The process is indicated by the following reactions:

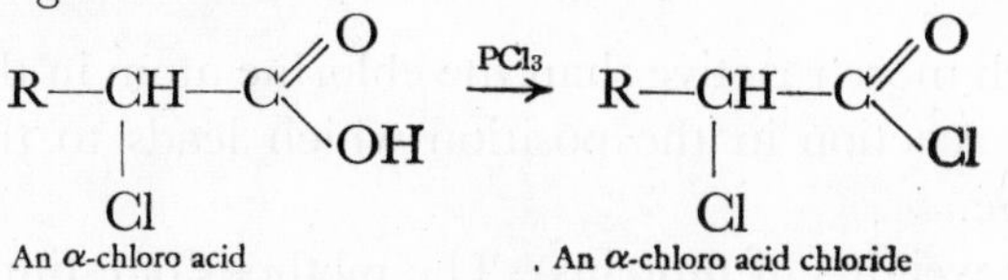

$$R—CH—C\underset{OH}{\overset{O}{\diagdown}} \quad \xrightarrow{PCl_3} \quad R—CH—C\underset{Cl}{\overset{O}{\diagdown}} \tag{1}$$

$$\underset{Cl}{\big|} \qquad\qquad\qquad\qquad \underset{Cl}{\big|}$$

An α-chloro acid . An α-chloro acid chloride

$$R—CH—C\underset{Cl}{\overset{O}{\diagdown}} + R'—CH—C\underset{OR}{\overset{O}{\diagdown}}$$

$$\underset{Cl}{\big|} \qquad\qquad\qquad \underset{NH_2}{\big|}$$

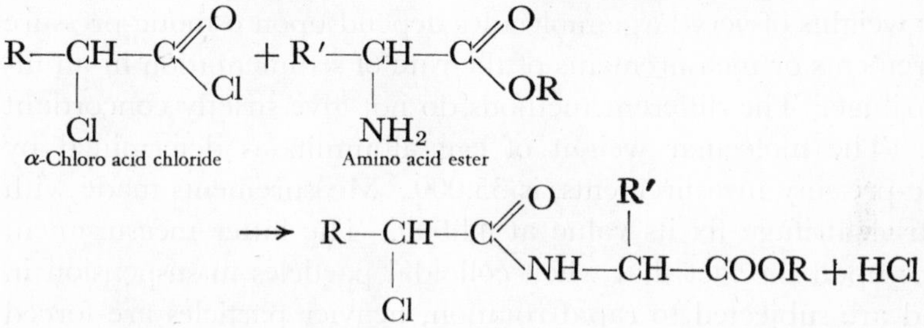

α-Chloro acid chloride   Amino acid ester

$$\longrightarrow \quad R—CH—C\underset{\diagdown NH—CH—COOR}{\overset{O \quad\;\; R'}{\diagdown \qquad |}} + HCl \tag{2}$$

$$\underset{Cl}{\big|}$$

The chlorine atom remaining in this condensation product is replaced by an amino group by treatment with ammonia:

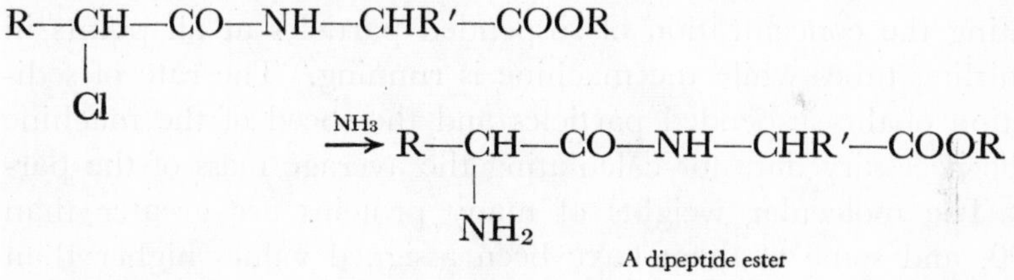

$$R—CH—CO—NH—CHR'—COOR$$

$$\underset{Cl}{\big|}$$

$$\xrightarrow{NH_3} R—CH—CO—NH—CHR'—COOR \tag{3}$$

$$\underset{NH_2}{\big|}$$

A dipeptide ester

The dipeptide ester will react with the same or a different chloro acid chloride to form a condensation product which, on treatment with ammonia and hydrolysis of the ester group, yields a tripeptide:

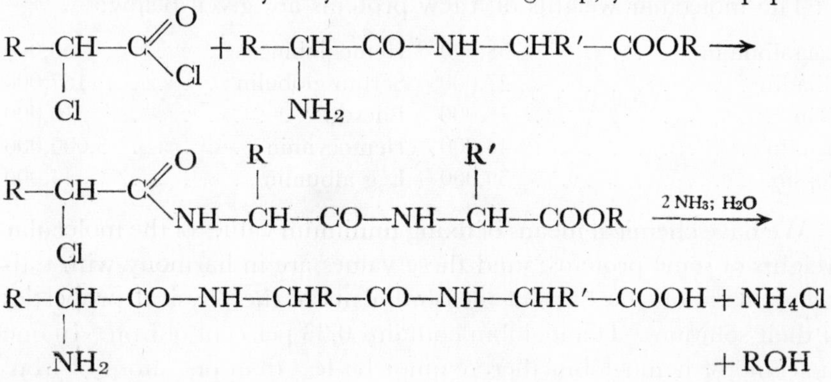

$$R—CH—C\underset{\diagdown Cl}{\overset{O}{\diagdown}} + R—CH—CO—NH—CHR'—COOR \longrightarrow$$

$$\underset{Cl}{\big|} \qquad\qquad\qquad \underset{NH_2}{\big|}$$

$$R—CH—C\underset{\diagdown NH—CH—CO—NH—CH—COOR}{\overset{O \quad\; R \qquad\qquad R'}{\diagdown \qquad | \qquad\qquad\quad |}} \xrightarrow{2\,NH_3;\;H_2O}$$

$$\underset{Cl}{\big|}$$

$$R—CH—CO—NH—CHR—CO—NH—CHR'—COOH + NH_4Cl$$

$$\underset{NH_2}{\big|} \qquad\qquad\qquad\qquad\qquad\qquad\qquad\qquad + ROH$$

In the chloro acid chloride the chlorine atom of the

$$-C\begin{matrix} \diagup O \\ \diagdown Cl \end{matrix}$$

group is much more reactive than the chlorine atom in the α-position. This ensures reaction in the position which leads to the peptide or amide linkage.

Molecular weights of proteins. The methods of estimating the molecular weights of very large molecules depend upon osmotic-pressure measurements or measurements of the rate of sedimentation in an ultracentrifuge. The different methods do not give strictly concordant results. The molecular weight of egg albumin, as determined by osmotic-pressure measurements, is 35,000. Measurements made with the ultracentrifuge fix its value at 44,000. The latter measurement depends upon the fact that when colloidal particles in suspension in a liquid are subjected to rapid rotation, heavier particles are forced away from the center of the rotating unit more rapidly than lighter ones. An ultracentrifuge operates at speeds as high as 70,000 revolutions per minute. The machine is provided with optical devices for estimating the concentration of suspended particles at all points in the whirling tubes while the machine is running. The rate of sedimentation of the suspended particles and the speed of the machine give the necessary data for calculating the average mass of the particles. The molecular weights of many proteins are greater than 100,000, and some of them have been assigned values higher than 5,000,000. The molecular weight of the tobacco mosaic virus, a protein substance, has been estimated as fifty million, but this estimate is subject to revision.

The molecular weights of a few proteins are given below:

Lactalbumin	38,000	Hemoglobin		68,000
Gliadin	27,000	Serum globulin		167,000
Zein	35,000	Edestin		310,000
Insulin	46,000	Hemocyanin		5,000,000
Pepsin	39,000	Egg albumin		44,000

We have chemical means of fixing minimum values of the molecular weights of some proteins; and these values are in harmony with estimates made on the basis of measurements of the physical properties of their solutions. Hemoglobin contains 0.33 per cent of iron. In one molecule of hemoglobin there cannot be less than one atom of iron.

From the proportion $0.33 : 100 = 56 : M$ the minimum value for the molecular weight, M, is 17,000. Hemoglobin contains sulfur (0.38 per cent). Cystine has been identified as one of the products formed when hemoglobin is hydrolyzed, and cystine contains two atoms of sulfur. There must be at least two atoms of sulfur in the hemoglobin molecule. From the proportion $0.38 : 100 = 64 : M$ we have for the minimum value 16,842. A measurement based upon sedimentation in an aqueous solution of hemoglobin, when subjected to a centrifugal force, gives a value of 68,000 for the molecular weight of the protein. Osmotic-pressure measurements indicate that in aqueous solution the molecular weight of hemoglobin is approximately 68,000. This means that each molecule of hemoglobin contains four atoms of iron and four cystine molecules.

Qualitative Tests for Proteins

The proteins form precipitates with many reagents, particularly with certain acids and with salts of heavy metals. Concentrated nitric acid and aqueous solutions of trichloroacetic acid, tannic acid, phosphotungstic acid, and picric acid form insoluble protein salts or they precipitate the proteins in denatured forms. Copper, iron, and mercury salts of proteins are insoluble in water. The reactions listed below are not specific tests for proteins, but any substance which responds to several of these tests may be regarded as a protein.

1. **Biuret reaction.** When a dilute copper sulfate solution is added to a protein solution and then dilute sodium hydroxide is added, a reddish-violet color is produced. The blue tone of the color increases with molecular complexity. This reagent produces a color in a solution of any compound which contains one of the following groups:

$$—NH—CO—NH—CO— \qquad —NH—CO—CHR—CO—NH—$$
$$—NH—CO—CO—NH— \qquad —NH—CR_2—CO—NH—$$

The color is due to the formation of a complex copper ion not unlike the cyclic ion of Fehling's solution.

2. **Heller's ring test.** This test is used to detect the presence of protein in urine. Concentrated nitric acid is added carefully to urine in a test tube; a white precipitate of denatured protein appears at the interface between the two solutions if protein (albumin) is present.

3. **Millon's reaction** is a test for the phenolic group or, in the case of proteins, for tyrosine. A solution of mercury in dilute nitric acid

produces a white precipitate with a protein. On heating the precipitate turns red.

4. Xanthoproteic reaction. Concentrated nitric acid in contact with a protein in the solid state produces a yellow color which deepens to orange when moistened with a solution of ammonia. Any compound which contains an aromatic ring usually responds to this test. Tyrosine and tryptophan are responsible for the color which develops when the test is applied to a protein; human skin gives the reaction readily.

EXERCISES

1. What is meant by each of the following terms?

a. α-Amino acid	*e.* Polypeptide
b. Peptide linkage	*f.* Denaturation
c. Dipolar structure	*g.* Simple protein
d. Amphoteric compound	*h.* Conjugated proteins

2. How is it shown that proteins are composed of amino acids? What is the composition of starch? of cellulose? of a fat? of natural rubber? (Refer to previous chapters.)

3. By what path does a vegetable protein become an animal protein? Is all the vegetable protein necessarily utilized in the production of the animal protein? Can man synthesize in his body all the amino acids which he requires?

4. Specify the general class of compounds to which each of the following belongs: (*a*) linen, (*b*) silk, (*c*) nylon, (*d*) rubber, (*e*) wool, (*f*) hair, (*g*) wood, (*h*) lard, (*i*) cotton, (*j*) rayon, (*k*) casein, (*l*) starch.

5. Write a general formula for a tetrapeptide. What type of amino acid would be present if the peptide were neutral? acidic? basic?

PROBLEMS

1. Express in equations the synthesis of (*a*) glycine (from acetic acid and any other reagents); (*b*) leucine (from malonic ester, isobutyl bromide, and any other reagents).

2. Write equations for the interaction of alanine with HCl and with NaOH.

3. Outline a synthesis of glycylalanine by Fischer's method.

4. Devise a test for cotton fiber in a cloth presumed to be wool. Base the test upon the facts that proteins are hydrolyzed by acids and by bases but that cellulose is hydrolyzed by acids only.

24 · COAL-TAR PRODUCTS

Benzene and Its Homologues

Benzene was first isolated in 1925 by Michael Faraday. The compound was discovered among the by-products of the manufacture, through the pyrolysis of animal and vegetable oils, of illuminating gas. Until 1949 benzene was obtained as a by-product of coke manufacture, along with many other substances which contain its cyclic nucleus; an additional source is the dehydrogenation of the cyclohexane in petroleum (see page 105).

The formula of benzene, C_6H_6, indicated to early investigators a high degree of unsaturation; but the inertness of the compound toward bromine and permanganate led to the conclusion that the structure of benzene must differ fundamentally from the structures of ethylene and acetylene. The same anomaly was observed in many fragrant substances of vegetable origin, such as oil of bitter almonds, cinnamon, and oil of wintergreen. These fragrant extracts were termed aromatic compounds because of their odors. Later it was discovered that the essential oils which had been classified as *aromatic* compounds were derivatives of benzene, and gradually the term *aromatic* came to be applied to all substances which contain the benzene nucleus.

The structure of benzene was discussed in Chapter 9; the pertinent facts are summarized below.

SUMMARY OF FACTS REGARDING THE STRUCTURE OF BENZENE

1. Symmetrical cyclic structure evidenced by (*a*) no isomers of monosubstitution products; (*b*) three isomeric disubstitution products.
2. Unsaturation evidenced by (*a*) conversion to cyclohexane by catalytic hydrogenation; (*b*) chlorine added photochemically to form $C_6H_6Cl_6$.
3. Heat of hydrogenation and heat of combustion are about 36 kg-cal less than that calculated for a Kekulé structure from corresponding measurements of alkanes and alkenes.
4. Observations in agreement with assumption of a mesomeric structure: (*a*) Carbon-carbon bond distance of 1.38 A lies between that of a single bond (1.54 A) and that of a double bond (1.32 A). (*b*) Benzene does not add Br_2 or reduce MnO_4^-. (*c*) It has a planar configuration (twelve atoms in a plane). (*d*) No isomers of 1,2-disubstitution products exist.

The abbreviated symbol for benzene (see page 105) is used to indicate the presence of the benzene nucleus in all aromatic compounds in spite of its implication of the presence of ordinary double bonds.

CH₃

Toluene
(C₆H₅—CH₃)

Naphthalene
(C₁₀H₈)

Biphenyl
(C₆H₅—C₆H₅)

Interest in aromatic compounds lies in the fact that derivatives of benzene and naphthalene comprise a great variety of useful products, including dyes, drugs, explosives, plastics, and solvents. This serves to emphasize the importance of coal tar and its associated products; for coal is the chief source of aromatic compounds, and the coking of coal makes them available. The aromatic hydrocarbons obtained from coal tar can be used directly as starting points in synthetic processes. This is not so generally true of aliphatic hydrocarbons.

The preparation of aromatic compounds from aliphatic sources is a recent accomplishment. Toluene, which is used in the manufacture of the explosive TNT, is now made in large quantities from the open chain and naphthenic hydrocarbons of petroleum. Conversely, open-chain compounds can be made from ring compounds. We no longer consider it necessary to begin with different source materials for the preparation of aliphatic and aromatic compounds. Gasoline can be made by hydrogenating coal, and benzene can be made through pyrolysis of gasoline. Factors such as cost and availability of raw materials determine the sources and methods which should be employed in the synthesis of any desired compound. As long as coke is used in the smelting of iron ore, benzene and many of its derivatives will be available as by-products. When our supplies of coal and petroleum have been exhausted, we shall still have, as raw materials, the carbohydrates—agricultural products which are produced by photosynthesis from carbon dioxide of the atmosphere and water.

Coal-tar production. When bituminous coal is heated to a temperature of about 1200° C in the absence of air, there distills from the hot mass gases, volatile liquids, and a black, viscous tar. When all volatile matter has been driven out, a residue of coke remains in the retort or oven. The heating process is referred to as the distillation of coal, but it is not a simple distillation process. Many of the compounds which appear in the tarry distillate are formed by chemical reactions during the heat treatment; they are not present, as such, in coal. Coke is used in enormous quantities as a fuel and as a reducing agent in the smelting of iron ore. Approximately fifty million tons of coal are annually converted into coke for this purpose in the United States.

The gases which are released when coal is heated consist mostly of hydrogen and methane; but the mixture contains also ammonia, hydrogen sulfide, and the vapors of many organic compounds, some of which are partially condensed to liquids as the gaseous mixture is cooled. The ammonia and hydrogen sulfide are washed out of the coal gas with water, and the remaining vapors are removed by solution in a nonvolatile organic oil. The gas, thus purified, is used as a fuel. The average composition by volume of the fuel gas obtained from coal is as follows: hydrogen 52 per cent, methane 32 per cent, carbon monoxide 5 or 6 per cent, nitrogen 4 or 5 per cent, carbon dioxide 2 per cent, and a small amount of alkene hydrocarbons.

YIELDS OF MAIN PRODUCTS OBTAINED FROM ONE TON OF COAL

Coke	1500 pounds
Fuel gas	11,000 cubic feet
Tar	60 pounds
Ammonium sulfate	25 pounds
Carbolic acid and cresols	25 pounds
Naphthalene	50 pounds
Benzene	2 to 3 gallons
Toluene	1 to 2 gallons

The tar obtained in the distillation of coal is subjected to fractional distillation for partial separation into its components. The residue, which amounts to about 60 per cent, is pitch. Each fraction is extracted with alkaline solutions to remove phenol, cresols, and other acidic compounds; it is then extracted with dilute acid solutions to remove organic bases, such as pyridine; finally the hydrocarbon residue is redistilled. The more volatile liquid products, benzene and toluene, are recovered largely from the scrubbed gases rather than from the tar. More than one hundred useful compounds are obtained from coal tar and associated products. A few of the more important members of the group are shown on page 282.

SOME COMPOUNDS OBTAINED FROM COAL TAR

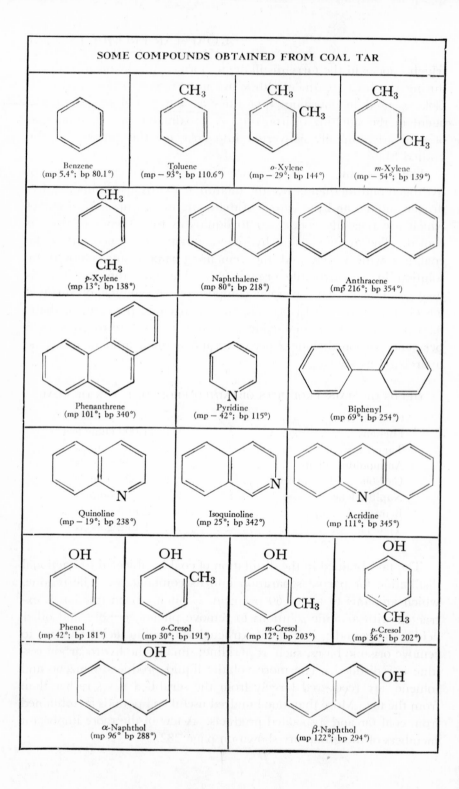

Benzene
(mp 5.4°; bp 80.1°)

Toluene
(mp − 93°; bp 110.6°)

o-Xylene
(mp − 29°; bp 144°)

m-Xylene
(mp − 54°; bp 139°)

p-Xylene
(mp 13°; bp 138°)

Naphthalene
(mp 80°; bp 218°)

Anthracene
(mp 216°; bp 354°)

Phenanthrene
(mp 101°; bp 340°)

Pyridine
(mp − 42°; bp 115°)

Biphenyl
(mp 69°; bp 254°)

Quinoline
(mp − 19°; bp 238°)

Isoquinoline
(mp 25°; bp 342°)

Acridine
(mp 111°; bp 345°)

Phenol
(mp 42°; bp 181°)

o-Cresol
(mp 30°; bp 191°)

m-Cresol
(mp 12°; bp 203°)

p-Cresol
(mp 36°; bp 202°)

α-Naphthol
(mp 96° bp 288°)

β-Naphthol
(mp 122°; bp 294°)

Substitution in Benzene

The number and kinds of substitution products of benzene not only prove the cyclic nature of its carbon skeleton, but also present other problems in molecular structure of practical and theoretical interest.

Number of substitution products. The substitution of an atom or group, X, for one hydrogen atom in benzene gives rise to a compound corresponding to the formula C_6H_5X. Only one substitution product of this composition exists; there are no isomers. The ring structure is in harmony with this experimental fact. If the six hydrogen atoms are equivalent,—that is, similarly placed in the benzene molecule,—it makes no difference which one is replaced.

When two hydrogen atoms in benzene are replaced by other atoms, the product may be any one of three forms or a mixture of three isomeric forms; but it never consists of more than three forms. (See page 102.) Here again the ring structure accounts for the experimental result. To deal with a specific case, let us assume that the substituent X is a chlorine atom. The ring of carbon atoms will be represented by a hexagon, and it must be understood that a hydrogen atom is attached at each angle of the hexagon unless some other atom is specifically indicated. We can have the following compounds of the formula $C_6H_4Cl_2$:

ortho-Dichlorobenzene,
or
1,2-dichlorobenzene

meta-Dichlorobenzene,
or
1,3-dichlorobenzene

para-Dichlorobenzene,
or
1,4-dichlorobenzene

The terms *ortho*, *meta*, and *para* are used to designate the relative positions of two atoms or groups substituted for hydrogen in benzene. Substituents on adjacent carbon atoms are in ortho positions; in a meta compound one carbon atom intervenes between the two positions of substitution; in a para compound the two substituents are across the ring from each other. The letters *o*, *m*, and *p* are used as abbreviations of *ortho*, *meta*, and *para* respectively. In another method of designating positions of substituents the carbon atoms are numbered from one to six, and the appropriate numbers are included in the name of the compound.

The number of possible disubstitution products is the same whether the substituents are alike or different, that is, whether the formula is $C_6H_4X_2$ or C_6H_4XY. A greater number of trisubstitution products can be made from benzene. The possibilities are as follows: for $C_6H_3X_3$, three isomers; for $C_6H_3X_2Y$, six isomers; for C_6H_3XYZ, ten isomers.

Determination of positions of substituents. There are three dichlorobenzenes, as indicated above, and three possible isomeric forms of every disubstitution product of benzene. How can we determine in any particular case which of the three isomers is the ortho compound and which has the meta structure or the para structure? Let us use the three xylenes, $C_6H_4(CH_3)_2$, to illustrate a method of dealing with a problem of this kind. One of the three xylenes melts at $-54°$, another at $-29°$, and the third at $+13°$. On treatment with concentrated nitric acid the xylene which melts at $-29°$ yields two different mononitro derivatives. It is possible to obtain three isomeric mononitroxylenes from the one that melts at $-54°$, but only one mononitroxylene is formed from the compound melting at 13°. Now *para*xylene can form only one monosubstitution product; for the four replaceable hydrogen atoms attached to carbon atoms in the ring are similarly located. The nitro group must enter the *para*xylene molecule in a position which is *ortho* to one methyl group and *meta* to the other:

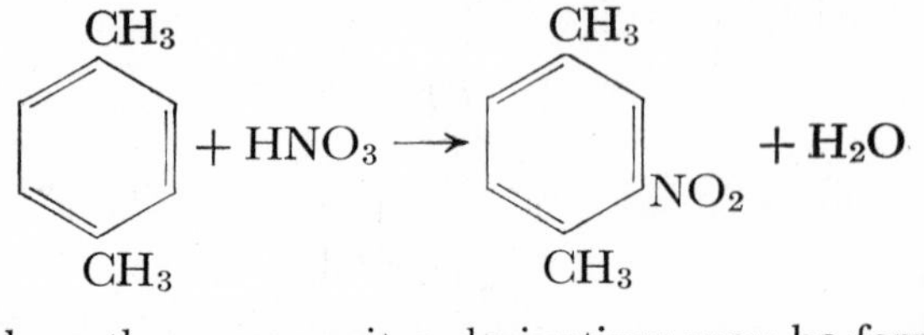

From *meta*xylene three mononitro derivatives may be formed:

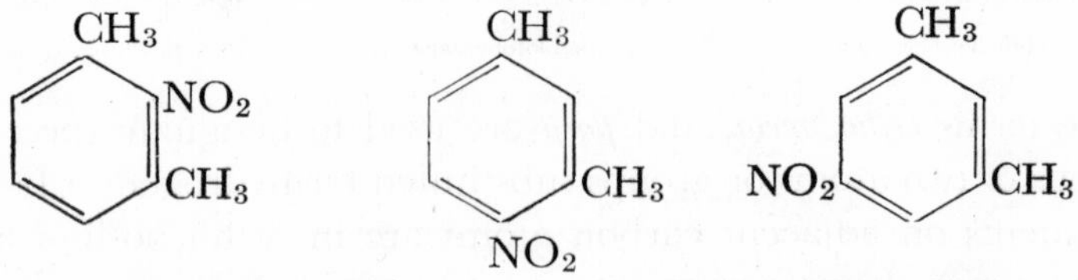

From *ortho*xylene two, and only two, mononitro derivatives can be prepared:

Hence the xylenes melting at $-54°$, $-29°$, and $13°$ are *meta*, *ortho*, and *para* compounds respectively.

After the structures of a few disubstitution products have been determined by the method shown above, a much simpler procedure can be followed. A compound of established structure can be used as a reference point in the synthesis of a new compound. For example, the methyl groups in the xylenes may be oxidized to carboxyl groups. The carbon atoms of the methyl groups remain attached to the ring, and the carboxyl groups of the oxidation products therefore occupy positions corresponding to the positions of the methyl groups of the xylenes. Thus, *o*-xylene is oxidized to *o*-phthalic acid:

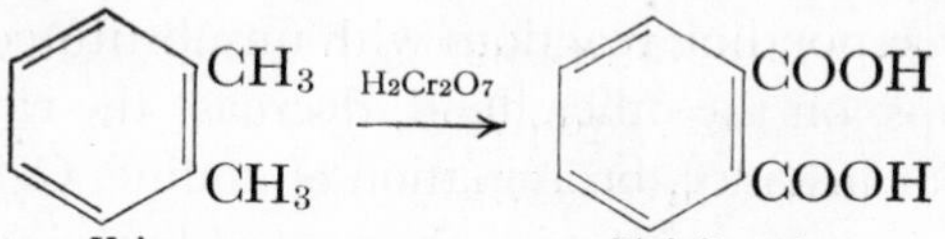

Orientation rules. When a monosubstitution product of benzene is converted into a disubstitution product, there exists the possibility of forming either an ortho, a meta, or a para compound, or a mixture of these. The three derivatives are not formed in equal quantities. The product formed is either a mixture of the ortho and para isomers with very little, if any, of the meta compound, or it is almost exclusively the meta compound. The character of the group present in the monosubstitution product seems to determine the position which the second substituent will occupy. Some atoms or groups, if already attached to the benzene ring, direct the next-entering group mainly to the ortho and para positions; others direct the second-entering group largely to the meta position. The principal substituents and the positions to which they direct the next-entering atom or group are shown below:

Groups Which Direct to the Ortho and Para Positions		Groups Which Direct to the Meta Position	
—NH$_2$	—OR	—NO$_2$	—COOH
—NHR	—Cl, Br, I	—CHO	—COOR
—NR$_2$	—R (CH$_3$, C$_2$H$_5$, etc.)	$-C\diagdown^O_R$	—CN
—NHCOR	—CH$_2$OH		—SO$_3$H
—OH		—CCl$_3$	—NR$_3^+$

The orientation rule indicates only the main products to be expected in a substitution reaction. Small yields of ortho and para products are obtained when a meta directing group is present, and some of the meta isomer is formed when an ortho-para directing group is already in the molecule. The rule is a useful qualitative guide only. The relative amounts of ortho, meta, and para derivatives formed with any particular directing group present vary with the conditions of the experiment. In general, groups which tend to draw electrons from the ring direct the next-entering atom or group to the meta position.

After an ortho-para orienting group has been introduced into benzene, a second and third substitution can be made more easily. Reactions involving positions ortho and para to the first substituent are more rapid than corresponding reactions with unsubstituted benzene. Meta directing groups, on the other hand, decrease the rate of substitution in the ring. For instance, bromination of aniline, $C_6H_5NH_2$, is a very rapid reaction as compared with the rate of bromination of benzene, and the bromination of nitrobenzene, $C_6H_5NO_2$, is much slower than the bromination of benzene.

Homologues of Benzene

Compounds derived from benzene by substitution of alkyl radicals for nuclear hydrogen atoms are homologues of benzene; in composition they differ from benzene by CH_2 or n times CH_2. Compounds of this type may be made in several ways.

1. **Friedel and Crafts reaction.** This is a reaction between an aromatic hydrocarbon and an alkyl halide under the catalytic influence of aluminum chloride. Benzene and ethyl bromide, for example, yield ethylbenzene:

$$+ \ CH_3 - CH_2Br \ \xrightarrow{\text{AlCl}_3} \ \text{(Ethylbenzene)} - CH_2 - CH_3 \ + \ HBr$$

Benzene   Ethylbenzene

The ethylbenzene reacts similarly, to form a mixture of ortho-diethylbenzene and para-diethylbenzene. This is not a satisfactory method for attaching long normal chains to the benzene ring, for aluminum chloride catalyzes the conversion of primary alkyl halides to secondary halides. Normal propyl chloride reacts with benzene in the presence of aluminum chloride to produce isopropylbenzene.

Fig. 13. Catalytic Cracking Units of the Baton Rouge Refinery

2. **Addition of an alkene.** A variation of the Friedel and Crafts reaction is found in the catalytic addition of an alkene to an aromatic hydrocarbon:

$$\text{benzene} + (CH_3)_2C{=}CH_2 \xrightarrow{\text{AlCl}_3} \text{tert-Butylbenzene}$$

2-Methylpropene — tert-Butylbenzene

3. **Use of metallic derivatives.** In the Fittig reaction a mixture of an aromatic halide and an aliphatic halide is warmed with metallic sodium. The process is an adaptation of the Wurtz reaction (p. 67).

$$C_6H_5Br + C_4H_9Br + 2\,Na \longrightarrow C_6H_5{-}C_4H_9 + 2\,NaBr$$

The butylbenzene, $C_6H_5{-}C_4H_9$, formed in this way is mixed with two other products, namely, $C_4H_9{-}C_4H_9$ and $C_6H_5{-}C_6H_5$. The three compounds, however, are easily separated.

A better method is based upon the use of a Grignard reagent:

$$C_6H_5Br \xrightarrow[\text{Ether}]{Mg} C_6H_5MgBr \xrightarrow{n\text{-}C_4H_9Br} C_6H_5\text{—}C_4H_9(n) + MgBr_2$$

This procedure gives good yields with primary halides, and particularly with reactive halides such as allyl chloride, $CH_2\text{=}CH\text{—}CH_2Cl$.

4. **Pyrolysis of an alkane.** When paraffin hydrocarbons are subjected to high temperatures, several types of reaction occur. The cracking process which results in the production of motor fuels from less volatile oils is an important application of pyrolysis. When the temperatures and pressures are properly adjusted and suitable catalysts are used, some open-chain compounds are converted into ring compounds. Toluene is made in large quantities by this method:

$$CH_3\text{—}CH_2\text{—}CH_2\text{—}CH_2\text{—}CH_2\text{—}CH_2\text{—}CH_3 \xrightarrow[\text{Heat}]{\text{Catalyst}}$$

n-Heptane

Toluene + 4 H_2

Chromium oxide, Cr_2O_3, supported on aluminum oxide, Al_2O_3, can be used to catalyze this type of reaction. A temperature of approximately 500° is required.

Physical constants of a few of the homologues of benzene are given in the following table:

NAME	FORMULA	MELTING POINT	BOILING POINT	SPECIFIC GRAVITY
Toluene	$C_6H_5CH_3$	− 95°	110.8°	0.866 (20°)
Xylene (o)	$C_6H_4(CH_3)_2$	− 29°	144°	0.893 (0°)
Xylene (m)	$C_6H_4(CH_3)_2$	− 53.6°	139°	0.881 (0°)
Xylene (p)	$C_6H_4(CH_3)_2$	13.2°	138°	0.861 (20°)
Hemimellitene	$C_6H_3(CH_3)_3$ 1, 2, 3	—	176.5°	0.895 (20°)
Pseudocumene	$C_6H_3(CH_3)_3$ 1, 2, 4	− 61°	169.8°	0.879 (20°)
Mesitylene	$C_6H_3(CH_3)_3$ 1, 3, 5	− 52.7°	164.5°	0.869 (10°)
Ethylbenzene	$C_6H_5C_2H_5$	− 92.8°	134°	0.883 (0°)
Cumene	$C_6H_5C_3H_7$ (*iso*)	—	153.4°	0.879 (0°)
Propylbenzene	$C_6H_5C_3H_7$ (*n*)	− 101.6°	157.5°	0.881 (0°)
Cymene	$C_6H_4CH_3C_3H_7$ 1, 4	− 73.5°	176°	0.872 (0°)
Pentamethylbenzene .	$C_6H(CH_3)_5$	53°	230°	0.847 (107°)
Hexamethylbenzene .	$C_6(CH_3)_6$	166°	265°	
Hexaethylbenzene . . .	$C_6(C_2H_5)_6$	129°	298°	0.831 (130°)

Reactions of benzene homologues. The reactions of benzene with the halogens, nitric acid, and sulfuric acid have been discussed (pp. 105–106). These and the Friedel-Crafts type of condensation are the most important of the reactions which concern substitution of hydrogen atoms in the benzene nucleus. The homologues of benzene react similarly. For instance, ethylbenzene will react as does benzene with all the reagents mentioned above. Benzene homologues, however, present a threefold problem: (1) Will a given reagent under stated conditions react with a carbon atom in the nucleus or with one in the side chain? (2) Will the entering group be found mainly in the ortho, meta, or para position? (3) Will the reagent react but once, or will two or three molecules of the reagent react successively with one aromatic nucleus? These questions must be answered by actual trial; but a few rules will emerge as we proceed to study the methods of preparation and the properties of specific classes of aromatic compounds.

Free Radicals

The attachment of three phenyl groups to a single carbon atom produces a compound of extraordinary properties. If the fourth bond of the carbon atom holds a hydrogen atom, the compound is easily oxidized; if it holds a hydroxyl group, the resulting carbinol reacts rapidly with hydrogen chloride; if it holds a chlorine atom, the halide borders on actual ionization and hydrolyzes rapidly.

$$(C_6H_5)_3CH \underset{Red.}{\overset{Ox.}{\rightleftarrows}} (C_6H_5)_3COH \underset{H_2O}{\overset{HCl}{\rightleftarrows}} (C_6H_5)_3CCl$$

Triphenylmethane   Triphenylcarbinol   Triphenylchloromethane

The greatest anomaly is found when one tries to prepare hexaphenylethane by subjecting a triphenylmethyl halide to the Wurtz reaction. In 1900 Gomberg tried this; and instead of getting a colorless benzene solution of a stable hydrocarbon, he obtained an orange-colored solution which absorbed oxygen from the air.

Reaction sought:

$$2(C_6H_5)_3CCl + 2 Ag \longrightarrow (C_6H_5)_3C—C(C_6H_5)_3 + 2 AgCl$$

Reaction obtained:

$$2(C_6H_5)_3CCl + 2 Ag \longrightarrow \text{colored solution}$$
$$\overset{O_2}{\longrightarrow} (C_6H_5)_3C—O—O—C(C_6H_5)_3 + 2 AgCl$$

He was able to show that the colored solution actually contained the desired product, hexaphenylethane; but it was not an ordinary hydrocarbon—it was partially and reversibly dissociated into free radicals.

$$(C_6H_5)_3C—C(C_6H_5)_3 \rightleftarrows 2(C_6H_5)_3C—$$
Hexaphenylethane   Triphenylmethyl

The fact that hexaphenylethane dissociates spontaneously into free radicals was established by the following observations: (1) the compound reacts rapidly with oxygen gas to form a peroxide; (2) it forms an addition product with bromine, and the compound formed has only one bromine atom per molecule; (3) it forms an addition product with nitric oxide, NO; (4) in solution its molecular weight is less than that calculated for the undissociated compound; (5) a solution of the compound in benzene is paramagnetic. Any substance which has an unpaired electron has magnetic properties. In forming a free radical a bonding pair of electrons splits, and one member of the pair goes to each radical. A radical, then, is a group of atoms which has an odd number of valence electrons. The triphenylmethyl radicals, as they appear in benzene solution, are not ions; they are electrically neutral groups. Hexaphenylethane in benzene is dissociated to the extent of a few per cent only. Hexabiphenylethane in benzene is completely dissociated into free radicals. The tribiphenylmethyl radical is represented by the following formula:

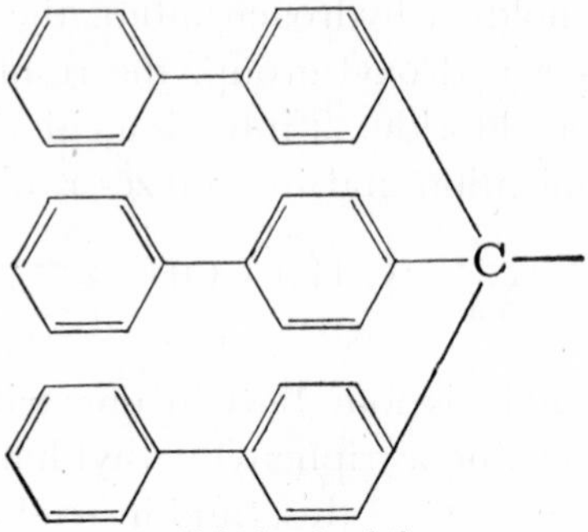

Tribiphenylmethyl

EXERCISES

1. Name several compounds which are formed when bituminous coal is heated. Write structural formulas for these compounds.

2. Is it possible to prepare aromatic compounds from aliphatic sources?

3. Account for the fact that there are no isomeric forms of bromobenzene, C_6H_5Br.

4. There are three dibromobenzenes, $C_6H_4Br_2$. How is it possible to assign a definite structural formula to each of the three compounds?

5. Write an equation to show how 1,4-methylethylbenzene may be made from toluene.

6. How is toluene made from a petroleum hydrocarbon? What is the major commercial source of benzene?

7. Write the structural formula of each of the following compounds: (a) anthracene, (b) naphthalene, (c) p-xylene, (d) pyridine, (e) biphenyl, (f) 1,2,4-trimethylbenzene, (g) phenol, (h) m-cresol, (i) triphenylmethyl radical.

8. Represent by balanced equations the reactions of benzene and of toluene with (a) bromine, (b) nitric acid, (c) sulfuric acid. If necessary refer to Chapter 9.

9. Is the same product formed by the two series of reactions shown below?

(a) $C_6H_6 \xrightarrow{Br_2} C_6H_5Br \xrightarrow{HNO_3} C_6H_4(NO_2)(Br)$

(b) $C_6H_6 \xrightarrow{HNO_3} C_6H_5NO_2 \xrightarrow{Br_2} C_6H_5(NO_2)(Br)$

Give a reason for your conclusion.

10. What reagents are usually employed in testing for unsaturation in hydrocarbons? Do benzene and toluene respond to these tests within the time limits commonly prescribed?

PROBLEMS

1. What is meant by the terms *ortho-para directing group* and *meta directing group*? Name from memory four groups in each classification.

2. Cite two evidences of resonance (conjugation) between the double bonds of benzene.

3. Triphenylmethane is $(C_6H_5)_3CH$. Represent its preparation from benzene, chloroform, and aluminum chloride through the use of the Friedel-Crafts reaction.

4. If you know the melting points of the ortho, meta, and para nitrotoluenes, $C_6H_4(NO_2)(CH_3)$, how could you assign structures to the isomeric nitrobenzoic acids, $C_6H_4(NO_2)(COOH)$?

5. What properties of hexaphenylethane indicate dissociation of the compound into free radicals?

25 · AROMATIC HALIDES, SULFONIC ACIDS, AND PHENOLS

The halogen derivatives of aromatic hydrocarbons fall into two classes: (1) those in which the halogen atom is attached to a carbon atom of the aromatic ring; (2) those in which the halogen atom is in a side chain. Benzene can form only the first type of halogen derivative; toluene can form both:

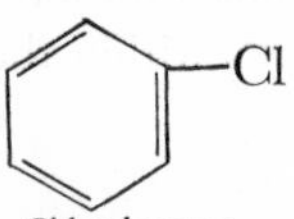

Chlorobenzene,
or
phenyl chloride

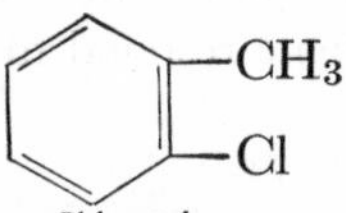

o-Chlorotoluene,
or
o-tolyl chloride

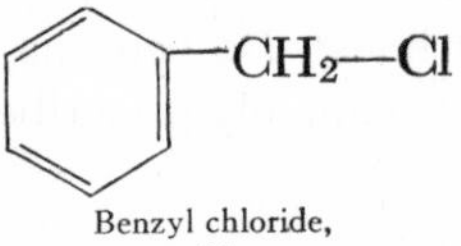

Benzyl chloride,
or
phenylchloromethane

Nomenclature. A monosubstitution product of benzene has the general formula C_6H_5X. It contains the phenyl radical, C_6H_5—. If X is a chlorine atom, the compound may be called phenyl chloride; or, as a derivative of benzene, it may be named chlorobenzene. In naming complicated structures it is a common practice to designate the positions of substituent groups by numbers.

Aromatic compounds in which aliphatic side chains are attached to the benzene ring are often treated as aliphatic compounds in which aromatic groups have been substituted for hydrogen atoms. Thus, the compound C_6H_5—CH_2—CH_3 may be regarded as a derivative of benzene or a derivative of ethane; it is ethyl benzene or phenyl ethane. There are two (isomeric) phenylethyl chlorides. They may be named as indicated below:

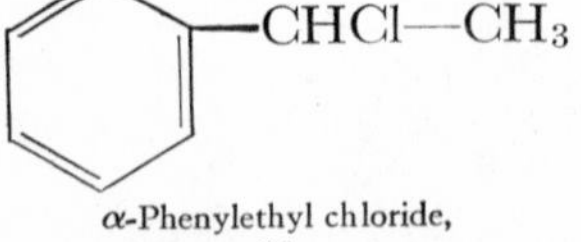

α-Phenylethyl chloride,
or
1-phenyl-chloroethane

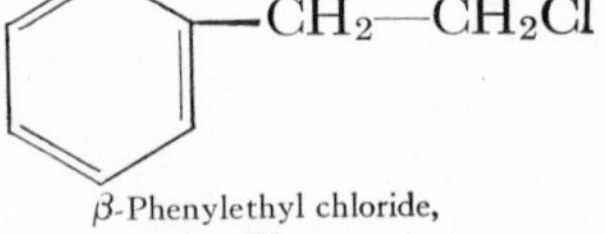

β-Phenylethyl chloride,
or
2-phenyl-chloroethane

Disubstitution products of benzene are often named as *ortho*, *meta*, and *para* compounds. Optional names are indicated in the following examples:

292

ortho-Dichlorobenzene,
or
1,2-dichlorobenzene

meta-Dichlorobenzene,
or
1,3-dichlorobenzene

para-Dichlorobenzene,
or
1,4-dichlorobenzene

For other examples see the tables below.

CHLORINE COMPOUNDS

NAME	FORMULA	MELTING POINT	BOILING POINT	SPECIFIC GRAVITY
Chlorobenzene	C_6H_5Cl	− 45.2°	132°	1.106 (20°)
1,2-Dichlorobenzene	$C_6H_4Cl_2$	− 17.6°	179°	1.325 (0°)
1,3-Dichlorobenzene	$C_6H_4Cl_2$	− 24.8°	173°	1.307 (0°)
1,4-Dichlorobenzene	$C_6H_4Cl_2$	52°	173°	1.241 (63°)
1,2,4-Trichlorobenzene . . .	$C_6H_3Cl_3$	17°	213°	1.446 (26°)
Orthochlorotoluene	$C_6H_4ClCH_3$	− 35.1°	159.4°	1.085 (18°)
Metachlorotoluene	$C_6H_4ClCH_3$	− 47.8°	162.4°	1.072 (20°)
Parachlorotoluene	$C_6H_4ClCH_3$	7.8°	162.5°	1.071 (18°)
Benzyl chloride	$C_6H_5CH_2Cl$	− 39°	179.4°	1.103 (18°)
Benzal chloride	$C_6H_5CHCl_2$	− 17.4°	214°	1.295 (16°)
Benzotrichloride	$C_6H_5CCl_3$	− 4.8°	220.7°	1.378 (15°)

BROMINE COMPOUNDS

NAME	FORMULA	MELTING POINT	BOILING POINT	SPECIFIC GRAVITY
Bromobenzene	C_6H_5Br	− 30.5°	156.2°	1.497 (20°)
1,2-Dibromobenzene	$C_6H_4Br_2$	1.8°	221°	2.003 (0°)
1,3-Dibromobenzene	$C_6H_4Br_2$	− 6.9°	217°	1.955 (20°)
1,4-Dibromobenzene	$C_6H_4Br_2$	86.8°	219°	1.954 (20°)
1,2,3-Tribromobenzene . .	$C_6H_3Br_3$	87.4°		2.658 (20°)
1,2,4-Tribromobenzene . .	$C_6H_3Br_3$	44°	276°	
1,3,5-Tribromobenzene . .	$C_6H_3Br_3$	120°	278°	
Orthobromotoluene	$C_6H_4BrCH_3$	− 28.1°	181.8°	1.422 (20°)
Metabromotoluene	$C_6H_4BrCH_3$	− 39.8°	183.7°	1.410 (20°)
Parabromotoluene	$C_6H_4BrCH_3$	28.2°	183.6°	1.310 (20°)
Benzyl bromide	$C_6H_5CH_2Br$	− 3.9°	199°	1.438 (22°)
Orthoxylyl bromide	$C_6H_4CH_3CH_2Br$	21°	217.7°	1.380 (22°)
Dibromometaxylene . . .	$C_6H_2Br_2(CH_3)_2$ (4, 6—1, 3)	72°	256°	
Tribromomesitylene	$C_6Br_3(CH_3)_3$ (2, 4, 6—1, 3, 5)	224°		

Distinction between nuclear and side-chain substituents. An aromatic halide is one in which the halogen atom is attached to the cyclic nucleus; if the halogen is in a side chain, the compound is really an aliphatic halide with an aromatic substituent. The latter displays the familiar substitution reactions characteristic of aliphatic halides, with this difference: if the halogen atom is in the α-position (on the carbon which is attached directly to the ring), the halogen atom will be more reactive than it would be in a simple alkyl halide. Thus benzyl chloride is much more easily hydrolyzed than methyl chloride. The phenyl group activates the adjacent carbon-halogen group.

The aromatic halides are relatively unreactive. For example, when the compound p-bromobenzyl chloride is boiled with dilute alkali, the chlorine atom only is removed. No bromide ion appears in the solution.

$$Br-\text{\large\Varangle}\text{\large\Varangle}-CH_2Cl + H_2O \xrightarrow{100°} Br-\text{\large\Varangle}\text{\large\Varangle}-CH_2OH + HCl$$

p-Bromobenzyl chloride p-Bromobenzyl alcohol

As a rule drastic treatment is required to replace a halogen atom by some other atom or group if the halogen atom is attached directly to an aromatic ring. As a consequence of this property aromatic halides are not as useful as aliphatic halides in synthetic processes.

The relative reactivities of a series of chlorides have been measured by Conant and co-workers by determining the rate of the substitution of chloride by iodide ion. In arbitrary numbers some of these are as follows:

HALIDE	RELATIVE REACTIVITY	HALIDE	RELATIVE REACTIVITY
C_6H_5Cl	0	$CH_2{=}CH{-}CH_2Cl$ . . .	79
$CH_2{=}CHCl$	0	$C_6H_5{-}CH_2Cl$	197
$(CH_3)_3CCl$	0.018	$CH_3{-}CO{-}CH_2Cl$ . . .	35,700
$CH_3{-}CH_2{-}CH_2{-}CH_2Cl$	1	$C_6H_5{-}CO{-}CH_2Cl$ . . .	105,000
cyclo-$C_6H_{11}Cl$	0.0001	$(C_6H_5)_3CCl$	38,000

A further distinction between aromatic and aliphatic halides lies in the methods of preparation of the two classes of compounds.

Preparation of aromatic halides. Halogenation of an aromatic hydrocarbon by chlorine or bromine leads to substitution either in the nucleus or in a side chain, according to the condition under which the reaction is carried out. Heat alone favors a reaction in the side chain, while certain catalysts, which are referred to as "halogen-carriers," promote nuclear substitution. The most useful catalysts for this purpose are iron, ferric chloride, aluminum chloride, and iodine.

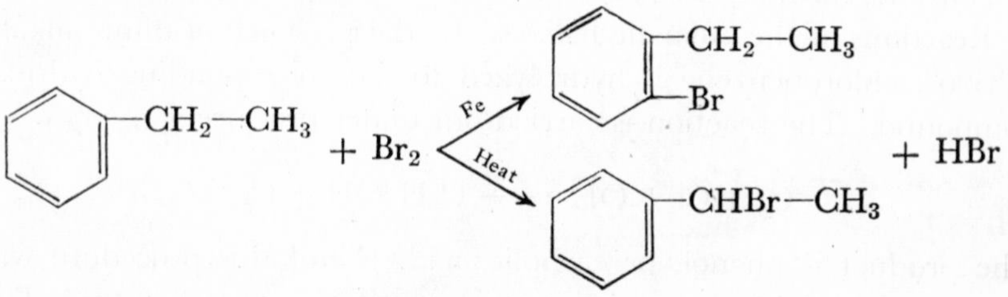

The position taken by the halogen atom in the ring is governed by the orientation rules which have been discussed (p. 285). In the above example both ortho and para derivatives would be formed. In the side chain the point of greatest reactivity is the α-position with respect to the ring.

The introduction of iodine and fluorine into the benzene ring requires procedures which are different from those employed for chlorine and bromine. This is because iodine rarely engages in direct halogenation of hydrocarbons, and fluorine reacts too vigorously. Both iodine and fluorine may be substituted for an amino group by way of the diazo reaction (p. 317). The same reaction may also be used to introduce chlorine and bromine. In some cases iodine may be used directly, provided a catalyst is present. For example, if benzene is to be converted to phenyl iodide, an oxidizing agent such as nitric acid serves as a catalyst:

$$C_6H_6 + I_2 \xrightarrow{HNO_3} C_6H_5I + HI$$

If an ortho-para directing group is present which activates the ring to a high degree, a weakly alkaline solution suffices to promote the substitution of iodine for nuclear hydrogen:

$$C_6H_5\text{—}OH + I_2 \xrightarrow{OH^-} I\text{—}C_6H_4\text{—}OH + HI$$

Phenol, C_6H_5OH, and aniline, $C_6H_5NH_2$, react with chlorine and bromine instantly in water solutions at room temperature, without the aid of catalysts.

Since benzene is represented as an unsaturated compound, one would suppose that addition of chlorine or bromine would compete seriously with the substitution processes. Actually addition is an extremely slow process under the conditions described above for the substitution reactions. In direct sunlight, at room temperature, and in the absence of a catalyst for substitution, chlorine and bromine add to benzene, forming $C_6H_6Cl_6$ and $C_6H_6Br_6$ respectively.

Reactions of the aromatic halides. In the presence of dilute alkali, at 300°, chlorobenzene is hydrolyzed to the corresponding hydroxy compound. The reaction is carried out under pressure.

$$C_6H_5Cl + OH^- \xrightarrow{300°} C_6H_5OH + Cl^-$$

The product is phenol, or carbolic acid. Until this procedure was discovered (1928), the major source of phenol was coal tar. The supply derived directly from coal tar had been supplemented with a synthesis of phenol by a process involving the sulfonation of benzene; but the use of chlorobenzene as a source of phenol greatly reduced the cost of the compound, and this has led to a notable expansion of the production of phenol-formaldehyde plastics. Most hydroxy derivatives of aromatic hydrocarbons are obtained by other paths.

Uses of aromatic halogen compounds. The aryl bromides and iodides can be used in the preparation of Grignard reagents, which in turn permit the introduction of aromatic nuclei into many types of compounds. The chlorides are not sufficiently reactive to form magnesium derivatives readily. Chlorobenzene finds use as a solvent and as an intermediate in the production of phenol. *p*-Dichlorobenzene is used as an insecticide. A compound known as 2,4-dichlorophenoxyacetic acid, commonly called 2,4-D, is used as a weed-killer.

2,4-Dichlorophenoxyacetic acid (2,4-D)

dichlorodiphenyltrichloroethane (DDT)
or
2,2-bis-(*p*-chlorophenyl)
1,1,1-trichloroethane

Herbicides which act selectively in killing certain types of plants and leaving others uninjured are becoming as important as insecticides in agriculture. The insecticide DDT is a halogen compound. It is prepared from chloral, CCl_3—CHO, and phenyl chloride, C_6H_5Cl. A 5 per cent solution of the compound in a hydrocarbon oil is commonly used as a spray. The oil evaporates and leaves a

Monsanto Chemical Company
Fig. 14. Spraying with a Solution of the Herbicide 2,4-D

solid film of the insecticide on the sprayed area. Flies, ants, and many other pests are poisoned by contact with the compound.

Among the naturally occurring iodine derivatives of benzene is thyroxine (p. 265), an amino acid of the thyroid hormone. This secretion of the thyroid gland has an important biological function in the control of metabolism, and the iodine is an essential constituent of the compound. Iodine deficiency in the diet leads to enlargement of the thyroid gland, or goiter. Faulty metabolism is often corrected by administration of an extract of the thyroid gland which contains the hormone.

Sulfonic Acids

Concentrated sulfuric acid acts upon an aromatic hydrocarbon, replacing hydrogen with the SO_3H group:

$$
\underset{\text{Benzene}}{\bigcirc} + \underset{\text{Sulfuric acid}}{SO_2\big\langle\begin{array}{c}OH\\[2pt]OH\end{array}} \xrightarrow{\text{Warm}} \underset{\text{Benzenesulfonic acid}}{\bigcirc\!\!-\!SO_2OH} + H_2O
$$

The reaction takes place rapidly at room temperature if fuming sulfuric acid is used. The sulfonation is reversible, but the reverse reaction is slow and usually requires a high temperature and an acidic catalyst:

$$C_6H_5SO_3H + H_2O \xrightarrow{HCl} C_6H_6 + H_2SO_4$$

In alkaline solution the hydrolysis takes a different course. Phenol, instead of benzene, is the final product:

$$C_6H_5SO_3H + NaOH \xrightarrow{\text{Cold}} C_6H_5SO_3Na + H_2O \qquad (1)$$

$$C_6H_5SO_3Na + NaOH \xrightarrow{\text{Hot!}} C_6H_5ONa + Na_2SO_3 \qquad (2)$$

$$C_6H_5ONa + HCl \longrightarrow C_6H_5OH + NaCl \qquad (3)$$

In acid solution the hydrolysis products are the hydrocarbon and a *sulfate*, while in alkaline solution they are a phenol and a *sulfite*. Both reactions find practical use, the one to recover aromatic hydrocarbons after sulfuric acid extractions, the other to prepare phenols.

The aromatic sulfonic acids are strong acids—as strong as sulfuric acid. They are isomeric with sulfite esters, such as C_6H_5—O—SO_2H. The fact that, in a sulfonic acid, carbon is attached to sulfur and not oxygen is shown by the oxidation of thiophenol, C_6H_5SH, the structure of which is known. The oxidation product is benzenesulfonic acid, $C_6H_5SO_3H$. The pure sulfonic acids are difficult to isolate, because of their high solubility in water.

Sulfonyl chlorides. Chlorides of sulfonic acids may be made from free sulfonic acids or from their salts by treatment with PCl_5, or from an aromatic hydrocarbon and chlorosulfonic acid:

$$\underset{\text{Sodium benzenesulfonate}}{3\ C_6H_5SO_3Na} + PCl_5 \xrightarrow{\text{Heat}} \underset{\substack{\text{Benzenesulfonyl}\\\text{chloride}}}{3\ C_6H_5SO_2Cl} + 2\ NaCl + NaPO_3$$

$$\underset{\text{Benzene}}{C_6H_6} + 2\ ClSO_3H \longrightarrow \underset{\substack{\text{Benzenesulfonyl}\\\text{chloride}}}{C_6H_5SO_2Cl} + HCl + H_2SO_4$$

Benzenesulfonyl chloride is a colorless liquid which has a disagreeable odor. Its vapor has an irritating effect upon the eyes and produces tears. It is used as a reagent for the separation of primary and secondary amines (p. 207).

Fusion of a sulfonate with a base. Phenols are readily prepared from salts of sulfonic acids by fusion with an alkali. Sodium hydroxide is the base commonly employed.

$$C_6H_5SO_3Na + NaOH \xrightarrow{300°-330°} C_6H_5ONa + NaHSO_3$$

Phenol, C_6H_5OH, is obtained by treating the sodium phenoxide, C_6H_5ONa, with hydrochloric acid:

$$C_6H_5ONa + HCl \longrightarrow C_6H_5OH + NaCl$$

Nitriles from sulfonic acids. A mixture of potassium cyanide and an aromatic sulfonate, when strongly heated, yields an aromatic cyanide, or nitrile. The mixed salts do not actually melt, but the nitrile distills from the hot mixture. The yield is often poor.

$$C_6H_5SO_3K + KCN \xrightarrow{Heat} \underset{\text{Benzonitrile}}{C_6H_5CN} + K_2SO_3$$

Sulfonic acid amides and imides. Benzenesulfonyl chloride and ammonia yield the crystalline benzenesulfonamide:

$$C_6H_5SO_2Cl + NH_3 \longrightarrow C_6H_5SO_2NH_2 + HCl$$

An application of this reaction to produce sulfanilamide will be found under sulfa drugs (p. 370). o-Toluenesulfonamide is used in the manufacture of saccharin, a crystalline compound which is more than five hundred times as sweet as cane sugar. The steps are briefly outlined as follows:

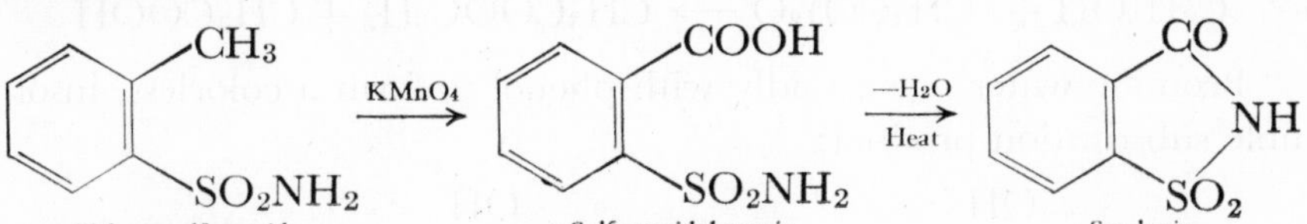

o-Toluenesulfonamide (mp 155°) →(KMnO₄)→ o-Sulfonamidobenzoic acid →(−H₂O, Heat)→ Saccharin (mp 229°)

Saccharin is an *imide* of o-sulfobenzoic acid. It is a valuable sweetening agent for persons who are suffering with diabetes or who for any other cause are unable to use sugar.

Phenols

The simplest hydroxy derivative of an aromatic hydrocarbon is hydroxybenzene, C_6H_5OH. It is called phenol or carbolic acid. The term *phenol* is not limited, however, to this particular compound; it is used as a class name for derivatives of benzene and its homologues in which at least one hydrogen atom of the ring has been replaced by a hydroxyl group. The phenols derived from toluene are called cresols; they are used as disinfectants.

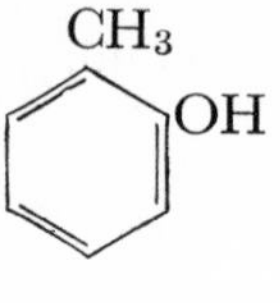

CH₃ OH

o-Cresol
(mp 30°; bp 191°)

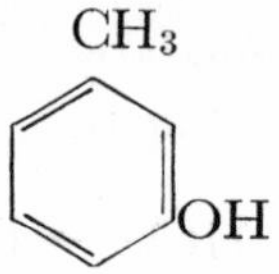

CH₃ OH

m-Cresol
(mp 10°; bp 203°)

CH₃ OH

p-Cresol
(mp 35°; bp 201°)

The phenols are weak acids, but they are sufficiently acidic to form salts in dilute aqueous solutions of sodium hydroxide. Water-insoluble phenols are usually soluble in dilute alkali.

$$C_{10}H_7OH + NaOH \longrightarrow C_{10}H_7ONa + H_2O$$
Naphthol   Salt of naphthol
(insoluble in water)   (soluble in water)

The dissociation constant of phenol, C_6H_5OH, is 1×10^{-10}. This figure is to be compared with the dissociation constant of a carboxylic acid of about 1×10^{-5} and of an alcohol of about 1×10^{-18}. Phenols are too weakly acidic to be titrated as acids. Alcohols are converted into alkyl halides by treatment with phosphorus trichloride; phenols form aromatic phosphorous esters with this reagent. In a few instances phenolic hydroxyl groups are replaced by chlorine when phosphorus pentachloride is used. Alcohols and phenols both react with acid chlorides and acid anhydrides to form esters:

$$C_6H_5OH + (CH_3CO)_2O \longrightarrow CH_3COOC_6H_5 + CH_3COOH$$

Bromine water acts rapidly with phenol to form a colorless, insoluble substitution product:

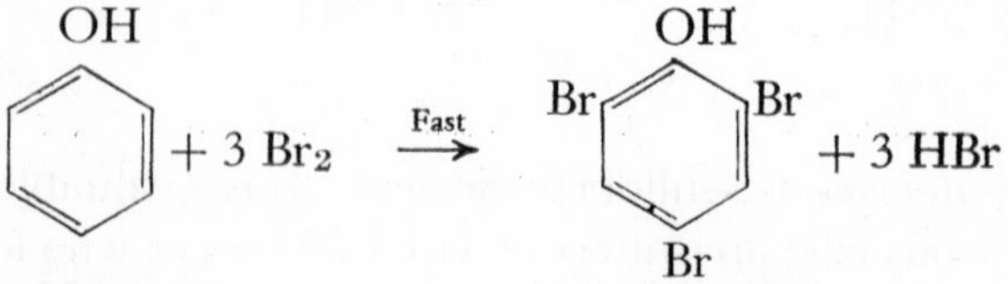

OH + 3 Br₂ $\xrightarrow{\text{Fast}}$ Br OH Br + 3 HBr
Br

Phenol
(mp 41°)

2,4,6-Tribromophenol
(mp 96°)

This nuclear substitution by bromine requires no catalyst and illustrates the fact that an ortho-para orienting group (in this case OH) increases the reactivity of the ortho-para positions. This effect is not marked in chlorobenzene, but is very strong in the phenols and amines.

The simple phenols give orange, red, or green colorations with ferric chloride in alcohol solution. The color is due to a complex ion formation and is used as a test for phenolic substances.

PHYSICAL PROPERTIES OF SOME PHENOLS

NAME	FORMULA	MP °C	BP °C	SOL. IN H₂O g/100 g 20°	K_a
Phenol	C_6H_5OH	41	182.6	8.3	1×10^{-10}
o-Cresol	$1,2-C_6H_4OHCH_3$	30	190.8	2.5	6.3×10^{-11}
m-Cresol	$1,3-C_6H_4OHCH_3$	10	203	2.6	9.8×10^{-11}
p-Cresol	$1,4-C_6H_4OHCH_3$	36	201.1	2.3	6.7×10^{-11}
o-Chlorophenol	$1,2-C_6H_4OHCl$	8.8	176	2.8	
m-Chlorophenol	$1,3-C_6H_4OHCl$	38.8	214	2.6	
p-Chlorophenol	$1,4-C_6H_4OHCl$	42.9	217	2.7	5.0×10^{-10}
o-Nitrophenol	$1,2-C_6H_4OHNO_2$	45	214.5	0.2	6.0×10^{-8}
m-Nitrophenol	$1,3-C_6H_4OHNO_2$	96		2.2	5.0×10^{-9}
p-Nitrophenol	$1,4-C_6H_4OHNO_2$	114		1.3	6.9×10^{-8}
Dinitrophenol	$1,2,4-C_6H_3OH(NO_2)_2$	113	Explodes		1×10^{-4}
Trinitrophenol (picric acid)	$1,2,4,6-C_6H_2OH(NO_2)_3$	122	Explodes	1.2	2.3×10^{-1}

Phenol is used in large quantities in the manufacture of synthetic resins. One of these, Bakelite, is a condensation product of phenol and formaldehyde. Phenol is an intermediate in the preparation of many drugs and dyes. Approximately 10 per cent of the supply is obtained from coal tar, and 90 per cent is made synthetically.

Synthesis of phenols. The best general methods for making phenols are (1) fusion of salts of sulfonic acids with alkali; (2) hydrolysis of diazonium salts. An example of the first process is shown on page 299. The second method will be outlined later in connection with the reactions of diazonium compounds (p. 316). Phenol itself is manufactured from benzene through chlorination and hydrolysis.

Dihydric phenols. The ortho and para dihydroxy derivatives of benzene are easily oxidized, and this property is responsible for their use as reducing agents. They are employed as photographic developers.

o-Dihydroxybenzene
(catechol)
(mp 104°; bp 240°)

m-Dihydroxybenzene
(resorcinol)
(mp 108°; bp 276°)

p-Dihydroxybenzene
(hydroquinone)
(mp 171°; bp 286°)

Catechol and hydroquinone occur as components of glycosides in plants. Lignins of wood contain catechol derivatives. Vanillin, the fragrant constituent of the vanilla bean, and piperonal (p. 326) contain the catechol nucleus. The meta compound is less susceptible to oxidation; its chief use is in the production of dyes. Even phenol itself is slowly oxidized in the air, as shown by the pink color which slowly develops in a colorless sample upon standing.

Oxidizing agents convert hydroquinone into a yellow compound called quinone. Reducing agents reverse the process.

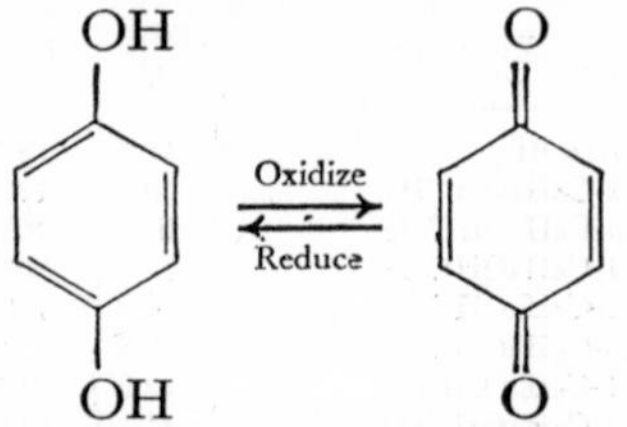

Hydroquinone
(colorless)

Quinone
(yellow)

This sort of reversible oxidation and reduction is common in animal and vegetable metabolism. The oxidation of polyhydroxy phenols often leads to the formation of deeply colored resinous products, particularly if the oxidation occurs in alkaline solution. The darkening of solutions of photographic developers and the discoloration of fruits are due to such oxidations.

Trihydric phenols. Pyrogallic acid and phloroglucinol are the best-known trihydroxy derivatives of benzene.

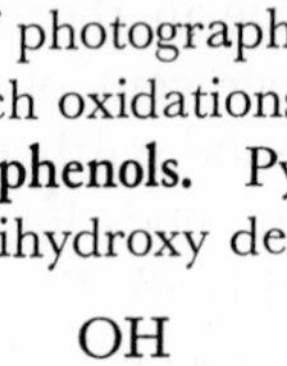

Pyrogallic acid,
or
1,2,3-trihydroxybenzene

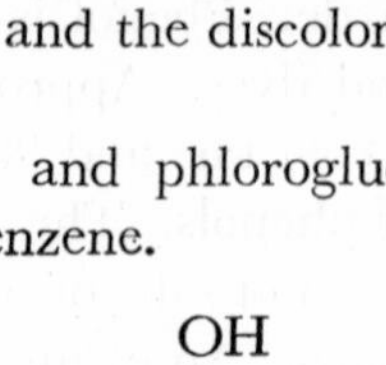

Phloroglucinol,
or
1,3,5-trihydroxybenzene

These compounds are colorless solids. In alkaline solution they are good reducing agents. Pyrogallic acid is used as a photographic developer, and in gas analysis it is used as a reagent for the absorption of oxygen. The naturally occurring tannins, which are used in the manufacture of leather, contain the pyrogallic acid nucleus.

Naphthols. The two monohydroxy derivatives of naphthalene are called naphthols. They are crystalline compounds which dissolve readily in alcohol, ether, and alkaline aqueous solutions. They are only slightly soluble in pure cold water. The naphthols are used extensively in the manufacture of dyes.

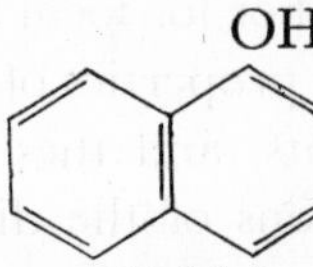

α-Naphthol
(mp 96°; bp 288°)

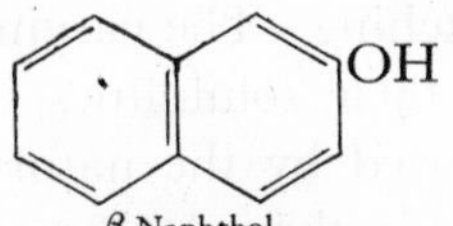

β-Naphthol
(mp 122°; bp 294°)

The naphthols may be made from naphthalene by first forming the naphthalenesulfonic acids and then fusing the latter with sodium hydroxide:

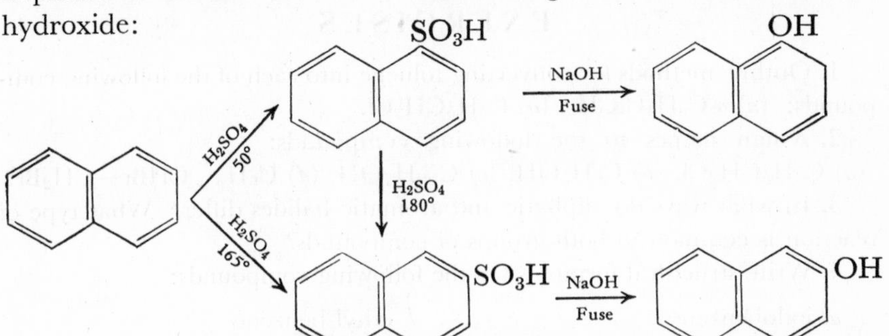

Antiseptic properties of phenols. Lord Lister, an English surgeon, was the first (1865) to use phenol as an antiseptic to combat infection during operations. Practically all phenolic substances are bactericidal, and the cresols, thymol, and carvacrol found early use in this capacity.

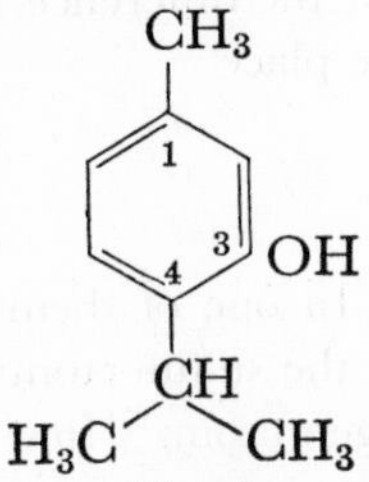

Thymol
(mp 51.5°)

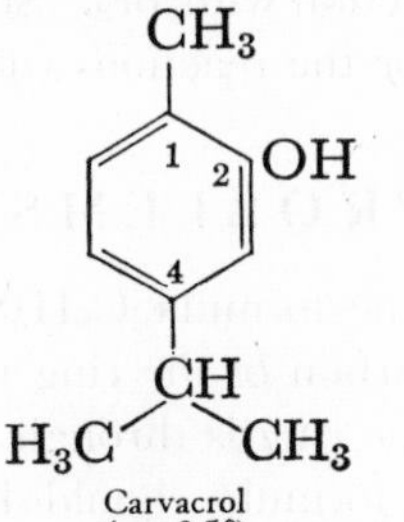

Carvacrol
(mp 0.5°)

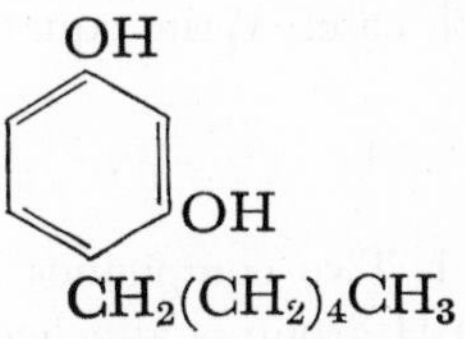

Hexylresorcinol
(mp 69°)

In 1921 Johnson and Lane reported that the antiseptic properties of alkyl-substituted resorcinols increased with increase in length of the alkyl chain. While resorcinol is only about one-third as effective as phenol, n-hexylresorcinol is rated as 50 to 100 times as effective. The relative potencies of antiseptics vary when tested with different organisms or under different conditions. Phenol itself now finds little application as an antiseptic.

Phenol and the cresols in high concentrations kill growing tissues; hence they may cause serious burns if applied to the skin. Phenol is often diluted with glycerol, olive oil, or camphor for local applications to relieve itching. The varying physiological properties of phenols are related to their solubilities in water and fats, and these solubilities may be varied by the nature and proportions of the diluent. The problem, as in the case of most germicides, is to produce a maximum lethal action on the unwanted organism with a minimum of harmful effects on the patient.

EXERCISES

1. Outline methods for converting toluene into each of the following compounds: (a) o-$C_6H_4ClCH_3$, (b) $C_6H_5CH_2Cl$.

2. Assign names to the following compounds:
(a) $C_6H_5CH_2Cl$, (b) C_6H_5OH, (c) $C_{10}H_7OH$, (d) C_6H_5—$CHBr$—CH_2Br.

3. In what ways do aliphatic and aromatic halides differ? What type of reaction is common to both groups of compounds?

4. Write structural formulas for the following compounds:

a. iodobenzene
b. 1,3,5-tribromobenzene
c. benzyl bromide

d. ethyl benzene
e. p-chlorotoluene
f. 2,4-dichlorotoluene

5. Write an equation representing the sulfonation of toluene. Use structural formulas.

6. Alcohols differ from phenols in the following properties: (a) acidity, (b) reaction with PCl_3, (c) reaction with Br_2. State what the difference is in each case. Write equations for the reactions which take place.

PROBLEMS

1. Two compounds have the formula $C_6H_5SO_3H$. In one of them the SO_3H group is attached to carbon of the ring through the sulfur atom; in the other the attachment to the ring is through an oxygen atom. How is it possible to determine which formula should be assigned to each of the compounds?

2. Show how phenol can be made from benzene in two different ways.

3. By what chemical reactions could the members of the following pairs of compounds be distinguished from each other?

a. C_6H_5—CH_2OH and HO—C_6H_4—CH_3
b. Br—C_6H_4—CH_2Cl and Cl—C_6H_4—CH_2Br
c. CH_3—C_6H_4—Br and C_6H_5—CH_2Br
d. $C_6H_5OC_2H_5$ and C_2H_5—C_6H_4OH

26 · AROMATIC NITRO COMPOUNDS, AMINES, AND DIAZONIUM SALTS

Nitration of an aromatic hydrocarbon is accomplished through the direct action of concentrated nitric acid on the hydrocarbon. The rate of the reaction is accelerated by the presence of concentrated sulfuric acid, and a mixture of the two acids is generally used.

$$C_6H_6 + HONO_2 \xrightarrow{H_2SO_4} C_6H_5NO_2 + H_2O$$

If a side chain is present in the hydrocarbon, the nitration still occurs at one of the nuclear positions. However, greater care must then be taken to control the temperature of the reaction mixture; for nitric acid is a strong oxidizing agent, and the side chains may be oxidized if the temperature becomes high.

In the *aliphatic* series, compounds of the formula RNO_2 exist in isomeric forms, RNO_2 and $RONO$, called nitro compounds and nitrites respectively. In *nitro* compounds the nitrogen atom of the NO_2 group is linked directly to carbon. In *nitrites*, which are esters of nitrous acid, the nitrogen is linked to carbon through an oxygen atom.

$$CH_3\text{—}CH_2\text{—}NO_2 \qquad\qquad CH_3\text{—}CH_2\text{—}O\text{—}NO$$

Nitroethane, bp 114°   Ethyl nitrite, bp 17°
(a nitro compound)   (a nitrous ester)

A nitrous ester is easily hydrolyzed to an alcohol and nitrous acid. Nitro compounds cannot be hydrolyzed. Nitrous esters yield alcohols and ammonia on reduction; nitro bodies are reduced to amines. The compounds formed by the action of nitric acid on *aromatic* hydrocarbons are nitro compounds. They are not susceptible to hydrolysis, and they can be reduced to amines.

Properties and uses. Most of the aromatic nitro compounds are colored. They range in color from a very pale yellow to orange. The nitro group, like the carboxyl group, promotes association of the molecules. One evidence of this association is a relatively high boiling point.

The mononitro compounds are neutral; they do not react with aqueous acids or bases. Polynitro compounds, however, become more deeply colored in basic solution, a fact which shows some sort of salt formation. This property makes 1, 3, 5-trinitrobenzene useful as an indicator for strongly basic solutions.

The nitro group is meta-orienting; it also represses the reactivity of remaining positions in the ring. This makes it easy to stop nitrations at the mononitro stage, as the introduction of a second nitro group requires a higher temperature or a longer time. Nitrobenzene does not engage in a Friedel and Crafts reaction, nor is it readily brominated.

The major use of simple nitro compounds is that of intermediates in syntheses. From them can be obtained aromatic amines, which in turn yield dyes and drugs. Some photographic developers are prepared from nitro compounds. A few nitro compounds can be used as explosives. An example is 2, 4, 6-trinitrotoluene, or TNT. Even more powerful explosives of this type were developed for use in bombs during the last war. These explosives differ in structure from gun cotton (nitrocellulose) and nitroglycerine, which also are used in the manufacture of explosives. Nitrocellulose and nitroglycerine are misnamed; they are esters of nitric acid, not true nitro compounds.

Nitrobenzene, $C_6H_5NO_2$, is a pale-yellow liquid (mp 5.7°, bp 211°, sp gr 1.204), almost colorless when pure. It is practically insoluble in water, but it dissolves in alcohol. Its odor resembles that of almonds. It is a commercial source of aniline, which is manufactured in large quantities for the production of aniline dyes.

Dinitrobenzenes. In the ordinary process of making mononitrobenzene a small quantity of dinitrobenzene appears as a by-product. To make dinitrobenzene the principal product, it is necessary to nitrate at a higher temperature or for a longer time, because of the reduced reactivity of the nuclear hydrogen atoms of nitrobenzene. Three compounds corresponding to the formula $C_6H_4(NO_2)_2$ are known; but direct nitration of benzene gives rise to the *meta* compound almost exclusively.

o-Dinitrobenzene   m-Dinitrobenzene   p-Dinitrobenzene

The ortho and para derivatives are prepared by taking advantage of the directing influence of the amino group. Nitration of aminobenzene (aniline) leads to the formation of ortho and para nitroanilines. The NH_2 group may then be replaced by NO_2 through the diazo reaction (p. 317).

AROMATIC NITRO COMPOUNDS			
Name	Formula	Boiling Point, °C	Melting Point, °C
Nitrobenzene	$C_6H_5NO_2$	211	5.7°
m-Dinitrobenzene	$C_6H_4(NO_2)_2(m)$	302	90
o-Nitrotoluene	$CH_3C_6H_4NO_2(o)$	222	− 10
p-Nitrotoluene	$CH_3C_6H_4NO_2(p)$	238	51
m-Nitrotoluene	$CH_3C_6H_4NO_2(m)$	231	16
2,4-Dinitrotoluene	$CH_3C_6H_3(NO_2)_2$	300	70
2,4,6-Trinitrotoluene (TNT)	$CH_3C_6H_2(NO_2)_3$		81

Nitrotoluenes. The nitration of toluene, at temperatures between 25° and 75°, leads to the production of the three possible mononitro compounds, but in unequal yields; the average proportions are *ortho* 58.8 per cent, *para* 36.8 per cent, and *meta* 4.4 per cent. All are low-melting solids. Nitration at a higher temperature with an excess of nitric acid produces dinitro compounds and finally one or more of the six isomeric trinitrotoluenes. Symmetrical trinitrotoluene, a powerful explosive, is made in this way:

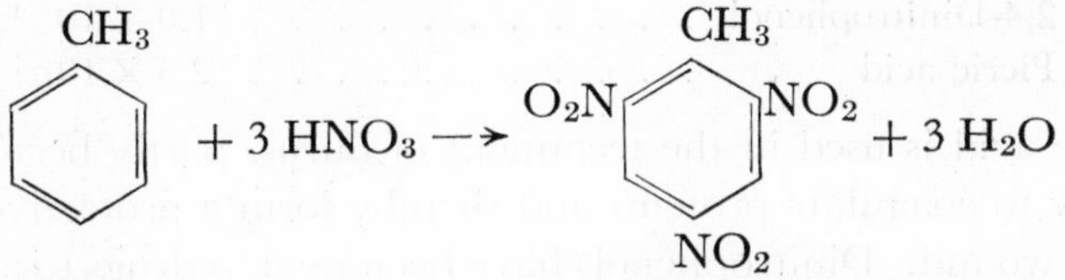

Toluene

2,4,6-Trinitrotoluene
(TNT, mp 81°)

Trinitrotoluene is a pale-yellow solid. It can be handled safely, for it is not detonated by an ordinary shock. A shell containing TNT can be fired from a cannon without danger of explosion. The explosion is induced later by the more sudden shock of a special detonator.

Nitrophenols. Dilute nitric acid suffices to convert phenol into a mixture of ortho and para nitrophenols. This is another example of the general rule that the reactivity of a ring compound is enhanced by the presence of groups which orient to the ortho-para positions. The ortho and para nitrophenols are readily separated by distillation with steam. The ortho compound is much more volatile than the para compound. On further nitration each of these compounds can be converted into the symmetrical 2, 4, 6-trinitrophenol known as picric acid.

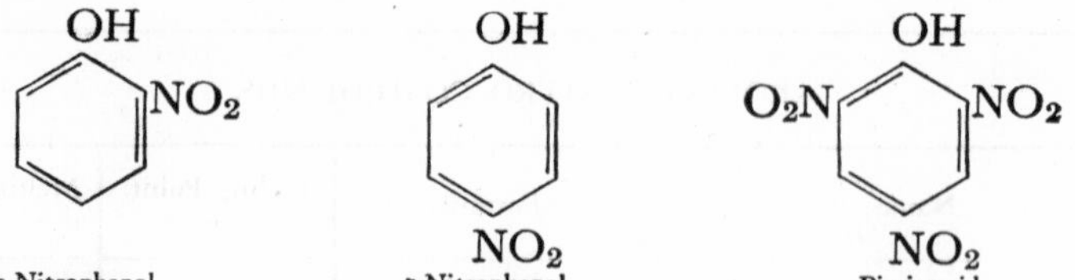

| o-Nitrophenol (mp 45°) | p-Nitrophenol (mp 114°) | Picric acid (mp 123°) |

The production of picric acid on a commercial scale is accomplished by dissolving phenol in cold concentrated sulfuric acid and then stirring into the mixture concentrated nitric acid. The first stage of nitration occurs readily at 0°; the final stage requires a temperature of 100°. Salts of picric acid are powerful explosives. The salts are very sensitive to shock; the free, crystalline acid is not easily detonated, but it should be handled with care.

The influence of the nitro group on the acidity of a phenol is indicated by the following tabulation of dissociation constants:

	K_a
Phenol	1.7×10^{-10}
o-Nitrophenol	6.0×10^{-8}
m-Nitrophenol	5.0×10^{-9}
p-Nitrophenol	6.0×10^{-9}
2,4-Dinitrophenol	1.0×10^{-4}
Picric acid	2.3×10^{-1}

Picric acid is used in the treatment of burns, partly because of its tendency to coagulate proteins and thereby form a protective coating over the wound. Dinitrophenols have been used as drugs to accelerate oxygen metabolism and raise the body temperature. This was at one time a common treatment for obesity. The practice has been discontinued, for serious disorders follow the use of the drug. The nitrophenols are poisons, and continued use of them as drugs leads to disorders of the liver and kidneys, and in many cases to cataracts in the eyes.

Salt formation of an ortho or para nitrophenol is accompanied by a marked change in color, generally from yellow toward red. This implies not only ionization but a change in structure. That is, the anion of the acid does not correspond in structure to that of the acid itself.

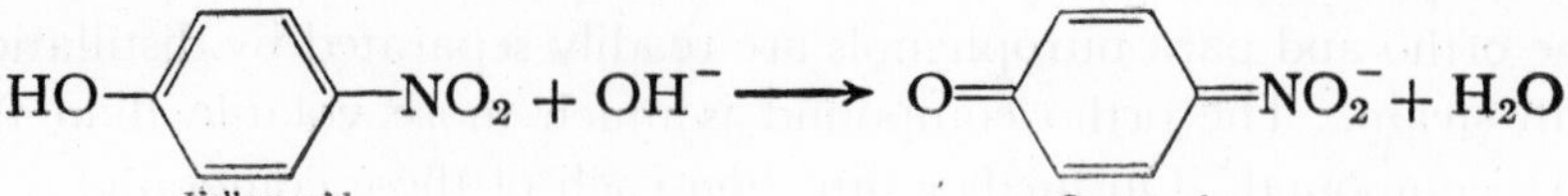

Yellow acid   Orange salt

To account for this we assume that the nitrophenol exists in tauto-meric forms:

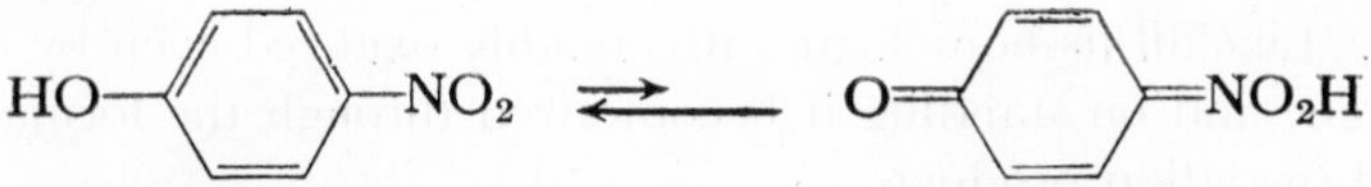

Benzenoid form   Quinonoid form

The undissociated compound is mainly in the benzenoid form, but the anion is largely in the strongly colored quinonoid form. Two forms of the compound may actually be isolated; one is much more acidic than the other, but the form which is the more acidic is un-stable. Only one salt can be isolated, because the two seemingly pos-sible anions are not isomers—they are resonance forms of a single ion. For their interconversion only electron shifts are required, not a shift of an atom.

Resonance forms of nitrophenolate ion

When nitric acid touches the skin, a yellow spot appears. Washing this spot with ammonia deepens the color. The phenomenon is due to the phenolic amino acid, tyrosine, in the protein of the skin, which forms a nitrophenolic derivative.

Aromatic Amines

An aromatic amine is a compound in which the nitrogen atom of one of the groups —NH_2, —NHR, or —NR_2 is attached directly to carbon in an aromatic nucleus. Amines are classified as primary, sec-ondary, or tertiary on the basis of the number of carbon atoms which are attached directly to the nitrogen atom. Examples are shown below:

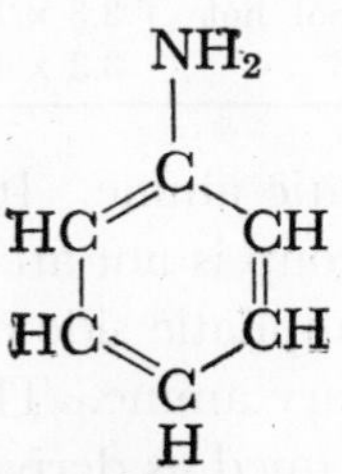

Aniline,
or
phenylamine
(a primary amine)

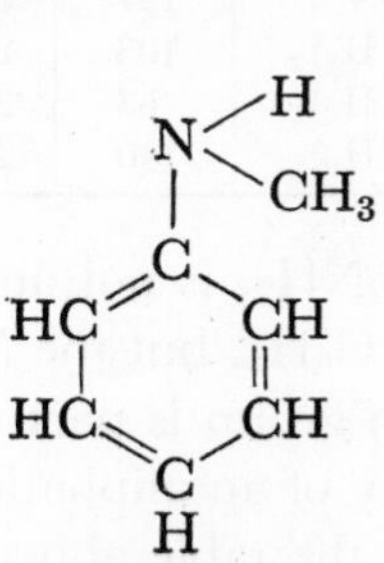

Methylaniline,
or
methylphenylamine
(a secondary amine)

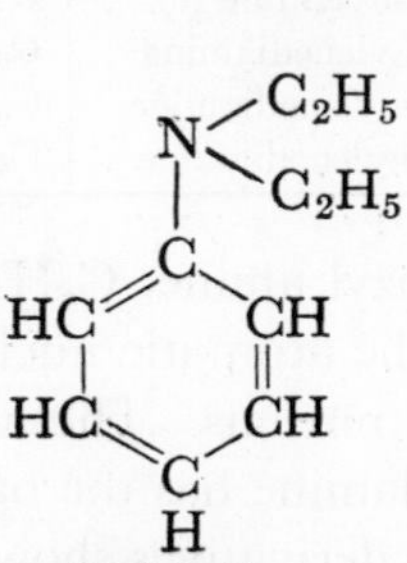

Diethylaniline,
or
diethylphenylamine
(a tertiary amine)

The simplest aromatic amine is aniline, a colorless, oily liquid which is sparingly soluble in water. It boils at 184.3° and melts at − 6.2°. Like all its homologues it is readily oxidized even by oxygen of the air, and on standing it becomes red through the formation of colored oxidation products.

An outstanding difference between aliphatic and aromatic amines is found in their properties as bases. While in aliphatic derivatives and in ammonia the basic dissociation constants vary from 1×10^{-3} to 1×10^{-5}, those of the aromatic amines are very much smaller. The table below presents some typical examples. The amines which are insoluble in water dissolve readily in dilute acids, that is, they form soluble salts:

$$C_6H_5NH_2 + H_2O \rightleftarrows C_6H_5NH_3^+ + OH^-$$

$$\overset{\text{HCl}}{\rightleftarrows} C_6H_5NH_3^+ + Cl^- + H_2O$$

Salt formation may be written also as follows:

$$C_6H_5NH_2 + HCl \rightleftarrows C_6H_5NH_3Cl \text{ (or } C_6H_5NH_2 \cdot HCl)$$

PHYSICAL CONSTANTS OF SOME AROMATIC AMINES

Name	Formula	Mp °C	Bp °C	Sol. Water g/100 g	K_b
Aniline	$C_6H_5NH_2$	− 6.2	184.3	3.5	4.6×10^{-10}
o-Toluidine	$CH_3C_6H_4NH_2$	− 21	201	1.5	3.5×10^{-10}
m-Toluidine	$CH_3C_6H_4NH_2$	− 32	203	Sl. sol.	6.0×10^{-10}
p-Toluidine	$CH_3C_6H_4NH_2$	45	200	0.74	2.1×10^{-10}
Benzyl amine	$C_6H_5CH_2NH_2$		185		2.4×10^{-5}
Methylaniline . . .	$C_6H_5NHCH_3$	− 57	196	V. sl. sol.	7.4×10^{-9}
Dimethylaniline . .	$C_6H_5N(CH_3)_2$	2.5	193	1.4	2.4×10^{-10}
Diphenylamine . . .	$(C_6H_5)_2NH$	52.9	302	V. sl. sol.	V. small
Triphenylamine . . .	$(C_6H_5)_3N$	127	348	Insol.	
o-Phenylenediamine .	$C_6H_4(NH_2)_2$	103	256	4.1	3.3×10^{-10}
m-Phenylenediamine	$C_6H_4(NH_2)_2$	63	287	Sol. hot	3.3×10^{-10}
n-Phenylenediamine .	$C_6H_4(NH_2)_2$	140	267	3	3.3×10^{-10}

Benzyl amine, $C_6H_5CH_2NH_2$, is not an aromatic amine. It contains the aromatic nucleus, C_6H_5, but the NH_2 group is not attached to this nucleus. The amino group is part of an aliphatic side chain. Benzylamine has the basicity of an aliphatic primary amine. The di-amino derivatives shown in the table above are named as derivatives of the divalent radical $\rangle C_6H_4$, which is called *phenylene*. Alternative names would be 1,2-diaminobenzene, 1,3-diaminobenzene, and 1,4-diaminobenzene. The toluidines are amino derivatives of toluene.

Preparation of amines. Primary aromatic amines are usually prepared by reduction of the corresponding nitro compounds. The reducing agents used are (1) metals, such as iron and tin, in acid solution; (2) stannous or titanous salts, particularly $SnCl_2$ and $TiCl_3$; (3) sulfides and sulfites, such as ammonium hydrosulfide, NH_4HS, and sodium hydrosulfite, $Na_2S_2O_4$; (4) hydrogen in contact with platinum. On a laboratory scale of operation, tin and hydrochloric acid give good yields of amine salts:

$$C_6H_5NO_2 + 3 Sn + 7 HCl \xrightarrow{Heat} C_6H_5NH_2 \cdot HCl + 3 SnCl_2 + 2 H_2O$$

Nitrobenzene   Aniline hydrochloride

The free base is obtained from the salt solution by the addition of sodium hydroxide followed by distillation with steam. On a commercial scale, reduction is accomplished by the use of iron and a trace of acid:

$$C_6H_5NO_2 + 2 Fe + 4 H_2O \xrightarrow[Heat]{HCl} C_6H_5NH_2 + 2 Fe(OH)_3$$

A reaction involving several equivalents of an oxidizing or reducing agent, such as the one shown by this equation, is not a single-step process. Intermediate products are formed, and with proper choice of reagents and conditions the intermediates may often be isolated. The change from a nitro compound to an amine may pass through the following stages:

$$C_6H_5NO_2 \longrightarrow C_6H_5NO \longrightarrow C_6H_5NHOH \longrightarrow C_6H_5NH_2$$

Nitrobenzene   Nitrosobenzene   Phenylhydroxylamine   Aniline

The conversion of aromatic halides to amines is difficult, owing to the low reactivity of the halides. Under high pressures, at high temperatures, and with cuprous oxide as a catalyst the replacement does occur:

$$2 C_6H_5Cl + 2 NH_3 + Cu_2O \xrightarrow{200°} 2 C_6H_5NH_2 + 2 CuCl + H_2O$$

Alkylation of amines. The mixed aromatic-aliphatic secondary and tertiary amines are prepared by application of the Hofmann reaction. An example is the formation of methylaniline from aniline:

$$C_6H_5NH_2 + CH_3I \longrightarrow C_6H_5NHCH_3 \cdot HI$$

$$C_6H_5NHCH_3 \cdot HI + NaOH \longrightarrow C_6H_5NHCH_3 + NaI + H_2O$$

Some dimethyl aniline is produced at the same time. In all applications of the Hofmann reaction mixed products are formed (p. 202). To obtain aromatic amines which are alkylated in the ring, one usually starts with the side chain already present, nitrates the hydrocarbon, and reduces the nitro compound.

Acylation of amines. The acetyl derivative of aniline, acetanilide, $C_6H_5NHCOCH_3$, is made by adding acetyl chloride or acetic anhydride to aniline, as in the general preparation of amides:

$$C_6H_5NH_2 + CH_3COCl \xrightarrow{\text{Pyridine}} C_6H_5NHCOCH_3 + HCl$$
$$\text{Aniline} \qquad\qquad\qquad\qquad\qquad \text{Acetanilide}$$

$$C_6H_5NH_2 + (CH_3CO)_2O \xrightarrow{\text{Heat}} C_6H_5NHCOCH_3 + CH_3COOH$$
$$\text{Aniline} \qquad\qquad\qquad\qquad\qquad \text{Acetanilide}$$

The product is a white crystalline solid which melts at 114°. Acetanilide has been used for many years to combat fevers, but more effective remedies for this purpose are now available.

Acetylation of the amino group is reversible; that is, the amide may be hydrolyzed and the amine recovered. Accordingly acetylation is often employed to protect the amino group while other reactions are being carried out. An example is found in the preparation of sulfanilamide (p. 370). The nitration and bromination of the ring in aniline are best carried out upon acetanilide, because in aniline itself the amino group so activates the ring that control of the reaction is difficult. The acetyl group not only protects the amino group from attack by the reagent but reduces the reactivity of the nuclear positions. Para nitroaniline is made as follows:

$$\text{NHCOCH}_3 \xrightarrow{\text{HNO}_3} \quad \text{NHCOCH}_3 \text{ (NO}_2\text{)} \xrightarrow{\text{H}_2\text{O(H}^+)} \quad \text{NH}_2 \text{ (NO}_2\text{)} + CH_3COOH$$

Acetanilide   p-Nitroaniline

Some ortho nitroaniline is formed at the same time. The meta nitroaniline is prepared by reduction of one of the nitro groups of meta dinitrobenzene. Ammonium hydrosulfide will reduce one NO_2 group and leave the other unchanged.

$$\text{NO}_2 \text{(NO}_2\text{)} + 3\,H_2S \xrightarrow[\text{H}_2\text{O}]{\text{NH}_3} \text{NH}_2 \text{(NO}_2\text{)} + 3\,S + 2\,H_2O$$

Aminophenols. The ortho and para aminophenols are widely used as photographic developers and as starting points in the manufacture of some drugs. They are very easily oxidized, and they consequently reduce Tollens's reagent and Fehling's solution. Alkaline solutions of these compounds become discolored if exposed to air for a short time. The aminophenols are amphoteric compounds; the NH_2 group is weakly basic, and an OH group, when attached to the benzene ring, is weakly acidic. Aminophenols therefore form salts with acids and with bases. The reactions of para aminophenol with sodium hydroxide and with hydrochloric acid may be represented as follows:

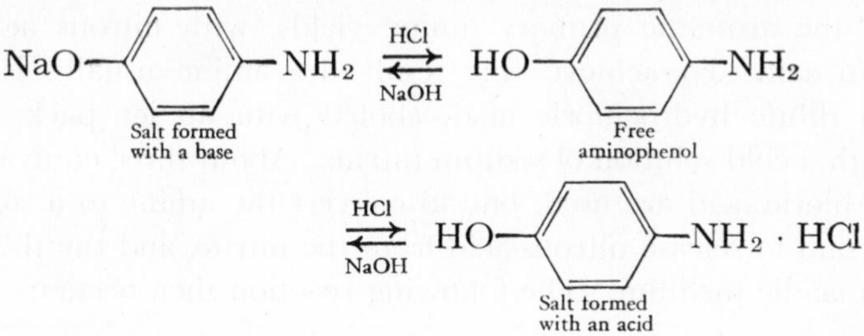

NaO—⟨benzene⟩—NH₂ ⇌(HCl/NaOH) HO—⟨benzene⟩—NH₂

Salt formed with a base   Free aminophenol

⇌(HCl/NaOH) HO—⟨benzene⟩—NH₂ · HCl

Salt formed with an acid

Para aminophenol may be prepared from phenol by treatment with nitric acid and reduction of the nitro group:

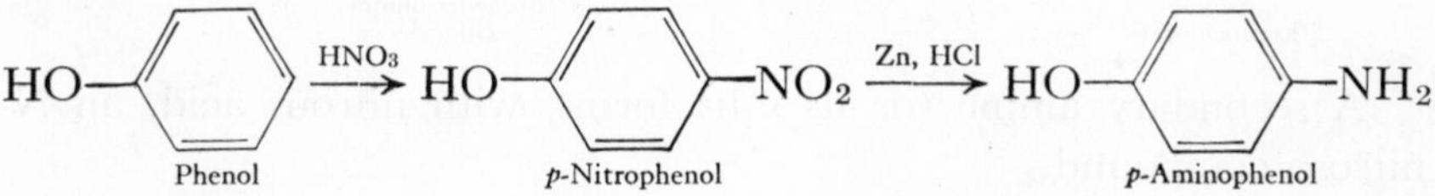

HO—⟨benzene⟩ —(HNO₃)→ HO—⟨benzene⟩—NO₂ —(Zn, HCl)→ HO—⟨benzene⟩—NH₂

Phenol   p-Nitrophenol   p-Aminophenol

A procedure which begins with nitrobenzene is also practical. Nitrobenzene can be reduced in neutral solution to phenylhydroxylamine, C_6H_5NHOH. The latter, when warmed with an acid, undergoes a rearrangement in which the hydroxyl group leaves the nitrogen atom and becomes attached to the para carbon atom of the ring. The hydroxyl group and the para hydrogen atom exchange places. This type of rearrangement (discovered by A. W. Hofmann in 1871) is peculiar to N-substituted aromatic amines.

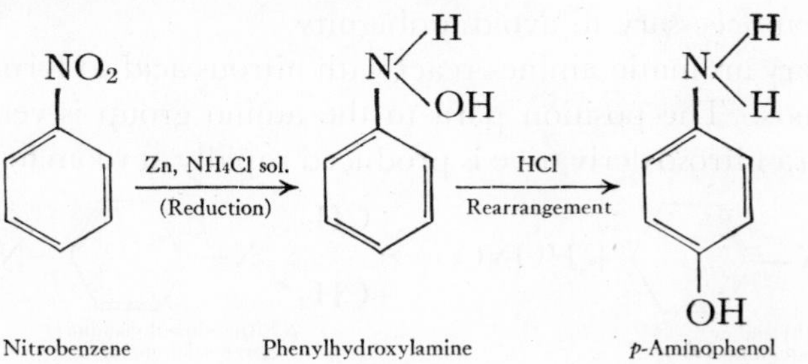

⟨benzene with NO₂⟩ —(Zn, NH₄Cl sol. / Reduction)→ ⟨benzene with N<H,OH⟩ —(HCl / Rearrangement)→ ⟨benzene with N<H,H and OH⟩

Nitrobenzene   Phenylhydroxylamine   p-Aminophenol

Reactions of amines with nitrous acid. Primary, secondary, and tertiary aromatic amines react differently with nitrous acid; the reagent may be used to distinguish between them. We shall use aniline, methylaniline, and dimethylaniline to illustrate the different results. At room temperature or at higher temperatures nitrogen gas is formed when a primary amine or its salt reacts with nitrous acid:

$$\underset{\text{Aniline}}{C_6H_5NH_2} + HNO_2 \longrightarrow \underset{\text{Phenol}}{C_6H_5OH} + N_2 + H_2O$$

An aliphatic primary amine reacts in the same way (p. 207).

At a lower temperature (0° to 5°) a reaction occurs, but no N_2 is evolved; the aromatic primary amine yields, with nitrous acid, a diazonium salt. To achieve this result the amine usually is dissolved in dilute hydrochloric acid, cooled with an ice pack, then mixed with a cold solution of sodium nitrite. About three equivalents of hydrochloric acid are used, one to convert the amine to a soluble salt, a second to release nitrous acid from the nitrite, and the third to assure an acidic medium. The following reaction then occurs:

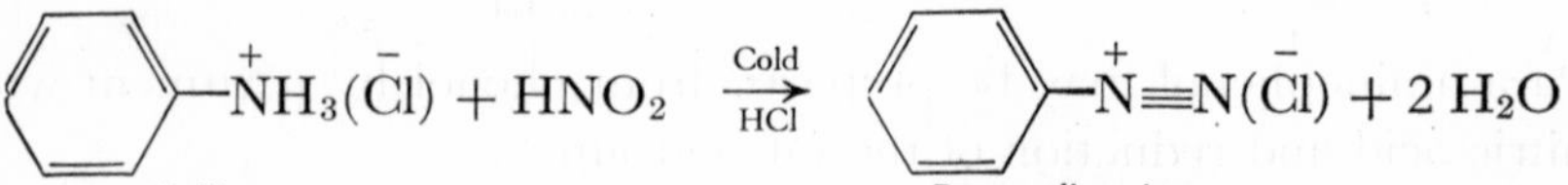

Aniline
hydrochloride

Benzenediazonium
chloride

A secondary amine (or its salt) forms, with nitrous acid, an N-nitroso compound:

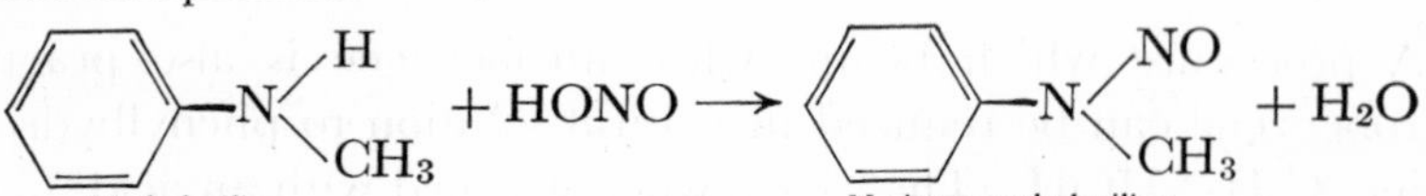

Methylaniline
(colorless, bp 195°)

N-nitrosomethylaniline
(yellow, mp 15°)

The letter N precedes the name of the product to indicate that the nitroso group, NO, is attached to the nitrogen atom of the amine. A compound in which the NO group is attached to a carbon atom is called a C-nitroso compound. The letters N and C are used, however, only when necessary to avoid ambiguity.

Tertiary aromatic amines react with nitrous acid to form C-nitroso compounds. The position para to the amino group is very reactive, and a para nitroso derivative is produced rapidly at room temperature:

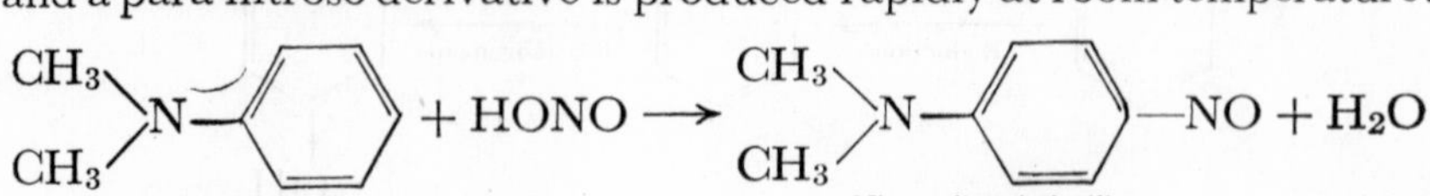

Dimethylaniline
(colorless liquid, bp 193°)

p-Nitrosodimethylaniline
(green solid, mp 87°)

Sulfanilic acid. Cold, concentrated sulfuric acid acts upon aniline to form a salt, aniline acid sulfate, $C_6H_5NH_3SO_4H$. When this salt is heated to a temperature of 200°, it undergoes a rearrangement and loses a molecule of water. The final product is sulfanilic acid:

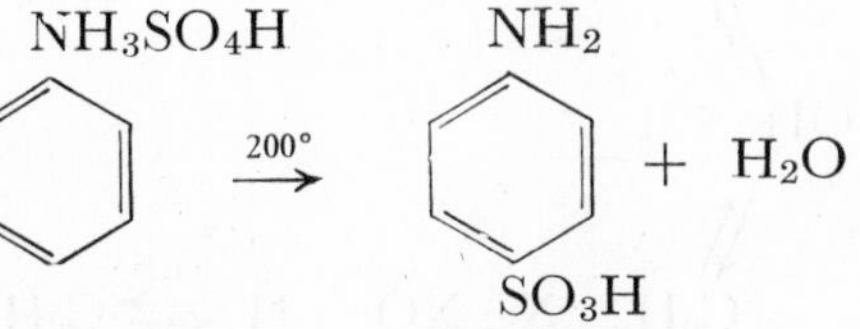

$$NH_3SO_4H \qquad NH_2$$

Aniline acid sulfate   Sulfanilic acid

Sulfanilic acid is a crystalline compound which is only slightly soluble in water and in organic solvents. It has no definite melting point. It is a dipolar compound, because it exists primarily in the form of an inner salt, $\overset{+}{H_3N}—C_6H_4—\overset{-}{SO_3}$.

Diazonium Salts

The process of converting a primary aromatic amine (or a salt of the amine) into a diazonium salt is called *diazotization*. As indicated above, this is accomplished by adding nitrous acid to a cold solution of the amine salt. We shall use the simplest aromatic amine, aniline, to illustrate diazotization and the reactions of diazonium salts, but it must be remembered that any compound in which an NH_2 group is attached directly to an aromatic nucleus will respond in the same way.

$$C_6H_5NH_2 \cdot HCl + HNO_2 \xrightarrow[\text{Cold}]{\text{HCl}} C_6H_5N_2Cl + 2\,H_2O$$

Amine salt   Diazonium salt
(aniline hydrochloride)   (benzenediazonium chloride)

In a weakly alkaline solution the diazonium salt is converted into an unstable diazohydroxide as follows:

$$C_6H_5—\overset{+}{N}\equiv\overset{-}{N(Cl)} + KOH \longrightarrow C_6H_5—N\!\!=\!\!N—OH + KCl$$

Diazonium salt   Diazohydroxide

In concentrated alkali the diazohydroxide itself forms a salt, since it is weakly acidic:

$$C_6H_5—N\!\!=\!\!N—OH + KOH \longrightarrow C_6H_5—N\!\!=\!\!N—OK + H_2O$$

Hence it appears that the diazohydroxide is amphoteric in the same sense that aluminum hydroxide is amphoteric; it can yield either hydrogen ion or hydroxide ion:

$$C_6H_5-\overset{+}{N}=N + OH^- \underset{H^+}{\overset{H^+}{\rightleftarrows}} C_6H_5-\overset{+}{N}=N + H_2O$$

Benzenediazonium ion

$$C_6H_5-N=N-OH$$
Benzenediazo hydroxide

$$C_6H_5-\overset{+}{N}=NO^- + H^+ \underset{}{\overset{OH^-}{\rightleftarrows}} C_6H_5-N=NO^- + H_2O$$

Benzenediazotate ion

An equilibrium exists between diazonium and diazo structures. We may represent the equilibrium in the simplest form as follows:

$$C_6H_5-\overset{+}{N}=N \underset{H^+}{\overset{OH^-}{\rightleftarrows}} C_6H_5-N=N-OH$$

Diazonium salt   Diazo compound

We shall hereafter write either of these in the form $C_6H_5N_2X$, with X representing the anion of any acid or the hydroxyl group.

Reactions of diazonium salts. Diazonium salts undergo two types of reaction. One type consists of a replacement of the group N_2X by another univalent group or by a single atom, with the evolution of nitrogen gas. The other type consists of a coupling process which leads to the production of a dye.

Replacement of the N₂X Group

Replacement by hydroxyl. A phenol is formed when a diazonium salt is warmed with acidified water. The solution is made strongly acidic before it is heated, to prevent a coupling reaction which would lead to the formation of a dye (see page 318).

$$C_6H_5N_2X + H_2O \overset{H^+}{\longrightarrow} C_6H_5OH + N_2 + HX$$

In some cases the dye formation persists, so that the process cannot always be used to prepare a phenol from an amine.

Replacement by chlorine or bromine. A solution of the diazonium salt is heated with a halogen acid and the corresponding cuprous salt, which is a catalyst:

$$C_6H_5N_2X + HCl \overset{CuCl}{\longrightarrow} C_6H_5Cl + N_2 + HX$$
$$C_6H_5N_2X + HBr \overset{CuBr}{\longrightarrow} C_6H_5Br + N_2 + HX$$

Fine copper powder may be substituted for the cuprous salts in these reactions. Replacement of the diazo group in the presence of a cuprous salt is known as the Sandmeyer reaction.

Replacement by iodine. Potassium iodide is added to a solution of the diazonium salt. No catalyst is necessary, and the reaction is rapid:

$$C_6H_5N_2X + KI \longrightarrow C_6H_5I + N_2 + KX$$

Replacement by the CN group. A solution of the diazonium salt is warmed with potassium cyanide. The catalyst may be copper powder or cuprous cyanide.

$$C_6H_5N_2X + KCN \xrightarrow{Cu} C_6H_5CN + N_2 + \overset{KX}{\cancel{H_2O}}$$

Replacement by fluorine. Fluoboric acid, HBF_4, acts upon a solution of a diazonium salt as follows:

$$C_6H_5N_2X + HBF_4 \longrightarrow C_6H_5N_2BF_4 + HX$$

The salt, $C_6H_5N_2BF_4$, precipitates and can be removed from the mixture. When heated, the salt dissociates, and boron trifluoride and nitrogen escape as gases:

$$C_6H_4N_2BF_4 \xrightarrow{Heat} C_6H_5F + N_2 + BF_3$$

Replacement by hydrogen. Reducing agents such as sodium stannite, hypophosphorous acid, formaldehyde, and ethyl alcohol replace the diazo group with hydrogen; the reducing agents are oxidized in the process:

$$C_6H_5N_2X + C_2H_5OH \longrightarrow C_6H_6 + N_2 + CH_3CHO + HX$$

In this way an amino group, through diazotization, may be removed from an aromatic ring.

Replacement by the NO_2 group. When sodium nitrite and freshly prepared cuprous oxide are added to a solution of a diazonium salt, the nitro group becomes attached to the ring:

$$C_6H_5N_2X + NaNO_2 \xrightarrow{Cu_2O} C_6H_5NO_2 + N_2 + NaX$$

Nitrobenzene is usually prepared in another way (p. 305); but this method of introducing a nitro group becomes important when a nitro group is wanted in a position it would not take if introduced by the direct action of nitric acid.

Coupling Reactions

When a diazonium salt is added to a solution of an aromatic amine or a phenol, a coupling reaction occurs with no evolution of nitrogen. The coupling of diazotized aniline with a phenol is accomplished by adding an acidic solution of the diazonium salt to an alkaline solution of the phenol. The net result may be represented as follows:

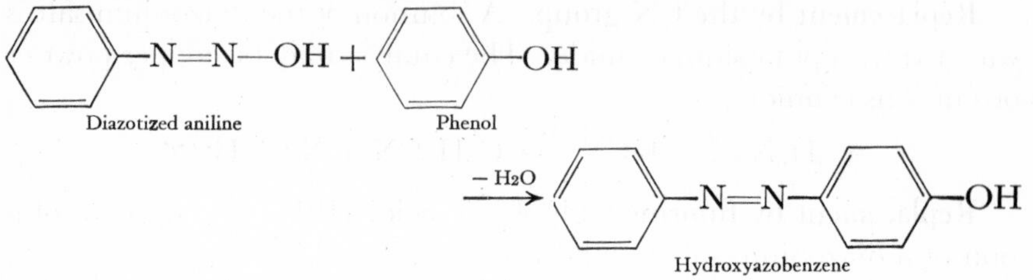

Diazotized aniline   Phenol

Hydroxyazobenzene

The product, C_6H_5—N=N—C_6H_4OH, which is formed in the above reaction is called hydroxyazobenzene; it is a derivative of the parent compound, azobenzene, shown below:

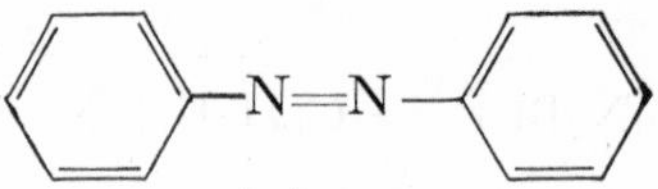

Azobenzene

A unit of this type is found in all azo dyes; but one or both of the aromatic nuclei may be naphthalene, biphenyl, or some other aromatic ring system. All molecules which contain such a unit are colored, but a colored derivative of azobenzene is not a dye unless there is a hydroxy group (OH or OR) or an amino group (NH_2, NHR, or NR_2) attached to at least one of the rings. Such groups not only enhance the color of the compound but also cause it to become more firmly fixed upon the fabric to be dyed. Carboxyl and sulfonic acid groups are also desirable, in that they improve the fastness of dyes.

Coupling occurs mainly in the position which is para to the hydroxyl group of the phenol. Some of the isomeric ortho compound also appears.

When an aromatic amine is coupled with a diazotized primary amine, it is necessary to mix the reagents in an acidic medium to keep the amine in solution. Then sodium acetate is added to reduce the hydrogen ion concentration (the weak acetic acid is formed). If the solution in which the reagents are mixed is very strongly acidic, the diazotized amine is held almost exclusively in the diazonium form, and the amine is held in the form of its salt. When the reagents are held in these forms, coupling does not occur.

Tertiary amines and phenols couple with diazotized amines without the formation of intermediate products. Dimethylaniline reacts with diazotized aniline as follows:

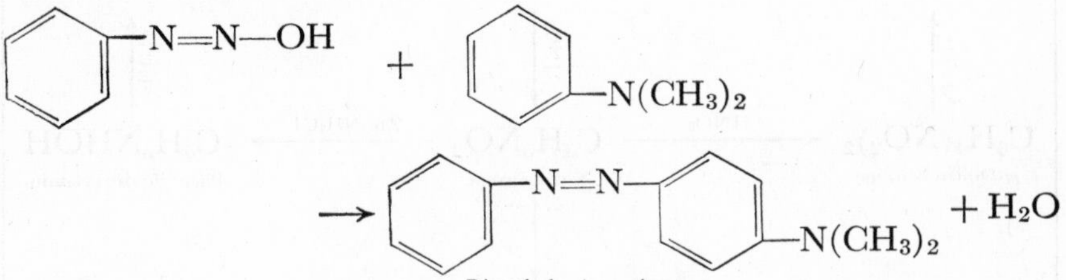

Dimethylaminoazobenzene

The products formed in these coupling reactions are dyes (see page 345).

Primary and secondary aromatic amines also yield dyes by coupling with diazotized amines, but in these cases intermediate products are formed. A hydrogen atom attached to nitrogen is more rapidly replaced than an ortho or para hydrogen atom. Diazotized aniline couples with free aniline as follows:

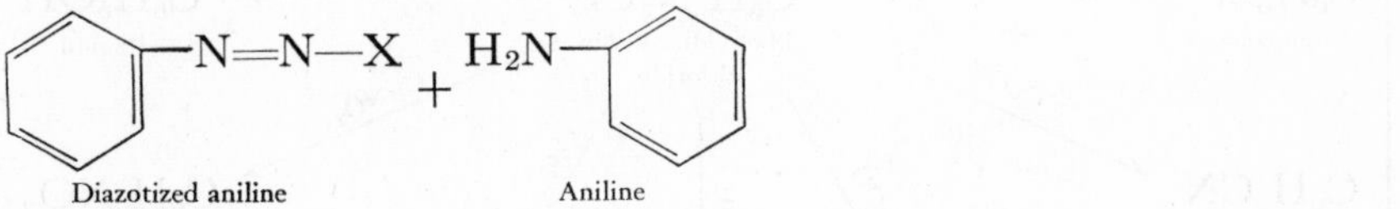

Diazotized aniline   Aniline

Diazoaminobenzene

The product of this reaction undergoes a rearrangement when warmed with hydrochloric acid, and a dye is formed:

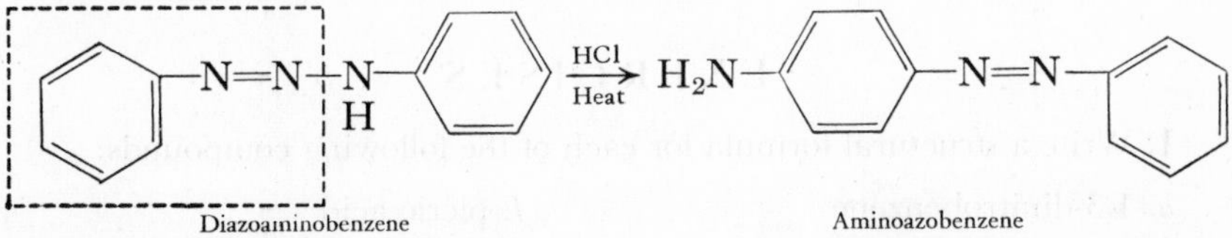

Diazoaminobenzene   Aminoazobenzene

The part of the molecule which is set off by dotted lines leaves the NH group and exchanges its position with that of the hydrogen atom attached to the para carbon of the aniline ring. This is a rearrangement in which a substituent attached to nitrogen in an aromatic amine shifts to the ring. (Compare this change with the conversion of phenylhydroxylamine to p-aminophenol, p. 313.)

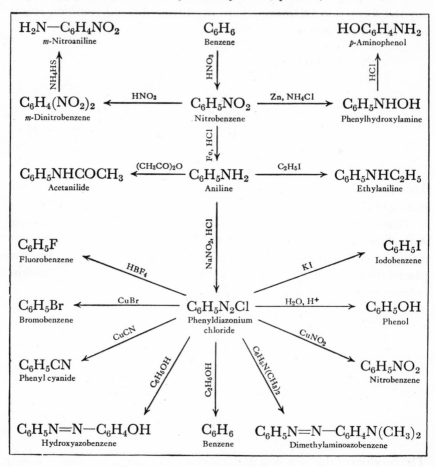

Compounds Derived from Nitrobenzene and Aniline

EXERCISES

1. Write a structural formula for each of the following compounds:

a. 1,3-dinitrobenzene

b. 2,4,6-trinitroaniline

c. meta phenylenediamine

d. hydroxyazobenzene

e. hydroquinone

f. picric acid

g. dimethylaniline

h. azobenzene

i. sulfanilic acid

j. acetanilide

2. Outline a method for making each of the following compounds. Use *p*-toluidine and any other compounds as needed in each case.

a. 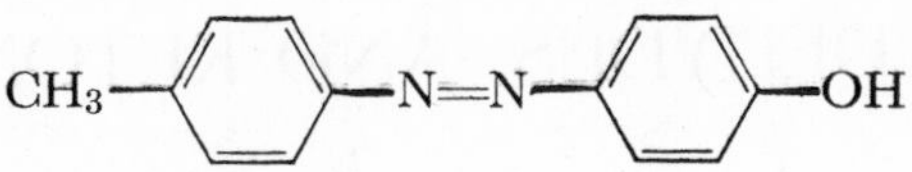 CH_3—⟨benzene ring⟩—$N{=}N$—⟨benzene ring⟩—OH

b. 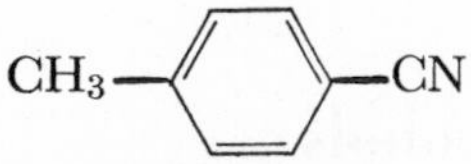 CH_3—⟨benzene ring⟩—CN

c. 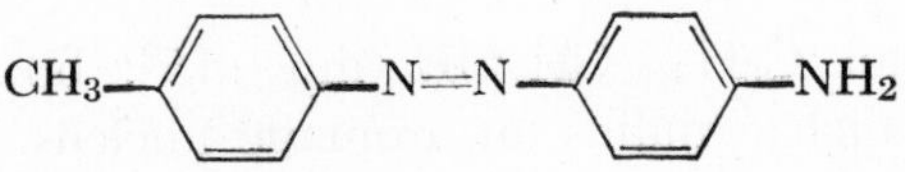 CH_3—⟨benzene ring⟩—$N{=}N$—⟨benzene ring⟩—NH_2

d. 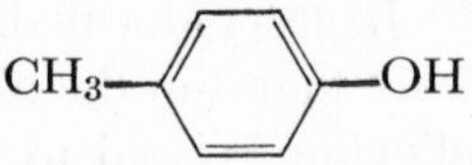 CH_3—⟨benzene ring⟩—OH

3. Outline procedures for making phenol (*a*) from nitrobenzene, (*b*) from benzenesulfonic acid.

4. Write structural formulas for the dyes which would be formed if benzenediazonium chloride were added to solutions of the following compounds: (*a*) dimethylaniline, (*b*) phenol, (*c*) *m*-toluidine.

PROBLEMS

1. How could you obtain a pure sample of picric acid, dinitrobenzene, and para toluidine from a mixture of the three compounds?

NOTE. Take advantage of insolubility in water and possible solubility in acid and base due to salt formation.

2. Write equations which represent the steps in the preparation of *m*-nitrobromobenzene from nitrobenzene.

3. Devise a method of making *o*-nitrobromobenzene from acetanilide.

4. What volume of nitrogen, measured at 20° and 740 mm, would be released if 23.25 grams of aniline were warmed with a mixture of sodium nitrite and hydrochloric acid?

5. How could you distinguish between the members of the following pairs of compounds?

a. 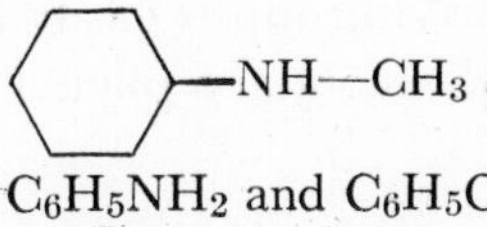 ⟨benzene ring⟩—NH—CH_3 and CH_3—⟨benzene ring⟩—NH_2

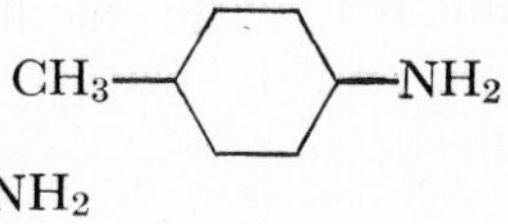

b. $C_6H_5NH_2$ and $C_6H_5CH_2NH_2$
c. C_6H_5OH and C_6H_5COOH
d. C_2H_5—NO_2 and C_2H_5—O—NO

27 · AROMATIC ALCOHOLS, ALDEHYDES, AND KETONES

Alcohols

Benzyl alcohol, C_6H_5—CH_2OH (mp − 15°; bp 205°), is the simplest alcohol which contains an aromatic nucleus. It is a colorless liquid with a faint, pleasant odor. Its esters formed with acetic, benzoic, cinnamic, and salicylic acids are found in the oils of some flowers and in fragrant resins. Benzyl salicylate is used to prevent sunburn. It absorbs the harmful ultraviolet rays of the sun, but transmits rays which tan without destruction of the cells of the skin. On standing exposed to the air benzyl alcohol acquires the odor of almond oil, owing to its oxidation to benzaldehyde.

Benzyl alcohol may be considered a derivative of carbinol (methyl alcohol) in which one hydrogen atom has been replaced by a phenyl radical. Further substitution of the same type produces benzohydrol and ultimately triphenyl carbinol:

$$
\begin{array}{ccc}
\text{H} & \text{H} & C_6H_5 \\
| & | & | \\
C_6H_5\text{—C—OH} & C_6H_5\text{—C—OH} & C_6H_5\text{—C—OH} \\
| & | & | \\
\text{H} & C_6H_5 & C_6H_5
\end{array}
$$

Benzyl alcohol,
or phenyl carbinol
(mp − 15°; bp 205°)

Benzohydrol,
or diphenyl carbinol
(mp 69°; bp 298°)

Triphenyl carbinol
(mp 162 ; bp 360°)

The phenyl group activates the α-carbon atom of a side chain. In an earlier chapter this was made evident by the easy bromination of ethylbenzene (see pages 107 and 295) and by the reactivity of the halogen atom in benzyl chloride (p. 294). The phenyl carbinols exhibit similar reactivity; the hydroxyl group is easily replaced by a halogen atom, and the primary and secondary phenyl carbinols are readily oxidized:

$$(C_6H_5)_3COH + HCl \text{ (conc)} \xrightarrow{20°} (C_6H_5)_3CCl + H_2O$$

Triphenyl carbinol   Triphenylchloromethane

$$3(C_6H_5)_2CHOH + 2\ MnO_4^- \longrightarrow$$

Benzohydrol

$$3(C_6H_5)_2CO + 2\ MnO_2 + 2\ OH^- + 2\ H_2O$$

Benzophenone

Preparation of aromatic alcohols. The standard procedures which were used in making aliphatic alcohols are applicable to the preparation of the aromatic alcohols. Some of these are summarized below:

PREPARATIVE PROCEDURES		
Method	Reagents	Products
Hydrolysis of halides	C_6H_5—CH_2Cl; H_2O	C_6H_5—CH_2OH
Grignard reaction	C_6H_5MgBr; R—CHO	C_6H_5—CHOH—R
	C_6H_5MgBr; C_6H_5—CHO	$(C_6H_5)_2CHOH$
	$RMgBr$; C_6H_5—CHO	C_6H_5—CHOH—R
	C_6H_5MgBr; $(C_6H_5)_2CO$	$(C_6H_5)_3COH$
Reduction of aldehydes and ketones	C_6H_5—CHO; H_2; Pt	C_6H_5—CH_2OH
	$(C_6H_5)_2CO$; H_2; Pt	$(C_6H_5)_2CHOH$

In the procedures indicated above, any aromatic nucleus may be substituted for C_6H_5, provided it contains no functional group which would introduce competitive reactions. Special procedures are available for specific compounds which cannot be made by the types of reactions given above.

Aldehydes

Any compound in which the aldehyde group, —CHO, is attached directly to a cyclic nucleus of the benzene type is an *aromatic aldehyde*. An aromatic compound which contains an aldehyde group in a side chain differs from a true aromatic aldehyde in some respects. The structural difference between them becomes evident upon examination of the following typical examples:

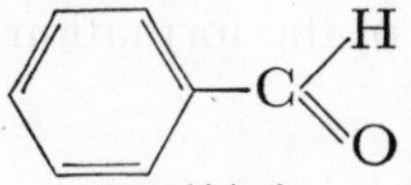

Benzaldehyde 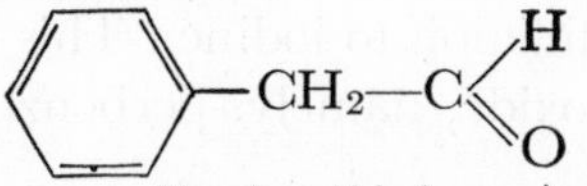   Phenylacetaldehyde

In benzaldehyde, which is the simplest aromatic aldehyde, there is no hydrogen attached to the α-carbon atom. The α-carbon in this case is a member of the ring. Hence benzaldehyde does not undergo the aldol condensation (p. 145), nor does it readily react with bromine (p. 295). In benzaldehyde the carbonyl group is in a position to conjugate with the unsaturated nucleus, while in phenylacetaldehyde such conjugation is impossible.

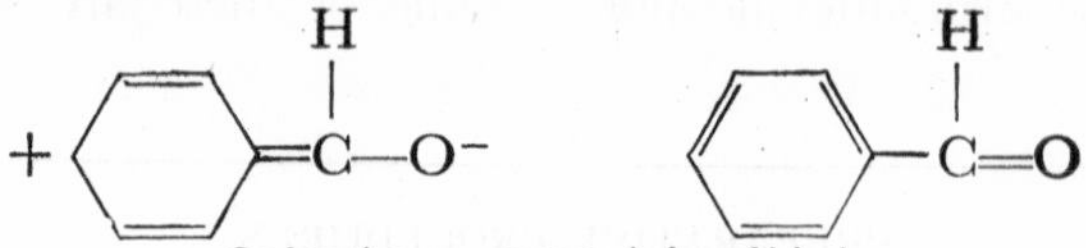

Conjugation, or resonance, in benzaldehyde

The result of this conjugation is a lowered reactivity of the aldehyde group, particularly with respect to reversible addition reactions.

Most reagents act in the same way upon aliphatic and aromatic aldehydes, but there is often a noticeable difference in the rates of reaction. In some cases reactions of aromatic aldehydes are slow and incomplete.

REACTIONS WHICH ARE COMMON TO ALIPHATIC AND AROMATIC ALDEHYDES

Reagent	Product
Hydrogen cyanide, HCN	Cyanohydrin
Sodium bisulfite, $NaHSO_3$	Addition product
Grignard reagent, RMgX	Secondary alcohol
Silver ammonia ion, $Ag(NH_3)_2^+$	Silver mirror and oxidation products
Hydroxylamine, NH_2OH	Oxime
Phenylhydrazine, $C_6H_5NHNH_2$	Phenylhydrazone
Alcohol, ROH (H^+)	Acetal
Oxidizing agent (MnO_4^-; $H_2Cr_2O_7$)	Acid
Oxygen gas, O_2	Peroxide
Reducing agent (H_2-Pt; Na-Alc)	Primary alcohol

The absorption of oxygen by benzaldehyde gives rise to two effects which can be observed. First, the liquid aldehyde changes to a solid acid. Second, during the process the mixture has the property of oxidizing iodide ion to iodine. This is a result of the formation of an organic peroxide, namely, perbenzoic acid.

C₆H₅—CHO + O₂ → C₆H₅—C⟨OOH⟩⟨O⟩ →(C₆H₅CHO)→ 2 C₆H₅COOH

Benzaldehyde   Perbenzoic acid   Benzoic acid

C₆H₅—C⟨OOH⟩⟨O⟩ + 2 HI → C₆H₅COOH + I₂ + H₂O

The process of oxidation by oxygen gas is called autoxidation, and it nearly always involves the formation of a peroxide as an intermediate product. Autoxidation is often catalyzed by light and by iron compounds and is inhibited by traces of hydroquinone. These same variables appear in the drying of paints, which also depends upon autoxidation.

Aromatic and aliphatic aldehydes differ in the following ways:

1. Aromatic aldehydes do not reduce Fehling's solution.

2. Aromatic aldehydes alone do not undergo the aldol condensation. In this respect they are like tertiary aliphatic aldehydes, which have no hydrogen on the α-carbon atom.

3. Aromatic aldehydes do not resinify when treated with strong bases. Instead of forming resins they undergo the Cannizzaro reaction. In this respect also they are like tertiary aliphatic aldehydes.

4. Aromatic aldehydes undergo the benzoin condensation.

5. Aromatic aldehydes condense with aromatic amines to form dyes (p. 349), and with anhydrides of carboxylic acids to form aromatic compounds with unsaturated side chains (see Perkin's synthesis of cinnamic acid).

Occurrence and nomenclature. Some aldehydes of interest are listed in the table below. In general the name is based upon the common name of the corresponding acid, as is the case with aliphatic aldehydes. For instance, we have benzoic acid and benzaldehyde, cinnamic acid and cinnamaldehyde, salicylic acid and salicylaldehyde, phenylacetic acid and phenylacetaldehyde. An approach to a systematic nomenclature is found in such names as *o-hydroxybenzaldehyde* for salicylaldehyde, and *3-methoxy-4-hydroxybenzaldehyde* for vanillin.

Natural sources. The aromatic aldehydes seldom exist as such in nature, but are readily recovered from natural products by oxidation or hydrolysis. Benzaldehyde, C_6H_5—CHO (mp − 26°; bp 179.5°), the best-known member of the group, is a colorless, oily liquid. It is present in bitter almonds and in cherry kernels in the form of amygdalin, C_6H_5—CH(CN)—O—$C_{12}H_{21}O_{11}$. Amygdalin is a glycoside, formed from the cyanohydrin of benzaldehyde and a sugar, $C_{12}H_{22}O_{11}$, called gentiobiose. On hydrolysis the glycoside yields the sugar, hydrogen cyanide, and benzaldehyde:

$$C_6H_5CH(CN)OC_{12}H_{21}O_{11} + H_2O$$
$$\longrightarrow C_{12}H_{22}O_{11} + C_6H_5CHO + HCN$$

/2

SOME NATURALLY OCCURRING ALDEHYDES		
Name	Formula	Source
Benzaldehyde	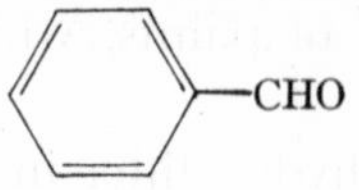 ⬡—CHO	Oil of bitter almonds; toluene oxidation
Cinnamaldehyde	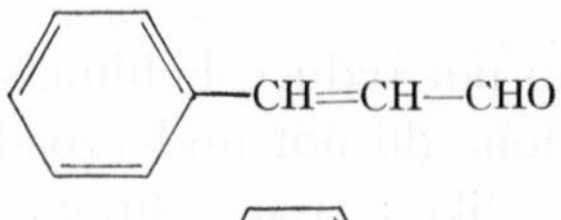 ⬡—CH=CH—CHO	Oil of cinnamon from the bark of a tropical laurel; reaction between benzaldehyde and acetaldehyde
Anisaldehyde	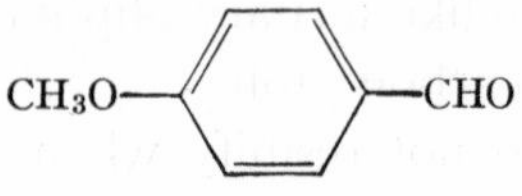 CH_3O—⬡—CHO	Oxidation of anethole from anise oil
Vanillin	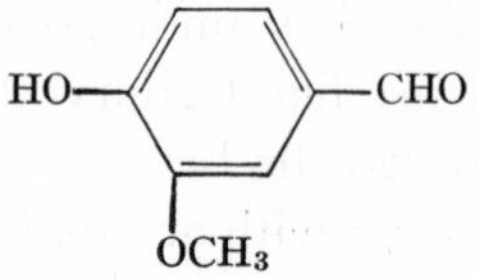 HO—⬡—CHO OCH_3	Oil of vanilla beans; oxidation of isoeugenol
Salicylaldehyde	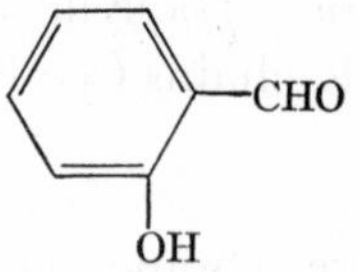 ⬡—CHO OH	Oil of spiraea; Reimer-Tiemann reaction; oxidation of o-cresol
Piperonal	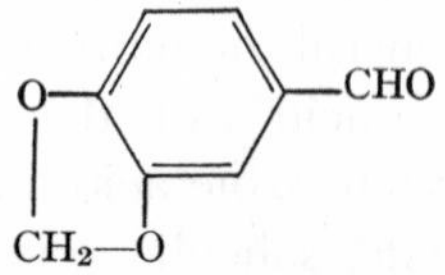 O—⬡—CHO CH_2—O	Prepared from oil of sassafras and by oxidation of piperic acid from pepper

Most of the compounds included in the table are familiar as components of certain flavors and perfumes. The synthetic preparation of these compounds has become a large-scale industry. Benzaldehyde has the odor of almond oil; cinnamaldehyde is responsible for the odor in cinnamon bark; piperonal has the odor of heliotrope and is often called heliotropin.

The Cannizzaro reaction. When an aromatic aldehyde is mixed with a concentrated aqueous solution of a strong base, and the mixture is shaken or allowed to stand for several hours at room temperature, half of the aldehyde molecules are oxidized to the corresponding acid, and half are reduced to an alcohol:

$$2\ C_6H_5CHO + KOH \longrightarrow C_6H_5COOK + C_6H_5CH_2OH$$

A result of this kind, in which a compound undergoes both oxidation and reduction, is called dismutation. Aliphatic aldehydes also react in this manner if the aldol condensation is impossible or incomplete. Formaldehyde yields methyl alcohol and formic acid; isobutyraldehyde is oxidized and reduced. Most aliphatic aldehydes resinify in the presence of strong alkali.

The benzoin condensation. When an alcoholic solution of benzaldehyde is warmed with a small quantity of potassium cyanide, it is converted almost quantitatively into benzoin:

$$2\ C_6H_5\!\!-\!\!CHO \longrightarrow C_6H_5\!\!-\!\!CHOH\!\!-\!\!CO\!\!-\!\!C_6H_5$$

Benzaldehyde (mp − 26°; bp 179.5°)   Benzoin (mp 137°; bp 344°)

The action of the cyanide ion is specific; no other catalyst for this reaction has been found. The benzoin condensation is accomplished in alkaline solution only; free hydrocyanic acid does not furnish a sufficient concentration of cyanide ions. The reaction differs fundamentally from the aldol condensation, for it is a reaction between aldehyde groups exclusively. In the aldol condensation hydrogen attached to the α-carbon atom takes part in the reaction. In aromatic aldehydes, and in tertiary aliphatic aldehydes, no hydrogen is present on the α-carbon atom, and the aldol type of condensation cannot occur.

The Perkin reaction. In 1877 William H. Perkin made cinnamic acid by heating a mixture of benzaldehyde, acetic anhydride, and sodium acetate. He interpreted the process as a condensation between the aromatic aldehyde and the acetic anhydride:

$$C_6H_5\!\!-\!\!C\!\!\begin{array}{c}H\\ \diagup\\ \diagdown\\ O\end{array} + CH_3\!\!-\!\!\overset{\overset{O}{\|}}{C}\!\!-\!\!O\!\!-\!\!\overset{\overset{O}{\|}}{C}\!\!-\!\!CH_3$$

Benzaldehyde   Acetic anhydride

$$\xrightarrow{CH_3COONa}\left[C_6H_5\!\!-\!\!\overset{\overset{H}{|}}{\underset{\underset{OH}{|}}{C}}\!\!-\!\!CH_2\!\!-\!\!\overset{\overset{O}{\|}}{C}\!\!-\!\!O\!\!-\!\!\overset{\overset{O}{\|}}{C}\!\!-\!\!CH_3 \right]$$

Condensation product

The condensation product, a β-hydroxy acid anhydride, yields cinnamic acid through loss of water and hydrolysis of the acid anhydride linkage:

$$\left[C_6H_5-\underset{\underset{OH}{|}}{\overset{\overset{H}{|}}{C}}-CH_2-\overset{\overset{O}{||}}{C}-O-\overset{\overset{O}{||}}{C}-CH_3 \right]$$

$$\longrightarrow C_6H_5-CH{=}CH-COOH + CH_3-COOH$$

Cinnamic acid

When propionic acid anhydride and sodium propionate are heated with benzaldehyde, α-methyl cinnamic acid is formed:

$$C_6H_5-CHO + \underset{\underset{CH_3}{|}}{CH_2}-\overset{\overset{O}{||}}{C}-O-\overset{\overset{O}{||}}{C}-CH_2-CH_3$$

$$\longrightarrow C_6H_5-CH{=}\underset{\underset{CH_3}{|}}{C}-COOH + CH_3-CH_2-COOH$$

The Perkin synthesis of unsaturated acids, therefore, is of the same character as the aldol condensation. The α-carbon atom of one molecule becomes attached to the carbonyl carbon atom of another.

The question has been raised as to whether the acid anhydride or the salt of the acid condenses with the aldehyde. The products would be the same in either case. When it is considered that esters and acid anhydrides are much more reactive toward reduction and toward addition of the Grignard reagent than are salts of acids, it appears that the activating effect of ester and anhydride groups upon their α-carbon atoms should also be greater. The salt is regarded as a catalyst.

Preparation of Aromatic Aldehydes

Methods of preparing aromatic aldehydes are of two types: (1) a side chain which is already in the ring is converted to an aldehyde group; (2) the aldehydic carbon atom is introduced into the ring by a substitution process.

1. **Oxidation of a methyl group.** Benzaldehyde is made from toluene by direct oxidation through the use of manganese dioxide and 65 per cent sulfuric acid:

$$C_6H_5-CH_3 + 2\ MnO_2 + 2\ H_2SO_4$$

$$\overset{40°}{\longrightarrow} C_6H_5-CHO + 2\ MnSO_4 + 3\ H_2O$$

Benzoic acid also is formed, and it can be made the chief product by altering the time, temperature, and concentration of sulfuric acid. A mixture of chromic acid in acetic anhydride is an alternative oxidizing agent.

An indirect oxidation of the methyl group can be accomplished by a preliminary treatment with chlorine gas. Benzyl chloride, C_6H_5—CH_2Cl, or benzal chloride, C_6H_5—$CHCl_2$, may be made from toluene by treatment with chlorine. Benzyl chloride is oxidized to benzaldehyde by an aqueous solution of lead nitrate; benzal chloride yields the aldehyde through hydrolysis:

$$C_6H_5—CH_3 \begin{cases} \xrightarrow{Cl_2} C_6H_5—CH_2Cl \xrightarrow{Pb(NO_3)_2} C_6H_5—CHO \\ \\ \xrightarrow{2Cl_2} C_6H_5—CHCl_2 \xrightarrow{H_2O;\ OH^-} C_6H_5—CHO \end{cases}$$

Benzyl chloride

Benzal chloride

2. The Gattermann-Koch reaction. The aldehyde group may be introduced directly into an aromatic hydrocarbon by a process analogous to the Friedel-Crafts reaction. A mixture of carbon monoxide and hydrogen chloride gases acts as if it were formyl chloride:

$$CO + HCl \longrightarrow \left[H—C\overset{\displaystyle O}{\underset{\displaystyle Cl}{\Big<}} \right]$$

The mixed gases are passed into the hydrocarbon in which $AlCl_3$ and $CuCl$ are suspended:

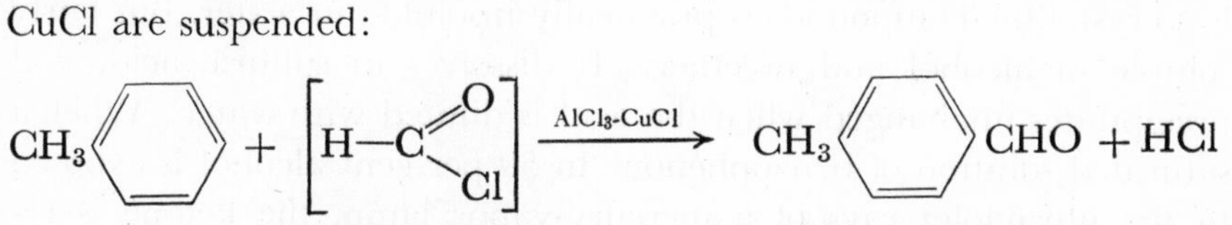

$$CH_3 \langle \bigcirc \rangle + \left[H—C\overset{\displaystyle O}{\underset{\displaystyle Cl}{\Big<}} \right] \xrightarrow{AlCl_3\text{-}CuCl} CH_3 \langle \bigcirc \rangle CHO + HCl$$

(CO + HCl) *p*-Tolualdehyde

3. The Reimer-Tiemann reaction. This is a reaction between a phenol and chloroform, in the presence of potassium hydroxide, which results in the introduction of an aldehyde group in the phenol. It cannot be carried out on a phenolic ether or a hydrocarbon.

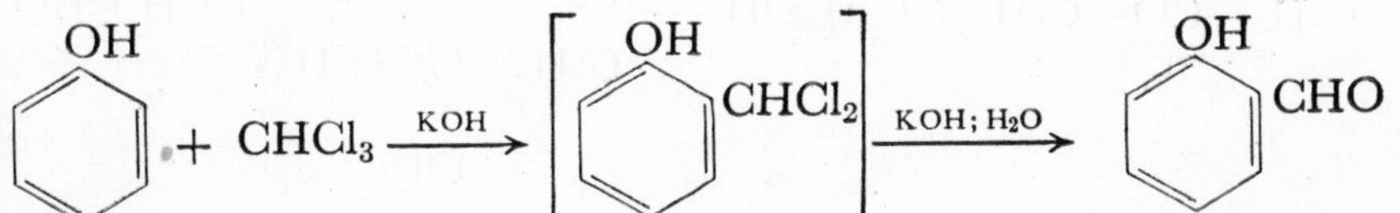

$$\underset{\text{Phenol}}{\overset{OH}{\bigcirc}} + CHCl_3 \xrightarrow{KOH} \left[\overset{OH}{\bigcirc}CHCl_2 \right] \xrightarrow{KOH;\ H_2O} \underset{\text{Salicylaldehyde}}{\overset{OH}{\bigcirc}CHO}$$

The intermediate product, written within brackets, has not been isolated. It undergoes immediate hydrolysis to form the aldehyde. Some *para*-hydroxybenzaldehyde is produced at the same time, but the ortho compound predominates. Salicylic aldehyde is manufactured for use in the synthesis of coumarin, which is employed extensively in the preparation of perfumes and flavors.

Ketones

The important aromatic ketones are of two types: (1) those with two aromatic nuclei attached to the carbonyl group; (2) ketones in which the carbonyl group is attached to one aromatic radical and one aliphatic radical. The two types are represented by benzophenone and acetophenone respectively:

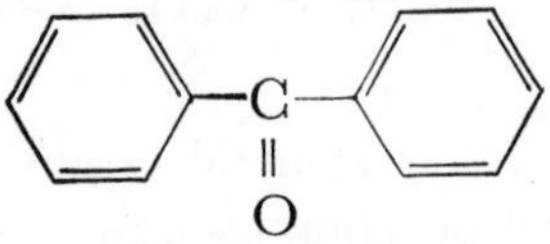

Benzophenone 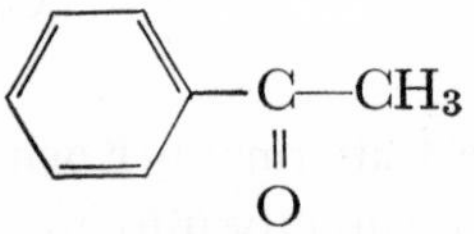   Acetophenone

Acetophenone, CH_3—CO—C_6H_5 (mp 20°, bp 202°), is a typical example of the mixed aliphatic-aromatic ketones. It is used in medicine as a soporific and is dispensed under the name of *hypnone*. Acetophenone is made by passing the mixed vapors of acetic acid and benzoic acid over thorium oxide at 450°.

Benzophenone, C_6H_5—CO—C_6H_5 (mp 48.5°, bp 306.1°), a colorless crystalline compound, is practically insoluble in water, but fairly soluble in alcohol and in ether. It dissolves in sulfuric acid, and precipitates unchanged when the acid is diluted with water. When a saturated solution of benzophenone in 50 per cent alcohol is exposed to the ultraviolet rays of a mercury-vapor lamp, the ketone is reduced by the alcohol to benzopinacol. The reduction product is less soluble than the ketone, and it precipitates in a very pure state:

$$2\ C_6H_5\text{—CO—}C_6H_5 + C_2H_5OH \longrightarrow \begin{array}{c} OH \\ | \\ C_6H_5\text{—}C\text{—}C_6H_5 \\ | \\ C_6H_5\text{—}C\text{—}C_6H_5 \\ | \\ OH \end{array} + CH_3CHO$$

Benzophenone
(mp 48.5°)

Benzopinacol
(mp 186°)

Pinacols are derivatives of ethylene glycol, $CH_2OH—CH_2OH$, in which the four hydrogen atoms attached to carbon have been replaced by carbon radicals. They can be made from many ketones by reduction with amalgamated magnesium. A magnesium derivative of the ketone is first formed, but the magnesium compound is hydrolyzed rapidly and completely when brought into contact with water:

$$
\begin{array}{ccc}
\underset{\text{Acetone}}{\begin{array}{c}CH_3\\ \quad\ \ \diagdown \\ \quad\ \ \diagup CO\\ CH_3\\[4pt] CH_3\\ \quad\ \ \diagdown \\ \quad\ \ \diagup CO\\ CH_3\end{array}} & \xrightarrow{\text{Mg-Hg}} \quad \underset{\text{Magnesium pinacolate}}{\begin{array}{c}CH_3\\ \quad\ \ \diagdown \\ \quad\ \ \diagup C—O\\ CH_3\quad |\\ \qquad Mg\\ CH_3\quad |\\ \quad\ \ \diagup C—O\\ CH_3\end{array}} \quad \xrightarrow{\ 2\ H_2O\ } & \underset{\substack{\text{Pinacol}\\(\text{tetramethylglycol})}}{\begin{array}{c}CH_3\\ \quad\ \ \diagdown \\ \quad\ \ \diagup C—OH\\ CH_3\quad |\\[6pt] CH_3\quad |\\ \quad\ \ \diagdown \\ \quad\ \ \diagup C—OH\\ CH_3\end{array}}
\end{array}
$$

The aromatic ketones respond to nearly all reactions of aliphatic ketones. Exceptions are found in some addition reactions. Benzophenone does not add HCN or $NaHSO_3$. Resonance involving the two benzene rings and the carbonyl group produces a condition which is adverse to the formation of the addition products.

The Clemmensen reduction process converts ketones into the corresponding hydrocarbons. Many aldehydes have been similarly reduced, but alcohols and acids usually are not reduced in this way.

$$\underset{\text{Acetophenone}}{C_6H_5—CO—CH_3} \xrightarrow{\text{Zn; HCl}} \underset{\text{Ethylbenzene}}{C_6H_5—CH_2—CH_3}$$

$$\underset{\text{Benzophenone}}{C_6H_5—CO—C_6H_5} \xrightarrow{\text{Zn; HCl}} \underset{\text{Diphenylmethane}}{C_6H_5—CH_2—C_6H_5}$$

Preparation of Aromatic Ketones

The following methods are commonly used in the preparation of aromatic ketones:

1. **The Friedel-Crafts reaction.** An aromatic hydrocarbon and an acid chloride are mixed; then powdered aluminum chloride is added:

$$\underset{\text{Benzene}}{C_6H_6} + \underset{\text{Acetyl chloride}}{CH_3COCl} \xrightarrow{\text{AlCl}_3} \underset{\text{Acetophenone}}{C_6H_5—CO—CH_3} + HCl$$

$$\underset{\text{Benzene}}{C_6H_6} + \underset{\text{Benzoyl chloride}}{C_6H_5COCl} \xrightarrow{\text{AlCl}_3} \underset{\text{Benzophenone}}{C_6H_5—CO—C_6H_5} + HCl$$

2. Pyrolysis of salts. A salt of a carboxylic acid or a mixture of salts is heated:

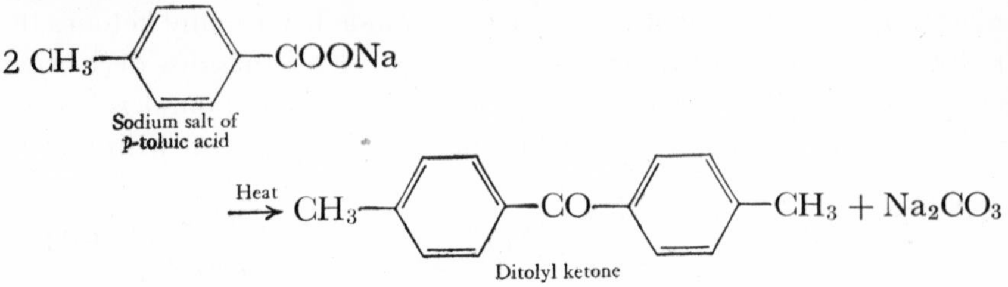

Sodium salt of
p-toluic acid

Ditolyl ketone

3. Oxidation of a secondary alcohol. Hot chromic acid converts a secondary alcohol into a ketone:

$$3\ C_6H_5-CHOH-C_2H_5 + Cr_2O_7^{--} + 8\ H^+$$

Phenyl ethyl carbinol

$$\longrightarrow 3\ C_6H_5-CO-C_2H_5 + 2\ Cr^{+++} + 7\ H_2O$$

Phenyl ethyl ketone

4. The pinacol rearrangement. Unsymmetrical ketones may be prepared from ditertiary alcohols (pinacols) by treatment of the latter with warm, dilute sulfuric acid. With tetraphenyl glycol (benzopinacol) the reaction proceeds as follows:

Benzopinacol, or
tetraphenylethylene glycol

Benzopinacolone, or
benzoyltriphenylmethane

The rearrangement involves an exchange of positions between a phenyl radical and a hydroxyl group, and simultaneous loss of a molecule of water.

The current interpretation of the course of the reaction presumes that the controlling step is rupture or loosening of a carbon-oxygen bond under the influence of the acid catalyst, and in this way an opportunity is made for placement upon that carbon atom of the migrating group. Hydrogen ion from the catalyst attaches to one of the hydroxyl groups, bestowing its positive charge upon that group. This is indicated in the formula below as occurring at carbon atom (2). This hydroxyl group splits off in the formation of a molecule of water, and simultaneously one of the carbon radicals passes with its pair of electrons from carbon (1) to carbon (2). This leaves carbon atom (1) with a sextet of electrons. It completes its octet by forming a double bond with the remaining oxygen atom. The establishment of this double bond is accomplished by drawing into the carbon-oxygen linkage a pair of electrons from the oxygen valence shell. The oxygen is thereby rendered positive, and the hydrogen atom attached to it dissociates as hydrogen ion.

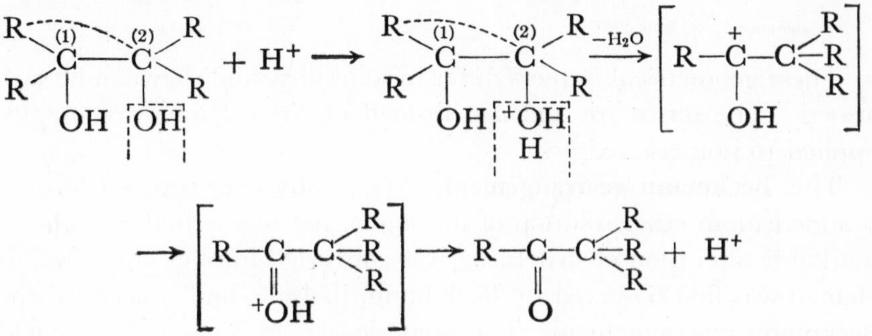

The selection of the migrating group or atom depends upon which hydroxyl is the more readily removed. In symmetrical glycols these reactivities are identical, but in unsymmetrical glycols the product formed is controlled by both the relative tendencies of the groups to migrate and the relative reactivities of the two hydroxyl groups. In many instances these variables lead to a good yield of one of the possible products.

Oximes and the Beckmann Rearrangement

Oximes. Hydroxylamine acts upon an aldehyde or ketone to form an oxime:

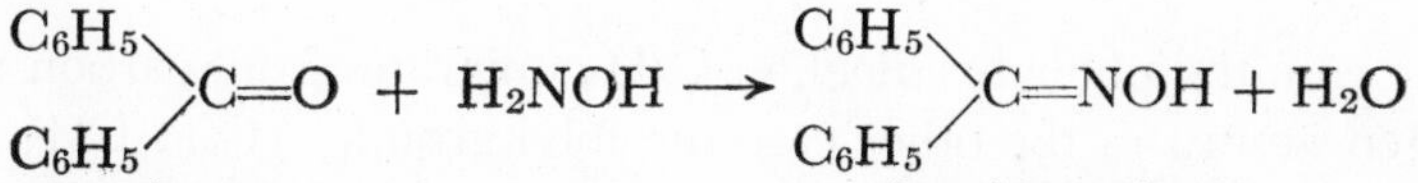

Benzophenone — Benzophenone oxime

Hydroxylamine hydrochloride is used in making an oxime; for the free base, NH_2OH, is unstable. The salt, $NH_2OH \cdot HCl$, is added to the ketone in aqueous solution, and a base (usually sodium hydroxide) is added to release the free hydroxylamine from the salt.

An unsymmetrical ketone forms two oximes (geometrical isomers); for the double bond between carbon and nitrogen holds the hydroxyl group in either of two positions. Thus there are two oximes of phenyl tolyl ketone. They correspond to the following structures:

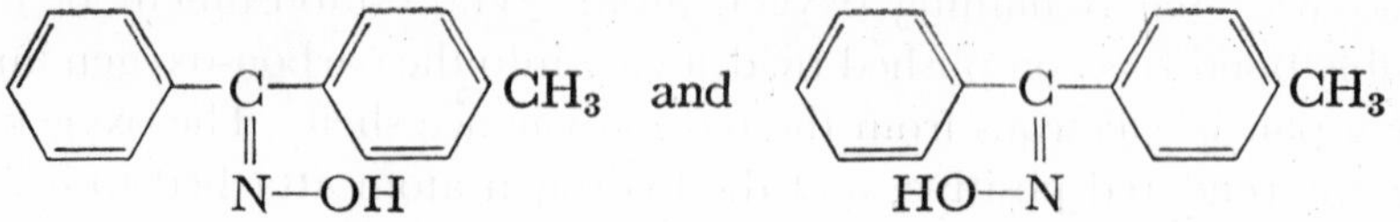

$$\text{C}_6\text{H}_5\text{—C(=N—OH)—C}_6\text{H}_4\text{—CH}_3 \quad \text{and} \quad \text{C}_6\text{H}_5\text{—C(=N—OH)—C}_6\text{H}_4\text{—CH}_3$$

I   II

syn-Tolyl phenyl ketoxime,   *syn*-Phenyl tolyl ketoxime,
or   or
anti-phenyl tolyl ketoxime   *anti*-tolyl phenyl ketoxime

These geometrical isomers differ in solubility, and they can be separated. The terms *syn* and *anti* instead of *cis* and *trans* are usually applied to isomeric oximes.

The Beckmann rearrangement. When phosphorus pentachloride is added to an ether solution of an oxime, the oxime undergoes a remarkable alteration of structure; it is converted into an amide. This change was first observed by Beckmann, in 1886, and it is called the Beckmann rearrangement. The isomeric oximes, shown above, yield different amides when subjected to the action of phosphorus pentachloride. The product obtained from I is the anilide of *p*-toluic acid,

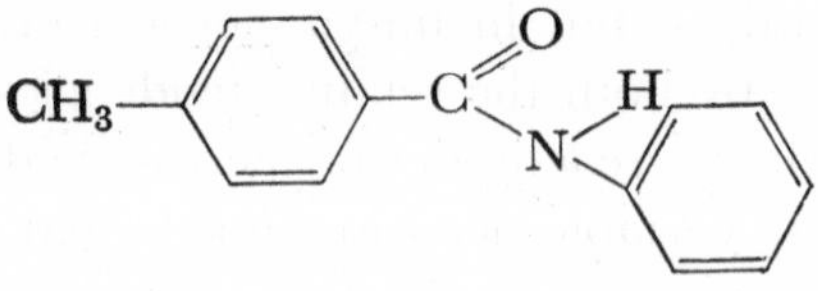

$$\text{CH}_3\text{—C}_6\text{H}_4\text{—C(=O)—N(H)—C}_6\text{H}_5$$

From oxime II the product obtained is a toluidine derivative of benzoic acid,

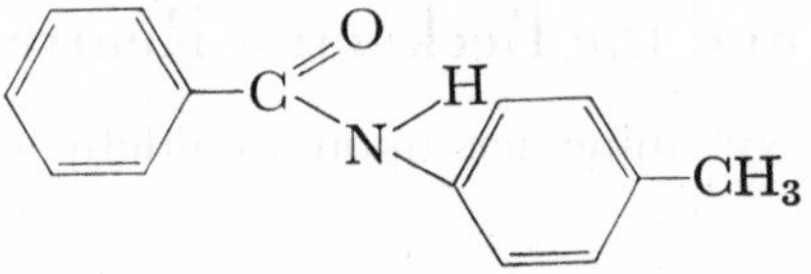

$$\text{C}_6\text{H}_5\text{—C(=O)—N(H)—C}_6\text{H}_4\text{—CH}_3$$

In one case the phenyl radical, $-\text{C}_6\text{H}_5$, migrates from carbon to the nitrogen atom; in the other case the tolyl group, $-\text{C}_6\text{H}_4\text{CH}_3$, shifts from carbon to the nitrogen atom. It seems to be an exchange of positions between a carbon radical and the hydroxyl group, followed by a tautomeric shift of the hydrogen atom from oxygen to nitrogen.

In 1891 Hantzsch reached the conclusion that the exchange of places between the hydroxyl group and a carbon radical in an oxime must occur between groups on the same side of the double bond (*cis* or *syn* position). He recommended the use of the Beckmann rearrangement as a means of determining the structures of the isomeric oximes, assuming in each case that the exchange of positions occurs between groups on the same side of the molecule—a cis-interchange. Over a period of more than thirty years this theory was applied, and structural formulas were assigned accordingly to all known oximes, the formulas being determined by identifying the rearranged products and assuming cis-interchange.

Between 1921 and 1930 Meisenheimer described experiments which proved that the interchange occurs between the hydroxyl group of an oxime and a carbon radical on the opposite side of the molecule—trans-interchange.

The steps in the rearrangement of oxime I (*syn-p*-tolyl phenyl ketoxime) may be formulated as follows:[1]

$$C_6H_5-C-C_6H_4CH_3 \longrightarrow \left[HO-C-C_6H_4CH_3 \atop N-C_6H_5 \right] \longrightarrow$$
$$\quad\quad\quad N-OH$$

$$O=C-C_6H_4CH_3$$
$$\quad\quad | $$
$$HN-C_6H_5$$

Many investigations have been made to determine the course of the Beckmann reaction; and in so far as the results can be interpreted, they support the Meisenheimer theory. On account of the capacity of oximes to isomerize (that is, the cis form to change to the trans form, and vice versa), it is not always possible to correlate the experimental results with a particular mechanism.

It is not difficult to determine which group is attached to nitrogen in the final product; for the product is an amide which is easily hydrolyzed to an acid and an amine. The amide $CH_3C_6H_4CONHC_6H_5$, for example, is hydrolyzed to *p*-toluic acid, $CH_3C_6H_4COOH$, and aniline, $C_6H_5NH_2$. The isomeric amide, $C_6H_5CONHC_6H_4CH_3$, yields benzoic acid, C_6H_5COOH, and *p*-toluidine, $CH_3C_6H_4NH_2$. The hydrolysis products are easily identified.

EXERCISES

1. Write a structural formula for each of the following types of compounds: (*a*) an aliphatic aldehyde, (*b*) an aromatic aldehyde, (*c*) an aliphatic ketone, (*d*) an aromatic ketone, (*e*) an amide, (*f*) a primary aromatic alcohol, (*g*) a secondary aromatic alcohol

2. Write a balanced equation to represent a reaction of each type of compound listed in Exercise 1.

3. Write a balanced equation for the action of each of the following reagents on acetophenone: (*a*) HCN, (*b*) NaHSO₃, (*c*) C₂H₅MgI, (*d*) NH₂OH.

4. Write an equation which represents the action of a concentrated sodium hydroxide solution on benzaldehyde.

5. Write the formula of the unsaturated aromatic acid which would be formed through the Perkin reaction from benzaldehyde, butyric anhydride, (CH₃—CH₂—CH₂—CO)₂O, and sodium butyrate, CH₃—CH₂—CH₂—COONa.

6. Write structural formulas for two oximes which may be made from acetophenone.

7. Write equations for the following transformations: (*a*) preparation of benzophenone from benzoic acid; (*b*) preparation of benzophenone from diphenyl carbinol.

8. Write structural formulas for the following compounds: (*a*) benzaldehyde, (*b*) cinnamic acid, (*c*) benzyl alcohol, (*d*) benzopinacol, (*e*) cinnamic aldehyde, (*f*) salicylaldehyde.

PROBLEMS

1. Write an equation for making ortho toluic aldehyde. Begin with toluene and any desired reagents.

2. Write the formula of the compound which would be formed by the action of PCl₅ on benzophenone oxime.

3. Define *cis-interchange* and *trans-interchange* as applied to the Beckmann rearrangement.

4. An anilide is a phenyl-substituted amide. How could benzanalide, C₆H₅—CO—NH—C₆H₅, be prepared from benzoic acid, C₆H₅COOH, and aniline?

5. Describe, with the help of balanced equations, the following:

a. The Cannizzaro reaction
b. The benzoin condensation
c. The Perkin reaction
d. The Beckmann rearrangement
e. The Gattermann-Koch reaction
f. The Reimer-Tiemann reaction
g. The Friedel-Crafts synthesis of ketones
h. The pinacol rearrangement

28 · AROMATIC ACIDS
AND THEIR DERIVATIVES

Any compound in which a carboxyl group is attached to an aromatic nucleus is called an aromatic acid. In chemical properties the aromatic acids are very much like the aliphatic acids, and the two classes of compounds are made by similar methods.

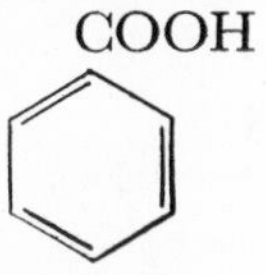

COOH   COOH   COOH

Benzoic acid   o-Toluic acid   p-Toluic acid   Phthalic acid
(mp 122°)   (mp 104°)   (mp 180°)   (mp 231°)

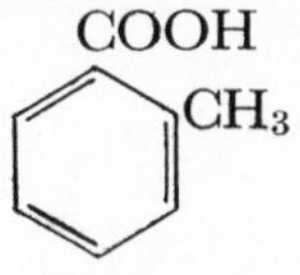

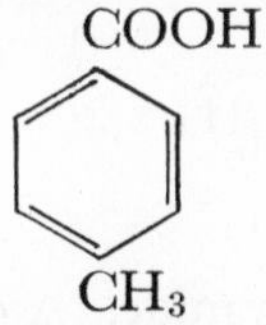

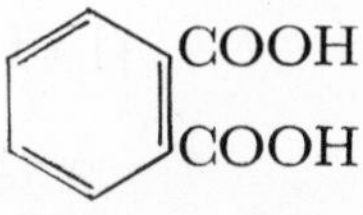

It is seen from the examples given above that the melting points of the aromatic acids are high. This is in contrast to the melting points of the monocarboxylic acids of the aliphatic series, which range from $-80°$ up to about $+70°$. Most aromatic carboxylic acids are readily crystallized from hot-water solutions. They are sparingly soluble in cold water, much more soluble in hot water, and they dissolve readily in dilute alkali.

Preparation of Aromatic Acids

1. **Oxidation of side chains.** A hydrocarbon in which an aliphatic side chain is attached to an aromatic nucleus can be oxidized to an acid:

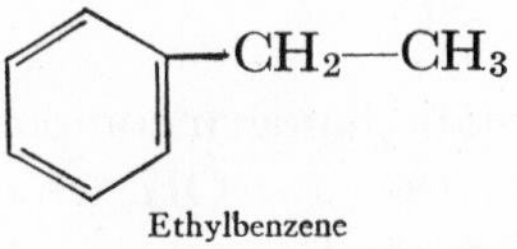

$$-CH_2-CH_3 \quad + 2\ Cr_2O_7^{--} + 16\ H^+$$

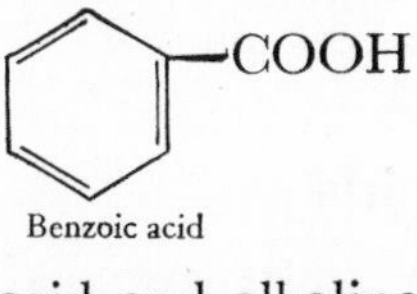

Ethylbenzene

$$\rightarrow \quad -COOH \quad + 4\ Cr^{+++} + CO_2 + 10\ H_2O$$

Benzoic acid

Chromic acid and alkaline permanganate are usually effective as oxidizing agents. If the side chain is a long one, two acids are formed by the oxidation; one is an aromatic acid and the other aliphatic.

337

Apparently the oxidation starts with the carbon atom which is directly attached to the ring, and the side chain is ruptured at that point. If there are several side chains, a carboxyl group is formed at the point occupied by each chain. The number of side chains in the hydrocarbon can be determined by identifying the acid which is produced by oxidation. For example, if an aromatic hydrocarbon with the formula C_9H_{12} yields a tribasic acid, we know that the hydrocarbon had three side chains attached to the ring. The oxidation proceeds as follows:

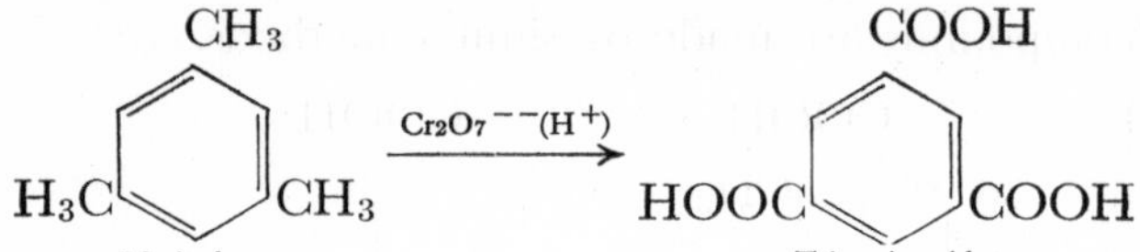

Mesitylene (mp − 52.7°; bp 164.6°) — Trimesic acid (mp 380°)

2. Hydrolysis of a cyanide. A cyanide or nitrile is hydrolyzed by a hot aqueous solution of hydrochloric acid:

$$C_6H_5CN + 2\,H_2O + H^+ \longrightarrow C_6H_5COOH + NH_4^+$$

3. The Grignard reaction. The carboxyl group may be formed through the use of carbon dioxide. Alkyl and aryl halides, in dry ether, combine with magnesium, forming Grignard reagents. When carbon dioxide is led into the ether solution, an addition product is formed, which is rapidly hydrolyzed by the addition of water or a dilute acid:

$$C_6H_5MgBr + CO_2 \longrightarrow C_6H_5{-}C\begin{matrix}\nearrow OMgBr \\ \searrow O\end{matrix}$$

$$C_6H_5{-}C\begin{matrix}\nearrow OMgBr \\ \searrow O\end{matrix} + HCl \longrightarrow C_6H_5{-}C\begin{matrix}\nearrow OH \\ \searrow O\end{matrix} + Mg^{++} + Br^- + Cl^-$$

This method is not applicable if the aromatic halogen compound contains a group like —CHO, —COOH, —NO_2, or —OH, which would react with the organo-magnesium compound.

Specific Acids

Benzoic acid, C_6H_5COOH (mp 122°, bp 250°), is a colorless crystalline compound which occurs in many resins and particularly in gum benzoin. It has been isolated from cranberries and some other fruits.

On a commercial scale it is made by chlorinating hot toluene, and then hydrolyzing the resulting benzotrichloride by treatment with hot water and calcium hydroxide:

$$C_6H_5CH_3 + 3\ Cl_2 \xrightarrow{Heat} C_6H_5CCl_3 + 3\ HCl$$

Toluene   Benzotrichloride

$$2\ C_6H_5CCl_3 + 4\ Ca(OH)_2 \xrightarrow{Heat} (C_6H_5COO)_2Ca + 3\ CaCl_2 + 4\ H_2O$$

Calcium benzoate

The acid is precipitated from a suspension or solution of the salt by the addition of hydrochloric acid:

$$(C_6H_5COO)_2Ca + 2\ HCl \longrightarrow 2\ C_6H_5COOH + CaCl_2$$

The sodium salt of benzoic acid has mild antiseptic properties, and it has been used extensively as a preservative for foods. The pure-food law permits this practice if the amount of sodium benzoate used is specified on the label of the container.

The acid chloride, benzoyl chloride, C_6H_5COCl (bp 197.2°), is a colorless liquid with a disagreeable odor. Its fumes have an irritating effect upon the eyes, causing tears. It is made by treating benzoic acid with phosphorus pentachloride (the trichloride is not effective):

$$C_6H_5COOH + PCl_5 \longrightarrow C_6H_5COCl + POCl_3 + HCl$$

Benzoic   Benzoyl
acid   chloride

Esters of benzoic acid are prepared by mixing an alcohol or a phenol with benzoyl chloride and aqueous alkali (Schotten-Baumann reaction).

o-Sulfobenzoic acid, $HOOC—C_6H_4—SO_3H$, is of interest as an intermediate in the preparation of indicators and as the parent compound from which saccharin is made. Sulfobenzoic acid is made from toluene by sulfonation, followed by oxidation of the toluenesulfonic acid:

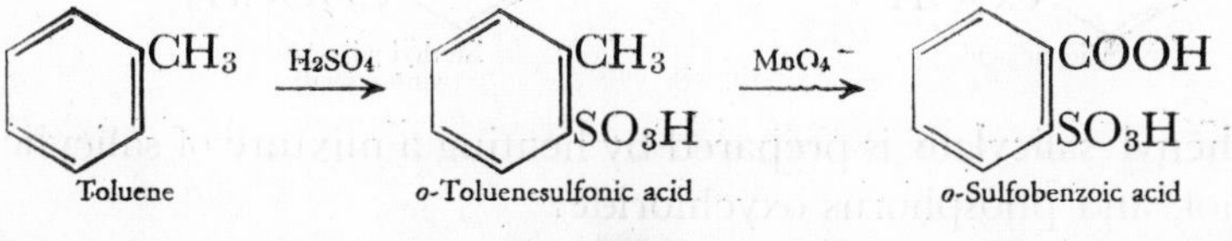

Toluene   *o*-Toluenesulfonic acid   *o*-Sulfobenzoic acid

Saccharin is the cyclic imide of *ortho*-sulfobenzoic acid, but it cannot be made directly from the acid. In the manufacture of saccharin, toluene is treated with chlorosulfonic acid, $ClSO_2OH$, instead of sul-

furic acid. This results in a sulfonic acid chloride, which is converted
to the amide by ammonia, as indicated below:

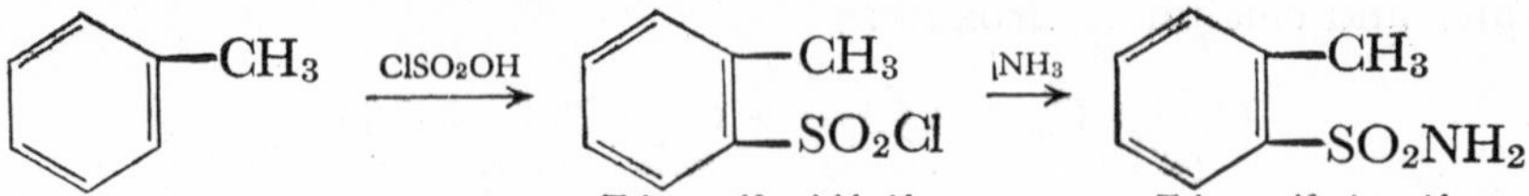

Toluene   Toluenesulfonylchloride   Toluenesulfonic amide

For the conversion of the amide to saccharin see page 299.

Salicylic acid, or ortho hydroxybenzoic acid, occurs in nature as a
constituent of the glucoside salicin, in the bark and leaves of the willow.
With ferric chloride, in neutral solution, it acquires a violet color.
This color test distinguishes *ortho*-hydroxybenzoic acid from the corresponding *meta* and *para* compounds.

Salicylic acid is prepared commercially by a reaction known as the
Kolbe synthesis. Sodium phenoxide is heated with carbon dioxide under pressure:

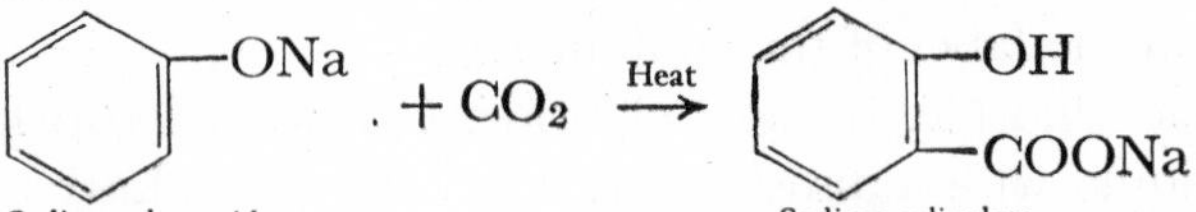

Sodium phenoxide   Sodium salicylate

Phenols generally may be converted to phenolic aromatic acids in
this way.

The methyl ester of salicylic acid is the principal component of oil
of wintergreen. It is a colorless liquid which boils at 224°. The ester
is made in large quantities for use in the manufacture of artificial
flavors and perfumes. Wintergreen is employed extensively in lini-
ments. It is believed that the ester penetrates the skin and hydrolyzes
in the subcutaneous tissues to liberate salicylic acid. The acid has a
physiological action which relieves pain. The ester is made by warm-
ing a mixture of salicylic acid and methyl alcohol. A little sulfuric
acid is used as a catalyst.

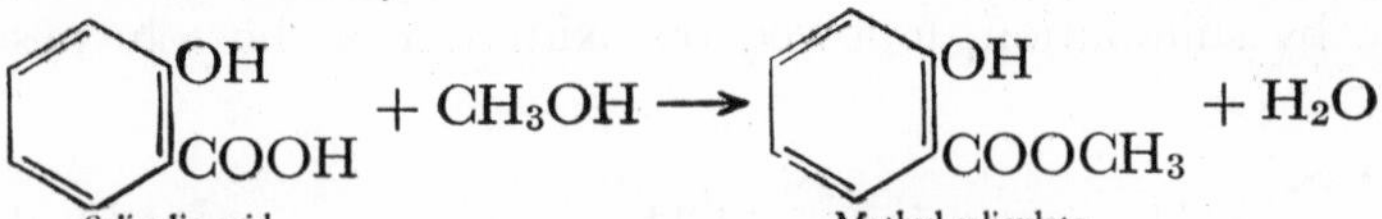

Salicylic acid   Methyl salicylate (wintergreen)

Phenyl salicylate is prepared by heating a mixture of salicylic acid,
phenol, and phosphorus oxychloride:

$$HO-C_6H_4-COOH + HOC_6H_5$$

Salicylic acid

$$\xrightarrow{POCl_3} HO-C_6H_4-CO-O-C_6H_5 + H_2O$$

Phenyl salicylate

Phenyl salicylate is an ester (mp 42°) which is not hydrolyzed by the acidic gastric juice of the stomach, but is readily hydrolyzed by the alkaline fluids of the intestines. The hydrolysis liberates salicylic acid and phenol, both of which are antiseptics. One other use of the compound is that of coating pills which, to be effective, must be delivered intact to the intestines. The ester coating does not dissolve in the stomach, but does dissolve in the alkaline media of the intestinal tract.

Acetylsalicylic acid, commonly called aspirin, is another derivative of *ortho*-hydroxybenzoic acid that has therapeutic value. It is made by heating salicylic acid with acetic anhydride:

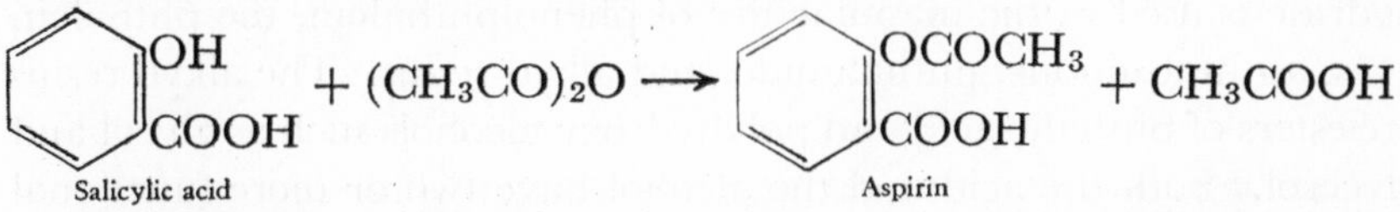

Salicylic acid   Aspirin

Phthalic acids. There are three dicarboxylic acids corresponding to the formula $C_6H_4(COOH)_2$:

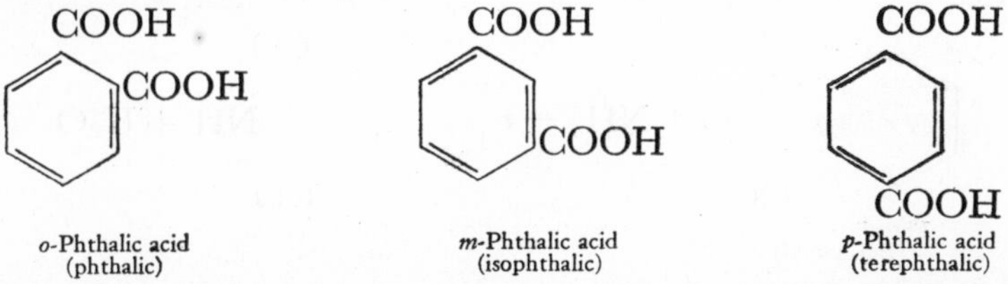

o-Phthalic acid   *m*-Phthalic acid   *p*-Phthalic acid
(phthalic)   (isophthalic)   (terephthalic)

They may be prepared from the corresponding xylenes through oxidation by hot dilute nitric acid, or from the corresponding methylbenzoic acids (toluic acids) by oxidation with alkaline permanganate solution. Catalytic oxidation of the xylenes by oxygen of the air is another practical method of making the phthalic acids.

Ortho phthalic acid, the only valuable member of the group, has been made commercially by oxidizing naphthalene with sulfuric acid. Mercury salts are effective catalysts in this process. In a newer process naphthalene is oxidized by atmospheric oxygen at 250°. The catalyst in this case is a mixture of the oxides of several metals, including vanadium oxide. Octane, a petroleum hydrocarbon, can be converted into *ortho*-xylene (see page 105), and the latter is readily oxidized to *ortho*-phthalic acid:

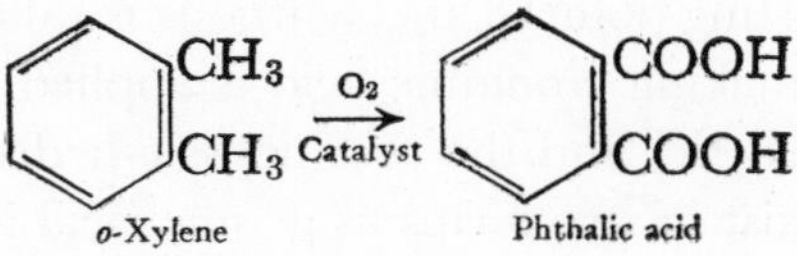

o-Xylene   Phthalic acid

Phthalic acid crystallizes in colorless prisms. If heated rapidly, it melts at about 231°. Failure to melt sharply is due to its gradual loss of water, with the production of an anhydride, which melts at 130.8°:

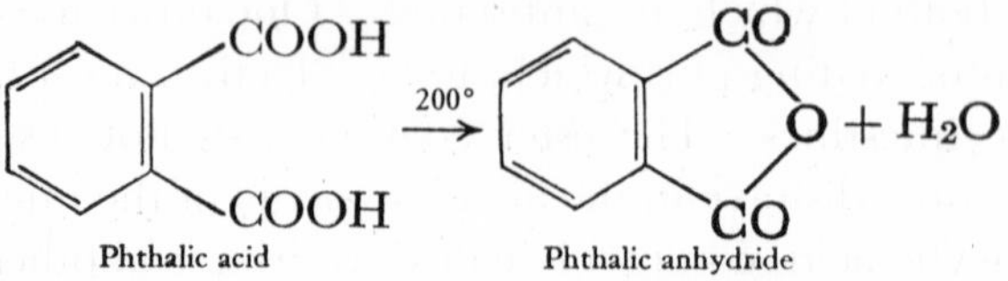

Phthalic acid $\xrightarrow{200°}$ Phthalic anhydride $+ H_2O$

Phthalic anhydride is the product formed when a mixture of air and naphthalene vapor is passed over hot vanadium oxide. The anhydride is used in the manufacture of phenolphthalein, the phthalein dyes, anthraquinone, phthalimide, and alkyd resins. The alkyd resins are esters of phthalic acid and polyhydroxy alcohols such as glycol and glycerol. Both the acid and the alcohol have two or more functional groups, which is a requirement for the building of large molecules.

Phthalimide is made by passing ammonia over hot phthalic anhydride:

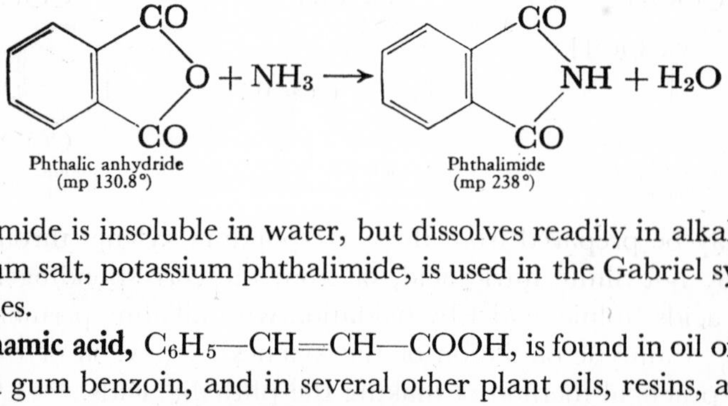

Phthalic anhydride $+ NH_3 \longrightarrow$ Phthalimide $+ H_2O$
(mp 130.8°)   (mp 238°)

Phthalimide is insoluble in water, but dissolves readily in alkali. The potassium salt, potassium phthalimide, is used in the Gabriel synthesis of amines.

Cinnamic acid, C_6H_5—CH=CH—COOH, is found in oil of cinnamon, in gum benzoin, and in several other plant oils, resins, and balsams. Its preparation by Perkin's method was outlined in connection with the chemistry of benzaldehyde (p. 327). Structurally it is not an aromatic acid, but in physical properties it resembles the aromatic acids. The carboxyl group is attached to a conjugated system of double bonds. There are two geometric isomers of cinnamic acid; one melts at 68° (*cis*), the other at 136° (*trans*).

Coumarin. A derivative of *ortho*-hydroxycinnamic acid, known as coumarin, is made in large quantities for use in artificial flavors and perfumes. The starting point in the synthesis is salicylaldehyde. The Perkin method of making cinnamic acid is applied to salicylaldehyde instead of benzaldehyde, and the product is *o*-hydroxycinnamic acid. Salts of this acid exist in two forms as geometrical isomers. The *trans* form, known as coumaric acid, is obtained in crystalline form when a solution containing a salt of the acid is acidified. The *cis* form of the acid, coumarinic acid, cannot be obtained in the free state; for as soon as it is released by acidifying a salt solution, it spontaneously loses water and precipitates in the form of the lactone, coumarin.

Coumarinic acid   Coumarin
(mp 67°; bp 291°)

Coumarin is described as having the odor of new-mown hay. It occurs naturally in the sweet woodruff and in tonka beans. The annual consumption of coumarin in this country amounts to more than 200,000 pounds. It is used with vanilla as a food flavor, and as a perfume for soaps and other toilet preparations. It is employed also to enhance the fragrance of tobacco.

EXERCISES

1. Represent the following substances by structural formulas:

a. Phthalic acid   *f.* Phthalic anhydride
b. Methyl salicylate   *g.* Cinnamic acid
c. Coumarin   *h.* Anthranilic acid
d. Salicylic acid   *i.* Saccharin
e. Aspirin

2. Show how a Grignard reaction may be employed in the synthesis of p-toluic acid, CH_3—C_6H_4—$COOH$. Begin with toluene and any desired reagents.

3. Show how p-toluidine, CH_3—C_6H_4—NH_2, may be used to prepare toluic acid. (Consider the diazo reaction as a possible step in the process.)

4. Indicate some of the uses of the following compounds: (*a*) phthalic anhydride, (*b*) salicylic acid, (*c*) benzoic acid.

PROBLEMS

1. Show how the esterification of phthalic acid by glycerol could lead to a resinous product.

2. Outline the production of saccharin from toluene, chlorosulfonic acid, ammonia, and potassium permanganate.

3. Apply the Perkin reaction (synthesis of cinnamic acid from benzaldehyde) to the synthesis of coumarin from salicylic aldehyde.

29 · DYES AND INDICATORS

A dye is a compound which is capable of imparting a permanent color to a textile fiber. An indicator is a compound which changes color rapidly and reversibly in response to changes in its environment.

The natural dyes which have been in use for centuries—indigo, alizarin, and Tyrian purple—are now synthesized or displaced by other synthetic substances. The practical dyer lists dyes in four principal groups: (1) those that dye fibers directly (substantive dyes), (2) those that require mordants (adjective dyes), (3) ingrain dyes, and (4) vat dyes.

Substantive dyes are fairly soluble in water, but they adhere so strongly to the textile that the fabric can be dyed by immersion in a hot solution of the dye. Most substantive dyes are applied to silk or wool, rather than to cotton, linen, or rayon.

Adjective dyes do not adhere directly to the fabric, but can be used in conjunction with mordants. A mordant is a substance which adheres strongly to both the fabric and the dye. The mordants commonly employed are salts of aluminum, iron, chromium, and tin, tannic acid, calcium phosphate, and finely divided silica. The choice of mordant is determined by the character of the dye. A compound is formed between the mordant and the dye, which is called a lake. The color of the lake varies with the mordant used.

Ingrain colors are formed in the fiber by saturating the fabric with a solution of one reagent and then immersing the fabric in a solution of the second reagent. The two reagents, which together produce the dye, come into contact with each other on and within the fibers. Ingrain dyes are insoluble in water. The same principle is applied in the use of the so-called "vat dyes," but the second reagent used in connection with vat dyes is oxygen of the air. Indigo is used as a vat dye. The fabric is immersed in a solution of a reduced form of indigo which is colorless and soluble; then the cloth is exposed to the air to permit oxidation of the soluble indigo white to the insoluble blue compound.

Adherence of a dye to a fiber may be due to what is loosely called adsorption or to actual compound formation. The former may be a variation of molecular association, achieved through hydrogen bonds

344

and dipolar attractions, and is almost the sole way in which cotton and linen are able to retain a dye. Wool and silk, on the other hand, are amphoteric substances, containing amino groups and carboxyl groups, and capable of salt formation. Dyes also are acidic or basic and thus able to enter into chemical reaction with such fibers. Substantive silk and wool dyes are relatively numerous as compared with substantive cotton dyes.

Azo Dyes

Any primary aromatic amine may be diazotized by nitrous acid (see page 315). The reaction is usually carried out by adding sodium nitrite to an acid solution of an amine salt. A diazonium salt is thus formed.

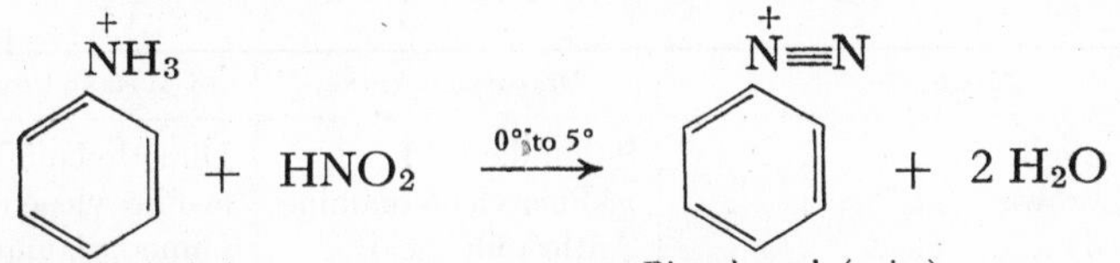

Amine salt (cation)

Diazonium salt (cation)

A diazonium salt or a diazo compound (p. 318) will couple with a phenol or naphthol to form a dye. A typical coupling reaction is represented by the following equation:

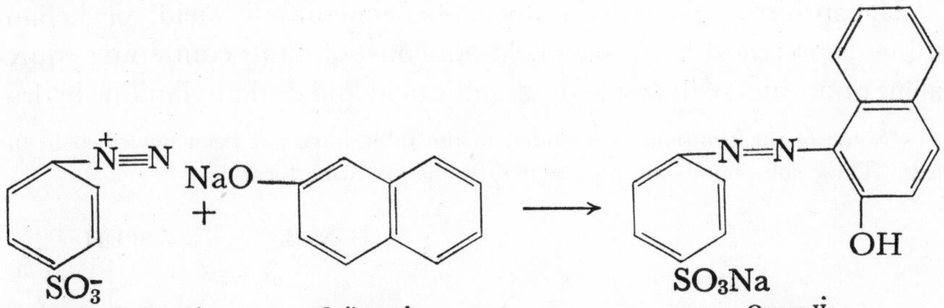

Diazotized sulfanilic acid

Sodium salt of β-naphthol

Orange II (a dye)

Tertiary aromatic amines couple in a similar way. In this case the acidic solution of the diazotized amine salt is added to a solution of the tertiary amine salt. Coupling is brought about by adding sodium acetate to reduce the acidity:

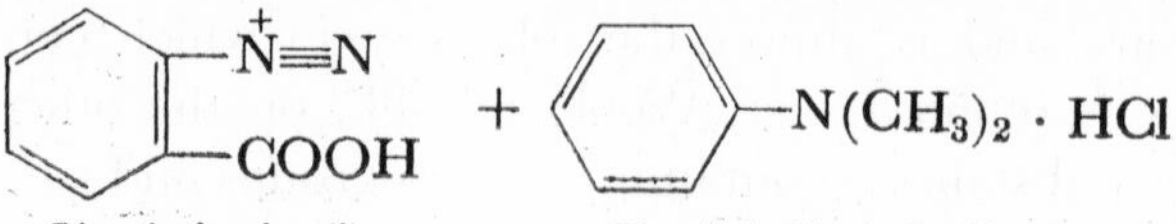

Diazotized anthranilic acid   Dimethylaniline hydrochloride

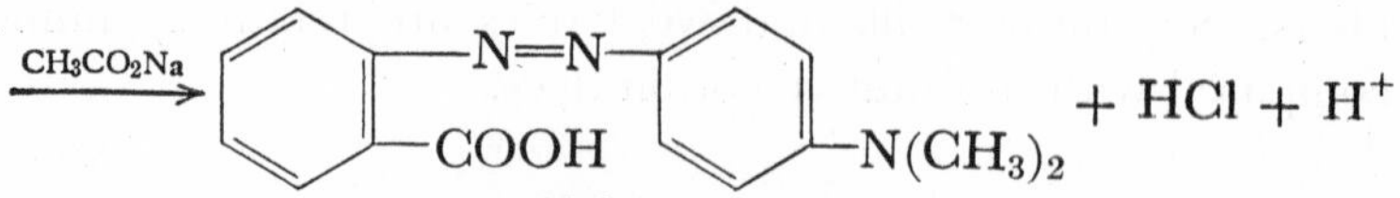

Methyl red

Coupling occurs in the para position with respect to a hydroxyl or an amino group unless that position is already occupied, in which case reaction occurs in the ortho position.

The following table lists some of the common azo dyes and the compounds from which they are derived:

AZO DYES AND INDICATORS*

NAME	DIAZOTIZED AMINE	COUPLING COMPOUND
Methyl orange	Sulfanilic acid	Dimethylaniline
Bismarck brown	m-Phenylene diamine	m-Phenylene diamine
Methyl red	Anthranilic acid	Dimethylaniline
Para red	p-Nitroaniline	β-Naphthol
Congo red	Benzidine	Naphthionic acid
Orange II	Sulfanilic acid	β-Naphthol
Alizarin yellow R	p-Nitroaniline	Salicylic acid
Benzopurpurin 4 B	o-Tolidine	Naphthionic acid

Helianthine. Dimethylaminoazobenzenesulfonic acid, or helianthine, is prepared by mixing cold aqueous solutions containing equivalent quantities of diazotized sulfanilic acid and dimethylaniline hydro-

*Some of the compounds included in the table have not been described in the text. These compounds are represented by the following formulas:

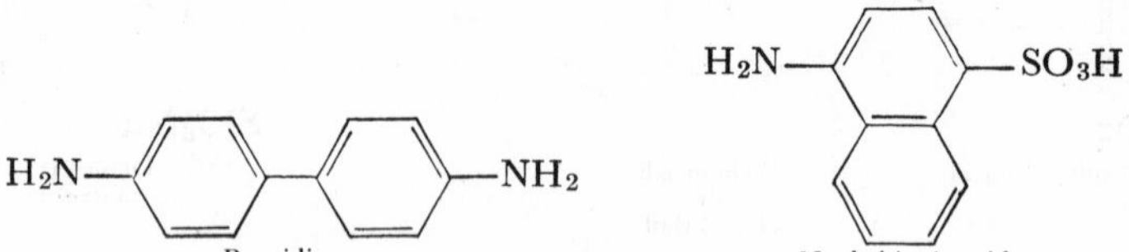

Benzidine

Naphthionic acid

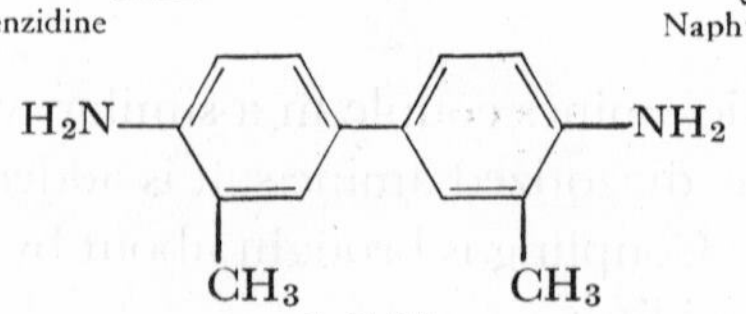

ortho-Tolidine

chloride. The sodium salt of the compound is the yellow dye known as methyl orange. It is used as an indicator in the titration of acids and bases. The preparation of methyl orange is represented by the equation below. Since the reaction is carried out in a buffer solution near the neutral point, the diazotized component may be represented as a diazo hydroxide or as a diazonium ion, and the dimethylaniline may be represented as a free base or as a salt.

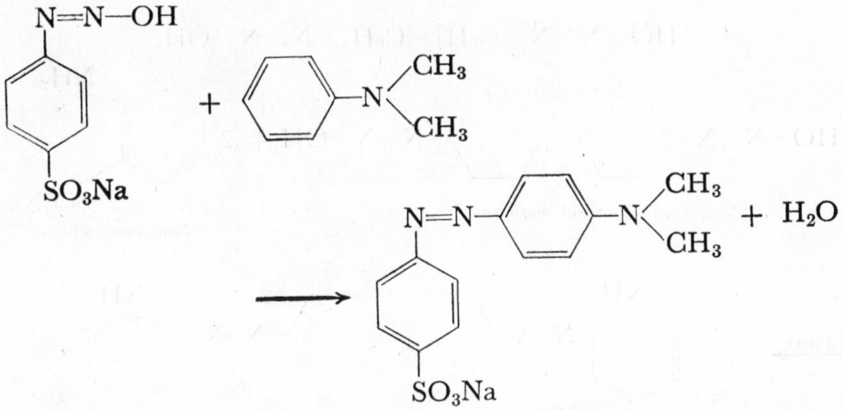

Methyl orange

In acid solution methyl orange is converted into the red dye helianthine. In alkaline solution the process is reversed. The color change is due to a structural rearrangement in the molecule. The equilibria involved in the color changes of methyl orange are indicated below:

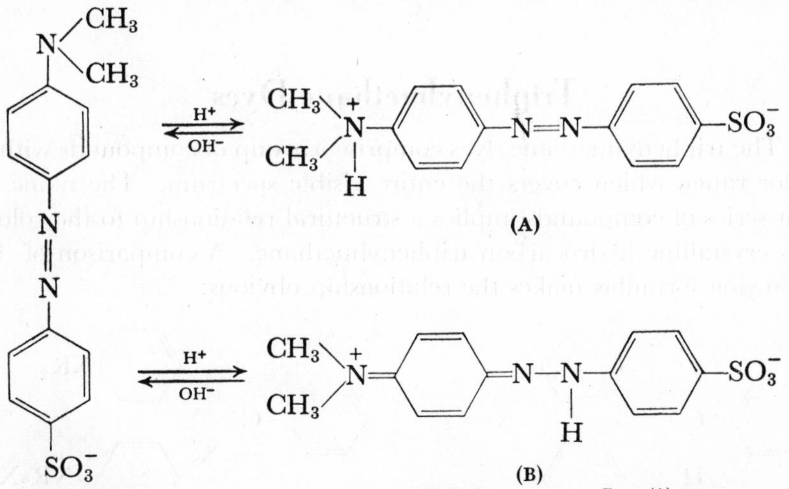

(A)

(B)

Methyl orange
(yellow anion of
sodium salt)

Helianthine tautomers. Form (A) orange,
small amount; form (B) red, predominating

Tetrazo compounds, formed from benzidine with the naphthols, naphthylamines, and related bodies, constitute the Congo group of dyes. They possess the valuable property of dyeing cotton without mordants.

Congo red is formed from diazotized benzidine and naphthionic acid. The reaction may be written with the diazonium ion, $N\equiv\overset{+}{N}$—C_6H_4—C_6H_4—$\overset{+}{N}\equiv N$, or with the diazo hydroxide,

HO—$N\equiv\overset{\cdot}{N}$—$C_6H_4$—$C_6H_4$—$N\equiv N$—$OH$:

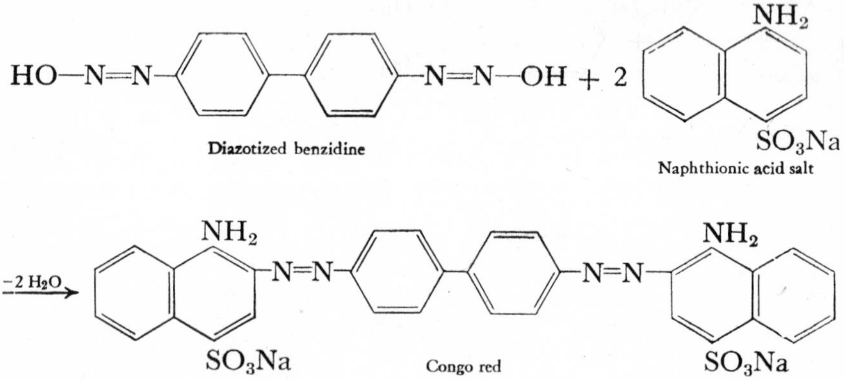

Diazotized benzidine

Naphthionic acid salt

Congo red

The presence of sulfonic acid groups in a dye renders the compound more soluble in water and at the same time enhances its capacity to combine with silk or wool.

Triphenylmethane Dyes

The triphenylmethane dyes comprise a group of compounds with a color range which covers the entire visible spectrum. The name of this series of compounds implies a structural relationship to the colorless crystalline hydrocarbon triphenylmethane. A comparison of the following formulas makes the relationship obvious:

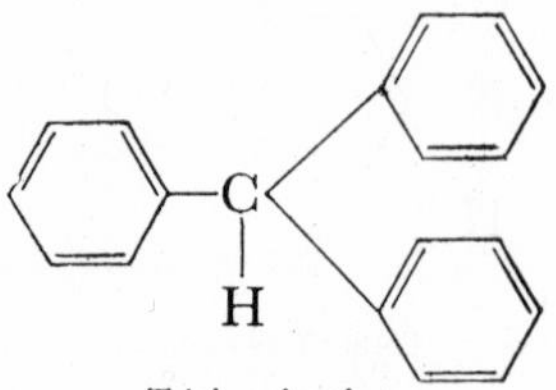

Triphenylmethane

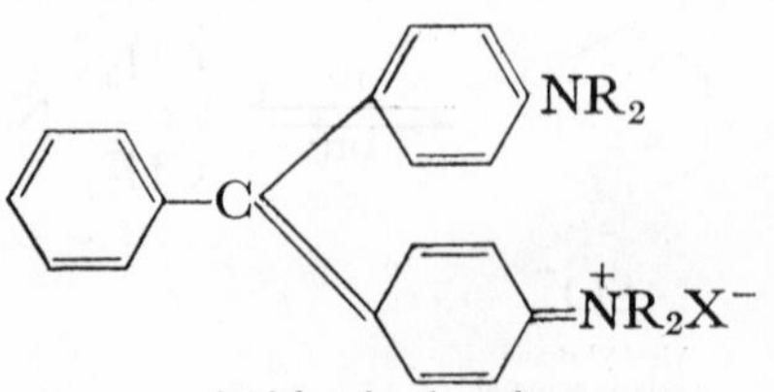

A triphenylmethane dye

The dyes differ from the parent hydrocarbon by the presence in each dye molecule of amino groups or hydroxyl groups in at least two of the benzene rings. Triphenylmethane is not actually used as a start-ing point in the manufacture of these dyes. Methods of making them will be outlined with reference to specific examples.

Malachite green. The first step in the preparation of this dye is accomplished through the action of zinc chloride on a mixture of benzaldehyde and dimethylaniline. The product of this condensation is a colorless compound called a *leuco base*. It is easily oxidized to the corresponding hydroxy compound (still colorless), which is called a *color base*. The color base is converted by a dilute acid to the green dye. The three steps are indicated by the following equations:

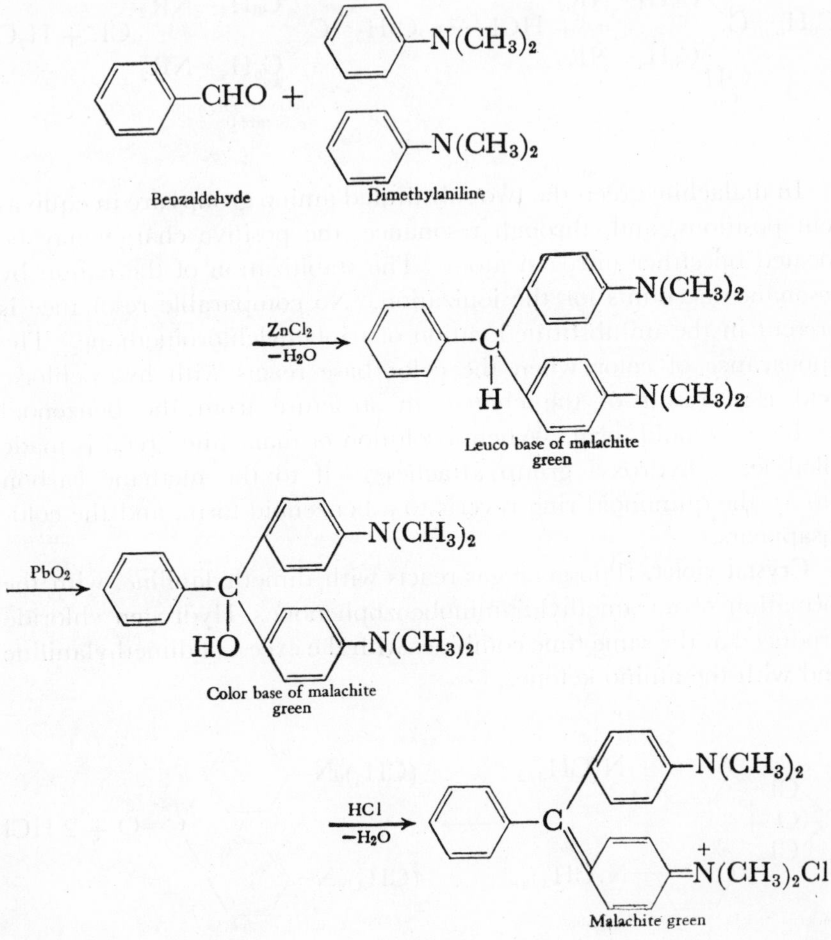

Benzaldehyde

Dimethylaniline

Leuco base of malachite green

Color base of malachite green

Malachite green

The action of hydrochloric acid on the color base of a triphenyl-methane dye is unusual in two respects: (a) the reaction is rapid; (b) the chlorine does not remain attached to the methane carbon atom. The effect of amino groups upon the dissociation of chloride ion from the methane carbon atom may be seen by comparing the following reactions:

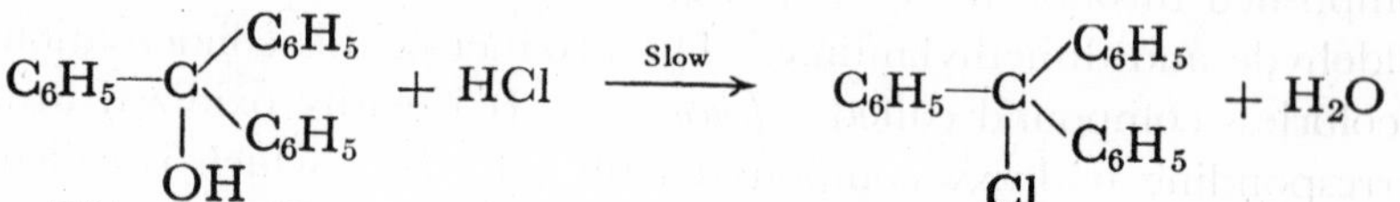

$$C_6H_5-C\begin{smallmatrix}C_6H_5\\\\C_6H_5\\|\\OH\end{smallmatrix} + HCl \xrightarrow{\text{Slow}} C_6H_5-C\begin{smallmatrix}C_6H_5\\\\C_6H_5\\|\\Cl\end{smallmatrix} + H_2O$$

Triphenyl carbinol   Triphenylchloromethane (un-ionized)

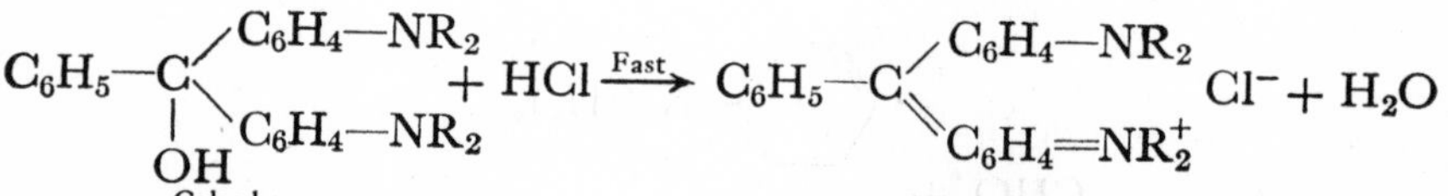

$$C_6H_5-C\begin{smallmatrix}C_6H_4-NR_2\\\\C_6H_4-NR_2\\|\\OH\end{smallmatrix} + HCl \xrightarrow{\text{Fast}} C_6H_5-C\begin{smallmatrix}C_6H_4-NR_2\\\\C_6H_4=NR_2^+\end{smallmatrix} Cl^- + H_2O$$

Color base   Malachite green (ionized)

In malachite green the two substituted amino groups are in equivalent positions, and, through resonance, the positive charge may be located on either nitrogen atom. The stabilization of the cation by resonance accounts for the ionization. No comparable resonance is present in the unsubstituted cation of triphenylchloromethane. The appearance of color when the color base reacts with hydrochloric acid is a result of the change in structure from the benzenoid to the quinonoid form. When a solution of malachite green is made alkaline, a hydroxyl group attaches itself to the methane carbon atom; the quinonoid ring reverts to a benzenoid form, and the color disappears.

Crystal violet. Phosgene gas reacts with dimethylaniline, with the formation of tetramethyldiaminobenzophenone. Hydrogen chloride produced at the same time combines with the excess of dimethylaniline and with the amino ketone.

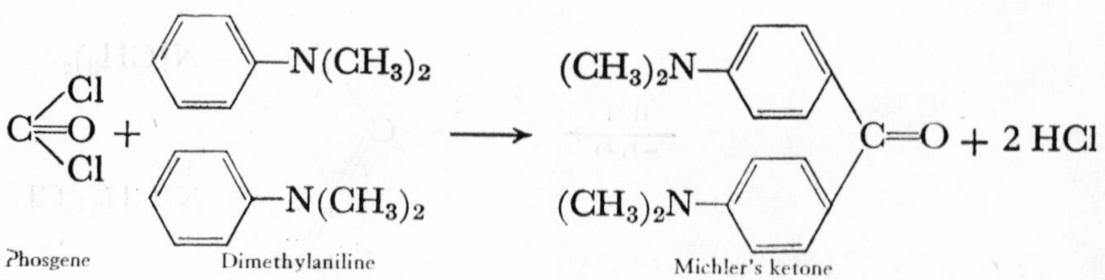

$$C\begin{smallmatrix}Cl\\=O\\Cl\end{smallmatrix} + \begin{smallmatrix}\bigcirc-N(CH_3)_2\\\\\bigcirc-N(CH_3)_2\end{smallmatrix} \longrightarrow \begin{smallmatrix}(CH_3)_2N-\bigcirc\\\\(CH_3)_2N-\bigcirc\end{smallmatrix}C=O + 2\ HCl$$

Phosgene   Dimethylaniline   Michler's ketone

When warmed with phosphorus oxychloride, a mixture of tetramethyl-diaminobenzophenone (Michler's ketone) and dimethylaniline yields the color base of crystal violet:

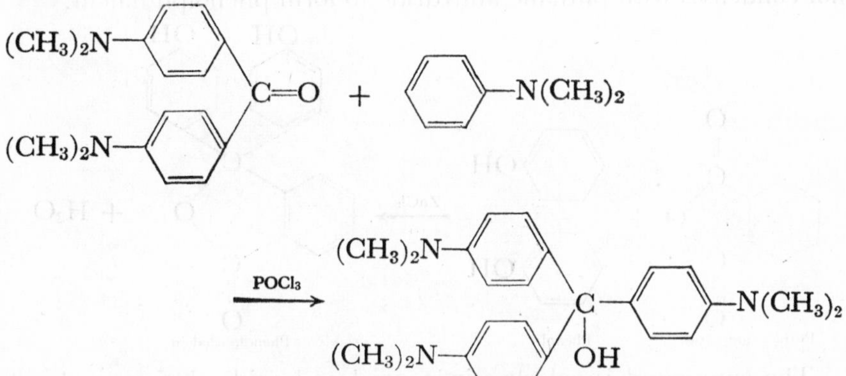

Color base of crystal violet

The carbinol, or color base, is converted into the dye by treatment with an acid:

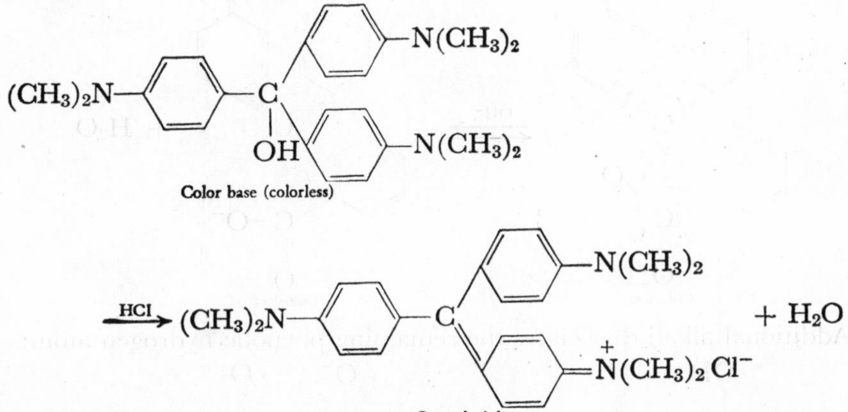

Color base (colorless)

Crystal violet

In this dye the positive charge may be located on any one of three nitrogen atoms. The above structure represents one of the three resonance forms. All strongly colored organic compounds possess a high degree of conjugation, or resonance, in the molecule. Like malachite green and other members of this class, crystal violet dyes silk and wool directly; but cotton is dyed only with the aid of a mordant, such as tannic acid.

The Phthaleins

Phenolphthalein. When heated with anhydrous zinc chloride, phenol condenses with phthalic anhydride to form phenolphthalein:

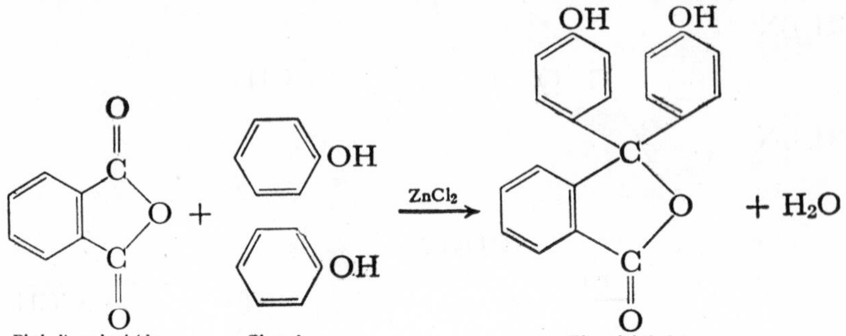

Phthalic anhydride   Phenol   Phenolphthalein

The compound is colorless in neutral and acid solutions and red in alkaline solutions. It is used extensively as an indicator. The first change to occur in alkali is hydrolysis of the lactone ring and dehydration of the resulting carbinol:

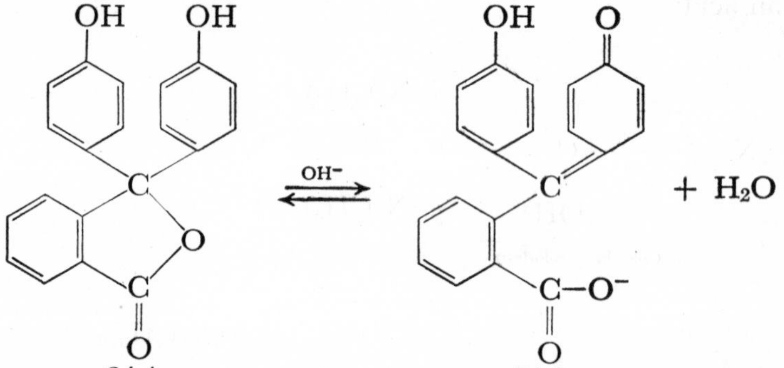

Colorless   Colorless

Additional alkali dissociates the remaining phenolic hydrogen atom:

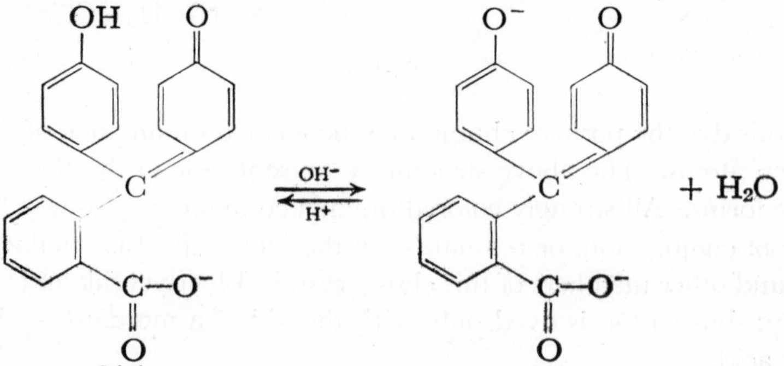

Colorless   Red

In the presence of a large excess of a base the red color of phenol-phthalein gradually fades until the solution becomes colorless. The mechanism of this change is indicated by the following equation:

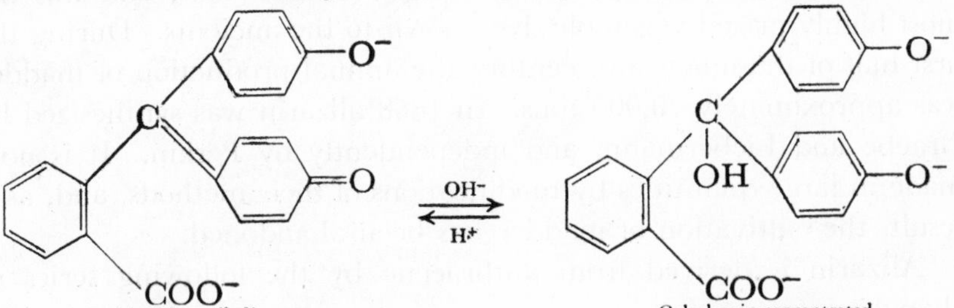

Red in dilute alkaline
solution

Colorless in concentrated
alkaline solution

Phenolphthalein is a colorless crystalline solid which melts at 261°. It dissolves readily in alcohol, but it is only slightly soluble in water. It is used in medicine as a laxative.

Fluorescein. Resorcin couples with phthalic anhydride, the point of attachment being ortho to one and para to the other of the hydroxyl groups. Water is then eliminated from the ortho hydroxyl groups, and fluorescein is produced. The second step is indicated by the following equation:

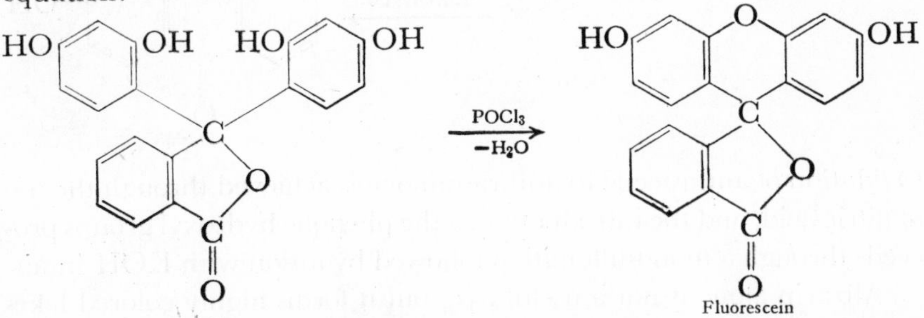

Fluorescein

An alkaline solution of the dye appears green by reflected light and red by transmitted light. It is easily brominated, being thereby con-verted into the beautiful red dye eosin:

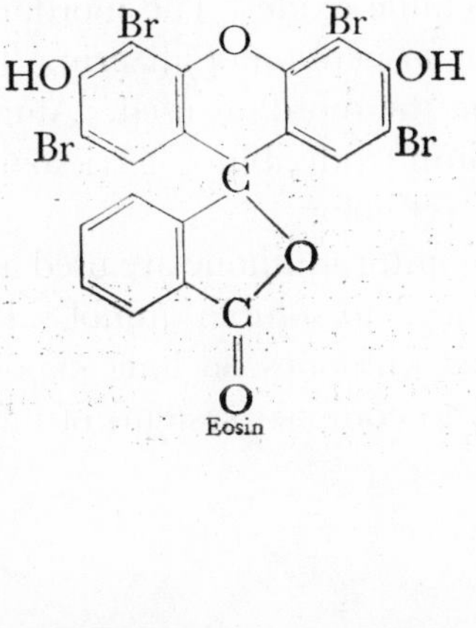

Eosin

Alizarin Dyes

Alizarin was formerly obtained from madder roots, and was the most highly prized vegetable dye known to the ancients. During the first half of the nineteenth century the annual production of madder was approximately 70,000 tons. In 1868 alizarin was synthesized by Graebe and Liebermann, and independently by Perkin. It is now made in large quantities by modifications of their methods, and, as a result, the cultivation of madder has been abandoned.

Alizarin is derived from anthracene by the following series of changes:

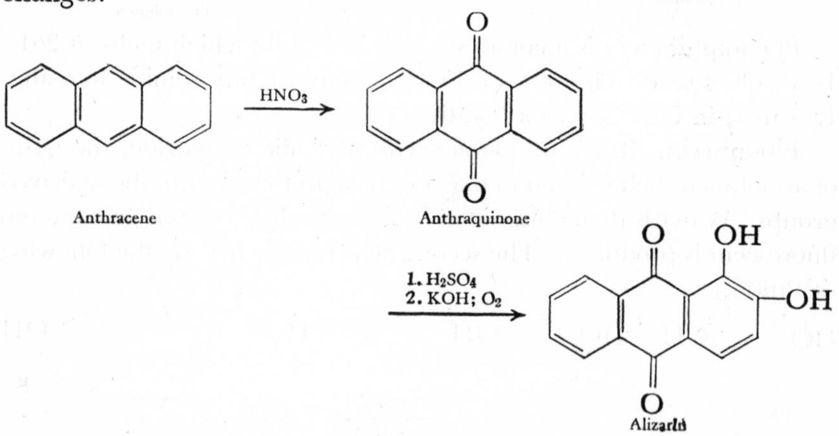

Anthracene $\xrightarrow{\text{HNO}_3}$ Anthraquinone $\xrightarrow[\text{2. KOH; O}_2]{\text{1. H}_2\text{SO}_4}$ Alizarin

Oxidation of anthracene to anthraquinone is achieved through the use of nitric acid, and the introduction of the phenolic hydroxyl groups proceeds through a monosulfonation followed by fusion with KOH in air.

Alizarin alone is not a useful dye, but it forms highly colored lakes with various metallic oxides which are used as mordants. Cloth to be dyed is immersed in a solution of a salt that is readily hydrolyzed. It is then steamed, to hydrolyze the salt and deposit on the textile fibers a film of the metallic oxide. The mordanted cloth is then immersed in a solution or suspension of alizarin. The color produced in the fiber depends upon the mordant used. Aluminum and tin oxides yield red colors; calcium oxide, blue; ferric oxide, violet-black; and chromium oxide, a claret color.

Many derivatives of anthraquinone are used as vat dyes. The quinone ring is easily reduced to soluble quinol salts, and the latter are oxidized to the colored quinones on long exposure to air. Some of these dyes correspond to compact systems of fused rings, highly conjugated, and oxidized to such an extent that no further change is effected by exposure to air and light. An example of such a complicated system is the blue dye known as indanthrene:

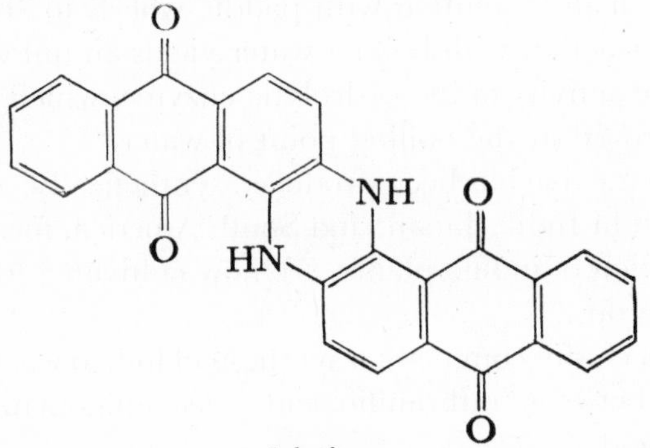

Indanthrene

Indigo

Indigo, obtained from the leaves of indigo plants, has been known for many centuries. Its value depends not only upon its beautiful blue color but also upon its stability. It is not changed by acids or alkalies, nor is it faded by light. It occurs in the plant as a glucoside, indican, $C_{14}H_{17}O_6N$, which, in the presence of an enzyme occurring with it, is hydrolyzed by warm water to dextrose, $C_6H_{12}O_6$, and indoxyl:

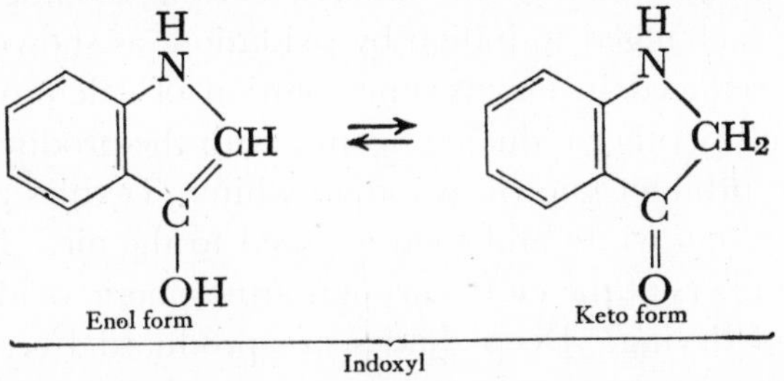

Enol form   Keto form

Indoxyl

Indoxyl, in alkaline solution, is readily oxidized by the air to indigo:

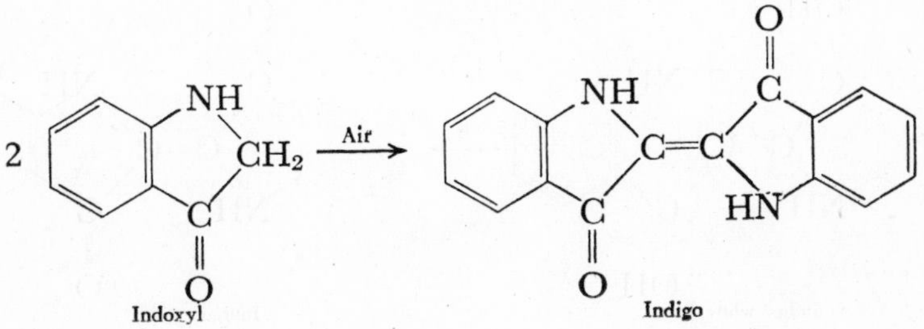

Indoxyl   Indigo

The commercial method of preparing the dye from natural sources consists in leaching the leaves of the plant with lukewarm water, rendering the aqueous extract alkaline by the addition of limewater, and churning the alkaline solution with paddle wheels to aerate and thus oxidize it. Extraction with boiling water yields an unhydrolyzed glucoside; for the activity of the hydrolytic enzyme, which the plant also yields, is destroyed at the boiling point of water.

Since 1900 the dye has been produced synthetically, and thousands of acres of land in India, Japan, and South America, formerly devoted to the production of indigo plants, are now cultivated for the production of other crops.

The first successful commercial synthesis of indigo was accomplished by a reaction between anthranilic acid (*ortho*-aminobenzoic acid) and chloroacetic acid:

$$C_6H_4 \begin{cases} NH \boxed{H + Cl} CH_2COOH \\ COOH \end{cases}$$

$$\longrightarrow \quad C_6H_4 \begin{cases} NH-CH_2-COOH \\ COOH \end{cases} + HCl$$

The product formed (phenylglycine-*o*-carboxylic acid), when fused with sodium hydroxide, yields indoxyl, carbon dioxide, and water. The indoxyl is changed to indigo by oxidation, as shown above.

Indigo is reduced in an alkaline solution of calcium hydrosulfite (CaS_2O_4) and by other reducing agents, with the production of a colorless soluble product known as indigo white. Textiles are soaked in solutions of indigo white and then exposed to the air. The color develops in the fibers of the cloth through atmospheric oxidation during the process of drying. Deep shades are produced by repeating the operation several times.

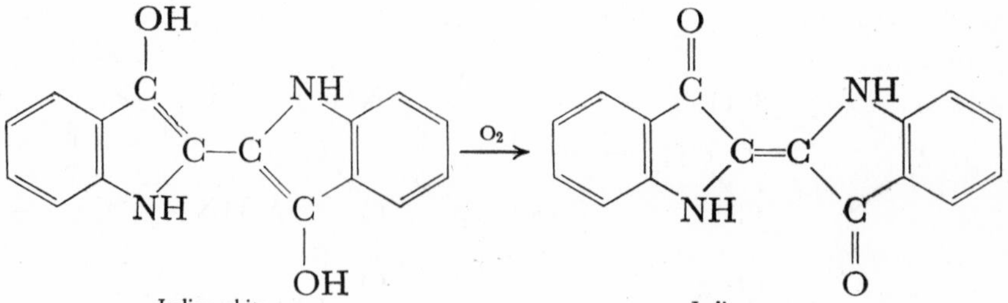

Indigo white   Indigo

Indicators

The indicators most commonly used are compounds which are sensitive to changes in the concentrations of hydrogen ions and hydroxide ions. Methyl orange and phenolphthalein, for example, are used to indicate the end points in the titration of acids and bases. Methyl orange changes from yellow, through orange, to red as the hydrogen ion concentration changes from about 0.00001 to 0.0001 equivalent per liter. A phenolphthalein solution begins to appear pink at hydroxide ion concentrations of about 0.000001 N and is red in 0.00001 N hydroxide ion. The one changes color in slightly acidic solution, and the other is colored in slightly basic solution. Some other indicators change color closer to the true neutral point; still others can be used to detect acidities and basicities up to 0.1 N.

The reason for these differences lies in the fact that indicators are themselves weak acids or weak bases. They form salts which ionize, and the anion of an acidic indicator and the cation of a basic indicator differ in color from the free acid and base.

Constitution and Color

Why are some compounds colorless and others colored? We can give at least a partial answer to this question. In 1776 Witt suggested that color in organic compounds is due to the presence of certain groups which he designated as chromophores. Some of these are as follows:

| *p*-Quinonoid ring | *o*-Quinonoid ring | Azo group | Nitro group |

$$-N{=}N-\qquad -NO_2$$

These alone, as we have seen, are not strongly colored; only as they become parts of extended unsaturated systems which include such groups as —OH or —NH$_2$ do they develop marked colors. Witt termed these accessory groups *auxochromes*, and their function has been observed in all the dyes considered. In their presence the color is intensified and is in general shifted toward the violet end of the spectrum.

All compounds absorb light in some part of the spectrum, but the human eye is sensitive to only a limited region of the spectrum. If absorption occurs within this region, a color visible to the eye is produced. The portion of the light which is not absorbed is reflected or transmitted, and it is the reflected or transmitted waves which we see. If the incident light is white light, the color which we perceive is complementary to the color absorbed. Thus a compound which we call red is one which absorbs in the blue-green end of the spectrum. The following table summarizes the colors to be expected in compounds which absorb in various regions of the spectrum:

COLOR AND LIGHT ABSORPTION

Color Absorbed	Complementary Color
Violet	Yellow-green
Blue	Yellow
Blue-green	Orange-red
Green	Purple
Yellow-green	Violet
Yellow	Blue
Orange	Green-blue
Red	Blue-green

Modern theories which deal with the relation between the color of a substance and its structure seek to explain why color is so, often associated not only with an extended series of conjugated double bonds but also with a conjugated series which includes an ionic charge. The study has made it possible in many cases to predict from the structure of a compound the positions and character of its absorption bands.

EXERCISES

1. What is the difference between colored compounds in general and dyes?

2. Write the formula of phenolphthalein as it exists in an acidic solution, and represent by an equation the change which takes place when dilute alkali converts the indicator to its colored form.

3. Outline the preparation of methyl orange from sulfanilic acid and dimethylaniline. Indicate by formulas the red form and the yellow form of the indicator.

4. Express the cause of color in compounds: (a) in terms of chromophore and auxochrome groups; (b) in terms of the incident light absorbed.

5. What is a mordant? a lake? a substantive dye? Why are silk and wool more readily dyed than cellulose fibers?

6. Use indigo as an example to illustrate the principle underlying the use of vat dyes.

PROBLEMS

1. Write the formula of a dye which could be made from benzidine and β-naphthol.

2. Outline in equations the preparation of crystal violet from phosgene and dimethylaniline. Point out the color base in the series of substances formed.

3. How, from any starting point, may the following azo dyes be prepared?

(a)

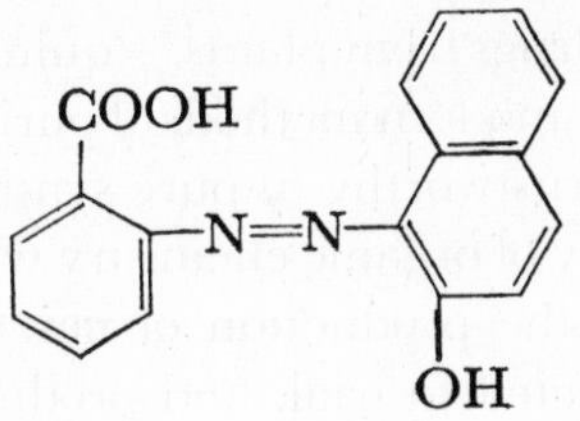

(b) O_2N- ⬡ $-N{=}N-$ ⬡ $-OH$, COOH

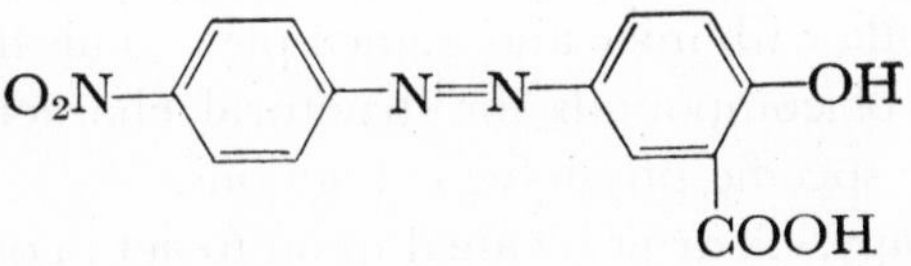

30 · NATURAL AND SYNTHETIC DRUGS

The preparation of useful drugs by synthetic methods is a twentieth-century accomplishment. Through all the earlier ages physicians were dependent upon extracts from plants, and these extracts usually were unstandardized mixtures of varying potencies. Even now we obtain some of the most valuable drugs from plants,—quinine, morphine, and digitalis are examples,—but modern methods of purification have made these natural products as trustworthy as pure synthetic medicinals.

Until the structure theory of organic chemistry was developed, there was no scientific basis for the production of new drugs. Nearly all available plants were subjected to trial, and products derived from a few of them were found to be physiologically active.*

No scientific basis for the selection of natural drugs has yet been found. The preliminary physiological experiments with new compounds are made with mice and guinea pigs. This makes it possible to test hundreds of compounds for structural characteristics which are responsible for specific physiological actions.

Chemotherapy. A drug is called upon to act in one of several ways. It may be required to increase or decrease the activity of some metabolic process; it may be used to destroy pathogenic microorganisms or inhibit their growth; it may have general antiseptic properties, or it may be more or less specific toward one type of organism; it may be needed to produce anesthesia. We do not include under chemotherapy the use of vitamins and hormones, even though, as in the case of ascorbic acid, a specific compound cures a condition once rated as a disease. And we are not concerned here with general disinfectants and antiseptics. Vaccines and serums act specifically in combating microorganisms; but they are very complex protein substances, of biological origin, which we are unable to synthesize. By chemotherapy we mean the use of chemical substances of known structure, to eliminate pathogenic microorganisms from a host.

*The *doctrine of signature* was one of the earliest guides in the search for remedies. It was believed that the Creator had stamped all medicinal herbs with a form or color which would reveal to the initiated the type of disorder the plant could cure. Yellow was the signature for jaundice, and teas made from yellow blossoms (usually administered in connection with mystic ceremonies) were supposed to relieve the symptoms of jaundice. Extracts of red plants or red blossoms were used for scarlet fever.

The principal pathogenic organisms are bacteria and protozoa. Amoebic dysentery, malaria, and sleeping sickness are disorders caused by protozoa. Bacterial diseases include diphtheria, typhoid fever, and tuberculosis. Measles, mumps, and influenza are virus diseases. More than two hundred microorganisms which are harmful to man have been identified, and so far only about a dozen have yielded to vaccines or serums. Robert Koch isolated the anthrax bacillus in 1876, and the possibility of immunizing cattle against anthrax was demonstrated by Pasteur in 1881. It seems that time enough has elapsed since then to accomplish control of all diseases by this method if such a panacea were possible. On the other hand, up to 1900 only a few chemical substances were known to have specific action. Mercury compounds had been used in the treatment of venereal diseases since the sixteenth century; quinine from cinchona bark was the only cure for malaria from the seventeenth century until very recently; emetine has been shown to be the active substance in ipecac, which has been used in the treatment of dysentery and diarrhea for three hundred years. The first synthetic drug to be intentionally developed for a specific purpose was introduced in 1909 by Paul Ehrlich; it was designed to control syphilis.

There is hope for unlimited success in chemotherapy. The problem, essentially, is to produce a substance which is more toxic to the microorganism in question than it is to the host. Of course, the more basic problem is diagnosis of an ailment as one of parasitic, dietary, metabolic, or psychopathic origin; but it is conceivable that a chemical treatment will someday be successful for every disorder which is caused by a microorganism or a virus.

The idea that synthetic products could be built up which would act specifically against microorganisms without appreciable toxicity to man was first systematically tested by Paul Ehrlich. He knew that methylene blue stains parasitic organisms to a greater degree than it stains tissues of the host, and he concluded that it might be possible to incorporate in such a dye organic or inorganic groups of high toxicity and thus aim the poison specifically at the parasite. The same principle is now being used in developing the therapeutic use of radioactive elements.

Methylene blue

The facts that an organic arsenic compound,

$$H_2N—C_6H_4—AsO_3HNa,$$

kills trypanasomes and that a complicated azo dye, trypan red, has the same effect suggested to Ehrlich that a combination of the two structures in one molecule would be particularly effective. He prepared, after six hundred trials, a compound of the required properties, called arsphenamine, or salvarsan. Later a more stable compound, neo-arsphenamine, was developed by him for the same use. Both compounds are arsenic analogues of certain derivatives of azobenzene.

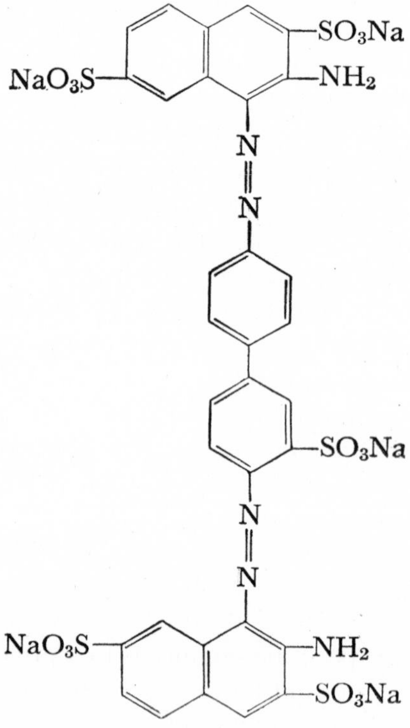

Trypan red, an azo dye

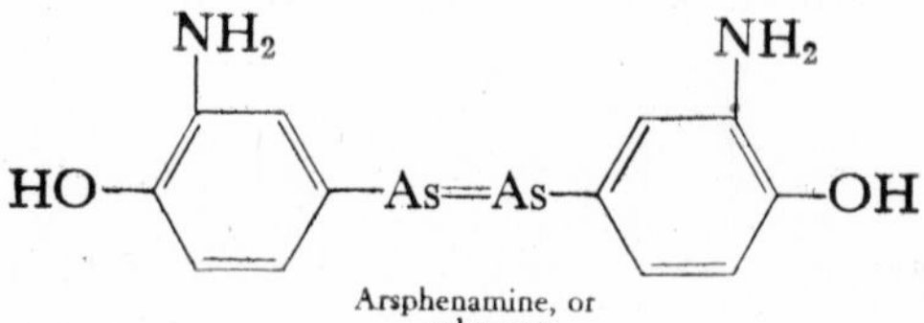

Arsphenamine, or salvarsan

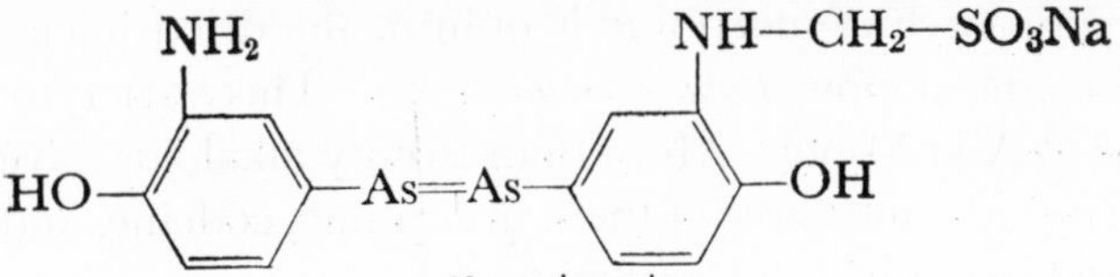

$$NH_2 \qquad\qquad NH-CH_2-SO_3Na$$

$$HO--As\!\!=\!\!As--OH$$

Neoarsphenamine

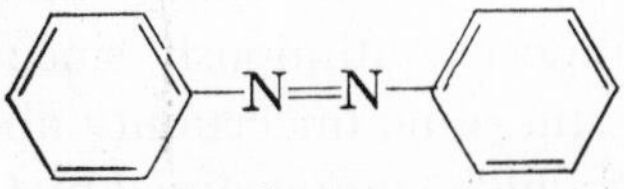

$$-N\!\!=\!\!N-$$

Azobenzene

Classification of drugs. Medicinal compounds may be classified on the basis of use, origin, or chemical structure. The commonest classification is based upon use or physiological function, as indicated by the list below:

A FEW VALUABLE DRUGS	
Uses or Functions	**Examples**
Anesthetics	Ether, chloroform, nitrous oxide, cocaine, avertine (tribromoethanol)
Hypnotics and sedatives	The barbiturates, chloral hydrate, codeine, morphine, novocain
Analgesics and antipyretics	Aspirin, acetanilide, cinchophen, morphine, codeine
Antimalarials	Quinine, atebrin
Stimulants	Digitalis, strychnine, camphor, caffeine, ephedrine
Antiseptics, germicides, and fungicides	Nicotine, phenol, cresols, salicylic acid, iodoform, mercury salts, methylene blue, formaldehyde, sulfa drugs, penicillin

Specific Drugs

Morphine. No other drug competes successfully with morphine in producing sleep and relieving pain, and no other drug has a greater tendency to develop addiction.*

*For fairly accurate descriptions of the habit-forming property of morphine read De Quincey's *Confessions of an English Opium-Eater* and Fanny Hurst's short story "She Walks in Beauty."

The chief source of morphine is opium, the dried juice of the unripe seeds of the poppy, *Papaver somniferum*. This variety of poppy is indigenous to Asia Minor. More than twenty alkaloids have been isolated from opium, and three of them, morphine, codeine, and papaverine, are used extensively in medicine.

Although the structure of the morphine molecule has been a subject of serious study almost continuously since the alkaloid was isolated in 1804, there is still some uncertainty about the configuration. The following formula, which was proposed by Gulland and Robinson in 1925, must be nearly correct:

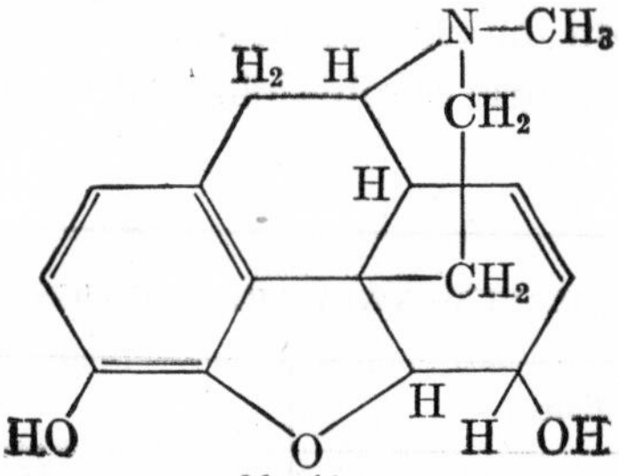

Morphine

This formula accounts for all the chemical reactions of the drug, but as yet the structure has not been confirmed by synthesis. Morphine contains the ring structures of phenanthrene and isoquinoline. These have been identified among the decomposition products of the alkaloid. In morphine, however, these ring systems are partially reduced (more nearly saturated than in phenanthrene and isoquinoline).

Morphine produces a variety of effects in various species of animals. In human beings it acts as a sedative, small doses causing sleep and toxic doses producing profound unconsciousness. Its most important therapeutic use is that of relieving pain, which is accomplished in most cases by administration of less than 0.01 of a gram. The ability to perceive pain is depressed by doses much too small to cause sleep.

Acute morphine poisoning is caused by doses ranging from 0.03 to 0.06 of a gram. The average lethal dose for an adult unaccustomed to its use is about 0.35 of a gram. The system acquires tolerance for morphine, and habitual users take large doses with impunity. The effects described above are produced by much smaller quantities of the alkaloid if administered by hypodermic injection.

Codeine is a methylated morphine in which the phenolic hydroxyl has been converted to a methoxyl group. In consequence codeine is less active than morphine and less likely to lead to drug addiction. It finds extensive use in cough medicines.

Heroin is a synthetic variant of morphine in which both hydroxyl groups are acetylated; it is a stronger narcotic than morphine.

Demerol. A synthetic derivative of piperidine called demerol has some of the properties of morphine. It is a habit-forming drug and is classed as a narcotic. It is the ethyl ester of 1-methyl-4-phenyl-piperidine-4-carboxylic acid. (See formula of piperidine below.)

The ring systems of pyridine, piperidine, quinoline, and isoquinoline are found as structural units in many compounds of vegetable origin. For the structure of phenanthrene see page 282; the formulas of the other compounds mentioned in this connection are shown below.

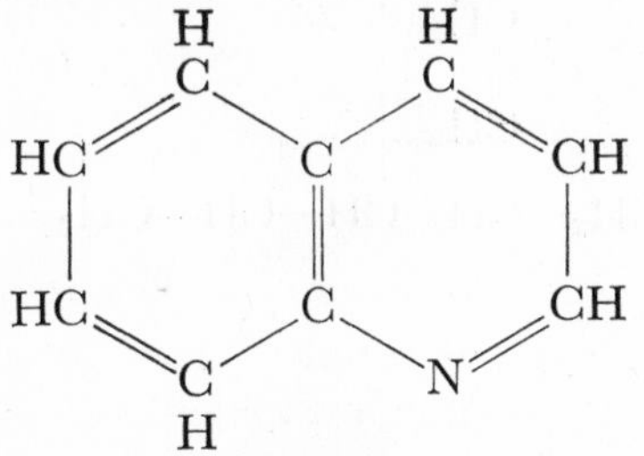

Quinoline
(bp 237.7°)

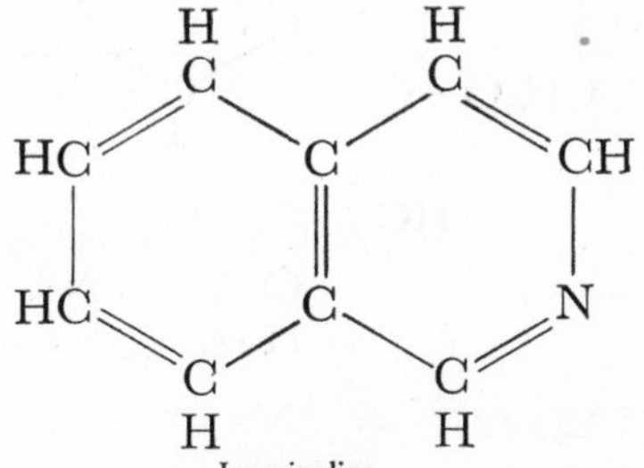

Isoquinoline
(bp 243°)

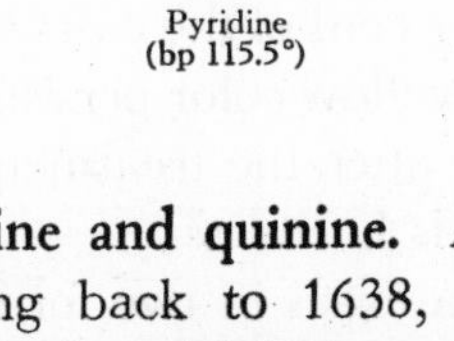

Pyridine
(bp 115.5°)

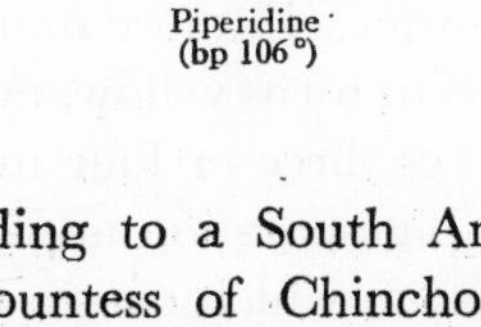

Piperidine
(bp 106°)

Cinchonine and quinine. According to a South American tradition dating back to 1638, the countess of Chinchon recovered from a fever after drinking an extract from the bark of a tree. The generic name *Cinchona* was later applied to the trees yielding similar products, and the first alkaloid isolated from the bark was called cinchonine.

Cinchonine, $C_{19}H_{22}N_2O$, crystallizes in prisms melting at 255°. It is a ditertiary base, dextrorotatory, almost insoluble in water, soluble in alcohol, and much like quinine in its chemical and physiological reactions. Quinine is a methoxy derivative of cinchonine. The two alkaloids occur together, and they are usually associated with traces of at least twenty other related bases.

Quinine is the most important member of the group. It is a drug of great therapeutic value. It is not a poison in the ordinary sense of the term; still it is far from harmless if taken in large doses. It retards all vital processes, inhibiting every type of metabolic change. Quinine is used quite generally to combat malarial fever. Its synthesis was accomplished in 1944, but the process is too expensive to be commercially useful at the present time.

$$CH_3O-C \overset{H}{\underset{\underset{H}{C}}{\overset{C}{=}}} \overset{C}{\underset{N}{C}} \overset{CHOH-CH-N-CH_2}{\underset{CH_2-CH-CH-CH=CH_2}{\overset{|\quad CH_2 \quad |}{\overset{|\quad CH_2 \quad |}{CH}}}}$$

Quinine

Cinchonine differs from quinine only in having a hydrogen atom in the place of the methoxy group in the quinoline unit.

Synthetic antimalarials. More than ten thousand compounds were tested for antimalarial properties between 1918 and 1940. Only two of them proved to be useful; they were plasmochin and atebrin. Plasmochin, a derivative of quinoline, was introduced into medicine in 1926; atebrin was used experimentally as early as 1930, but it did not become a drug of great importance until 1942. Atebrin is a yellow, bitter powder. In more than 50 per cent of the cases treated with this drug the skin turns yellow, and the yellow color persists for several days (sometimes three or four months) after the treatment is discontinued. This pigmentation apparently is harmless.

The protozoan which causes malaria exists in two forms, a sexual and an asexual form. The sexual form does not multiply in a human being, but does multiply in the blood stream of the anopheles mosquito. The chills and fever typical of malaria occur when the asexual forms undergo division. In this process of division only a few sexual forms of the organism develop, and these must be transferred back to the blood of the mosquito for multiplication. Quinine and atebrin alike attack the asexual forms of the organism. These drugs bring relief to the patient, restoring the normal body temperature; but the blood of the patient is still infectious for mosquitoes. Plasmochin, on the other hand, attacks both forms of the organism. It is superior to quinine or atebrin in this respect, but it is also more toxic and far more likely to produce harmful effects upon the blood cells.

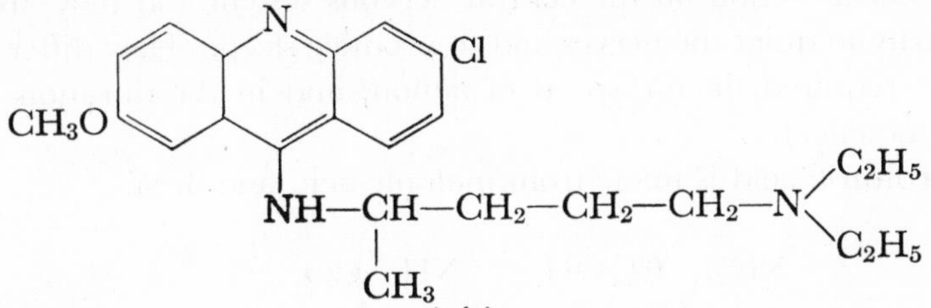

Atebrin

Strychnine and brucine. Strychnine, $C_{21}H_{22}N_2O_2$, occurs with brucine, $C_{23}H_{26}N_2O_4$, in the nuts or seeds, leaves, and bark of the plants of the genus *Strychnos*. The seed of *Strychnos nux vomica* contains more than 1 per cent of strychnine and as much brucine. Curare, a resin extracted from many species of trees, contains strychnine, brucine, curarine, and other poisonous bases.

Strychnine crystallizes in prisms which are soluble in alcohol and practically insoluble in water. Salts of strychnine, on the other hand, dissolve readily in water. The base is levorotatory, and has an alkaline reaction and a bitter taste.

Nicotine. $C_{10}H_{14}N_2$, when pure, is a colorless, odorless liquid. It acquires a brown color and a tobacco odor on standing. It boils and gradually decomposes at 247°. It has an alkaline reaction, produces

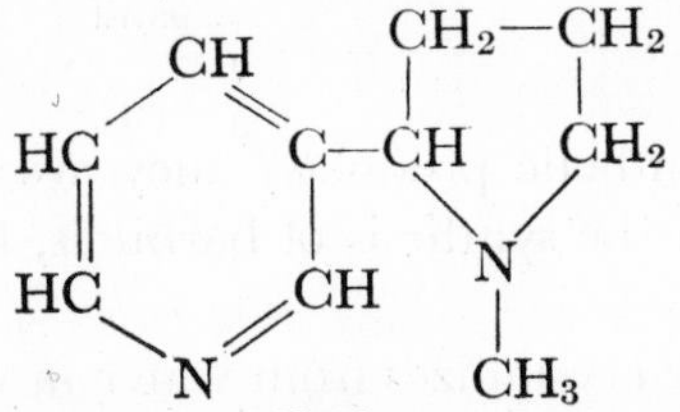

Nicotine

a burning sensation in the mouth, and causes profuse salivation. Acute nicotine poisoning gives rise to mental confusion, vomiting, and finally convulsions. It is the toxic ingredient in many insecticides.

Nicotine occurs in the leaves of the tobacco plant, principally in the form of salts of malic and citric acids. The tobacco plant is the chief source of this alkaloid. The plant is indigenous to America and was unknown in Europe until 1650.

The barbiturates. The first derivative of barbituric acid to be used in medicine was veronal (1903). A few years later phenobarbital, or luminal, was placed on the market. Since then a large number of barbiturates have been made available for clinical use. They all have a depressant action on the central nervous system and they are used primarily to quiet the nerves and to produce sleep. They differ in the dosage required, in the speed of action, and in the duration of the hypnotic effect.

Barbituric acid is made from malonic acid and urea.

$$
\begin{array}{ccccc}
NH_2 & COOH & & NH-CO & \\
| & | & & | \quad | & \\
CO & + CH_2 & \xrightarrow{POCl_3} & CO \quad CH_2 & + 2\,H_2O \\
| & | & & | \quad | & \\
NH_2 & COOH & & NH-CO & \\
\text{Urea} & \text{Malonic acid} & & \text{Barbituric acid} &
\end{array}
$$

The hydrogen atoms of the methylene group (CH_2) in barbituric acid are readily replaced by alkyl or aryl radicals (see malonic ester synthesis, p. 190). The substitution products formed in this way are the barbiturates or barbitals.

$$
\begin{array}{cc}
NH-CO & \\
| \quad | \diagup C_2H_5 & \\
CO \quad C\diagdown & \\
| \quad | \diagdown C_6H_5 & \\
NH-CO & \\
\text{Phenobarbital} &
\end{array}
\qquad
\begin{array}{cc}
NH-CO & \\
| \quad | \diagup C_2H_5 & \\
CO \quad C\diagdown & \\
| \quad | \diagdown C_5H_{11} \; \text{(isoamyl)} & \\
NH-CO & \\
\text{Amytal} &
\end{array}
$$

The barbitals are synthetic products; they are not found in plants. Since urea is used in the synthesis of barbitals, these compounds are often called *ureids*.

Caffeine. Caffeine crystallizes from water in white needles having a silky luster and a bitter taste. It sublimes under atmospheric pressure at 178°, and melts in a sealed tube at 237°. Caffeine occurs in coffee (0.5 per cent to 1.5 per cent) and in tea leaves (2 to 4 per cent). There is approximately the same amount of caffeine in a cup of coffee as in a cup of tea, for a greater weight of coffee is used in preparing the beverage.

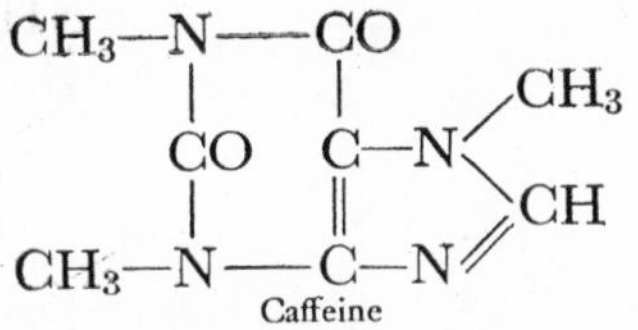

$$\begin{array}{c} CH_3-N-\!\!\!-CO \\ | \qquad | \qquad CH_3 \\ CO \quad C-N{<} \\ | \qquad || \qquad CH \\ CH_3-N-\!\!\!-C-N{/} \end{array}$$

Caffeine

Caffeine acts upon the central nervous system, upon the kidneys, and upon the heart. It is a cerebral stimulant; it overcomes drowsiness and relieves fatigue. Intravenously injected it quickens the heart action and temporarily produces a stronger pulse. Upon the kidneys it acts as a diuretic.

The sulfa drugs. Certain derivatives of sulfanilic acid, popularly called the sulfa drugs, have become important agents in combating infections due to the types of bacteria classified as *cocci*. Various types of streptococcus infection, including pneumonia and gonorrhea, are among the disorders which have been promptly relieved through the use of these drugs. They have been used in the form of sprays or dusts on open wounds; they are administered also orally and by injection.

Sulfanilamide. The first sulfanilic acid derivative to be recognized as valuable in medicine was sulfanilamide, or para-aminobenzenesulfonamide. The formula of this crystalline compound is now used as a basis of reference in naming all sulfa drugs. The numbering of the carbon and nitrogen atoms is as follows:

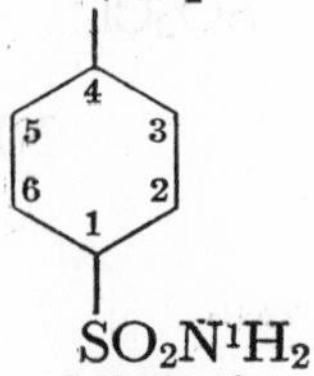

$$N^4H_2$$

(benzene ring numbered 4, 5, 3, 6, 2, 1)

$$SO_2N^1H_2$$

Sulfanilamide

The numbering begins with the carbon atom to which the sulfonic acid group is attached, for this is regarded as the principal functional group in the molecule. The nitrogen atoms are differentiated by superscripts, N^1 referring to the amido nitrogen atom, N^4 to the amino nitrogen atom.

The principal radicals derived from this formula are the following:

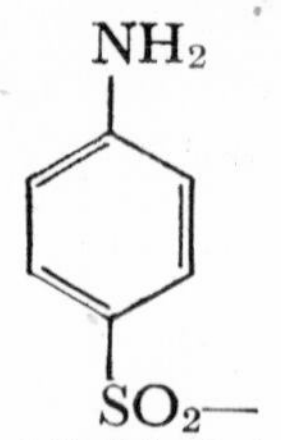

NH_2

SO_2—

Sulfanilyl radical

NH_2

SO_2—NH—

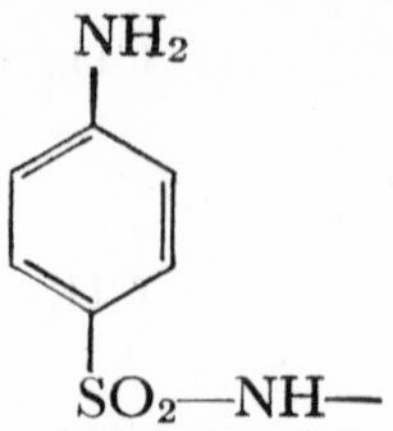

Sulfanilamide radical

The system of naming derivatives is illustrated below:

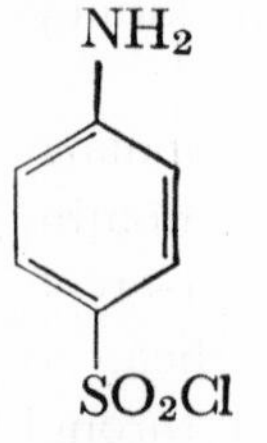

NH_2

SO_2Cl

Sulfanilyl
chloride

$NHCH_3$

SO_2NH_2

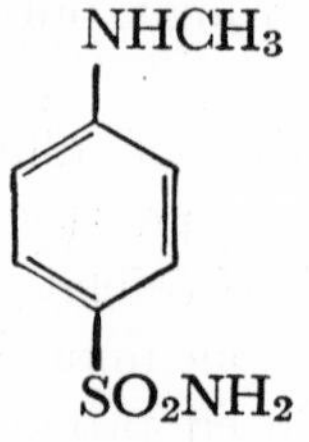

N4-Methyl-
sulfanilamide

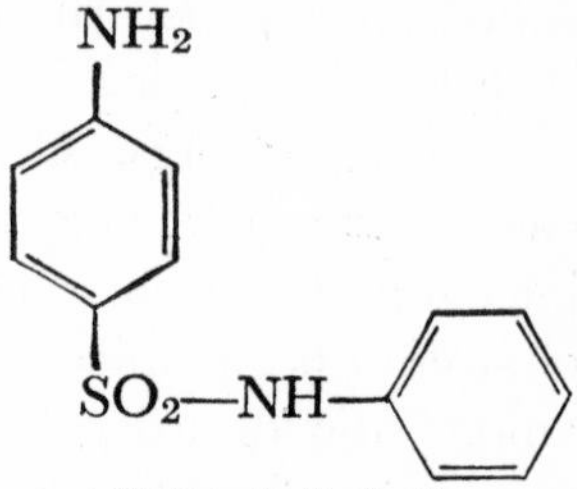

NH_2

SO_2—NH—

N1-Phenyl-sulfanilamide

Sulfanilamide is prepared from acetanilide as follows:

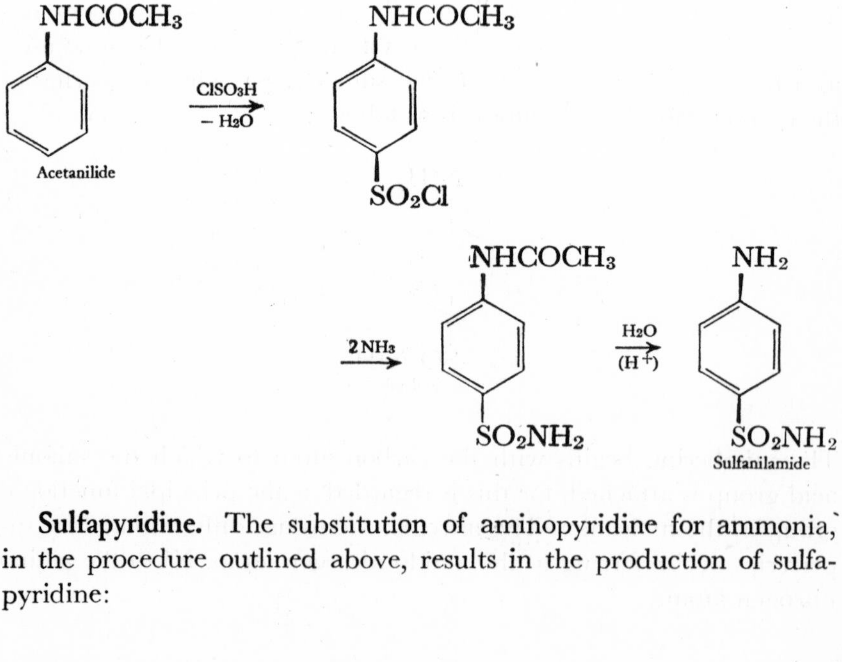

$NHCOCH_3$

Acetanilide

$\xrightarrow[-H_2O]{ClSO_3H}$

$NHCOCH_3$

SO_2Cl

$\xrightarrow{2\,NH_3}$

$NHCOCH_3$

SO_2NH_2

$\xrightarrow[(H^+)]{H_2O}$

NH_2

SO_2NH_2

Sulfanilamide

Sulfapyridine. The substitution of aminopyridine for ammonia, in the procedure outlined above, results in the production of sulfa-pyridine:

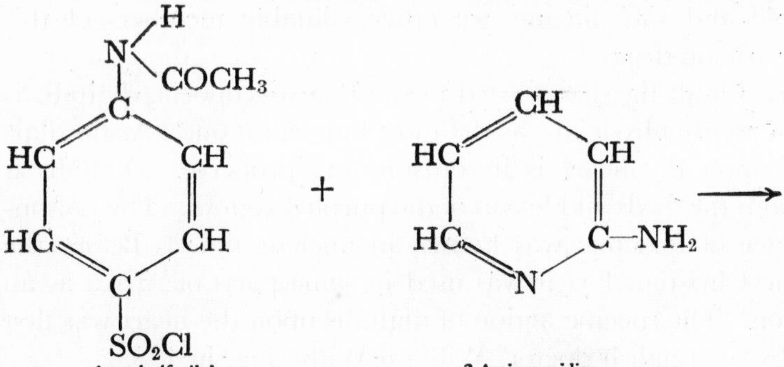

Acetylsulfanilyl
chloride

2-Aminopyridine

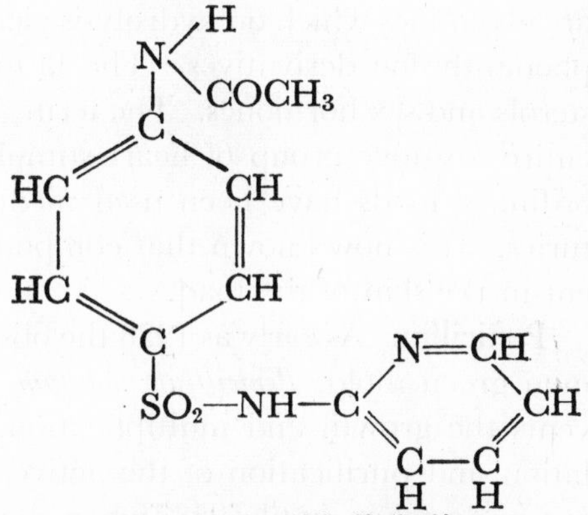

N^4-Acetyl-N^1-pyridyl-sulfanilamide

The acetyl group, having served its purpose in preventing coupling with the sulfanilic acid amino group, is now removed by hydrolysis, and the useful drug is obtained in crystalline form. Its formula is written, in compact form, as follows:

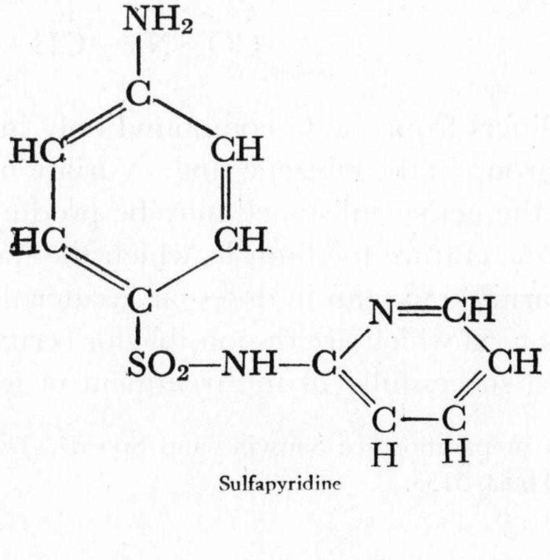

Sulfapyridine

Sulfathiazole and sulfadiazine are other valuable members of this group of synthetic drugs.*

Digitalis. Of all the drugs listed in the Pharmacopoeia, digitalis is regarded by many physicians as the most important one. A stimulating action upon the heart is its outstanding property. Digitalis is obtained from the seeds and leaves of the purple foxglove. The poisonous character of foxglove was known in ancient times. Before the dawn of the Christian Era it was used in some parts of Africa as an arrow poison. The specific action of digitalis upon the heart was first described by an English doctor, William Withering, in 1785.

Several closely related compounds occur together in foxglove. They are glycosides which on hydrolysis yield simple sugars and complicated phenanthrene derivatives. The latter are chemically related to the sterols and sex hormones. The term *digitalis* is generally applied to the entire foxglove group of heart stimulants. Dried, powdered skins of ordinary toads have been used medicinally in China for many centuries. It is now known that compounds related to digitalis are present in the skin of the toad.

Penicillin. As early as 1928 the observation was made that the common green mold, *Penicillium notatum*, secretes a substance which prevents the growth and multiplication of some types of bacteria. Isolation and purification of the active compound called penicillin was not undertaken until 1938, when the need for harmless antiseptics in the army became urgent. The chemical nature of penicillin is indicated by its structural formula,

$$\text{C}_6\text{H}_5\text{—CH}_2\text{—CO—NH—CH—CH} \quad \overset{\text{S}}{\underset{\text{CO—N——CH—COONa}}{\text{C}}} \overset{\text{CH}_3}{\underset{\text{CH}_3}{}}$$

Penicillin G

Penicillin X differs from the G compound only in the presence of a para hydroxyl group in the benzene ring. Variations in composition and structure of the active substance may be produced by changing the character of the culture medium in which the mold is grown.

Penicillin is harmless to man in doses far greater than are required to combat the bacteria which are responsible for certain diseases. The compound is used successfully in the treatment of wounds. The or-

*For methods of preparation see Sausville and Spoerri, *Journal of the American Chemical Society* (1941), **63**, 3153.

Oxford University, England

Fig. 15. Penicillin Crystals

ganisms which infect open wounds and cause blood poisoning are among those most effectively eliminated by penicillin; hence the popularity of this drug on the battlefield. Anthrax, pneumonia, diphtheria, and gonorrhea are among the diseases which have been cured with the aid of penicillin. Among the organisms which are not sensitive to penicillin are those causing typhoid fever and tuberculosis. The drug apparently acts by preventing multiplication of the pathogenic organisms, rather than accomplishing a destruction of those already present. The ordinary defense mechanisms of the body can eliminate organisms from the blood if the process of multiplication is stopped.

EXERCISES

1. What is chemotherapy?

2. To what class of compounds does salvarsan belong?

3. To what class of drugs does each of the following compounds belong: (a) ether, (b) cocaine, (c) aspirin, (d) phenobarbital, (e) morphine, (f) nicotine, (g) digitalis, (h) strychnine, (i) quinine, (j) sulfapyridine?

4. Write a structural formula for each of the following compounds: (a) urea, (b) quinoline, (c) phenanthrene, (d) isoquinoline, (e) piperidine, (f) sulfanilic acid.

31 · ENZYMES, VITAMINS, AND HORMONES

The classes of compounds which we recognize as necessary foods in human nutrition are proteins, fats, carbohydrates, salts, and water. With these the cells of the living organism are built and are kept in repair. Through the many chemical transformations of metabolism the body temperature is maintained and energy for work is made available. The mechanisms by which these foods are converted into living cells and body fluids, and the processes involved in replacing waste materials, are governed by extremely small amounts of other substances known as enzymes, vitamins, and hormones. These are the catalysts and the regulators of vital processes. They are present in quantities too small to be significant sources of building materials in cell formation or useful sources of muscular energy or heat, but they are just as essential to health as are the more substantial components of our diets.

The three classes of organic catalysts have some properties in common, but they differ widely in origins, specific functions, and composition. The enzymes are proteins, and in most cases conjugated proteins; that is, the protein molecules are in combination with other types of compounds. Enzymes are therefore compounds of extremely complex structures. They are produced in the body as needed. Amylase, for example, is synthesized in the salivary glands and is ready to start the process of digestion of starch as soon as food of this kind is taken into the mouth. Pepsin, which promotes the hydrolysis of proteins to peptones, is a component of the gastric juice; it is secreted by the mucous membrane of the stomach. Trypsin, which converts proteins and peptones into polypeptides, is produced in the pancreas, and it is delivered to the intestinal tract through the pancreatic duct.

The vitamins are much simpler in structure than the enzymes, and unlike the enzymes they are not produced in the body as needed. They must be supplied in the diet or taken into the system as accessories to the diet. The vitamins do not belong to any one class of compounds; they are chemically unrelated substances. Most of the known vitamins have been produced synthetically; their structural formulas are known. Vitamins are delivered by the blood to the cells where they are needed.

374

Hormones are definite chemical compounds which are secreted by the ductless glands and which are transported by the blood. They stimulate activity at points remote from their origins, and each hormone performs some specific function. When, for example, food mixed with the acidic gastric juice passes from the stomach to the intestine, a hormone is released which enters the blood stream; and as soon as blood containing this compound reaches the pancreas, it stimulates the secretion of pancreatic juice. When the food reaches the point where the pancreatic duct enters the intestine, the necessary enzymes from the pancreas are there to aid in the digestive process. The hormone which regulates this activity of the pancreas can be prepared by immersing a washed segment of the intestine of a recently killed animal in very dilute hydrochloric acid. The injection of a few cubic centimeters of the extract into the blood causes an immediate flow of secretions from the pancreas. Dilute hydrochloric acid alone, when introduced into the blood stream, does not have this effect; a neutral aqueous extract of the intestinal mucosa also fails to stimulate the pancreas.

Enzymes

Enzymes are organic compounds which are capable of catalyzing chemical reactions involved in physiological processes. A catalyst increases the rate of a reaction by altering the mechanism of the process. A change which is accomplished without a catalyst through one or two slow steps may, with the aid of a catalyst, be accomplished through several very rapid steps. In at least one of the steps the catalyst itself enters into the formation of an unstable intermediate product. Ultimately the catalyst is released from the intermediate product, and it can go through the cycle again. Gradual loss of the catalyst through side reactions accounts for the fact that there is a limit to the amount of material which may be changed by a specified quantity of the catalyst. Invertase, an enzyme produced by yeast, will convert 200,000 times its own weight of cane sugar into glucose and fructose; and rennin, obtained from the stomach of a calf, will precipitate more than 400,000 times its own weight of casein from milk.

One of the first cases of enzyme action to be carefully studied was that of the production of alcohol from glucose through fermentation induced by yeast (see pages 111, 112). Enzymes are produced by reactions in living organisms, but they can perform their functions as catalysts in the absence of living things.

It is the present practice to indicate in the name of an enzyme the substrate upon which the enzyme operates and to terminate the name in *ase*. Thus the enzyme which catalyzes the conversion of urea into ammonia is called urease. Names which were established before this system was adopted are still in use.

The table on page 377 shows some of the enzymes now recognized. Some have been isolated as pure homogeneous compounds.

Vitamins

The history of exploration over a period of three centuries following the discovery of America is filled with reports of suffering and deaths due to a disease known as scurvy (*scorbutus*). It was in this period that men first ventured far beyond the sight of land and lived for many weeks at a time on diets which included no fresh fruits or vegetables. In the eighteenth century it was recognized that the disease was due to some deficiency in the diet and that the trouble seldom appeared when fruits and vegetables were available. Citrus fruits were known to be especially effective in preventing scurvy, and in 1795 the British Parliament issued an order which required the inclusion of lime juice in the food supplies of all ships in the navy. British sailors are still called "limeys." In 1931 the active component of citrus fruits was isolated; it was later identified as an unsaturated derivative of gulonic acid and thus shown to be related to the sugar gulose. The compound was classified as a vitamin, and called cevitamic acid, ascorbic acid, or vitamin C. Prior to the isolation of this compound the name *vitamin* had been applied to two other dietary accessories found in yeast and bran. Thus, although it had been known for a century that some component of limes was necessary in the diet, the compound, when isolated, was given third place in the alphabetical list of these important regulators.

Vitamin A. The first substances to be called vitamins were an oil-soluble compound (vitamin A) and a water-soluble compound (vitamin B) found in yeast and in rice polishings. It soon became evident that the substances to which these designations had been applied were not pure chemical compounds—they were mixtures. We now have two members in the A group, and the B complex contains at least ten different active components.

The two closely related fat-soluble vitamins are most abundant in fish-liver oils. They are separately designated as vitamins A_1 and A_2;

CLASSES AND EXAMPLES OF ENZYMES			
Name	Source	Substrate	Products
Diastases		Starches	Maltose and dextrins
Amylase	Malt		
Diastase	Saliva		
Ptyalin	Pancreas		
Maltase	Malt, yeast, saliva, pancreas	Maltose and α-glucosides	Glucose
Invertase	Yeast, plant cells	Sucrose	Glucose and fructose
Emulsin	Plant cells (almond)	β-Glucosides (amygdalin)	Glucose
		β-galactosides	Galactose
Phosphorylase	Starchy vegetables	Hexose-6-phosphate	Starches and H_3PO_4
Inulase	Fungi	Inulin	Fructose
Lipases	Pancreas	Fats, esters	Acids and alcohols (glycerol)
Phosphatase	Intestinal wall	Nucleotides*	Nucleosides* and H_3PO_4
Pepsin	Gastric juice	Proteins	Peptones
Trypsin	Pancreas	Proteins and peptones	Peptones and peptides
Erepsin	Intestinal wall	Peptones	Peptides
Urease	Soybean	Urea	Ammonia, carbon dioxide
Arginase	Liver	Arginine	Ornithine,† urea

*Nucleotides are esters formed between phosphoric acid and substances of the type of riboflavin (p. 379). Nucleotides, in combination with particular proteins, become enzymes. Nucleosides are substances of the riboflavin type, that is, hydrolyzed nucleotides.

†The formation of ornithine and urea from arginine is given by the equation

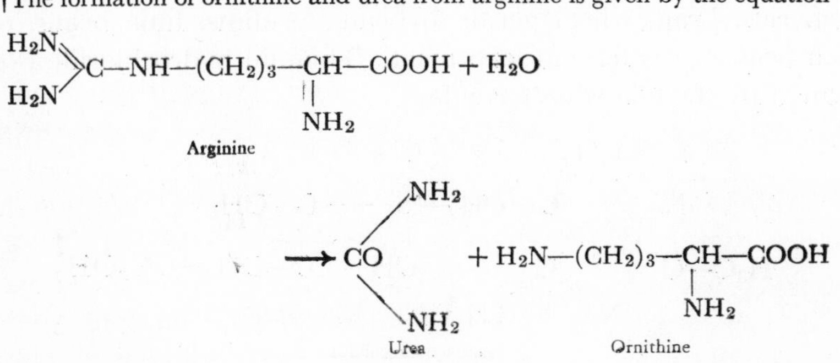

$$H_2N{>}C-NH-(CH_2)_3-CH-COOH + H_2O$$
$$\overset{|}{\underset{NH_2}{|}}$$

Arginine

$$\rightarrow CO\overset{NH_2}{\underset{NH_2}{<}} + H_2N-(CH_2)_3-CH-COOH$$
$$\underset{NH_2}{|}$$

Urea   Ornithine

but they are almost identical in composition, structure, and functions, and we shall deal with them collectively as vitamin A. Cream, eggs, green leaves, bananas, carrots, and sweet potatoes have high vitamin-A values, although they contain very little of the free vitamin. These foods are rich in carotenes, which, upon hydrolysis, yield the vitamin:

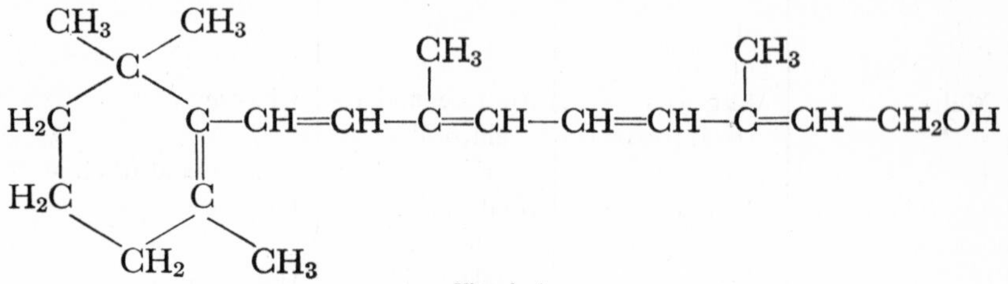

Vitamin A

The earliest symptom of vitamin A deficiency is subnormal vision in dim light (night blindness). Ability to see in the dark is dependent upon the presence in the eye of a pigment called visual purple. This substance is destroyed by exposure to bright light, and it develops again in the dark. The rate of development of visual purple, up to a certain maximum, is proportional to the amount of vitamin A delivered to the eye by the blood stream. Many individuals experience difficulty in driving at night. The glare of an approaching headlight destroys the visual purple in the eyes, and, owing to vitamin-A deficiency, the restoration of the pigment is retarded. For a short time after encountering the glaring light the driver is blind. Symptoms of vitamin-A deficiency in children are skin eruptions, eye infections, and retarded growth.

Vitamin B. The members of the vitamin-B complex of importance in human nutrition are thiamin, riboflavin, nicotinic acid, and nicotinic acid amide.

Thiamin (vitamin B_1). The best natural sources of thiamin are yeast, rice, bran, wheat germ, soybeans, peanuts, lima beans, oats, green peas, egg yolk, and lean meat. Thiamin hydrochloride is represented by the following formula:

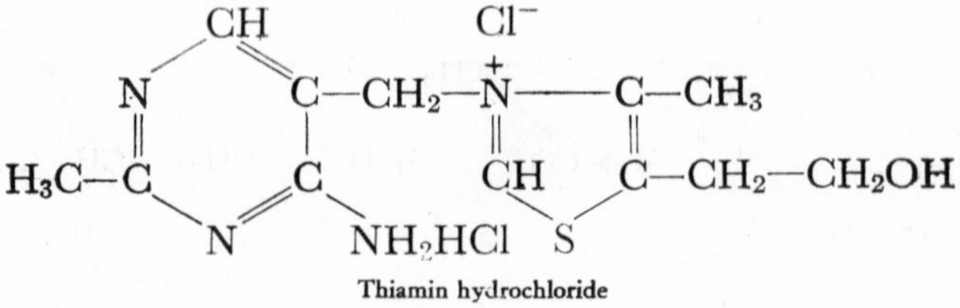

Thiamin hydrochloride

It is available as a synthetic product. Deficiency of thiamin in the diet leads to the disease known as beriberi and to weakness and loss of appetite.

Riboflavin (vitamin B₂). Riboflavin is found in many foods, especially in liver, kidney, oysters, fish roe, egg white, beet greens, broccoli, spinach, lean meats, and cheese. The compound is on the market as a synthetic product. Riboflavin is essential for normal growth and vitality. A disease of the eye which leads to opacity of the cornea is the most specific result of deficiency in riboflavin.

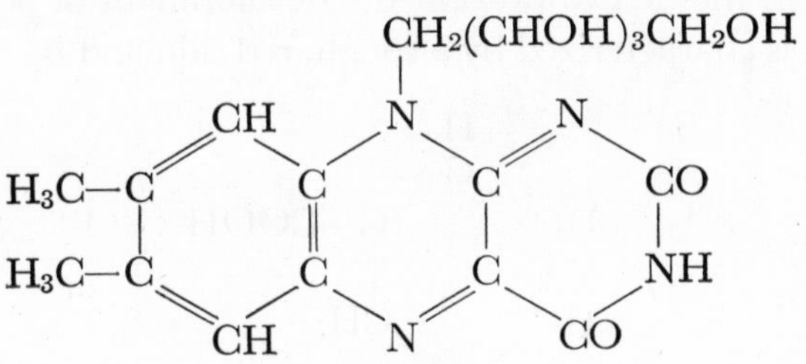

$$CH_2(CHOH)_3CH_2OH$$

Riboflavin

Vitamin C. The occurrence of ascorbic acid in citrus fruits has been mentioned in connection with the early history of scurvy. Other good sources of this compound are beet greens, cabbage, mustard greens, asparagus, pineapples, and tomatoes.

Deficiency in vitamin C results in hemorrhages, which may occur in any part of the body. This seems to be due to a weakening of the walls of the capillaries. The bones become soft, and symptoms which may be mistaken for rickets often appear. Connective tissues fail to develop normally, and the patient becomes weak.

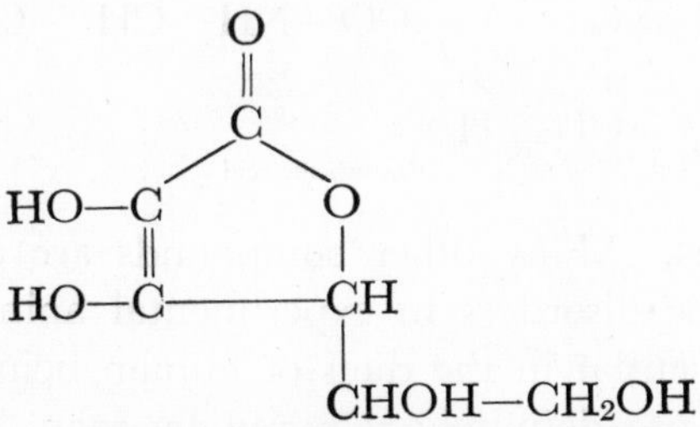

l-Ascorbic acid (cevitamic acid, or vitamin C)

Vitamin D. Rickets is a disease of the bones—a failure properly to incorporate calcium and phosphorus in the skeleton. It is a common cause of bowlegs and other deformities in children. The vitamins which prevent rickets are sterol derivatives, and they can be made from certain sterols in the skin by exposure to sunlight or ultraviolet radiation. There are several sterols in the vitamin-D group, each of which has some value as a regulator of calcium and phosphorus metabolism. Vitamin D_2 is made from ergosterol by irradiation with ultraviolet light (see page 386). Fish oils are the best natural sources of vitamin D. Halibut-liver oil and tuna-liver oil are especially rich in the antirachitic compounds.

Nicotinic acid. Either nicotinic acid or the amide derived from it is necessary in the diet to prevent the development of pellagra, a disorder which is characterized by a rough, red skin and by inflammation

$$
\begin{array}{c}
\text{H} \\
\text{C} \\
\text{HC}^{\diagup \diagdown}\text{C}-\text{COOH} \\
\text{HC}_{\diagdown \diagup}\text{CH} \\
\text{N}
\end{array}
$$

Nicotinic acid

of the tongue. The disease is accompanied very often by nervous indigestion.

Pantothenic acid. This substance stimulates the growth of yeast, and it operates as an antidermatitis factor in the chick. It is a compound of great importance in the poultry industry. Pantothenic acid consists of β-aminopropionic acid (β-alanine) in combination with αγ-dihydroxy-ββ-dimethylbutyric acid:

$$
\begin{array}{c}
\quad\quad\text{CH}_3 \ \ \text{OH} \\
\quad\quad | \quad\quad | \\
\text{HO}-\text{CH}_2-\text{C}---\text{C}-\text{CO}-\text{NH}-\text{CH}_2-\text{CH}_2-\text{COOH} \\
\quad\quad | \quad\quad | \\
\quad\quad\text{CH}_3 \ \ \text{H}
\end{array}
$$

Pantothenic acid

Other vitamins. Many other compounds are active in the prevention of specific disorders in experimental animals, and some of these may be essential in the diets of human beings. The vitamins described above are definitely required by man. Among the compounds listed as vitamins are pyridoxin, α-tocopherol, biotin, choline, p-aminobenzoic acid, inositol, folic acid, and two derivatives of naphthoquinone. A discussion of these substances is beyond the scope of this book.

Hormones

A hormone is a chemical substance which is secreted by a ductless, or endocrine, gland and which is capable of inducing activity in some organ of the body remote from the source of the compound. Hormones are carried to the organs they stimulate by the blood and lymph.

Adrenaline, or epinephrine. This substance is produced by several glands, notably the adrenals or suprarenal glands, which are situated at the upper ends of the kidneys. Its secretion is a part of the mechanism for control of blood pressure. Adrenaline is used in surgery to

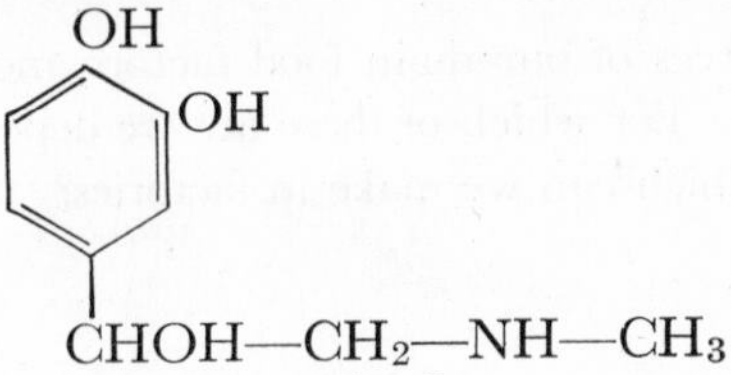

$$\begin{array}{c} OH \\ \bigcirc OH \\ \\ CHOH—CH_2—NH—CH_3 \end{array}$$

Adrenaline

reduce bleeding, since it causes constriction of the blood vessels near the point of injection. A number of drugs have been produced which, in some of their effects, are more useful than adrenaline. Among these are ephedrine and benzedrine:

$$\begin{array}{ccc} C_6H_5—CH—CH—CH_3 & & C_6H_5—CH_2—CH—CH_3 \\ \quad | \quad | & & | \\ \quad OH \quad NH—CH_3 & & NH_2 \end{array}$$

Ephedrine   Benzedrine

Insulin is secreted by the pancreas and is necessary for control of the storage of carbohydrates in the process of animal metabolism. With the help of insulin the liver extracts glucose from the blood stream whenever the concentration of glucose exceeds a certain value (about 0.1 per cent). The glucose is deposited as glycogen, or animal starch. The glycogen undergoes hydrolysis and releases glucose as needed. Absence of insulin is the cause of diabetes, and its administration to a diabetic patient provides a partial substitute for the hormones produced in the proper functioning of the pancreas. Banting and Best in 1922 showed that insulin is a protein.

The sex hormones and the hormone of the thyroid gland are considered in other chapters.

EXERCISES

1. Name the three classes of organic compounds which constitute the major types of food needed as fuel and as structural material. Which is used largely for the latter purpose? Are the others consumed completely upon digestion, or are they stored for use between meals?

2. Describe the roles played by the vitamins, enzymes, and hormones. Give some examples of each of the three types of compounds.

3. Why is it essential that vitamins be present in the diet?

4. Name an enzyme that catalyzes the hydrolysis of each of the following: (*a*) starch, (*b*) proteins, (*c*) fats. What are the hydrolysis products in each case?

5. Review the sources of our main food factors and of the vitamins, enzymes, and hormones. For which of these are we dependent upon the vegetables or animals? Which can we make in factories?

32 · STEROLS

Complex alicyclic alcohols known as sterols are found in all plants and animals. They belong to a more general class of compounds known as steroids, corresponding to the formula shown below. This is the formula for cyclopentanoperhydrophenanthrene with three hydrogen atoms replaced by R, R′, and R″. The saturated hydrocarbon cyclopentanoperhydrophenanthrene is regarded as the parent substance from which all steroids are derived.

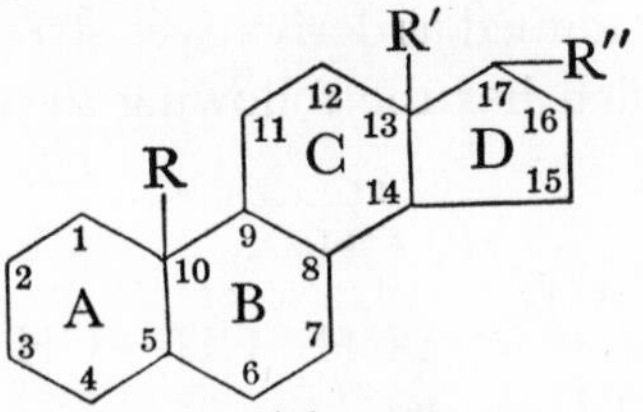

Steroid ring system

The steroids are waxy solids or oils, and they appear with fats in plant and animal extracts. Separation of the fats is accomplished by solvent extraction or saponification. The nonsaponifiable fractions do not dissolve in water or alkali and are further fractionated by distillation, crystallization, and the formation of derivatives. When heated with zinc, the most common pyrogenic product is phenanthrene; when dehydrogenated with selenium, a small yield of hydrocarbon, known as the Diels hydrocarbon, is formed:

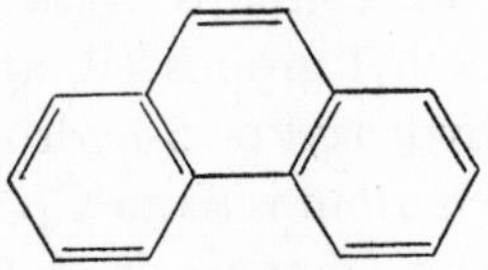

Phenanthrene

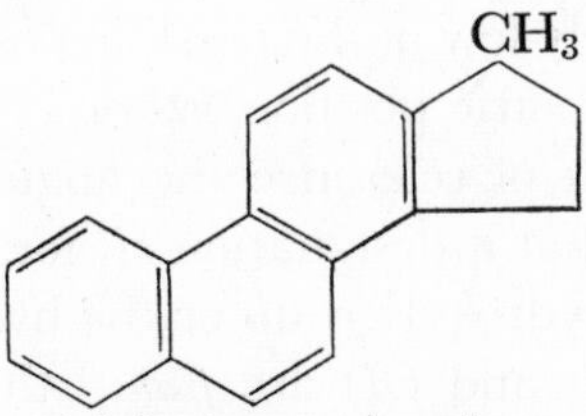

Methyl cyclopentenophenanthrene
(the Diels hydrocarbon)

These compounds furnished early clues to the structure of the steroids; but because of the drastic conditions of their formation, the conclusions had to be confirmed by simpler oxidations and reductions, and finally by syntheses of the compounds.

The steroids are found, in the free state or in combination with other types of compounds, as components of the bile acids, the cardiac aglucones, the sex hormones, the fat-soluble vitamins, brain tissue, the spinal cord, the secretions of the adrenal glands, and the blood. The chart on page 385 summarizes the structural relationships of some of these with reference to the parent hydrocarbon. The group R' is invariably methyl, while R and R'' are variable.

The sterols of animal origin are classified as *zoosterols;* those found in plants are *phytosterols.* They have in common a five-membered ring and three six-membered rings—the same ring system which characterizes the reduced cyclopentenophenanthrene. They differ in degree of unsaturation in the rings and in the composition and structures of side chains. They are named as derivatives of a saturated hydrocarbon called cholestane, which has the following formula:

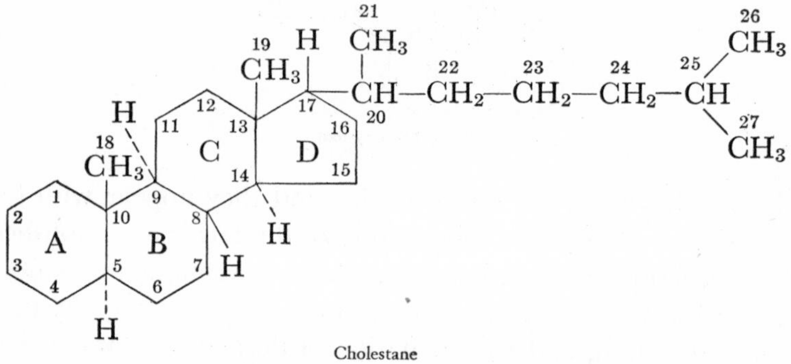

Cholestane

For reference the rings are labeled *A, B, C,* and *D,* and the carbon atoms are numbered.

Hydroxyl groups are present in many sterols, but they are located at relatively few of the possible positions. These hydroxyl groups may be in geometric positions *cis* or *trans* to other groups in the same ring. As a point of reference the angular methyl groups (R and R') are used, so that a designation *cis* for a 3-hydroxyl or 5-hydrogen means that the hydroxyl group or the hydrogen atom is *cis* to C_{18}. The ring fusions *BC* and *CD* are *trans;* this means that C_{11} and C_{14} are on opposite sides of ring *B,* and C_{17} and C_{15} are on opposite sides of ring *C.* The variable geometric isomerism lies in the ring fusion *AB,* which may be *cis* or *trans;* that is, the relative positions of C_{18} and the hydrogen atom attached to C_5, conforming to the ring fusion of *AB,* may be on the same side or on opposite sides of the plane of ring *A.*

STEROID DERIVATIVES

Type	Position of Hydroxyl Groups	Position of Double Bonds	R	R'' (Type)
Sterols	3, 7, or 20	4, 5, 6, or 22	$-CH_3$	$-\overset{\underset{22}{CH}}{\underset{\underset{CH_3}{\|}}{}}-CH_2-CH_2-\underset{24}{CH}-\overset{\underset{26}{}}{C}\Big\langle{}^{CH_3}_{CH_3}$ (with R and CH_3)
Bile acids	3, 6, 7, 8, 12, or 23	None present	$-CH_3$	$-\underset{\underset{CH_3}{\|}}{C}-CH_2-CH_2-COOH$
Heart poisons . .	3, 5, 8, 11, 14, or 16	None present	$-CH_3$ $-CH_2OH$ $-CHO$	$-C=CH$ with $CH_2-C=O$ and $>O$
Toad poisons. . .			$-CH_3$	$-C=CH-O$ with $CH=CH-C=O$ and CH_3
Digitalis sapogenins	2, 3, or 6	None present	$-CH_3$	$-CH-CH-CH-CH_2$ with O (C_{16}), O (CH_2), $CH-CH_3$
Adrenal secretions (cortin)	(11?), 21, (3-keto)	4 or 6	$-CH_3$	$-\overset{OH}{\underset{}{CH}}-CH_2OH$ or $-\overset{O}{\underset{}{C}}-CH_2OH$
Sex hormones (estrogenic)	3, 16, or 17	1, 3, 5, and 6, 7, or 8		$-OH$ or $=O*$
Corpus luteum .	(3-keto)	4	$-CH_3$	$-CO-CH_3$
Androgenic types	(3-keto)	4	$-CH_3$	$-OH$ or $=O*$

Cholesterol. The molecular formula for cholesterol is $C_{27}H_{46}O$. It is an unsaturated secondary alcohol which, with bromine, readily forms an addition product corresponding to the formula $C_{27}H_{46}OBr_2$. The double bond is in ring B, and the hydroxyl group is attached to carbon atom number 3.

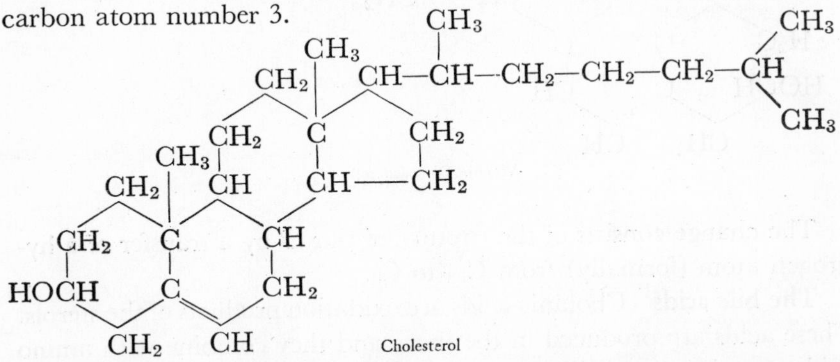

Cholesterol

*When R'' is —OH, the compound is a cyclic, secondary alcohol. The alcohol can be converted into a cyclic ketone, —OH and —H being replaced by =O.

Cholesterol crystallizes in needles melting at 148°–150°. It is insoluble in water, but soluble in alcohol, ether, and chloroform.

The cholesterol content of normal animal tissues varies between a trace and as much as 5 per cent. The brain of an adult man contains about 28 g of cholesterol (approximately 2 per cent of the weight of the organ).

Ergosterol. The principal sterol of yeast is ergosterol, $C_{28}H_{44}O$. It is present in all animal tissues, especially in the skin. Irradiation of ergosterol with ultraviolet light converts the compound into vitamin D_2:

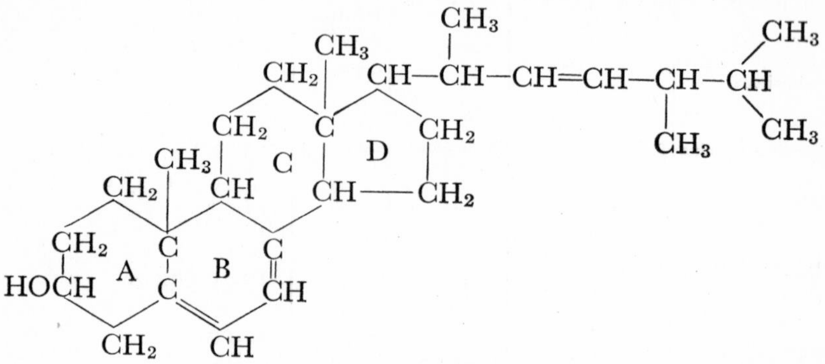

Ergosterol (mp 160°)

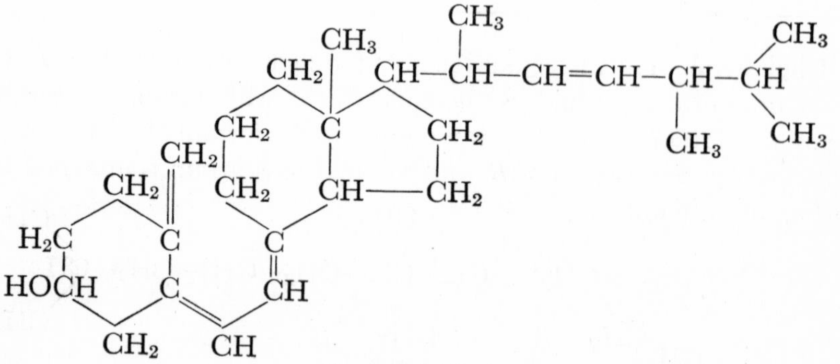

Vitamin D₂ (calciferol)

The change consists of the rupture of ring B by a transfer of a hydrogen atom (formally) from C_{18} to C_9.

The bile acids. Cholanic acids are oxidation products of the sterols. These acids are produced in the liver, and they combine with amino acids, forming "conjugated acids." Glycine (H_2N—CH_2—$COOH$) and taurine (H_2N—CH_2—CH_2—SO_3H) are the principal amino acids which are involved. The union is an amide or peptide linkage involving the carboxyl group of the cholanic acid and the amino group of the glycine or taurine.

Cholanic acids from different sources differ in the number and in the positions of hydroxyl groups attached to the rings. In common with all sterol derivatives, they exist also in *cis* and *trans* isomeric forms. The methyl group attached to carbon atom 10 and the hydrogen atom on carbon 5 are on the same side (*cis*) of the molecule.

One of the cholanic acids corresponds to the following formula:

Cholic acid, or 3, 7, 12-trihydroxy cholanic acid

Cardiac aglucones. Cholanic acids combine with carbohydrates, amino acids, and alkaloids, forming a great variety of paired, or conjugated, molecules. Among the natural products of this kind are digitalis and strophanthus. These are used in medicine as heart stimulants. The complete structures of these compounds have not been established with certainty, but they are known to be sterol derivatives.

The sex hormones. Internal secretions of the ovaries and testicles contain sterol derivatives which stimulate the activity of the reproductive organs. They are responsible for the development of secondary sex characters, such as differences in plumage of male and female birds and differences in the development of wattles, spurs, and combs in domestic fowls. There are several hormones in this group, each performing some special function in the processes of reproduction and growth. From ovarian extracts and from pregnancy urine, active principles have been isolated. The compounds, some of which are given on the next page vary in potency. The estrogenic hormones control the functioning of the ovaries and uterus.

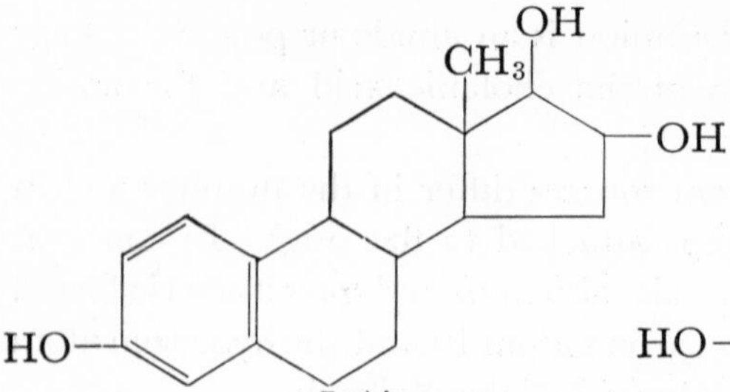

OH

CH$_3$

—OH

HO—

Estriol

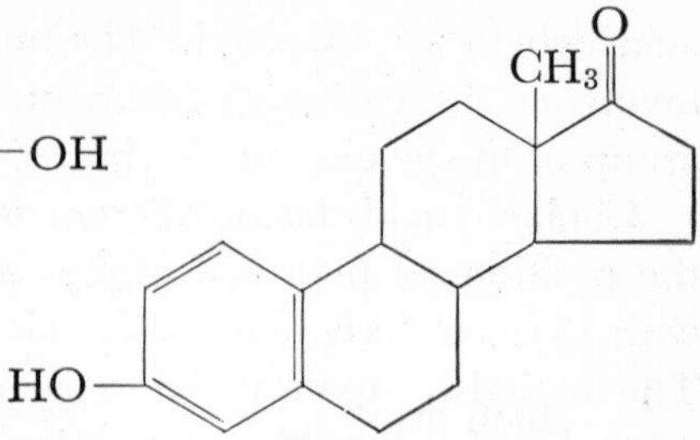

O

CH$_3$

HO—

Estrone

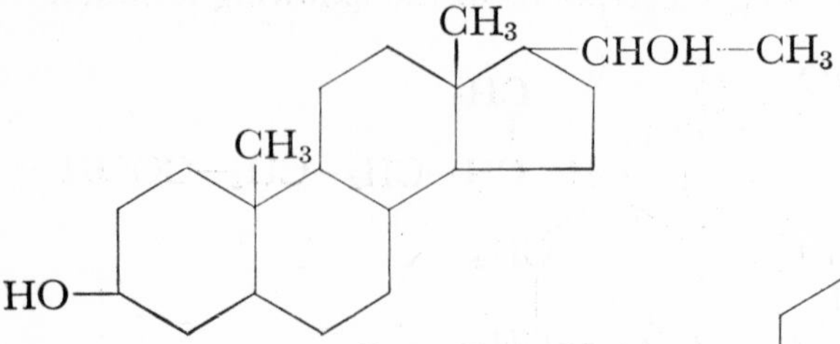

CH$_3$

—CHOH—CH$_3$

CH$_3$

HO—

Pregnandio

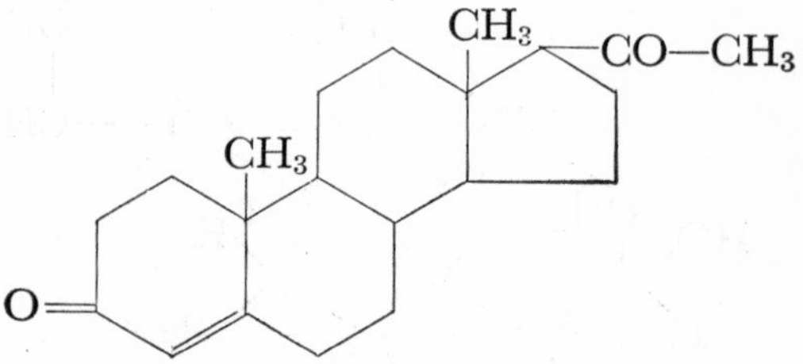

CH$_3$

—CO—CH$_3$

CH$_3$

O=

Progesterone

The estrogenic hormones are not produced after menopause; and the disturbances of that period, caused by readjustments of metabolism, have been alleviated by administration of the hormone.

The control of secondary male characteristics is achieved through the male sex hormones. They are isolated from urine and extracts of testicular tissue. Of the two represented below, testosterone is the more active.

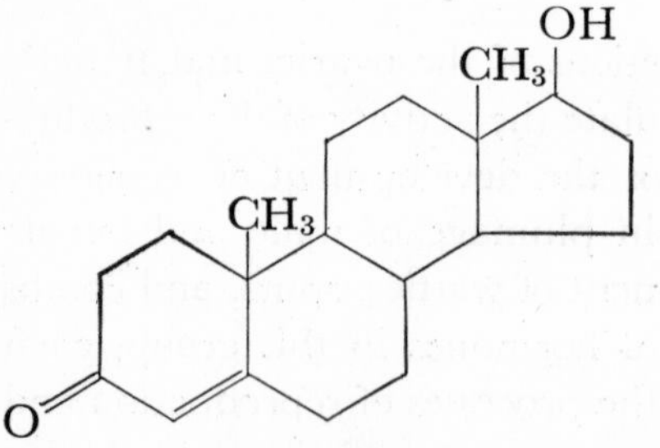

OH

CH$_3$

CH$_3$

O

Testosterone

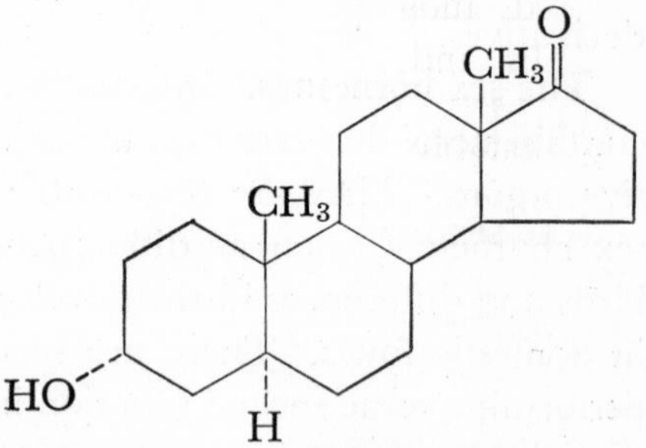

O

CH$_3$

CH$_3$

HO

H

Androsterone

The male and the female sex hormones are obtainable from animals, and both types have been synthesized from cholesterol.

INDEX

[Principal references are in black type.]

Acetaldehyde, 33, 40, 41, 137, 140, **153**, 155
Acetals, 143, 239, 255
Acetamide, 183, 205
Acetanilide, 312, 370
Acetic acid, 33, 41, 161, **169**
Acetic anhydride, 91, 177
Acetoacetic acid, 226
Acetoacetic ester, 227, 229, 230
Acetone, 137, 138, 140, **156**
Acetophenone, 330
Acetyl bromide, 174
Acetyl chloride, 174
Acetyl fluoride, 174
Acetyl iodide, 174
Acetylation, 254, 312
Acetylene, 33, 34, 37, 44, **88–91**, 177
Acetylsalicylic acid, 341
Acid anhydrides, 165, **176**
Acid chlorides, 166, 173, 175
Acids, aliphatic monobasic, 160–171; aromatic, 337–343; dibasic, 187; dissociation constants of, 161, 164, 187; hydroxy, 211–225; sulfonic, 298; unsaturated, 196
Acridine, 282
Acrolein, 157
Acyl halides, 166, **173**, 175
Acyl radicals, 162
Acylation, 207, 254, 312
Addition reaction, 36, 73, 89, 90
Adipic acid, 187, **192**, 193; nitrile of, 193
Adrenaline, 381
Alanine, 264
Albumins, 268
Alcohols, aliphatic, 38, 81, **108–117**; aromatic, 322
Alcoholysis, 115, 132, 175, 176
Aldehydes, aliphatic, 40, **136–148**; aromatic, **323–330**
Aldol condensation, 145
Alizarin, 354
Alkane hydrocarbons, 49–57; preparation of, 65–69; reactions of, 60–65
Alkene hydrocarbons, 70–85; isomerism, 82–85; preparation of, 81–82; reactions of, 73–81; reduction of, 66
Alkyl halides, **128**, 130; preparation of, 129; reactions of, 131, 134
Alkyl radicals, 54
Alkylation, 78, 206, 255
Alkyne hydrocarbons, 88
Amides, 166, **183**
Amines, 199, 309; aliphatic, 199–206; aromatic, 309–315
Amino acids, 263, **264**, 269
Aminoazobenzene, 319
Aminophenols, 313
Ammonolysis, 132, 175, **176**
Amygdalin, 325
Amyl alcohols, 109
Amyl bromide, 130
Amyl butyrate, 178
Amyl chloride, 130
Amyl ether, 122
Amyl iodide, 130
Amylamine, 199

Amylase, 112, 377
Amylenes, 71
Amylopectin, 243, **245**
Amylose, 243, 245
Androsterone, 388
Aniline, 309, 310, 311
Anisaldehyde, 326
Anthracene, 282, 354
Anthraquinone, 354
Antimalarials, 366
Arabinose, 233, 243, 252, **260**
Arginase, 377
Arginine, 266, 377
Aromatic hydrocarbons, 98, **100**, 279
Ascorbic acid, 379
Aspartic acid, 266
Aspirin, 341
Associated molecules, **121**
Atebrin, 367
Auxochromes, 357
Azelaic acid, 187
Azobenzene, 318

Barbiturates, 368
Barbituric acid, 368
Beckmann rearrangement, **334**
Benzal chloride, 293, 329
Benzaldehyde, 323, 326, 327, 328, **349**
Benzedrine, 381
Benzene, 92, **100–107**, 279, 283
Benzene hexachloride, 106, 296
Benzenediazonium chloride, 314
Benzenesulfonic acid, 106, 208, **298**
Benzenesulfonyl chloride, 207, **299**
Benzoic acid, 337, 338
Benzoin condensation, 327
Benzophenone, 322, 330, **333**
Benzopinacol, 330
Benzotrichloride, 293, **339**
Benzoyl chloride, 339
Benzoylacetic acid, 226
Benzyl alcohol, 322
Benzyl bromide, 293
Benzyl chloride, 293, **329**
Benzylamine, 310
Berthelot reduction, **66**
Bile acids, 386
Biotin, 380
Biphenyl, 282
Bismarck brown, **346**
Bisulfite addition, **144**
Biuret reaction, 277
Bonds, 10, 15, 16, **43–46**, 92–94, 101–104, 279
Bromobenzene, 105, 293
Bromobenzyl alcohol, 294
Bromobenzyl chloride, **294**
Bromoform, 147
Bromopropane, 98
Bromotoluene, **293**
Brucine, 367
Buffer solutions, 164
Butadiene, 94, **96**, 193
Butanal, 140
Butanes, **50**, 53

389